ENCYCLOPEDIA OF
FLIGHT

Encyclopedia of *FLIGHT*

Volume 2

Guidance systems - Sputnik

Indexes

Edited by
Tracy Irons-Georges

Consulting Editor
James F. Marchman III
Department of Aerospace and Ocean Engineering
Virginia Polytechnic Institute and State University

Project Editor
Heather Stratton Williams

SALEM PRESS, INC.
Pasadena, California   Hackensack, New Jersey

Managing Editor: Christina J. Moose
Developmental Editor: Tracy Irons-Georges
Project Editor: Heather Stratton Williams
Copy Editor: Leslie Ellen Jones
Assistant Editor: Andrea E. Mitchell
Acquisitions Editor: Mark Rehn
Photograph Editor: Philip Bader
Research Supervisor: Jeffry Jensen
Research Assistant: Jeff Stephens
Production Editor: Cynthia Beres
Page Design: James Hutson
Layout: Eddie Murillo
Cover Design: Moritz Design, Los Angeles, Calif.

629.13
En 19
v. 2

Copyright © 2002, by SALEM PRESS, INC.

All rights in this book are reserved. No part of this work may be used or reproduced in any manner whatsoever or transmitted in any form or by any means, electronic or mechanical, including photocopy, recording, or any information storage and retrieval system, without written permission from the copyright owner except in the case of brief quotations embodied in critical articles and reviews. For information address the publisher, Salem Press, Inc., P.O. Box 50062, Pasadena, California 91115.

∞ The paper used in these volumes conforms to the American National Standard for Permanence of Paper for Printed Library Materials, Z39.48-1992 (R1997).

ISBN 1-58765-046-0 (set : alk. paper)
ISBN 1-58765-048-7 (v. 2 : alk. paper)

First Printing

PRINTED IN THE UNITED STATES OF AMERICA

Contents

Guidance systems 309
Gulf War 311
Gyros 314

Hang gliding and paragliding 318
Harrier jets 320
Heavier-than-air craft 322
Helicopters 326
High-altitude flight 330
High-speed flight 333
Hijacking 336
Hindenburg 340
History of human flight 343
Hornet 349
Hot-air balloons 351
Hovercraft 353
Howard R. Hughes 356
Human-powered flight 357
Hypersonic aircraft 360

Iberia Airlines 364
Icing 365
Insects 367
Instrumentation 370

Japan Airlines 373
Jennys 374
Jet engines 376
Jet packs 380
Jet Propulsion Laboratory 381
Amy Johnson 384
Johnson Space Center 385
Jumbojets 387

Kamikaze missions 391
Kennedy Space Center 394
Kites 396
KLM 398
Korean Air 400
Korean War 402

Landing gear 405
Landing procedures 407
Samuel Pierpont Langley 409
Learjets 410

Leonardo da Vinci 411
Lighter-than-air craft 413
Otto Lilienthal 417
Charles A. Lindbergh 419
Lockheed Martin 420
Lufthansa 423
Luftwaffe 425

McDonnell Douglas 429
Mach number 431
Maintenance 433
Manufacturers 436
Marine pilots, U.S. 440
Beryl Markham 442
MD plane family 444
Mercury project 446
Mergers 449
Messerschmitt aircraft 451
Microgravity 453
Military flight 455
Missiles 460
Billy Mitchell 463
Model airplanes 464
Monoplanes 465
Montgolfier brothers 467

National Advisory Committee for
    Aeronautics 469
National Aeronautics and Space
    Administration 472
National Transportation Safety Board 476
Navy pilots, U.S. 479
Ninety-nines 481
Northwest Airlines 483

Hermann Oberth 485
Orbiting 486
Osprey helicopter 488
Overbooking 490

Pan Am World Airways 493
Paper airplanes 495
Parachutes 497
Parasailing 499
Passenger regulations 501

Pearl Harbor, Hawaii, bombing	502
Auguste Piccard	506
Pilots and copilots	507
Piper aircraft	510
Wiley Post	513
Ludwig Prandtl	514
Propellers	515
Propulsion	517
PSA	522
Qantas	524
Radar	526
Ramjets	530
Raptor	533
Reconnaissance	534
Record flights	537
Reentry	541
Hanna Reitsch	544
Rescue aircraft	545
Manfred von Richthofen	547
Eddie Rickenbacker	549
Sally K. Ride	551
Rocket propulsion	552
Rockets	554
Roll and pitch	558
Rotorcraft	560
Royal Air Force	562
Rudders	565
Runway collisions	566
Runways	569
Russian space program	570
Burt Rutan	574
Safety issues	576
Antoine de Saint-Exupéry	579
Alberto Santos-Dumont	581
SAS	582
Satellites	584
Saturn rockets	588
Seaplanes	591
707 plane family	594
Alan Shepard	598
Igor Sikorsky	599
Singapore Airlines	600
Skydiving	601
Skywriting	603
Sopwith Camels	605
Sound barrier	607
Southwest Airlines	609
Space shuttle	611
Spaceflight	616
Spanish Civil War	620
Spirit of St. Louis	623
Spitfire	625
Spruce Goose	626
Sputnik	630
Alphabetical Index of Entries	XV
Categorized Index of Entries	XIX

ENCYCLOPEDIA OF
FLIGHT

Guidance systems

Definition: Systems that aid in navigation, that is, in finding and keeping to a route and schedule.

Significance: Guidance systems enable an aircraft to fly its route safely, even when visibility conditions are less than favorable.

The purpose of guidance systems is to aid in navigation. It is a simple point but one that can easily be lost in the overall complexity of some new guidance systems. Navigation has simple, specific objectives. The navigator should select a route and a schedule. There should be a continuous succession of points against which the navigator can check the progress of the voyage. Next, the planned movement is executed; that is, the craft is kept to the route or course set. Guidance systems enable these simple but important tasks to be accomplished accurately.

External Observation Guidance Systems

Guidance systems comprise many parts, including instrument landing systems (ILS), air traffic control (ATC) systems, radar and database systems, and voice communication controls. Satellite landing systems are increasingly important in providing landing guidance. From the earliest days of air flight to the present, there have been consistent improvements in guidance systems.

The constant monitoring and correction of position is termed a closed loop. Finding the aircraft's position is achieved by measuring distance or direction or both. Additionally, guidance systems need to measure altitude. The transmission of sound and light waves, as well as other electromagnetic waves, is used in this process.

There are guidance systems to aid in speed measurement, altitude, and every other possible variable for flight. High-speed computers aid in the process, warning pilots and navigators when an aspect of the flight requires attention. The Kalman filtering system weights each datum according to its expected quality. It aids in the process of dead reckoning, speed, and direction, as well as continuously updating the craft's position. It also determines the speed of the plane, its heading, rate of climb or descent, and how each of these must be maintained or adjusted to stick to the flight plan.

Air traffic controllers keep a dead reckoning check on each aircraft, using strips that show the height, speed, and timing of each plane. The strips break down the flight plan of each aircraft. Radio navigation uses signals in a true beam system. Narrow beams about 3 feet long are used for landing, even in near-zero visibility. Improved microwave systems allow for even narrower beams and aid instrument landing systems.

Laser guidance systems provide pilots with a visual navigation flight path from as far as 20 miles from the runway, with the precision of an advanced instrument landing system. Best of all, the installation of laser guidance and cold cathode technologies to replace or enhance conventional landing light systems requires no additional aircraft equipment, and is cheaper to maintain than conventional lighting. For example, the lifetime cost of cold cathode lights is only 20 percent of that of incandescent lights. The combination of enhanced vision technologies with the latest ground proximity warning systems dramatically reduces the number of controlled-flight-into-terrain accidents.

Inertial Guidance Systems

Inertial guidance is a method of navigation used to guide rockets and airplanes, submarines, and other vehicles. Unlike other methods of navigation, inertial guidance does not rely on observations of land or the stars, on radio or radar signals, or on any other information from outside the vehicle. Instead, a device called the inertial navigator provides the guidance information. An inertial navigator consists of gyroscopes, which indicate direction, and accelerometers, which measure changes in speed and direction.

The principles of inertial guidance have been known since the early 1900's. Gyroscopes have been used as compasses on ships since that time. They can be set so that they point constantly in one direction, such as toward the North Star. Unlike magnetic compasses, these gyrocompasses always indicate true north and are not affected by steel. In 1923, the German engineer Max Schuler described a method for establishing a vertical line that would not tilt when a vehicle changes speed or direction. If the line tilts, it cannot be used to measure distance. Schuler's theory is used to build electronic systems that prevent tilting of the vertical line. During World War II, German scientists built an inertial guidance system that guided their V-2 rockets against England. In the late 1940's and early 1950's, Charles S. Draper and other scientists at the Massachusetts Institute of Technology built the first highly accurate inertial guidance systems. Space shuttles and other spacecraft are also equipped with inertial navigators. Inertial guidance systems are required on U.S. commercial overseas flights.

The advantages of inertial guidance can be explained by the example of an airplane flight. To reach its destina-

Guidance systems

tion, an airplane must both fly in the correct direction and cover the correct amount of distance. Without inertial guidance, a pilot has to rely on compasses or on signals from radio beacons at known positions on the ground to be sure the airplane is flying in the right direction. With inertial guidance, pilots need only consult the navigation equipment inside the airplane. They can find their way in spite of poor visibility, faulty communications, and the absence of landmarks. In time of war, enemies cannot jam an inertial guidance navigation system with false or confusing information.

The inertial navigator automatically measures changes in a vehicle's speed and direction, and sends the information to the computer. The computer calculates the effect of all the changes and keeps track of how far and in what direction the vehicle has moved from its starting point. Three gyroscopes inside the inertial navigator spin in different directions on axles. The axles are placed so that they form 90-degree angles with each other, like three edges of a box meeting at a corner. The axles keep their directions as long as the gyroscopes continue to spin. Each gyroscope is supported by gimbals (movable frames) so that it stays in position as the vehicle rolls, pitches, or turns. Together, the gyroscopes establish an inertial reference system (a stable set of lines). The accelerometers detect changes in the vehicle's motion in reference to the stable lines defined by the gyroscopes. The inertial navigator measures how far a vehicle has traveled by recording the changes in the position of a vertical line. This line indicates the direction to the center of the earth. Vertical lines from any two points on the earth meet at the center of the earth. The angle between the lines indicates the distance between the points. Each minute (one-sixtieth of a degree) of angle indicates a surface distance of one nautical mile (6,076.1 feet, or 1,852 meters). New York City is 3,006 nautical miles from London. Therefore, a pilot flying from New York City to London knows the airplane has gone far enough when the vertical line of the inertial navigator has moved through an angle of 3,006 minutes (50 degrees, 6 minutes).

Inertial guidance systems are subject to errors that grow over time. In some systems, a computer periodically combines the system's outputs with an independent source of

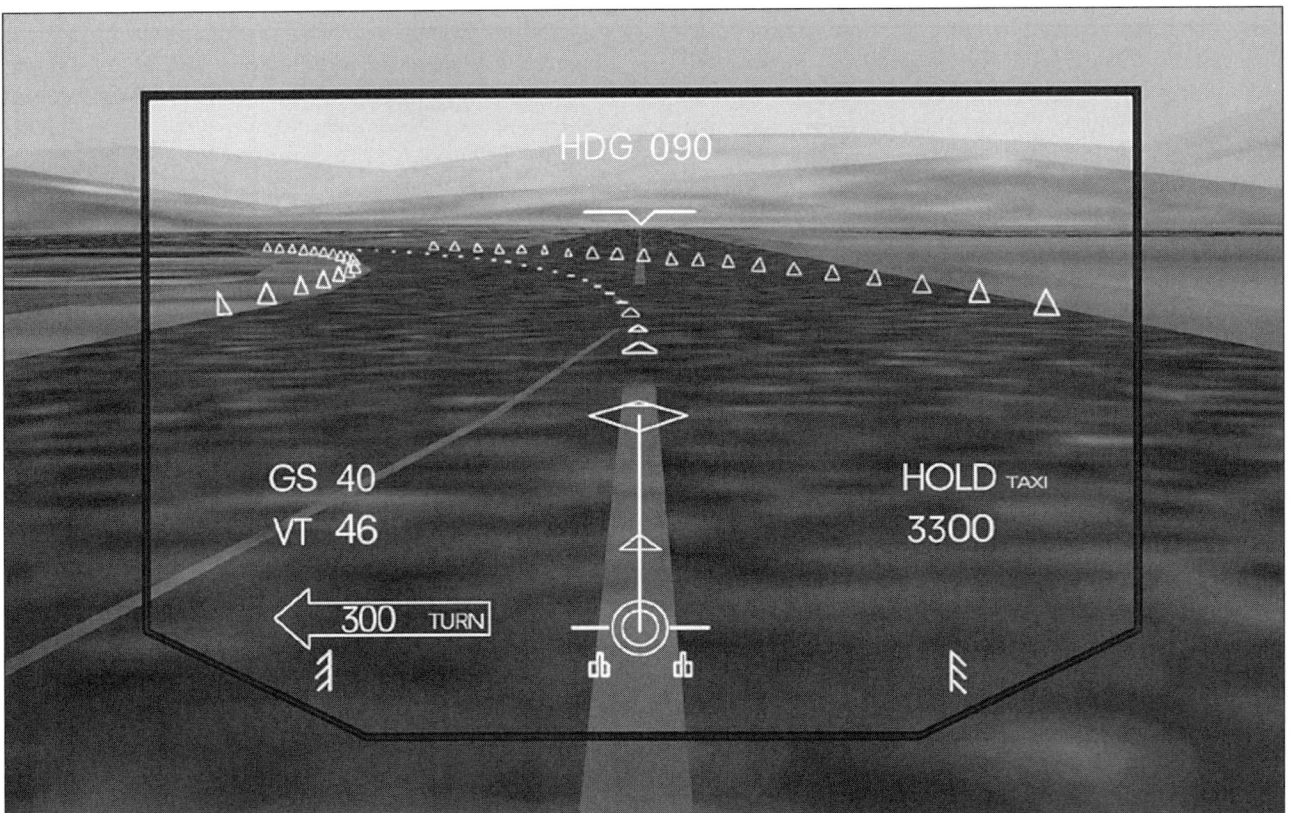

Guidance system technology helps pilots safely take off and land their planes in bad weather, when visibility is low. (Rockwell Collins)

position, such as a radio beacon. This procedure helps minimize the size of navigation errors.

Gyroscopes

Gyroscopes are essential in the working of inertial guidance systems. The gyroscope functions as a compass when the gyroscope is considered to be mounted at the equator of the earth. The spinning axis lies in the east-west plane; the gyroscope continues to point along the east-west line as the earth rotates. Laser gyros provide guidance in the most advanced aircraft systems. These gyros are not really inertial devices. Instead, they measure changes in counter-rotating beams of laser light, caused by changes in the aircraft's direction. The electrically suspended gyro, another advanced system, uses a hollow beryllium sphere suspended in a magnetic cradle. There are also fiber-optic systems in the works to aid in navigation.

The gyroscope also aids in the automatic pilot program of a plane through detecting and correcting variations in its selected flight plan, and it supplies corrective signals to the ailerons, elevator, and rudder. There are, in fact, a number of gyroscopes to detect changes in altitude, barometric pressure, and other factors. These gyroscopes transmit electrical signals to a computer, which combines and amplifies them, and then transmits these corrective signals to servomotors attached to the control surfaces of the aircraft. The pilot is thus able to use an autopilot to make corrections and to combine navigation and radio aids, such as inertial navigation systems, Doppler radar navigation systems, and radio navigation beacons. The autopilot can also couple beams of instrumental landing systems used in airport runways.

Frank A. Salamone

Bibliography

Biezad, Daniel J. *Integrated Navigation and Guidance Systems*. Reston, Va.: American Institute of Aeronautics & Astronautics, 1999. A navigation textbook, with excellent coverage of Global Positioning Systems (GPS) and inertial navigation systems.

Clausing, Donald J. *Aviator's Guide to Navigation*. 3d ed. McGraw-Hill, 1997. An advanced guide to air navigation, covering all types of systems that an aviator can encounter in modern aircraft.

Kayton, Myron, ed. *Avionics Navigation Systems*. 2d ed, New York: John Wiley & Sons, 1997. A systematic overview of modern navigation and sensing systems, written for engineers and professional navigators. Very thorough, but requires some familiarity with the systems to begin with.

See also: Air traffic control; Airplanes; Airports; Autopilot; Avionics; Communication; Doppler radar; Flight plans; Instrumentation; Landing procedures; Radar; Satellites; Takeoff procedures

Gulf War

Also known as: Persian Gulf War
Date: From January 16, 1991, to February 28, 1991
Definition: U.S. and U.N. aerial operations in which Iraqi command control centers, supply depots, and reinforcement forces were repeatedly bombarded for five and one-half weeks in retaliation against Iraq's invasion of Kuwait.
Significance: The 1991 Gulf War demonstrated the overwhelming and decisive role of air power in modern warfare. As the first major international crisis following the Cold War, the war demonstrated that a cooperative effort between the United States and the Soviet Union, along with the support of China, could enable the United Nations to quell a world crisis in a volatile area such as the Middle East.

Background and Overview

At 2:00 A.M. on August 2, 1990, Iraqi military forces occupied the tiny, oil-rich nation of Kuwait, Iraq's Arab neighbor on the Northern Persian Gulf. Ordered by Iraqi president Saddam Hussein, the invasion employed hundreds of tanks and surprised nearly the entire world. Within twenty-four hours, Iraq had taken complete control of Kuwait and moved thousands of Iraqi troops to Kuwait's Saudi Arabian border. Industrialized nations, such as the United States, that depended heavily on Kuwaiti and Saudi petroleum immediately terminated its foreign policies that had previously benefited Iraq. The United States and the United Nations organized a coalition of thirty-nine countries, including Egypt, France, Great Britain, Canada, Australia, Saudi Arabia, and Syria, that expelled Iraq within just six weeks and restored Kuwaiti independence without stripping Hussein of power. The United States made the unusual request that other countries contribute financially to the campaign. More than fifty-three billion dollars was received, with Saudi Arabia and Kuwait the largest donors. Several countries donated resources but not personnel.

Military Buildup

Immediately following the Iraqi occupation of Kuwait,

King Fahd of Saudi Arabia invited U.S. troops onto Saudi soil for protection against further aggression. This coalition, termed Operation Desert Shield, deployed 1,800 combat aircraft, 3,500 tanks, and 670,000 troops (425,000 of which were American), into the Gulf region by mid-January. The coalition also had moved 200 warships in the Gulf region, including six U.S. aircraft carriers and two battleships. By contrast, Iraq mobilized between 350,000 and 550,000 troops into Kuwait and southern Iraq, along with 550 aircraft, 4,500 tanks, and a small navy.

Had Hussein taken advantage of his initial military leverage and invaded Saudi Arabia in August, 1990, no military force in the immediate area could have deterred him. Any immediate American retaliation would have been limited to air and missile attacks from the USS *Independence* aircraft carrier in the Gulf and by B-52 bombers stationed on Diego Garcia Island, 2,500 miles away in the Indian Ocean. Hussein's unexplained delay gave U.S. president George H. W. Bush time to organize the largest deployment of air power and troops since World War II. Fifty thousand air and ground troops were sent to bases in Saudi Arabia in addition to three aircraft carrier fleets: the *Independence*, the USS *Eisenhower*, and the USS *Saratoga*. The number of American troops in the region had increased to more than 200,000 by November, after which Bush tried to scare Hussein into retreating by doubling the size of the American force.

Operation Desert Storm began with 539,000 American troops in the Gulf, along with 270,000 other coalition troops. There were 545,000 Iraqi troops in and around Kuwait. U.S. general H. Norman Schwarzkopf commanded the non-Arab units and Saudi general Khalid Sultan commanded the Arab units.

Air Power Strategies

The primary goal of the coalition air command was to destroy Iraq's ability to launch either offensive or defensive air campaigns. Secondary goals included the elimination of Iraq's weapons facilities and the disruption of Iraq's ability to gather information about coalition forces and to communicate internally. Coalition aircraft first bombed the Iraqi capital of Baghdad before attacking strategic military targets throughout Iraq and Kuwait. The allies focused their heaviest bombing on Iraqi troops, artillery centers, tanks, transportation routes, and supplies of ammunition, food, fuel, and water, as Hussein attempted to shield his military behind civilians. Iraq then launched crude Scud missiles at populated areas in Israel and Saudi Arabia, enraging many by killing civilians.

Operation Desert Storm

Hussein was given a deadline of January 15, 1991, to exit Kuwait. When he made no attempt to honor this deadline, Operation Desert Shield was upgraded to the military offensive Operation Desert Storm.

On January 16, 1991, at 6:40 P.M. eastern standard time, the White House announced that "the liberation of Kuwait has begun." Intensive air attacks continued for five and one-half weeks, concluding with a ground assault that began on February 23, 1991, at 8:00 P.M. eastern standard time, and lasted for exactly one hundred hours. The United States flew most of the campaign's sorties, and the British, French, and Saudis flew most of the rest. The coalition deployed unprecedented technological weapons systems, such as the unmanned Tomahawk cruise missile, the antimissile version of the Patriot antiaircraft system, and advanced infrared targeting that illuminated Iraqi tanks buried in the sand. Iraqi forces were overwhelmed by the use of new aircraft such as the British Tornado and the U.S. F-117A stealth fighter.

Other new technology included coalition smart bombs, which utilized previously untested laser guidance systems and accounted for 7 percent of all bombs dropped. Modern media coverage enabled the entire world continually to view coalition bombing raids. As Hussein desired, Iraq's long-standing neighbor and enemy, Iran, did not make a stand. As the bombing intensified, Iraq evacuated to Iran 137 aircraft, all of which Iran kept after the war.

For its initial thirty-seven days, Operation Desert Storm was almost exclusively a war of air bombardment. Iraq's military installations, communications facilities, air bases, armed forces in the field, missile launchers, weapons-producing factories, and nuclear production facilities were relentlessly bombed by more than 100,000 sea-launched sorties and missiles from the Persian Gulf. The Iraqi air force had surprisingly been grounded by Hussein after only the one day of bombing. Iraq's only offensive effort after its initial invasion of Kuwait was to launch eighty-five Scud missiles against Israel and Saudi Arabia. They resulted in a relatively minimal loss of life. Some were intercepted by American Patriot antimissile rockets, and others broke up upon reentry or missed their targets.

Operation Desert Saber

The land offensive Operation Desert Saber was launched on February 23, 1991, and lasted for four days. Deployment of ground troops was restrained until nearly the entire Iraqi infrastructure, including bridges, highways, electric power systems, water filtration plants, and airports, had been destroyed. With thousands of Iraqis already

Gulf War, 1991

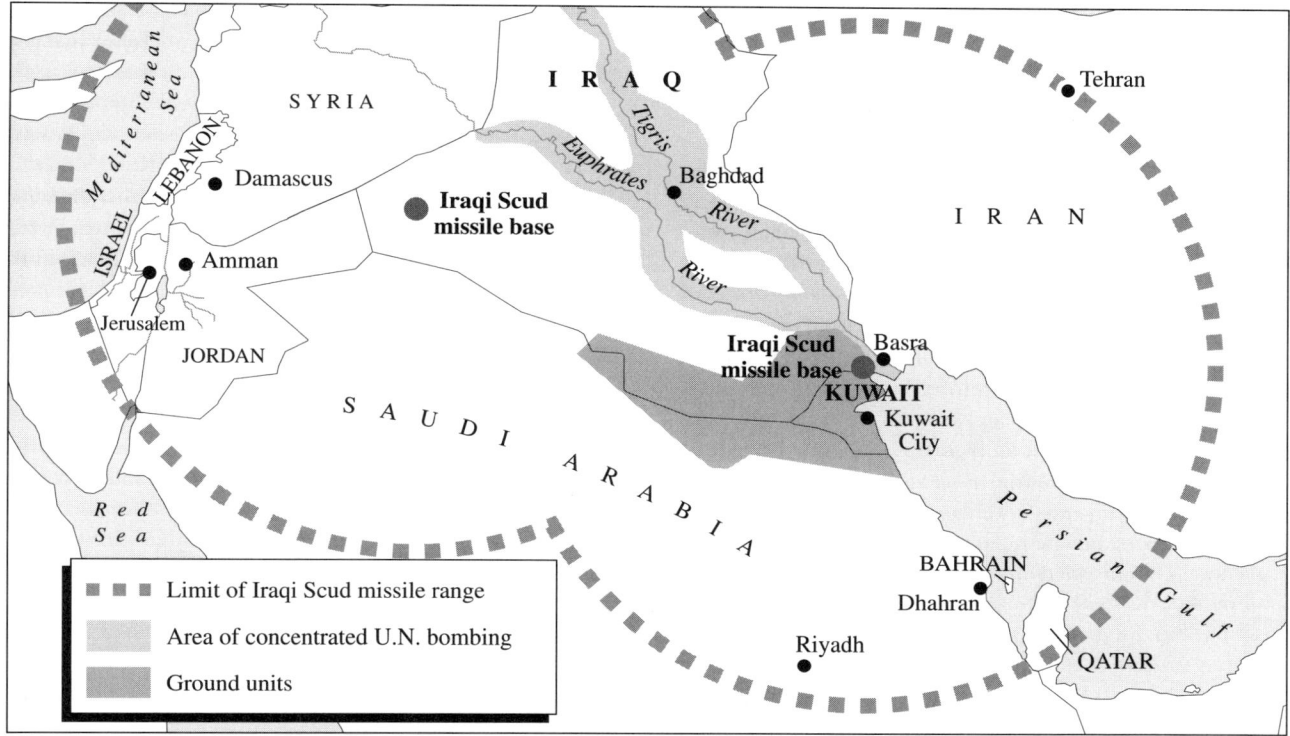

dead, surviving troops surrendered by the tens of thousands. The few Iraqi troops, including many of the elite Republican Guard, who continued to fight while retreating, shot their surrendering comrades in the back. When President Bush ordered a cease-fire on February 27, Kuwait was liberated, and the most extensive air bombardment and land offensive since World War II was over. Bush's early termination of the ground war was later criticized, as Baghdad was able to rescue a substantial amount of military equipment, which was later used to suppress postwar Shiite and Kurdish rebellions as Hussein remained in power.

Military Warcraft

Initial air attacks led by the United States included Tomahawk cruise missiles launched from warships in the Persian Gulf, F-117A stealth fighter-bombers armed with smart bombs, and F-4G Wild Weasel aircraft loaded with antiradar missiles. These attacks permitted F-14, F-15, and F-16 fighter-bombers, and F/A-18 Hornet fighters to gain air superiority. Bombing missions were timed to reduce the effectiveness of Iraqi ground radar defenses. The A-10 Thunderbolt, with its Gatling gun and heat-seeking or optically-guided Maverick missiles, effectively provided support for ground units. Other essential coalition support was provided by the AH-64 Apache, Black Hawk, AH-1 Cobra, and Super Cobra helicopters, which fired laser-guided Hellfire missiles, the E-3A airborne warning and control system (AWACS), and a modernized fleet of older B-52G's. The coalition's 2,250 combat aircraft, including 1,800 U.S. planes, were no match for Iraq's 500 Soviet-built MiG-29's and French-made Mirage F-1's. Coalition combat missions dropped more than 88,000 tons of bombs. Precision-guided missiles, night-vision devices, an infrared navigation and target designation system, and target sensors enabled round-the-clock bombing by the coalition. Ground-based firepower included the multiple-launch rocket system, the M-2 Infantry Fighting Vehicle, the M-60A3 main battle tank, the M-109 self-propelled howitzer tank, the M-1A1 main battle tank, and ninety Patriot missile launchers.

Casualties and Aftermath

Immediately following the Gulf War, the United States Defense Intelligence Agency estimated that 100,000 Iraqi soldiers had been killed, 300,000 wounded, 150,000 de-

313

serted, and 60,000 taken prisoner. U.S. representatives later stated these estimates could be off as much as 50 percent following claims by various human rights organizations of significantly different numbers. U.S. casualties included 148 killed in action, 407 wounded, and 121 killed in nonhostile activities, such as friendly fire.

Coalition bombing severely damaged Iraq's transportation systems, communication systems, and petroleum and other industries. Much of Iraq's electric power and clean water were destroyed, resulting in many civilian deaths from lack of food or medical treatment. Severe environmental pollution resulted after Hussein ordered approximately six hundred Kuwaiti oil wells set afire. The blazes took more than twelve months to extinguish and caused severe air pollution. Huge amounts of Kuwaiti oil were dumped into the Persian Gulf as the war ended. Postwar economic sanctions continued to cause great hardship to the civilians of Iraq and neighboring countries, as efforts to strip Hussein of power repeatedly failed. The operation had another, unintended effect: The presence of U.S. troops angered Osama bin Laden and other Islamic fundamentalists. The terrorist attacks of September 11, 2001, that killed more than five thousand were tied to the Gulf War.

Following Gulf War duty, many veterans complained of physical and psychological ailments, including memory loss, fatigue, and joint pain, collectively known as Gulf War syndrome. In 1996, the Pentagon warned five thousand veterans of the war that these symptoms might have been caused by exposure to nerve gas during an attack on a weapons depot.

Daniel G. Graetzer

Bibliography

Christy, Joe. *American Aviation: An Illustrated History*. Blue Ridge Summit, Pa.: Tab Books, 1987. An excellent review text on U.S. aviation history, with interesting insights into the past and potential future of air warfare.

Cooksley, Peter G., and Bruce Robertson. *Air Warfare: The Encyclopedia of Twentieth Century Conflict*. London, England: Arms and Armour Press, 1998. A chronology of significant events, inventions, and aeronautic milestones in armed flight.

Donald, David, ed. *The Complete Encyclopedia of World Aircraft*. New York: Barnes & Noble Books, 1997. A superb text with essays that examine the critical role of air power in international security by looking systematically at strategy and targeting. Includes photos, drawings, and statistics on essentially every airplane ever constructed.

Keaney, Thomas A., and Eliot A. Cohen. *Revolution in Warfare? Air Power in the Persian Gulf*. Annapolis, Md.: Naval Institute Press, 1995. A comprehensive account of the 1991 Gulf War, containing a revised edition of the Persian Gulf War Air Power Survey Summary Report created by Secretary of the Air Force, Donald B. Rice.

Price, Alfred. *Sky Battles: Dramatic Air Warfare Battles*. Dulles, Va.: Continuum, 1999. This fascinating text for the lay reader sensationally and accurately lives up to its title.

See also: Aircraft carriers; Apache helicopter; Eagle; Hornet; Missiles; Stealth fighter; Stratofortress

Gyros

Also known as: Gyroplanes, gyrocopters, autogyros, autogiros

Definition: An aircraft that, during most of its flight, derives a substantial part of its lift force from a free-spinning rotor system not provided with any form of direct power drive.

Significance: Historically, the gyroplane is significant in that its invention preceded that of the helicopter and was largely responsible for the helicopter's success. The need for hinges at the root of helicopter blades was first successfully accomplished in the gyroplane. Many homebuilt sport gyroplanes exist in the United States and throughout the world. The gyroplane's success as a homebuilt aircraft is largely due to its simplicity as compared to that of the helicopter.

Terminology

As recognized by the Federal Aviation Administration (FAA), "gyroplane" is the correct generic term for a type of aircraft that, during most of its flight, derives a substantial part of its lift force from a free-spinning rotor system not provided with any form of direct power drive. The term "gyrocopter" is actually a proprietary name originally used by Bensen Aircraft Corporation to designate its B8-M Gyrocopter. The B8-M was the predecessor of most amateur-built sport gyroplanes. "Autogyro" is an older term, often used for this type of aircraft, but it, too, is actually a proprietary name used by the Autogyro Company of America, which built some of the first gyroplanes. "Gyro" is a nickname applied to all these types of aircraft.

Features

The gyroplane is any type of aircraft that relies primarily on an unpowered, freewheeling (or autorotating) rotor as the main source of lifting force and has a separate propeller and engine combination providing forward thrust. Modern gyroplanes look much like helicopters with conventional-appearing tail surfaces. An example of a gyroplane is the Air and Space 18-A, which has these typical characteristics.

The gyroplane was invented by Juan de la Cierva, an early twentieth century civil engineer born in Spain. Cierva's first successful flight was made near Madrid, Spain, on January 9, 1923. The first gyroplane to be certified by the FAA in the United States was the Pitcairn PCA-2 gyroplane, which, at that time, was called an autogyro. Early gyroplanes looked much like double-wing aircraft with the top wing removed and replaced with a rotor. They had a conventional engine and propeller in front for forward thrust, a small lower wing for auxiliary lift and control, and conventional-looking tail surfaces, with a large rotor on top of the fuselage for primary lift.

The performance features of gyroplanes are a combination of those of helicopters and fixed-wing aircraft. The rotor is usually in autorotation, turned by the wind, much like the blades of a windmill that has been turned edgewise to the wind. There must be airflow through the rotor to keep it turning, and thus the gyroplane requires separate forward propulsion to keep it moving through the air. For this reason, gyroplanes cannot hover or take off and climb vertically like a helicopter. Although they can make fully controlled vertical descents, the speed is somewhat high, and landings are not performed in this manner. A gyroplane can fly very slowly and has a very short landing roll. Most gyroplanes temporarily use the engine to spin up the rotor before the takeoff run, thus allowing a very short takeoff roll. Engine power is removed from the rotor just before takeoff. A few gyroplanes also have a jump-takeoff capability. In a jump takeoff, the rotor is oversped with the rotor blades in a low pitch setting while the gyroplane is sitting on the ground. Power is then removed from the rotor and transferred to the forward propulsion system. The blade pitch is then rapidly increased to the normal cruise flight setting, and the gyroplane literally jumps off the ground, perhaps 10 to 15 feet into the air before transitioning to forward flight.

Amateur-built sport gyroplanes are often single-seat, open-cockpit aircraft that look much like flying lawn chairs, with a rotor on top and engine, propeller, and tail surfaces in the rear. An example of this type of gyroplane is the Brock KB-2.

Rotor Systems

A gyroplane's rotor "disk" is the tip path plane swept out by the individual rotor blades as they spin. The rotor disk is approximately perpendicular to the rotor shaft. A fundamental difference between the rotor disks of helicopters and gyroplanes is that a gyroplane rotor disk is tilted slightly rearward when viewed from the side. This angle provides both upward lift and rearward drag that must be overcome by the forward propulsion system. The individual rotor blades of a gyroplane are set at a low-pitch angle, which allows them to operate in autorotation. In a helicopter, the rotor disk is tilted slightly forward, providing upward lift as well as a component of the forward thrust for propulsion. The helicopter's engine spins the rotor and must provide the torque necessary to turn the rotor. Because the rotor blades of a helicopter have a higher pitch angle than those of a gyroplane, they require a power input in order to rotate.

A number of different rotor systems are in use in gyroplanes. All gyroplanes must have hinges on the blades where they attach to the rotor hub. In forward flight, the blade moving into the wind (advancing blade) would create more lift than the blade moving away from the wind (retreating blade). Without hinges, this would cause a dissymmetry of lift that would tend to roll the gyroplane over. This was the source of many problems in early attempts at rotary wing flight. Hinging the individual rotor blades allows them to flap up and down slightly as they move into the wind and away from the wind. This equalizes the lift and allows controlled flight.

Smaller gyroplanes usually have a rotor system that consists of two blades rigidly attached together. The two blades are hinged to the rotor shaft at their center, much like the pivot on a seesaw, and allow the blades to flap as a unit to equalize the lift. In larger gyroplanes, with three or more rotor blades, each blade is individually hinged to the rotor hub, so the blades can flap up and down slightly as they rotate. Flapping stops designed into the rotor hub prevent the flapping motion from becoming excessive and keep the blades from drooping excessively when the gyroplane is on the ground and the rotor is not turning.

Propulsion

The forward propulsion in gyroplanes is usually provided by a conventional reciprocating engine turning a pusher propeller located behind the rotor mast and ahead of the tail surfaces. The pusher propeller arrangement has three advantages over an arrangement with the engine and propeller mounted in front, known as a tractor arrangement. First, the pusher propellor system allows for a more bal-

Performance Specifications for Two Gyroplane Models

	Air & Space 18-A	*Brock KB-2*
Number of rotor blades	3	2
Rotor diameter	35 feet	22 feet
Overall length	19.8 feet	12 feet
Overall height	9.7 feet	6.6 feet
Seating capacity	2	1
Engine horsepower	180 @ 2,700 rpm	90 @ 4,100 rpm
Gross weight	1,800 pounds	600 pounds
Empty weight	1,280 pounds	230 pounds
Fuel capacity	28.4 gallons	10 gallons
Takeoff run	50 feet, run or jump	300 feet
Landing roll	Short roll or full stop	0 to 10 feet
Minimum level speed	20 miles per hour	20 miles per hour
Maximum speed	100 miles per hour	95 miles per hour
Cruising speed	95 miles per hour	70 miles per hour
Maximum rate of climb	700 feet per minute	1,000 feet per minute
Endurance	3 hours at 65 percent power	2 hours at 65 percent power
Service ceiling	12,000 feet	13,500 feet

anced gyroplane design, with cabin and crew weight in front of the rotor mast and the engine weight behind the rotor mast. Second, it provides better forward visibility for the pilot. Third, in the pusher propeller arrangement, the propeller slipstream hitting the tail surfaces provides better directional control and stability. Most early gyroplanes of the 1930's vintage had propellers pulling from the front. Some gyroplanes have rotary Wankel-type engines, and one, the Groen Brothers Hawk 4 Gyroplane has a gas-turbine engine driving a three-bladed propeller.

Tail Surfaces

The tail surfaces, or empennage, on a gyroplane are used more for stability than for control purposes. As do fixed-wing aircraft, gyroplanes display a wide variety of tail surface designs. Conventional tail designs, as well as V-tail, H-tail, and triple-tail designs can be found. Vertical stabilizers usually have rudders on them that can be deflected to cause the nose of the gyroplane to yaw to the left or right. Large rudder surface areas are usually used to take advantage of the propeller slipstream to provide yaw control at low forward speeds. Unlike in an airplane, the horizontal tail surfaces of a gyroplane are not usually movable, but rather are fixed surfaces provided for stability. Because a gyroplane can fly very slowly, relatively large tail surfaces are usually necessary for stability at low speeds. For this reason, it is not uncommon to see double or even triple rudders on a gyroplane, used to increase the total surface area without having a single, excessively large tail. Occasionally a large single vertical fin is used if it is centrally placed in the propeller slipstream.

Control Systems

The main flight controls of a gyroplane consist of a joystick, rudder pedals, and a throttle. Variations of these do occur. The throttle controls the engine power output and thus the forward thrust of the propeller, much as in a conventional fixed-wing aircraft. This arrangement is different from that of a helicopter, in which the throttle controls the engine power input to the main rotor, usually operating at a constant rate of revolutions per minute.

A gyroplane's joystick, also called a cyclic stick, controls the tilt of the rotor disk either by tilting the rotor shaft or by individually changing the pitch of the blades as they cyclically rotate (hence the term cyclic pitch). Tilting the stick to the left effectively causes the rotor disk to tilt to the left, causing a sideward component of rotor thrust that makes the gyroplane turn and bank to the left. Tilting the stick to the right does just the opposite. Pulling back on the cyclic stick tilts the rotor disk more rearward, causing an increase in rotor thrust due to the increased angle of attack to the airflow. This makes the gyroplane climb, assuming that sufficient thrust is produced by the propeller. Pushing forward on the cyclic stick tilts the rotor disk more forward, causing a decrease in rotor thrust and making the gyroplane descend. In essence, the cyclic stick controls the mechanical operation of the main rotor much the same as it would in a helicopter, but because the rotor is unpowered, it causes the gyroplane to respond much like an airplane to similar control stick inputs. Some gyroplanes have an overhead stick that requires movement in directions just the opposite of a joystick to control the rotor.

Rudder pedals operate the rudder as they would in an airplane, causing a yawing motion from right to left. In a helicopter, the rudder pedals are used to control yawing of the helicopter by changing the tail rotor blade pitch.

The gyroplane does not use a collective pitch lever in the same way a helicopter does. Instead, the collective pitch of the gyroplane's rotor blades is factory preset at an optimum angle for normal flight operation. Gyroplanes that have a rotor prespin or jump-takeoff capabilities will usually have a two-position collective pitch control. One position, with the blades in flat pitch, is used for rotor spinup while on the ground. The other position, for normal flight, is engaged just before starting the takeoff roll or making a jump takeoff. In a helicopter, a collective pitch lever is provided to manually change the pitch of all the rotor blades simultaneously, thus changing the rotor thrust as needed.

Typical Gyroplanes

The following gyroplanes designed for production have been developed in the United States or Canada: Kellet, Pitcairn, Umbaugh (later designated the Air and Space 18-A), the Canadian Avian, McCulloch J-2, and the Groen Brothers Aviation Hawk 4 Gyroplane.

Amateur-built sport gyroplanes can be licensed with the FAA in the experimental category if the aircraft is at least 51 percent amateur-built. A number of companies—including Air Command International, Joe Souza Gyroplanes, Barnett Rotorcraft, Ken Brock Manufacturing, Rotor Flight Dynamics, Rotor Hawk Industries, and Rotary Air Force—have developed sport gyroplane kits, which can be assembled in various combinations to suit the homebuilder's ability. The number of companies in the amateur-built field has proliferated so much that one must use care to select a well-proven and time-tested design.

Eugene E. Niemi, Jr.

Bibliography

Gablehouse, Charles. *Helicopters and Autogiros*. Philadelphia: J. B. Lippincott, 1967. A chronicle of rotary-wing aircraft, written in layperson's language and illustrated with a number of photographs, with coverage of gyroplane history, designs, predictions for the future, helicopter airlines, and some technical descriptions of control systems and rotor mechanisms.

Jackson, P., ed. *Jane's All the World's Aircraft*. Alexandria, Va.: Jane's Information Group, 1996. An excellent summary of most types of aircraft in the world, with photographs and descriptions in easy-to-read form. Gyroplanes appear in various editions from early to the present.

McCormick, Barnes W., Jr. *Aerodynamics of V/STOL Flight*. New York: Academic Press, 1967. Suitable primarily as a textbook for engineering students, this book discusses many principles applicable to gyroplanes as well as helicopters and describes the concept of autorotation.

U.S. Flight Standards Service. *Rotorcraft Flying Handbook*. Washington, D.C.: U. S. Department of Transportation, Federal Aviation Administration, Flight Standards Service, 2000. A well-illustrated technical manual for applicants seeking various levels of pilot ratings in helicopters or gyroplanes, with descriptions of how to fly gyroplanes and how gyroplane systems work.

See also: Airplanes; Helicopters; Propellers; Propulsion; Rotorcraft; Rudders; Tail designs

H

Hang gliding and paragliding

Definition: Unpowered aircraft derived from sailplane gliders and double-surfaced sport parachutes. Hang gliders are kitelike; paragliders are made of airfoil cells inflated by passing through the air.

Significance: Hang gliders and paragliders utilize basic principles of aerodynamics to fly without an external power source. The same basics of gliding underlay the early development of heavier-than-air flight.

Traditional gliders, progenitors of hang glider and paraglider flight, are unpowered, heavier-than-air craft that attain sustained flight via the aerodynamic forces acting on them. Gliders look like airplanes but are much lighter; they have low ratios of weight to wing area; and their wings are much longer and narrower than those of powered aircraft. Gliders include primary, secondary, and cargo types. Primary gliders have girder frameworks with attached wings, controls, stabilizers, and open seats at the framework's front. Popular secondary gliders (sailplanes) have fuselages and cockpits, and look like airplanes with very long, narrow wings. Cargo gliders (CGs) are towed by powered planes and carry heavy commercial loads in tow, which they can land where powered craft cannot.

Modern sailplanes lose only a few feet of altitude per second and ascend air currents, rising just 2 to 3 miles per hour. Beginning in the 1870's, pioneer aeronauts built successful gliders to define efficient wing and control system design. The best known is the German Otto Lilienthal, who studied air buoyancy and resistance, wing shape, and tail stabilization. In 1891, his crewed craft, capable of flying after a downhill run into the wind, made the first of thousands of flights. American glider pioneers Octave Chanute, the Wright brothers, and John Montgomery made many glider innovations.

Most modern glider design arose in post-World War I Germany. Its aircraft engineers, forbidden by treaty to build powered aircraft for military use, explored the great efficiency of light gliders with single, long wings and the weather conditions that optimized soaring flight. They found that strong ridge or thermal upcurrents provided the motive power gliders needed. Ridge currents form when steady winds blow against ridges or hills, but are limited to areas near their windward edges. Thermal currents (thermals) form by heat rising from the ground and are always present under cumulus clouds.

For traditional flight, a glider is accelerated to the speed needed to overcome gravity by means of a catapult or by being towed by a winch, automobile, or powered airplane. After launch, the craft disengages from the towline at a desired height and the pilot seeks thermals. The pilot turns into a thermal, and after reaching the maximum altitude possible seeks the next useful thermal. Good gliders move 20 miles horizontally for each mile of altitude attained and can stay aloft for many hours.

Hang-Gliding Essentials

Although some hang gliders have small engines, most hang gliding is unpowered flight in a kitelike craft based on the structure of the sailplane. The name derives from the fact that early pilots hung onto the gliders. The designed evolved so that hang gliders have an aluminum frame, a fabric sail, and a comfortable harness for the pilot. In order to take off, the pilot dives from a hill, cliff, or mountain. The hang glider was born in the 1960's, based on designs by Francis Rogallo of the National Aeronautics and Space Administration (NASA) for flex-wing parachutes for space vehicle reentry. Many design variations followed, and hang gliding, first merely a recreational activity, has become a competition sport, with flight-duration, distance, and altitude-gain events. Annual world championships are governed by the International Aeronautical Federation. The hang glider's limited ability to maneuver and handle wind change, as well as the fact that pilots fly without protective body coverings, make the sport somewhat dangerous.

Hang glider construction begins with a light, strong airframe of aluminum tubes which support a sail (its airfoil) made of Dacron or another polymer, creating two joined wings. The airframe has five parts. First, a leading-edge tube (LET) runs along the front edge of the wings. The sail wraps around the LET and is secured to it. A crossbar tube connects the LET of each wing and the third part of the airframe, a keel. The keel runs from the glider nose to the center of its rear end, above the pilot. The fourth and fifth parts of the frame are the king post and control bar. They connect to the airframe where crossbar and keel intersect. The

> ## The Aerodynamics of Gliding
>
> Heavier-than-air craft must conquer gravity before controlled flight is possible. Three forces are involved. The first, thrust, is caused in conventional aircraft by engines and in gliders by catapults, tows, or jumps. Thrust enables forward motion of the aircraft as long as it exceeds the second force, drag, which is caused by air viscosity. The third force, lift, is the key to flight. It operates upward, at a right angle to the direction of aircraft motion. Thrust is supplied by airfoils (wings), designed so the angle of attack, at which they meet the passing airflow, causes more rapid airflow past the upper airfoil surface than past its lower surface. This lowers air pressure above the airfoil, compared to that below it, engendering lift that raises properly designed aircraft into flight.
>
> To properly split passing air, an airfoil has a rounded leading edge and a sharp trailing edge. Unsymmetrical airflow is produced by a curved, or cambered, airfoil shape and the angle of attack at which it meets approaching air. The importance of the angle of attack is shown by its use and misuse during flight. An aircraft's angle of attack is changed by altering the airfoil's position in space. Angles of attack of up to 15 degrees provide increased lift, enabling faster climbs but slowing airspeed. When this angle is excessive, air eddy currents atop airfoils cause large lift decreases, which make aircraft drop toward the ground in stall. This stall may cause a crash unless the pilot quickly decreases the angle to safe values.

king post rises vertically from the keel and supports the glider when it is on the ground. The triangular control bar is used for support in flight, and is used by the pilot to guide the glider's movement. Usually, ten stainless-steel cables tie the airframe tubes together, supporting the hang glider's load. There are six "positive" wires running from the base of the control bar to the airframe and four "negative" wires running from the top of the king post to the airframe. They support the glider in its normal flight and in rare inverted flight. A third set of wing wires support the LET at all times.

Hang glider sails are made of polymer panels joined to create airfoils when stretched out on an airframe. Often a sail has riblike battens to help the airfoil keep its shape and to reduce drag. The hang glider is controlled by moving the pilot's weight by means of the control bar. Forward pulls drop the glider nose and cause acceleration or dives. Back pulls raise the glider nose, slow it down, and can cause stall. Lateral pulls to right or left tilt the respective wing, causing right or left turns. These movements, when well choreographed, allow expert hang glider pilots to carry out complex aerial maneuvers.

Prolonged hang glider glide, especially in cross-country glides, uses ridge currents and thermals to provide lift. Whether in short flights or cross-country soars, hang glider pilots wear comfortable supine or prone harnesses fastened to the glider. Harnesses suspend the pilot near the point where keel, crossbar, control bar, and king post meet. The harness is made of padded Dacron cloth with a seat-beltlike support of nylon webbing. Harnesses allow for comfortable flight, weight movement in any direction needed for control, and the carrying of emergency parachutes.

Paragliding

Paragliding began in France in the 1980's with canopies derived from double-surfaced Parafoil sport parachutes made of airfoil cells inflated by passing through the air. Paragliders are much longer than they are wide, and their wind-catching cells are inflated by gentle breezes. Their light weight and canopy softness make paragliding safer than hang gliding. The paraglider pilot, attached to a canopy by a seat harness, launches from a hill or another gentle slope using a canopy preinflated by the wind. The canopy behaves like an airfoil and can stay aloft for hours, a primary aim of paraglider enthusiasts. Paragliding is under control of the Fédération Aéronautique Internationale (FAI) hang-gliding commission.

A paraglider wing contains ten to seventy cells, joined side-by-side and closed along the entire trailing edge. The cells have inflation ports at the leading edge. Their walls also have interior ports that allow air to pass between them to maintain even internal pressure. Airfoil shape is maintained by this pressure, created by air entering the leading-edge ports kept open by stiff Mylar reinforcements. As long as the ports are clear, the airfoils keep their shape, and after full inflation, the internalized air stays put.

About 30 percent of paraglider lift is "plate lift," created when passing air is met with the leading edge higher than the trailing edge, and 70 percent is "induced lift," created by an airfoil shape which makes air pass over its top more slowly than underneath. The lines connecting airfoil and pilot are placed carefully to suit two requirements. First, many attachment points help keep the wing in an efficient shape when loaded. Second, as the lines cause drag, their number is minimized as much as possible. Also, paraglider operation depends on the match between pilot weight and aerodynamic forces. For optimization, the lines are joined to the harness by two to four pairs of webbing straps (risers).

As long as air flows evenly past the airfoil, lift keeps a paraglider moving upward, while gravity moves it forward and down. A paraglider descends slowly, due to the counterthrust of lift. Climb is only possible upon flight through thermal or ridge currents moving upward faster than a glider is dropping. Drag, due to pilot weight and the nonairfoil components, increases with the square of paraglider speed. Drag is also due to inequities of air passage around airfoils. Total drag is calculated by adding number values of the two drag types. The lift-to-drag ratio identifies the glide performance of the wing. A lift-to-drag ratio of five to one indicates that in still air, a paraglider moves forward 5 feet for every foot of descent.

The basic controls of paragliders are brakes. When they are not used, motion is straight forward at the best glide speed possible. Speed adjustment uses the brakes one-quarter on for minimum-sink speed and fully on to stall in a light-wind landing. Pulling the brakes causes the trailing edge to curve down, increasing camber and angle of attack. This increases lift but can cause stalls.

To steer, pilots pull down the brake on the side to they wish to turn into, increasing drag on that wing half. They can also assist steering by leaning in the direction of a turn. As to speed adjustment, most often it is useful to glide at less than the fastest glide speed. This is done by pulling the brakes down equally on both sides to increase the angle of attack. Speed increase is more difficult and uses a speed system, a foot stirrup connected to the front risers. Pushing on the stirrup shortens the front risers, reducing the angle of attack and increasing speed. Regardless, paragliders are slow aircraft and have only a small speed range.

Sanford S. Singer

Bibliography

Fair, Erik, Rod Stafford, and Rick Zimbelman. *Right Stuff for New Hang Glider Pilots*. Laguna Beach, Calif.: Publitec, 1987. A hang gliding manual full of important data on launching, soaring, wind effects, cross-country trips, forced and crash landings, and repairs.

Pfeiffer, Rich, Maggie Rowe, and Rod Stafford. *Hang Gliding According to Pfeiffer: Skills for the Advancing Pilot*. Laguna Beach, Calif.: Publitec, 1984. Thoroughly covers useful aspects of hang glider flying, such as soaring, cross-country, and contest flying, equipment, and flight calculations.

Poynter, Dan. *Hang Gliding: The Basic Handbook of Skysurfing*. Santa Barbara, Calif.: Parachuting Publications, 1977. Contains much useful information on hang gliding history, machine options, and flying.

Sollom, David, and Matthew Cook. *Paragliding from Beginner to Cross Country*. Marlborough, England: Crowood Press, 1998. Contains information on paragliding equipment, techniques, and competitions.

Whittall, Noel. *Paragliding: The Complete Guide*. New York: Lyons Press, 1995. Contains excellent information on paragliding theory, design, operation, and rules, as well as a useful glossary.

See also: Aerodynamics; Forces of flight; Gliders; Heavier-than-air craft; Ultralight aircraft

Harrier jets

Also known as: Harrier I, Harrier II (GR7 and AV-8B), Harrier II Plus
Date: First flight on August 31, 1966
Definition: Single-engine, vertical and short takeoff and landing (V/STOL) aircraft designed in Britain and manufactured in Britain and the United States.
Significance: Versatile aircraft used primarily by the United States, Great Britain, Spain, and Italy, Harrier jets can take off from aircraft carriers or land bases without the traditional reliance on runways. Used for air and ground support during combat, reconnaissance, fleet air defense, and maritime attack.

Development

In 1957, the British manufacturer Hawker-Siddley Aviation built the first Kestrel, the design of which would later be used for the Harrier jets. The construction of a prototype of the Harrier proceeded without government funding until after the development of an engine capable of vertical lift. In 1960, the British Royal Air Force expressed interest in the aircraft providing funds for continued research and development. Four additional planes were ordered after the potential for North Atlantic Treaty Organization (NATO) allies became apparent. The Harrier, a small ground-attack aircraft capable of vertical takeoffs achieved by the use of four swiveling nozzles on a Pegasus engine, flew for the first time on August 1, 1966. After the successful completion of the flight tests in Great Britain, six planes arrived in the United States for evaluation, with the National Aeronautics and Space Administration (NASA) examining two of them. Manufactured by British Aerospace, the Harrier I included two models, the Sea Harrier FA2 and the AV-8A. Both the Royal Air Force and the United States Marine Corps deployed the Harriers for defense and attack missions. The Sea Harrier, used primarily by the British Royal Navy as a defense fighter, utilized the Blue Vixen Radar that offered beyond visual range (BVR) capability and was able to shoot airborne and seaborne targets with its four AIM-120 BVR missiles. Capable of achieving speeds as high as Mach 1.3, the Harrier I had a wing span of 25 feet, 3 inches, a length of 46 feet, 5 inches, and a height of 11 feet, 10 inches. The British Royal Navy deployed the Sea Harrier during the Falkland Islands War in 1982. In the year 2000, the Harrier I was still being used by the Indian Navy and the Royal Thai Navy.

Second-Generation Harriers

By 1973, Hawker-Siddley and McDonnell Douglas Aircraft, an American contractor, initiated improvements on the original Harrier that resulted in the development of a composite wing structure. The original Pegasus motor, manufactured by Rolls Royce, continued to power the aircraft even though the maximum payload increased. The Harrier AV-8B flew for seven minutes at an altitude of 130 feet on November 9, 1978, at Lambert International Airport in St. Louis, Missouri. Before the production of the Harrier AV-8B commenced in 1981, the aircraft underwent extensive testing during a three-year period. The plane, measuring 46 feet 4 inches in length, with a wingspan of 30 feet 4 inches, is equipped with forward-looking infrared (FLIR) sensors, and the pilot can utilize night vision goggles, making the Harrier effective during both day and night missions. The aircraft is outfitted with free fall, retarded, cluster, and laser-guided bombs, air-to-air Sidewinder missiles, air-to-surface Maverick, HARM, and ALARM missiles, and a 1-by-25-millimeter Aden Cannon for the Royal Air Force or a 1-by-25 millimeter GAU-12 cannon for the United States Marine Corps. In addition to low-level missions at subsonic speeds, the Harrier II is also deployed for some medium-level operations where its accurate angle rate bombing system (ARBS) can be effectively utilized. British and NATO forces utilized the Harrier II in Bosnia and Serbia. The United States Marine Corps and the British Royal Navy deployed the Harrier II during Operation Desert Storm in 1991, where the eighty-

A Harrier jet, a vertical and short takeoff and landing (V/STOL) aircraft, rises straight into the air.

six aircraft flew 3,380 combat missions during forty-two days, dropping more than 6 million pounds of ordnance.

Harrier II Plus

Although the Harrier II proved effective, the United States and two of its NATO allies, Italy and Spain, cooperated on the development of the Harrier II Plus, which first flew on September 22, 1992. Manufactured by McDonnell Douglas and British Aerospace, the new aircraft relied on a more powerful engine, the Rolls-Royce Pegasus F402-RR-408, and included the advanced APG-65 radar system and avionics that allow the plane to fly a variety of missions during night or adverse weather conditions. Initially, the United States purchased twenty-seven, Italy sixteen, and Spain eight Harrier II Plus aircraft. Capable of engaging multiple targets simultaneously, the Harrier II Plus operates with free fall, retarded, cluster, and laser guided missiles, medium range air-to-air missiles (MRAAM) and short range air-to-air missiles (SRAAM), antishipping missiles, air-to-surface missiles, electronic counter measure (ECM) pods, and a 25-millimeter GAU-12 cannon. Since 1992, the United States Marine Corps has initiated a program to remanufacture all of its Harrier II planes, upgrading the systems to comply with the specifications of the Harrier II Plus. Boeing delivered the first Harrier II Plus in July, 1993, with the first updated Harrier II arriving in 1996.

Cynthia Clark Northrup

Bibliography

Chant, Christopher. *Fighters and Bombers*. Philadelphia: Chelsea House, 1999. A general reference source that provides drawings, photographs, and descriptions of all military fighters and bombers, including the Harrier jets.

Davies, Peter E., and Anthony M. Thornborough. *The Harrier Story*. Annapolis, Md.: Naval Institute Press, 1996. Excellent reference source for the design, development, and operational history of the Harrier jet. Interviews with engineers involved in the development of the aircraft provide firsthand accounts of the difficulties associated with VTOL technology.

Jenkins, Dennis R. *Boeing/BAe Harrier*. North Branch, Minn.: Speciality Press, 1998. Jenkins's work provides a look at the technical and engineering details involved with the production of the Harrier jet.

See also: Aircraft carriers; Boeing; Fighter pilots; Gulf War; Marine pilots, U.S.; Royal Air Force; McDonnell Douglas; Vertical takeoff and landing

Heavier-than-air craft

- **Definition:** A vehicle driven through the air by a self-carried power source, supported by air pressure against the wings or rotors, and controlled in flight path and destination by the pilot.
- **Significance:** Heavier-than-air craft, such as airplanes and helicopters, are faster, more controllable, and safer than lighter-than-air craft, and thus have become the dominant instrument in aerial transportation and warfare.

Early Experiments

In religion, mythology, legend, and imagination, human levitation and flight are old and familiar concepts. Birds, bats, and insects were visible proof that flying through the air with wings was possible in nature, and for centuries humans imitated birds by attempting to fly with flapping, birdlike wings carried by human arms. These "ornithopters," frequently launched from hillsides, towers, or barns, formed a long and frequently farcical or fatal tradition in humankind's attempt to fly.

Some early Greek physicists appreciated that a compressed jet of air could be a motive force, but saw no practical way to achieve this. During the Renaissance, Leonardo da Vinci sketched out a few ideas regarding helicopters and propellers, but with no suggestion for a power source. Still, the evidence that moving air could exert a tangible and useable force on sails, kites, and windmills was plain enough. In the eighteenth century, some "whirling arm" experimenters, such as John Smeaton, began to quantify the lift and drag forces exerted by moving air upon flat surfaces. In France, Launoy and Bienvenu devised a model helicopter in 1784. Late eighteenth century technology developed steam as a power source, but by 1783 Jacques-Étienne Montgolfier's balloons had captured public interest and also had given the French the premier place in aeronautics development.

Practical Applications

Significant heavier-than-air research was done in early nineteenth century England by Sir George Cayley, an inventor, scholar, and publicist whom many authors describe as "the father of modern aviation." Cayley's studies and experiments confirmed that a curved-wing, or cambered, surface supplied more lift than did a flat one, that low pressure on the upper surface exerted considerable lift, and that air pressure on an adjustable plane surface in an airstream varied in extent and location. He drew attention to the problem of stability, and also built model helicopters and gliders. One glider was capable of supporting his coachman in a short airborne hop. The pioneer pilot's verdict was "Please, Sir George, I wish to give notice. I was hired to drive, not to fly." Cayley's extensive publications were not widely known in his lifetime, but they had later influence. Cayley's English followers, such as William Samuel Henson and John Stringfellow, attempted an aerial steam carriage, but of greater importance was the first wind tunnel, built in 1871 by Francis Herbert Wenham and John Browning.

Frenchmen dominated aeronautical study and experimentation in the nineteenth century, but their more elaborate machines were less successful than a device of great simplicity. In 1871, Alphonse Pénaud employed twisted rubber as a power source for a model aircraft. His "planophore" was a stick fuselage holding curved and angled monoplane wings with their extremities tipped up, a vertical rudder, and a pusher propeller at the rear, powered by a twisted rubber band directly under the fuselage. In an apparently simple toy, Pénaud incorporated the essentials of airplane structure, including lift, inherent stability, and elementary vertical and horizontal control. The major challenge remained to find a better power source. One key to the progress of aviation was the development of the internal combustion engine by Nikolaus August Otto, Gottlieb Daimler, and Carl Benz.

Gliders and Powered Craft

In the 1890's, hang gliding was greatly developed and popularized by the exploits of Germany's Otto Lilienthal. The author of *Des Vogelflug als Grundlage der Fliegekunst* (1889; *Bird Flight as the Basis of Aviation*, 1911), Lilienthal believed that gliders copying bird wings would lead to successful powered flight. From 1891 to 1896, he built five monoplane gliders and two biplane gliders and made two thousand flights with them, measuring lift and drag. These glides of up to 750 feet in distance drew spectators, reporters, and photographers. The "German bird-man" was a hero to the air-minded, especially in the United States, and remained an inspiration even after his August 9, 1896, fatal crash.

Other European aviation pioneers were concentrating on powered flying machines. Alexander Feodorovich Mozhaiski attempted a steam-powered hop in 1884. In the 1890's, Victor Tatin and Charles Rivet built a steam-powered model plane, which in one test flew about 460 feet. Clément Ader claimed to have flown about 50 meters in 1890 in his steam-powered *Eole* and to have surpassed this distance on October 14, 1897, with a flight of 300 meters in his government-financed *Avion III*. Whether this was a continuous flight or the total length of a series of hops in unclear, but the French army observers were less impressed than Ader was, and the project was dropped.

In the 1890's considerable press attention was given to the construction and testing of a £30,000 steam airplane by Sir Hiram Maxim. It had a lifting area of 4,000 square feet, two 180-horsepower steam engines, twin propellers of 17.8 feet, a 1,800-foot launching track, and a total weight of 8,000 pounds. On July 31, 1894, with a steam pressure of 320 pounds per square inch, this monster barely left the ground, colliding with the guard rails. Maxim's craft had ample power, but lacked all the other requirements for flight. This experiment was not pursued further and made no advance in aviation technology, but it did keep attempts to fly in the public mind.

At the turn of the century, European aviation interests were turning to semirigid powered airships of increasing size, culminating in the German zeppelin. Hang gliding was continued, however, by Percy Pilcher, a Lilienthal disciple and English engineer. Pilcher was briefly joined by Lawrence Hargrave of Australia for testing some of the latter's box-kite designs. Pilcher's career was ended by a fatal crash in 1899. The next major experiment in heavier-than-air flight was made in America.

American Experiments

The gliding school of aviation in America was continued, encouraged, and publicized by Octave Chanute, a French-born American civil engineer. He improved glider design, using the ideas of Lilienthal, Pilcher, Hargrave, and others. Collecting information on past and current aviation experiments in the United States, France, and England, he developed the Chanute biplane glider using the Pratt truss used in bridge building. Augustus Moore Herring acted as Chanute's assistant and pilot for several hundred glides launched from the Indiana dunes in 1896 and flew up to 350 feet. In 1900, Chanute was contacted by the Wright brothers and gave them information and encouragement, while he was also in communication with the telephone inventor Alexander Graham Bell and the Smithsonian secretary Samuel Pierpont Langley regarding their own aviation projects. Thanks largely to Chanute, meetings and publications began to connect American aeronautical researchers into an informal group of scientific minds.

Langley, secretary of the Smithsonian Institution and respected in academic circles as America's leading expert in aeronautic science, succeeded in the 1890's in constructing steam-powered model airplanes. In 1898, during the Spanish-American War, he succeeded in gaining a grant from the U.S. Army for building a human-lifting, power-driven, controllable airplane. The result was the Pénaud-type aerodrome, with tandem wings, a tailpiece rudder, and twin-pusher propellers driven by a water-cooled gasoline engine of radial design, with five cylinders providing 52 horsepower.

On October 7, 1903, at Widewater on the Potomac River, witnessed by officials and the press, the 850-pound craft, with Charles Manly as pilot, was propelled from the roof of a houseboat, and in *The Washington Post*'s description, "simply slid into the water like a handful of mortar." *The New York Times* decided that a practical flying machine "might be evolved . . . in from one to ten million years." After a repetition of this failure on December 8, one congressman described Langley's aerodrome as a "mud duck which will not fly fifty feet." The U.S. Army quickly cancelled Langley's project, and he died in 1906 a disappointed man. However, the Smithsonian Institution until 1948 prominently displayed the great aerodrome as "the first aircraft in history capable of flight with a pilot and several hundred pounds of useful load."

The First Successful Flight

Wilbur Wright and his brother Orville were bachelors, living with their father, Milton Wright, a bishop in the United Brethren Church, and their sister Kate in Dayton, Ohio. The brothers operated a shop for building, selling, maintaining, and repairing the popular safety bicycles of the 1890's. Their joint interest in aviation may have been sparked by a childhood gift of a toy helicopter. It was certainly inspired by Otto Lilienthal, whose personal role in practical gliding they admired, and whose inductive, step-by-step approach to airplane design they followed. The Wrights were competent enough in algebra, solid geometry, trigonometry, and physics to understand the aeronautical problems involved in aviation, and as practical mechanics they were able to do most of the production themselves, saving expense and minimizing errors. They attacked the task in stages, concentrating first on the problem of wing lift, then on mastering flight control, and finally on adequate propulsion.

In May, 1899, Wilbur Wright wrote to the Smithsonian Institution requesting titles of books and articles on flying, and a current list was sent to him. The following August, the Wrights built their first aircraft, a biplane box kite 5 feet wide, with a fixed-tail plane, in order to test wing twisting, later called wing warping, as a method of controlling side roll. In May, 1900, Wilbur wrote to Chanute to ex-

---

Events in the History of Heavier-Than-Air Craft

1784: The French design a model helicopter.
1891: German Otto Lilienthal helps to develop and popularize hang gliders.
1900: Influential engineer Octave Chanute advises Orville and Wilbur Wright, Alexander Graham Bell, and Samuel Langley in their aviation projects.
1903: Samuel Langley makes unsuccessful attempt at flight in his *Aerodrome*; the Wright brothers succeed at Kitty Hawk with their *Flyer*.
1908: Orville Wright wins U.S. Army contract to produce military aircraft.

---

change ideas on gliding, and the Wrights' later gliders somewhat resembled Chanute types.

In September, 1900, the off-season in the bicycle trade, the Wrights took a camping vacation at Kitty Hawk, a sparsely inhabited stretch of sand dunes and mosquitoes on the Outer Banks of North Carolina. Here they flew their *Glider I*, mostly as a kite. The following year, a larger model, *Glider II*, failed to achieve the lift and drag results reported by earlier experimenters. The Wrights decided to check existing aeronautic tables with their homemade wind tunnel. These tests indicated that the Smeaton coefficient and the Lilienthal and Chanute tables from which they had been working were significantly inaccurate. Developing their own (confidential) tables, the Wrights built their successful 1902 *Glider III*. This craft included the mechanical linkage of wing warping to rear rudder control, which formed the chief basis of their 1902 patent application, granted in 1906. By a process of research, experiment, and checking for flaws, the Wrights developed an air frame which solved the problems of lift and flight control. The Wrights were then ready to attempt powered flight in 1903.

Much of their 1903 season, however, was consumed by problems and delays. Not finding a gasoline engine meeting their lightweight, high-power needs, they designed their own four-cylinder, water-cooled, in-line engine, weighing about 150 pounds, producing 12 horsepower, and linked by bicycle chains to a pair of pusher propellers. Marine propellers being entirely unsuitable, the Wrights used their wind tunnel to design propellers as "moving wings" traveling in a forward spiral. Altogether, testing the new machine, *Flyer I*, at Kitty Hawk was delayed until December 17, 1903. That day's consecutive flights were Orville's initial hop of 120 feet, Wilbur's of 175 feet, Orville's flight of 200 feet, and Wilbur's flight of 852 feet into a wind of 20 to 27 miles per hour for 59 seconds. These straight-line distances at a low level were not revolutionary, but to take off and be airborne under power for nearly a minute was new in the annals of aviation. There were photographs and five witnesses, but the press generated only a few garbled reports.

In 1904, the Wrights practiced on a new *Flyer II* with a slightly larger engine, flying at Huffman Prairie near Dayton. These low-altitude flights culminated in successful circles and, on November 9, a flight of five minutes. The 1905 *Flyer III* had a wing area of 503 square feet, a 40-feet, 6-inch span, and wing camber of 1 in 20. Its wings were horizontally flat, with a built-up elevator and rudder, and with an engine of about 20 horsepower. Another series of Huffman Prairie flights included one of 24 miles in 38 minutes. The local audience and photographs increased, and as one foreign visitor put it, "Dayton knows the Wrights fly, but America isn't sure."

The 1905 *Flyer III* represented the completion of the Wrights' project to build a human-carrying, powered flying machine capable of controlled flight. The Wrights offered the plane to the U.S. Army, then the British, French, and Germans. Their asking price of $250,000 or more was too steep for the war departments, who shrewdly suspected that the Wrights were reluctant to demonstrate their machine for fear of easy copying. Octave Chanute's 1903 Paris lecture on the Wrights' gliding experiments, Wilbur Wright's U.S. lectures, and visits to the Wrights by European observers gradually spread the conviction that powered aviation was indeed at hand.

Improving the Wright *Flyer*

Meanwhile, powered glider hops, particularly of box-kite construction types, increased in Europe. Some models were advertised for sale as "Wright-type flyers." The popular Brazilian sportsman Alberto Santos-Dumont was hailed for his 1906 flight at Bagatelle, France, as the "the first to fly." The Wrights brought a flyer plane to Europe in 1907, but left it in storage, deciding that in 1908 Orville would compete for a U.S. Army contract, while Wilbur would demonstrate the model which they left in France.

In 1908, Orville won the U.S. Army contract to considerable public acclaim, while in France, Wilbur had a Cinderella experience. Ridiculed for weeks for his lengthy delays in assembling and repairing the stored plane, Wilbur's August 8 demonstration flight at Le Mans, with circles, figure eights, and graceful landings under complete control, came as a revelation to Europeans who had not gotten beyond short, straight-line hops. Aviators, press, and public hailed Wilbur Wright as a hero and companies were quickly formed in France, Britain, and Germany to build Wright biplanes under license.

The 1908 Wright *Flyer* clearly outclassed its European counterparts in construction, performance, and controllability. However, at the Rheims air exhibition of 1909, there were several French types which had improved on the Wright *Flyer*. Henri and Maurice Farman offered stable biplanes, and Louis Blériot showed the monoplane type with which he would cross the English Channel to become the French hero of the year. Gabriel Voisin promised quick delivery and reliable construction. Leon Levavasseur's *Antoinettes* were becoming popular. Glenn H. Curtiss upheld the United States' reputation by winning the Gordon Bennet Speed Trophy. All these represented some form of advancement over the 1908 Wright machine. Several nations also established airplane sections in their armies in 1909.

The year 1910 saw a great increase in the number of airplane manufacturers, but a more modest growth in airplane sales. Clearly, even the largest firms would not survive without large government orders for military purposes, so patriotic public agitation was organized to that end. This brought about a major change in production types. Pre-1914 war departments wanted planes which excelled in range, stability, load, and altitude, solid and simple in design, built for careless handling with easy maintenance and repair under wartime conditions. From 1911 on, Europe's war departments were deciding which plane types and which manufacturing firms would survive, and trying to find a remedy for the French predominance in the light engine market.

By 1913, airplanes had wheeled landing gear, more efficient tractor propellers were replacing pusher types, and cantilevered wings were the key to larger monoplanes. Monocoque fuselage construction made possible the airliners of the future, and ailerons were beginning to replace wing warping, which would clearly not be practical with the heavy wings of a large plane. Also, Igor Sikorsky had already built a four-engine plane and would later build a practical helicopter. None of these improvements on the Wright *Flyer* matched the difficulty or importance of the problems of flight which the Wright brothers had solved, but they marked modern aviation as a field of constant and rapid change.

K. Fred Gillum

Bibliography

Christienne, Charles, and Pierre Lissarague. *A History of French Military Aviation*. Washington, D.C.: Smithsonian Institution Press, 1986. A popular edition of a scholarly work providing a French view of military aviation.

Crouch, Tom D. *A Dream of Wings: Americans and the Airplane, 1875-1905*. New York: W. W. Norton, 1981. A scholarly but readable text on American aviation up to the Wright brothers.

Gibbs-Smith, Charles Harvard. *Aviation: An Historical Survey from Its Origins to the End of World War II*. London: Her Majesty's Stationery Office, 1970. A comprehensive, readable, and scholarly history by an author who has published extensively in the field of Anglo-American aviation history.

Jakab, Peter L. *Visions of a Flying Machine: The Wright Brothers and the Process of Invention*. Washington, D.C.: Smithsonian Institution Press, 1990. An analysis of the aeronautical problems faced by the Wright brothers and their probable methods of solving them.

See also: Airplanes; Sir George Cayley; Octave Chanute; Glenn H. Curtiss; Leonardo da Vinci; Forces of flight; Gliders; Hang gliding and paragliding; Helicopters; History of human flight; Samuel Pierpont Langley; Otto Lilienthal; Propellers; Alberto Santos-Dumont; Igor Sikorsky; Wing designs; Wright brothers; Wright *Flyer*; Ferdinand von Zeppelin

Helicopters

Also known as: Choppers, helos, whirlybirds, copters
Definition: Any rotary-wing aircraft having powered, fixed rotors that provide lift and propulsion for the aircraft.
Significance: The helicopter was the first operational vertical takeoff and landing (VTOL) aircraft and remains the most prevalent.

Configurations

The helicopter is the principal VTOL aircraft in service throughout the world. The name "helicopter" was coined by a Frenchman, Viscomte Gustave de Ponton d'Amecourt, circa 1863. Helicopters can be distinguished from other rotary-wing aircraft by the fact that their rotors are fixed in position on the aircraft fuselage and simultaneously provide lift and propulsion. The vast majority of modern helicopters have either one or two rotors that provide lift and propulsive force.

Although helicopters can take off and land vertically, their maximum forward speed is much lower than that of fixed-wing aircraft. This limitation is due to the fact that the rotor or rotors must provide both propulsion and lift. Under high-speed flight conditions, the vibratory forces on the rotor blades become very large, thereby limiting the top speed of the helicopter. In order to increase the top speed, some helicopters, known as compound helicopters, have been equipped with auxiliary means of propulsion, such as propellers or jet engines.

Helicopters are built in a variety of configurations, including the single-rotor, the tandem, the coaxial, and the side-by-side helicopters. The single-rotor helicopter is the most common configuration currently in use. It can be identified by the single main rotor that provides thrust and propulsion, as well as pitch and roll control. A smaller tail rotor usually provides antitorque directional yaw control. However, other devices may be used instead of a tail rotor.

Another common configuration is the tandem helicopter. The tandem helicopter has two large rotors, one at the forward end of the helicopter and the other at the aft end. The two rotors rotate in opposite directions, thus eliminating the need for an antitorque device, such as a tail rotor. This configuration is particularly well-suited for the transport of heavy cargo, because the two rotors can accommodate large changes in the aircraft center of gravity due to the cargo load.

Less common configurations include side-by-side and coaxial helicopters. Like the tandem helicopters, side-by-side helicopters have two main rotors, but one is located on the right side of the aircraft, and the other is located on the left side. The rotors rotate in opposite directions, again eliminating the need for a tail rotor.

A variant of the side-by-side helicopter is the synchropter, on which the two rotors are placed close together, so that the rotors intermesh. The synchropter has the advantage of being able to take off and land in more confined areas than either a side-by-side or tandem helicopter, because the close proximity of rotor masts reduces the area required for clearance around the rotors.

The coaxial helicopter has two counterrotating rotors that share a common mast. Because the rotors rotate in opposite directions, no tail rotor is needed for this configuration either. Coaxial helicopters also have the advantage of being able to land in more confined areas than any other configuration, because the swept area of the rotors is the smallest of all configurations.

Missions

Because helicopters are able to take off vertically, hover in midair, and land vertically, they are ideal vehicles for a wide variety of missions. They do not require prepared landing areas, so they can take off and land in forest clearings, on the tops of buildings, and on ships at sea. As a result, they can be used in civil and military applications for which fixed-wing aircraft are unsuitable.

The transportation of passengers is one of the primary missions of helicopters. The largest civilian user of helicopter transportation is the petroleum industry. Helicopters regularly transport petroleum workers to and from offshore oil platforms, because they are much faster and more cost effective than boats. Many large corporations use helicopters to ferry their executives between sites. Commercial helicopter operators in scenic locations, such as the Grand Canyon and Hawaii, regularly carry passengers on sight-seeing tours, although increasingly stringent noise regulations have somewhat curtailed their business.

Commercial helicopter airlines have not been economically viable, despite the obvious advantages of ferrying passengers between airports and between airports and inner-city heliports. The U.S. military services, particularly the Army and the Marines, make extensive use of helicopters for troop transport. Naval helicopters are often used for ship-to-shore and ship-to-ship transportation of personnel. In all services, helicopters are used for the insertion and extraction of special-operations forces at remote sites.

Cargo transportation is another important helicopter function. In the logging industry, helicopters are used to transport logs from remote areas either directly to a mill or to rivers in which the logs are floated to a mill. Construction projects often use helicopters to transport heavy equipment, such as heating, ventilation, and air conditioning units, to the tops of tall buildings. The Statue of Freedom, atop the U.S. Capitol Building, was removed by helicopter in 1993 for restoration and was later replaced in the same manner. Helicopters with large buckets slung beneath them are used to transport water from nearby lakes to the site of a forest fire. On the military side, the Army and Marines use helicopters to transport supplies and even small- and medium-sized vehicles from rear areas to troops in the field. The Navy uses helicopters to transport supplies from shore to ships at sea and between ships at sea.

Many police departments, particularly in large cities, use helicopters for airborne patrol and surveillance. Because they operate at altitude, helicopters have a wider field of view than ground patrols. In cases of pursuit, it is much easier for a helicopter to keep a fleeing suspect in view and safer for the ground units and the general public. In addition, when on patrol, a helicopter can often reach the crime scene more rapidly than can a ground unit. In a similar application, radio and television stations use helicopters for acquiring traffic reports and news gathering. News helicopters can often reach the scene of a news event more rapidly than can ground vehicles.

Another mission for which helicopters are particularly well-suited is search and rescue. Although this is primarily a military mission, police departments and the U.S. National Park Service will use helicopters to find and rescue hikers, campers, and others who find themselves in dangerous situations. The U.S. Coast Guard is very active in search and rescue, patrolling the waters off the coast of the United States. A typical Coast Guard rescue mission would be to extract passengers from foundering sailing vessels. Combat search-and-rescue missions are flown primarily by the Air Force and the Navy to locate and return aircrews of aircraft downed in combat. During the Vietnam War, the Jolly Green Giant (CH/HH-3E) helicopters were a welcome sight for many pilots who had been shot down while flying over North Vietnam.

Combat close air support and antiarmor are purely military missions. Close air support involves using helicopters to support friendly ground troops by directing fire on enemy troops in the near vicinity. Helicopters used in antiarmor missions are equipped with ordnance that is capable of disabling or destroying tanks and other armored vehicles. The Marines use the AH-1 and the Army uses the AH-64 for these missions.

Flight Control

One of the first problems of helicopter flight control that must be solved is the question of how to keep the fuselage from rotating opposite the rotor. In order to spin the rotor, torque is applied by the engine to the rotor driveshaft. Therefore, the rotor has an angular momentum, which must be counteracted in some manner. If the angular momentum of the rotor is not equalized, the fuselage will begin to rotate in the opposite direction to the rotor rotation. Single-rotor helicopters equalize the angular momentum with countertorque devices, such as a tail rotor or a NOTAR (no tail rotor) system. The tail rotor is a smaller rotor mounted vertically at the end of a tail boom that generates a lateral thrust. The NOTAR system also generates lateral thrust but does so using the slipstream of the rotor and air ejected from a slot in the tail boom to produce the Coanda effect. Helicopters with more than one rotor, such as the tandem, side-by-side, and coaxial types, equalize the angular momentum by employing equally sized rotors rotating in opposite directions.

Helicopters

In order to fly a helicopter, the pilot must be able to control the translation of the aircraft in the vertical, lateral (side-to-side), and longitudinal (forward-and-back) directions, as well as rotation in roll, pitch, and yaw. The pilot's controls include a collective lever beside the pilot seat, a cyclic stick between the pilot's knees, and foot pedals. It is interesting to note that in helicopters, the pilot sits in the right seat and the copilot sits in the left. In fixed-wing aircraft, the pilot sits in the left seat, and the copilot sits in the right. This seating arrangement is an artifact from one of Igor Sikorsky's early helicopters, which had such "backward" seating.

To explain helicopter control, consider a single-rotor helicopter. The main rotor of a single-rotor helicopter produces a thrust, which acts in a direction roughly normal to the rotor disk. Therefore, in order to control the helicopter, the pilot must be able to control the magnitude and direction of this thrust. The magnitude of the thrust is controlled by the collective lever, which equally increases or decreases the pitch angle of all rotor blades, thereby increasing or decreasing the thrust. In order to control the direction of the thrust, the pilot must be able to control the orientation of the rotor disk. One way to change the orientation of the rotor disk is to physically tilt the rotor hub.

For very small helicopters, hub tilt is a practical control method. However, for larger helicopters, the rotor acts like a large gyroscope, which makes tilting the hub extremely difficult. The alternative is to increase the thrust on one half of the disk, while simultaneously decreasing the thrust on the other half. This cyclic change in thrust causes the rotor disk to tilt and does so with much less effort than hub tilt.

In all but a few modern helicopters, the pilot's cyclic stick, acting through a swashplate, is used to change the cyclic pitch of the rotor blades. The swashplate consists of two parts: a nonrotating plate and a rotating plate. The nonrotating plate, which is connected to the pilot collective and cyclic pitch controls, slides up and down for collective-pitch changes and tilts for cyclic-pitch changes. The rotating plate sits on top of the nonrotating plate and spins with the rotor. Pitch links, attached to the rotating plate and the rotor blades, mechanically change the pitch angle of the blades. Yaw control is obtained through the foot pedals, which are connected to the collective pitch controls for the tail rotor.

Helicopters use rotors rather than wings to achieve vertical takeoff and landing. (NASA)

History

Although the development of an operational helicopter is a relatively recent accomplishment, many of the concepts necessary for designing a practical helicopter have been known for a very long time. In fact, one could argue that a maple seed falling from a tree is nature's model for the helicopter. The Chinese top, which predates the Roman Empire, is perhaps humankind's first step toward modern helicopters. In addition, Leonardo da Vinci considered the possibility of vertical flight, and made a sketch of his concept for such a vehicle.

The development of a practical helicopter was made possible by overcoming three major technology barriers. The first barrier, and the easiest to overcome, was the design of a rotor system with rotor blades and a rotor hub that were strong but lightweight, with adequate aerodynamic efficiency. The second was to engineer a power plant with a sufficiently high ratio of power to weight, required in order to lift the aircraft off the ground. This barrier was overcome with the invention of the internal-combustion engine. The third technology barrier was to devise a method for controlling the helicopter in flight. The principles leading to controlled helicopter flight were developed gradually by helicopter pioneers.

Early helicopter pioneers tried a variety of power plants in their helicopter designs. During the latter half of the eighteenth century, Mikhail Vasilyevich Lomonosov in Russia, Launoy and Bienvenu in France, and Sir George Cayley in England provided power to their helicopters by using different spring mechanisms. While spring-driven power plants have a good ratio of power to weight, they cannot provide sufficient sustained power for long flights.

In the nineteenth century, steam-powered helicopters were designed by Horatio Frederick Phillips in England, d'Amecourt and Alphonse Pénaud in France, Enrico Forlanini in Italy, and Thomas Edison in the United States. In contrast to spring power, steam power could provide sufficient sustained power, but its ratio of power to weight was very low.

Like that of the airplane, the concept of the helicopter did not become truly feasible until the invention of the internal combustion engine. Developments leading to a practical helicopter began to be achieved not long after Orville and Wilbur Wright flew their first airplane, but the availability of an adequate power plant brought problems of control to the fore. Paul Cornu and Charles Renard in France, Emile and Henry Berliner in the United States, and Igor Sikorsky and Boris Yuriev in Russia made significant contributions prior to 1920.

Renard introduced the flapping hinge, which improved rotor control; and Yuriev introduced the antitorque tail rotor for yaw control. In 1907, Cornu made the first piloted, free-flight, vertical takeoff, but the aircraft had to be stabilized manually by a ground crew. In the 1920's and early 1930's, George de Bothezat in the United States, Etienne Oemichen and Louis-Charles Breguet in France, Raoul Pescara in Spain, Emile and Henry Berliner in the United States, Louis Brennan in England, A. G. von Baumhauer in Holland, and Corradino D'Ascanio in Italy, M. B. Bleeker in the United States, and Yuriev in Russia all built prototype helicopters. Unfortunately, all of these designs either had controllability problems or were too complex to be practical.

However, important contributions toward improved control were made by Bothezat, in differential collective pitch control; Pescara, in cyclic pitch control; von Baumhauer, in the area of the swashplate; and d'Ascanio, in servotab cyclic pitch control.

In 1936, German aircraft designer Heinrich Focke introduced the first practical helicopter, the Focke-Achgelis Fa-61, a side-by-side design in which all of the stability problems had been solved. In 1938, Hanna Reitsch flew the Fa-61 inside the Deutschland-Halle in Berlin, demonstrating its flying precision. In 1939, in the United States, Igor Sikorsky introduced the VS-300, a single-rotor helicopter, which may have been the world's first useful helicopter. Germany continued its development of the helicopter during World War II, and Anton Flettner's synchropter design, the FL-282 Kolibri, became the first production helicopter.

At about the same time, other individuals, including Arthur Young, Frank Piasecki, and Stanley Hiller in the United States, and Nikolai Kamov, Mikhail Mil, and Ivan Bratukhin in the Soviet Union were developing their own independent helicopter designs.

Modern Helicopters

The basics of helicopter design have not changed greatly since the early days of helicopters in the 1940's. However, technological improvements have been incorporated that make the modern helicopter safer, easier, and more efficient to fly. One of the most significant advances in helicopter performance resulted from the introduction of the gas-turbine engine. The maximum power-to-weight ratio achievable with piston engines by the end of World War II was approximately 1 horsepower per pound. However, by the 1960, turbine engines had achieved power-to-weight ratios of 3 horsepower per pound, and by 2000 they had achieved weight ratios of up to 6 horsepower per pound.

Helicopter rotor systems have also undergone significant changes. In the early years, rotor blades were made exclusively of wood, one of the principal materials used for aircraft construction. In 1944, Hiller introduced metal rotor blades on the XH-44, but it was not until 1952 that metal blades were delivered on a production aircraft, the Sikorsky S-52.

The use of composite materials for rotor blade construction began in the early 1960's, and, by the 1970's, the Messerschmitt-Bölkow-Blohm company in Germany had built all-composite blades for the BO-105 helicopter. Virtually every modern helicopter is now equipped with composite blades. The rotor hub has also undergone changes in the way that the blades are attached. Many helicopter rotors are fully articulated. That is, each blade has physical hinges, which allow the blade to flap out of the plane of rotation and lag in the plane of rotation. A bearing also allows the blade to pitch. The concepts of a hingeless rotor that eliminates the flap and lag hinges and a bearingless rotor, which is basically a hingeless rotor without a pitch bearing, have found their way into the designs of many modern helicopters.

Technological improvements, such as vibration control devices in the rotor system and the fuselage, have improved the comfort level for passengers, as well as the performance of the flight crew due to reduced fatigue. Crashworthy structural design, seats, and fuel systems have improved the safety of helicopters in emergency situations. Hydraulic control systems have replaced the mechanical control systems of early helicopters, and modern helicopters are often equipped with electronic flight control and stability augmentation systems to reduce pilot workload. Digital fly-by-wire and fly-by-light control systems, as well as glass cockpits, have begun to be introduced in advanced production helicopters.

Donald L. Kunz

Bibliography

Fay, John. *The Helicopter, History, Piloting, and How It Flies.* London: David & Charles, 1976. A description of the fundamentals of helicopter design and flight, using simple explanations of aeronautical theory.

Gablehouse, Charles. *Helicopters and Autogiros: A Chronicle of Rotating-Wing Aircraft Since 1907.* London: Scientific Book Club, 1967. A history of rotorcraft, including both helicopters and autogiros.

Hirschberg, M. J. *The American Helicopter, An Overview of Helicopter Developments in America, 1907-1999.* Arlington, Va.: ANSER, 2000. An historical account of twentieth century helicopter developments, with pictures and descriptions of many different designs.

Liberatore, *Helicopters Before Helicopters.* Malabar, Fla.: Krieger, 1998. A historical account of helicopter development from early concepts to practical models, updated with interpretations based on current knowledge.

Taylor, Michael J. *History of Helicopters.* London: Hamlyn, 1984. A chronicle of helicopter development.

See also: Apache helicopter; Bell Aircraft; Sir George Cayley; Firefighting aircraft; Gyros; Leonardo da Vinci; Hanna Reitsch; Rescue aircraft; Rotorcraft; Igor Sikorsky; Vertical takeoff and landing

High-altitude flight

Definition: Flight at altitudes higher than most flights but lower than orbital flight; roughly between 50,000 feet (9 miles) and 100 miles.

Significance: High-altitude flight has often been the frontier of aviation technology, meteorology, astronomy, and aerial reconnaissance. Many tasks can still be done more cheaply, or can only be done, in high-altitude flight.

High-Altitude Characteristics

The meaning of the term "high altitude" has changed over the years. Balloonists struggled to reach altitudes between 20,000 and 30,000 feet, yet by the last third of the twentieth century these altitudes were routine for commercial and military jet transports. The only constant is that the frontier always lies at the current definition of high altitude.

Decreasing pressure is the most important feature of high altitude. Most of the earth's atmosphere is in the troposphere, roughly the first 40,000 feet from the surface, and 99 percent of the atmosphere is below 127,000 feet. This has many implications. For high-speed jet aircraft, lesser air density allows greater speed, reduces heating problems, and allows greater engine efficiency until the available oxygen is too dilute to support combustion. For rockets, which require no external oxidizers, there is no limit except available fuel and oxidizer.

For slower aircraft utilizing maximum lift for minimum energy, progressively less air density requires progressively wider wingspans, bigger control surfaces, cleaner aerodynamics, or more power to lift the same payload. For lighter-than-air (LTA) craft, such as balloons and dirigibles, decreasing air density with increasing altitude means there is less lift available per unit volume, so LTA craft must be larger to carry a given payload to higher altitudes.

For living creatures, such as human crewmembers, a low-pressure (hypobaric) environment can be deadly. For instance, at about 18,000 feet the total air pressure is halved from that at sea level, and the amount of oxygen available to the body is similarly halved. The result is hypoxia (low oxygen) with progressively more severe symptoms as pressure declines: euphoria, headache, nausea, irritability, confusion, unconsciousness, and death. Aircraft crews can compensate for low pressure by breathing a greater percentage of oxygen. However, above 49,000 feet even pure oxygen does not have sufficient pressure to sustain life, so crews must have either pressurized cabins or pressure suits.

Flying above much of the atmosphere means that much of the radiation usually stopped by the atmosphere will impact the craft. The lack of atmosphere allows clearer astronomical observations at light wavelengths stopped by the atmosphere, such as infrared. However, increased radiation in ultraviolet and shorter wavelength bands can attack a number of plastics that might be used in aircraft structures, and flight crews are subject to higher doses of ionizing radiation than people on the ground.

Cold is another feature of high altitude. A rough formula is that in temperate zones every thousand feet of altitude is equivalent to traveling 75 miles farther from the equator. Temperatures drop steadily with altitude in the troposphere, stay the same or even rise slightly in the lower stratosphere, and then become somewhat irrelevant as declining air density begins to approach vacuum. Cold is not a serious problem for supersonic craft, for which avoidance of overheating is the prime concern. However, it can be life-threatening for slower craft.

Lastly, every mile of altitude yields roughly 33 miles of line-of-sight to the horizon. This has great importance for airborne radars and communications platforms. A radar plane flying at 40,000 feet has a range 260 miles, compared to 520 miles for a craft at 80,000 feet. In communications, an aircraft holding position or flying in tight circles to stay nearly in the same place can replace satellite communications service at lower cost and allow for ground stations that use much less power. They can also be put in place or upgraded more quickly than can satellite launches.

There are three types of high-altitude craft: highly efficient propeller and jet craft, supersonic jets and rockets, and lighter-than-air craft, such as balloons and dirigibles.

The U-2 and Its Competitors

The Lockheed U-2, sometimes called the Dragon Lady, is the most famous formerly secret high-altitude aircraft. In the early 1950's, during the most intense part of the Cold War, the U.S. intelligence community wanted a spy aircraft that could fly higher than any interceptors in the Soviet Union. Kelly Johnson at Lockheed proposed radically reconfiguring an F-104 Starfighter as a glider body with an 82-foot wingspan and a jet engine so it could fly at 70,000 feet. Johnson and his "Skunk Works" flew the first craft in August, 1955. On July 5, 1956, a U-2 flew over Moscow, the Soviet capital. Although the Soviets protested, they could do nothing about the overflights, and the United States denied its existence.

However, the U-2 flew slowly, turned slowly, had not been designed for stealth by minimizing its radar and infrared signature, and Soviet antiaircraft missiles improved. On May 1, 1960, the Soviets downed a U-2 one thousand miles inside their border, and captured the pilot, precipitating a major diplomatic incident. Another U-2 was shot down during the Cuban Missile Crisis in 1962, and the U-2's were pulled back from well-defended areas. However, they continued to be used into the twenty-first century as high-flying signal-intelligence craft, obtaining data without crossing into hostile territory, and as conventional reconnaissance craft once air superiority was achieved, as in the Gulf War of 1991.

This long life required a series of upgrades. The most important was the U-2R, beginning in 1967, which was a larger, stealthier aircraft that accomodated a two-person crew, a fourteen-hour maximum mission operations time, and a ferrying range of 8,000 miles. The civilian U-2 is the ER-2, which has done mapping and atmospheric sensing for several decades.

The most recent U-2 competition has come from two planes from the company Scaled Composites: the *Raptor* and the *Proteus*. Both use lightweight composite materials and advanced aerodynamics pioneered by Burt Rutan, designer of the nonstop world-circling *Voyager*. The remotely controlled *Raptor* is a propeller-driven slower competitor, but it is stealthier than the U-2, and it can linger over an area for forty-eight hours. It demonstrated an 8,000-mile flight range in 2001.

The *Proteus* is a direct, cheaper competitor to the U-2, with jet propulsion, a 2,000-pound payload, a fourteen-hour operations length, and an operational altitude of nearly 70,000 feet. As with its shape-changing namesake in Greek mythology, the *Proteus* can be configured for several other missions. Most important, it is a telecommunications repeater station, and for this mission, the *Proteus* demonstrated stable flight at 55,000 feet in late 2000.

A new altitude record of 96,500 feet was set on August 13, 2001, by the *Helios*, a robotic flying wing designed by Paul MacCready of AeroVironment. (MacCready had also designed the human-powered *Gossamer Condor*.) Although its payload is only 220 pounds, the *Helios* is direct competition for the Scaled Composites' *Proteus* repeater stations. *Helios* has solar cells for daylight power and for electrolyzing water into hydrogen and oxygen for nighttime fuel-cell power. Consequently, *Helios* can fly for six months at a time.

Lighter-Than-Air Craft at High Altitudes

Balloons were the first craft capable of reaching high altitude. On December 1, 1783, Jacques-Alexander-César Charles made the first flight in a hydrogen balloon and also made the first high-altitude flight, limited only by the uncomfortable cold he encountered. For the next 120 years, balloons were the only means of observing the atmosphere.

Swiss balloonist Auguste Piccard demonstrated the first pressurized cabin on May 27, 1931, when he and an assistant reached 51,793 feet, making them the first fliers ever to reach the stratosphere. More importantly, they discovered that cosmic rays increased with altitude, proving that they came from somewhere in space rather than the other suggested source, radioactivity within the earth.

American and Soviet flights from the 1930's through the 1960's carried personnel and instruments to steadily greater heights and developed many technologies later used in the space race. In fact, on May 4, 1961, the American *Stratolab V* reached an altitude of 113,700 feet with an open gondola, testing space suits in near-space conditions for the Mercury orbital-flight program.

After the 1960's, improved robotic instrumentation allowed LTA craft to shed the weight of the balloonists and their life support gear. By the late twentieth century, the National Aeronautics and Space Administration (NASA) began using super-pressure balloons for relatively small payloads in balloons weighing several tens of pounds. These balloons are different from zero-pressure balloons that expand when warmed by the sun and contract at night. When warmed at high altitude, zero-pressure balloons must vent excess helium to prevent bursting. This gas loss limits mission duration to only several days. With stronger materials, super-pressure balloons keep the same maximum shape even when warmed. Because no gas is lost such balloons can operate for months, and some of these balloons have circled the globe several times. By the early twenty-first century, NASA began flying large super-pressure balloons in a program called the Ultra Long Duration Balloon (ULDB), with balloons carrying several tons of instrument payload. These balloons compete with spacecraft for carrying astronomic payloads because they are cheaper, turnaround time is shorter, and awkward payloads can be accommodated that might not fit in a rocket or aircraft fuselage.

Dirigibles have greater difficulty reaching high altitudes because the volume of buoyant gas needed to lift the payload as well as a body structure, engines, and control surfaces can become truly immense compared to the weight of payload being carried. Yet, dirigibles can fly slowly enough into the wind to remain stationary over one spot for weeks, ideal for communications repeating stations. Thus, by the early twenty-first century, Sky Station International was building a dirigible to compete against those of AeroVironment and Scaled Composites.

Supersonic High-Altitude Craft

The most important supersonic high-altitude craft was the North American X-15 rocket-propelled research airplane, used from 1959 through 1968 to test materials and aerodynamics at speeds as great as 6.7 times the speed of sound (Mach 6.7, or 4,520 miles per hour) and altitudes as high as 354,000 feet. Lessons learned from these tests were later applied to the space shuttle and many supersonic airplanes.

High-altitude supersonic flight development reached a peak in the early 1960's and then languished until the beginning of the twenty-first century. As noted, supersonic craft operate best in high-altitude regimes because thinner air causes less heat through friction and allows greater efficiency. Higher altitudes had also been a general direction of military flight since World War I (1914-1918).

These two trends led to the North American XB-70, planned as a heavy bomber flying at Mach 3 and a flight ceiling of 70,000 feet. The XB-70 flew in the early 1960's. By 1964, the Soviet Union responded with the Mach-2.8 Mikoyan MiG-25 interceptor.

After the 1960's, other developments intervened. First, intercontinental ballistic missiles (ICBMs) were widely deployed. ICBMs could deliver bombs much faster than could aircraft. Furthermore, they did not require the expensive high-temperature alloys and vast amounts of fuel in operational training. Second, increasingly effective surface-to-air missiles caused large military aircraft to switch from high-altitude flight to flying low while ducking around missile sites. The XB-70 was never produced in volume, and the F-25 became largely a high-speed reconnaissance craft. The Lockheed SR-71 Blackbird was the best high-speed reconnaissance craft, with a maximum speed of more than Mach 3 (2,200 miles per hour and a maximum altitude of 90,000 feet).

The XB-70 also demonstrated that no matter how high supersonic transports flew, sonic booms were a major irritant to people on the ground. The booms and the cost of heavy fuel use both limited the market for commercial supersonic transports, such as the Concorde and the similar Tupolev Tu-144.

However, research has continued to develop better supersonic craft as the first stages for launch into orbit because oxygen carried by rockets weighs eight times as much as hydrogen fuel whereas jets get their oxygen from the atmosphere. Also, there have been reports of secret military craft with speeds of Mach 5 through Mach 10 and flight ceilings of 148,000 feet.

Roger V. Carlson

Bibliography

Hagland, Mark. "Helios: A State-of-the-Art Solar Plane." *Solar Today* 5, no. 3 (May/June, 2001): 32-35. Describes AeroVironment flying wings, with emphasis on the integrated power system of solar cells and fuel cells.

Hutheesing, Nikhil. "Airship Internet." *Forbes* 59, no. 9 (May 5, 1997): 170-171. Describes Skyship International's dirigible-borne telecommunications repeating stations; applies to all airborne telecommunications stations.

Jenkins, Dennis R. *Lockheed U-2 Dragon Lady.* Stillwater, Minn.: Specialty Press and Wholesalers, 1998. Summarizes the technology of the various U-2 variations and their role in history.

Ryan, Craig. *The Pre-Astronauts: Manned Ballooning on the Threshold of Space.* Annapolis, Md.: Naval Institute Press, 1995. Describes the lives spent and the lives lost working at progressively higher altitudes developing equipment that was later used in space flight.

Smith, I. Steve, Jr., and James A. Cutts. "Floating in Space." *Scientific American* 281, no. 5 (November, 1999): 132-139. Describes the scientific uses of superpressure balloons at high altitudes.

Thompson, Milton O. *At the Edge of Space: The X-15 Flight Program.* Washington, D.C.: Smithsonian Institution Press, 1992. Describes the operations, technologies, and implications of the rocket plane that flew the highest and fastest.

See also: Balloons; Dirigibles; Experimental aircraft; Jet engines; Lighter-than-air craft; Military flight; Auguste Piccard; Propellers; Reconnaissance; Rockets; Burt Rutan; Spaceflight; Supersonic aircraft; Andrei Nikolayevich Tupolev; X planes

High-speed flight

Definition: Flight airspeeds greater than the average, especially speeds close to the maximum attainable speed for the era.

Significance: The utility of civilian or military aircraft is always enhanced by increases in practical flight airspeeds. Much of the historic progress in aviation has revolved around solving the aerodynamic, structural, power, and heat problems associated with ever increasing speeds. Races and speed records, with their promise of prize money or prestige, have often stimulated individuals and governments to advance the art and science of high-speed flight.

As the first humans to make a controlled, powered flight in 1903, Orville and Wilbur Wright held the first unofficial speed record, at 30 miles per hour. Official speed records, though, are those that have been authenticated by the rules of the Fédération Aeronautique Internationale (FAI), formed in Paris in 1906, and these speed records begin with Alberto Santos-Dumont's 26 miles per hour in 1906, increasing to 83 miles per hour by 1911, 119 miles per hour in 1913, 192 miles per hour in 1920, 469 miles per hour on the eve of World War II in 1939, 606 miles per hour with the first jets in 1945, 1,526 miles per hour with second-generation fighter aircraft in 1959, and 2,194 miles per hour by the SR-71A in 1976.

Early High-Speed Flight

Initially, flight speeds were limited primarily by the lack of lightweight power plants, not surprising in view of the fact that development of the gasoline engine was still in its infancy. Thus, the first airplanes required a very large wing area and the most efficient structure was the bridge-based biplane, but its large size and attendant struts and wires generated a great deal of drag. By 1909, Glenn H. Curtiss was able to take his draggy biplane to first place in the first Gordon Bennett closed-circuit race at Rheims, France, with a speed of 47 miles per hour, mostly due to his development of a 50-horsepower V-8 engine that bettered the Wright brothers' original 12-horsepower engine.

Invention of the relatively lightweight, reliable, air-cooled rotary engine, in which the crankshaft is bolted to the aircraft and the cylinders and propeller rotate, led to the next great increment in high speed, culminating in a winning 124.5 miles per hour by a special Deperdussin monoplane racer in the last prewar Gordon Bennett race in 1913.

High-speed flight

World War I led to improvements in structures and power plants but negligible increases in speed because of the emphasis on climb rate and maneuverability, which favored biplanes.

After World War I, the Schneider Trophy race for seaplanes inspired great advances in engines. The liquid-cooled engine assumed prominence because of its low frontal area. By 1927, Reginald Mitchell's 900-horsepower Supermarine S.5 had established an absolute speed record of 282 miles per hour; it was the last time a biplane would win the race. The Supermarine S.6 retired the Schneider Trophy with an uncontested win at a speed of 340 miles per hour in 1930, with 2,300 horsepower available from its supercharged, liquid-cooled Rolls-Royce V-12. These racers, however, were impractical aircraft because they used low-drag skin radiators to dissipate the tremendous heat from their liquid-cooled engines.

The winning Rolls-Royce V-12 engine in the S.6 had been inspired by the Curtiss V-12 engine that had powered the Curtiss CR-2 biplane to first place in the Pulitzer race of 1921 (and later to an absolute speed record of 198 miles per hour) and by the CR-3 that won the Schneider Trophy in 1923 at 178 miles per hour. In the United States, however, by the mid-1920's, water-cooled engines were taking second place to newly developed, reliable, air-cooled radial engines that were much lighter and much more suited to commercial applications, but presented a great deal more frontal area and accompanying drag. Charles A. Lindbergh's historic New York-to-Paris flight in 1927 was made possible by a 220-horsepower Wright Whirlwind radial engine, for example.

The monoplane route to higher speeds, now that brute power had accomplished about all it could do, was shown by the features of the unheralded, trouble-prone Dayton-Wright RB-1 racer of 1921: a small unbraced (cantilevered) wing that used flaps to yield acceptable takeoff and landing speeds, a closed cockpit for less drag, and a retractable landing gear. With a low-drag NACA cowling for its radial engine (developed by the National Advisory Committee for Aeronautics or NACA, the predecessor of NASA), the 450-horsepower TravelAir Mystery Ship won the 1929 National Air Races in Cleveland, besting all the military biplanes. James H. "Jimmy" Doolittle set a land plane record of 294 miles per hour in 1932 in the small-winged, bottle-shaped GeeBee R-1, using an 800-horsepower Pratt & Whitney radial engine. By 1939, however, Lockheed had flown the aerodynamically clean prototype of its P-38 twin-engined Lightning to a top speed of 413 miles per hour, and civilian aircraft were forever out of the race for the highest speeds.

In World War II, piston-engined fighters reached speeds of around 500 miles per hour, but only at altitudes above about 20,000 feet, where their supercharged or turbocharged engines could take advantage of the less dense air. The liquid-cooled P-51H Mustang reached 487 miles per hour at 25,000 feet using water/methanol injection and high-octane fuel. An experimental version of the Republic P-47 Thunderbolt, using an 18-cylinder, air-cooled radial engine, reached a speed of 504 miles per hour at 34,450 feet. The Goodyear F-2G, developed from the Chance Vought F-4U Corsair, could reach speeds close to 500 miles per hour. Nonetheless, two facts threatened to forever prevent higher speeds: propeller and wing compressibility (Mach) effects.

The Sound Barrier

Propellers were becoming less and less efficient as their tips approached the speed of sound; the air would break away from the tips and form ear-splitting shock waves. Worse, planes and pilots were being lost when the airflow over the wing approached the speed of sound. Because air is speeded up over the top surface of a wing to produce a lower air pressure there and thereby generate lift, the speed of sound is reached at that point before (sometimes well before) aircraft speed reaches sonic speed (Mach 1). Shortly after a local airspeed of Mach 1 is exceeded, a shock wave is formed where the air suddenly has to be slowed back to subsonic speeds; because the pressure waves that inform the air that it must change its speed or direction cannot propagate into the region ahead of this point, the shock wave represents an extremely narrow region perpendicular to the wing surface where the pressure and density and temperature of the air greatly increase. Shock wave formation not only greatly increases the power requirement, it also causes the airflow to break away from the wing at that point, producing effects very similar to the low-speed stall created when the wing is at a high angle relative to the oncoming air.

At less than 70 percent of the speed of sound (Mach 0.675), a speed easily reached in a dive, the P-38 became uncontrollably nose-heavy as the wing lost lift and the horizontal tail surface lost its downward force; dive flaps were added to the sides of nacelles to save future pilots. Of U.S. fighters, the P-51 Mustang suffered the least from compressibility, thanks to its laminar-flow wing with the thickest point well back from the leading edge, but its pilots were warned that in high-speed dives, uncontrollable violent porpoising preceded a loss of altitude of 10,000 feet or more, at which point a recovery might be possible, because the Mach number decreased as the air temperature increased. The British Spitfire, with its very thin wing section, was eventually dived successfully to Mach 0.9, but it still was not at all clear that controlled supersonic flight would ever be possible.

The propulsion problem was solved by the invention of the turbojet engine by the British and Germans, an engine which obtains thrust by taking in air and using it to burn fuel, with the byproducts exiting to the rear at a much higher speed. The thrust generated is equal to the rate of change in momentum (the product of mass and speed) generated by the engine. The jet engine is most efficient in the less dense air at altitudes above 20,000 feet.

Rocket engines produce even more short-term thrust than jet engines, for their weight, and were used for the earliest transonic and supersonic flights. (Transonic flight is flight for which there is mixed subsonic and supersonic flow, approximately Mach 0.8 to Mach 1.2.) By 1944, the German rocket-powered Messerschmitt Me-263B had reached a speed of 703 miles per hour and the much more practical, jet-powered Messerschmitt Me-262 had reached 624 miles per hour.

Higher speeds required better aerodynamics, including a recognition of the advantages of the swept-back wing and solutions for its disadvantages. Adolf Busemann, in 1935, first published the finding that a swept wing permits a wing to be effectively thinner because the chord (width) of the wing is greater than for a similar unswept wing. It spreads the lift and the cross-section of the wing over a greater percentage of the fuselage, reducing the suddenness of the drag rise and the pitch-down tendency. However, the spanwise flow on a swept wing also tends to cause the wingtips to stall first at low speeds or when maneuvering, making the ailerons ineffective and producing a violent pitch-up tendency. The swept wing also suffers from a Dutch roll (coupled yaw and roll) tendency, which can be serious enough to destroy the aircraft. The stall problem can be treated by using high-lift devices (slats) on the leading edge of the outer wing panels and by chordwise plates (fences). The Dutch roll tendency can be treated by a gyroscopic-based yaw damper, as well as aerodynamically. In May, 1948, the swept-wing, jet-powered North American F-86A Sabre jet achieved an official world speed record of 670 miles per hour.

Supersonic Flight

The sound barrier, however, was still to be breached. The United States chose the bullet-shaped, rocket-propelled Bell X-1 to make the attempt. (Bullets were known to reach supersonic speeds in flight, but they had to spiral for stability and they did not try to use lift to stay in the air.) With only 2.5 minutes worth of rocket fuel, the only available route was to use an air launch from a modified B-29 bomber and glide to a landing afterward. This was possible only because the United States had California's clear skies and vast Muroc Dry Lake (the present Edwards Air Force Base) for landing. On October 14, 1947, test pilot Charles E. "Chuck" Yeager reached Mach 1.06 at 43,000 feet and the first human-generated sonic boom was heard. He glided back at 250 miles per hour, approached at 220 miles per hour, and landed at 190 miles per hour.

The Russian MiG-19 was the first fighter capable of supersonic flight in level flight, followed shortly by the Republic XP-91 and North American's F-100 Super Sabre. The secret was obtaining a short burst of extra thrust by dumping raw fuel directly into the exhaust (after the turbine), a practice called afterburning in the United States and reheat in Great Britain. However, the Super Sabre also had to be cured of a new disease: inertia coupling. With a long, heavy fuselage supported by short, light wings, an aircraft has roll inertia (resistance to changes in roll around the nose-to-tail axis) that is much less than its pitch and yaw inertia, and rolling motion can induce a pitching moment that sends an aircraft into a disastrous tumble. Additional tail and wing area solved the problem for the Super Sabre.

The FAI set new rules for speed records at high altitudes and Great Britain quickly claimed an absolute speed record in March, 1956, when its Fairey Delta 2 (FD.2) flew at 1,132 miles per hour. The official speed record as of 2001 was held by Lockheed's SR-71 Blackbird (a reconnaissance aircraft capable of over Mach 3 at 100,000 feet altitude); in 1976 it averaged 2,194 miles per hour, but probably could have gone even faster.

Transport aircraft have followed in the path blazed by research and fighter aircraft. The Douglas DC-2 almost won the London to Melbourne race in 1933 against specialized racing aircraft. The Boeing 707 was the first successful jet transport, going into service in the late 1950's. The French/British Concorde began Mach 2 airline service in 1976; it uses a highly swept delta planform with sharp leading edges generating vortices that greatly enhance lift at low speeds (vortex lift).

Hypersonic Flight

Hypersonic flight (greater than Mach 4 or 5) is the new frontier and in this flight realm, heat is the primary foe. Even on the Concorde, skin temperatures of 260 degrees Fahrenheit are reached and the fuselage lengthens by 9 or 10 inches in flight. On the titanium SR-71, temperatures reach 600 degrees Fahrenheit.

The North American X-15 showed that a rocket-powered research aircraft could reach hypersonic speeds; by 1967 the X-15 had flown to 354,000 feet and Mach 6.7, but it had also been seared by 3,000-degree-Fahrenheit temperatures. Ablative (sacrificial) coatings were used; they melt away at high temperatures while absorbing and dissipating the heat.

After the Soviet Union sent Yuri Gagarin into Earth orbit in 1961, beginning the race to the Moon, spaceflight, rather than higher-speed atmospheric flight, became the next U.S. challenge. It was followed by space stations and the space shuttle, the latter of which must attain just the right speed for its orbital height and then, with braking rockets, reenter the atmosphere at about 140,000 feet and Mach 6.7.

The X-43, making its first flight in 2001, is an uninhabited hypersonic research aircraft. It remains to be seen whether it will make hypersonic flight a regular occurrence.

W. N. Hubin

Bibliography

Berliner, Don. *Victory over the Wind: A History of the Absolute World Air Speed Record*. New York: Van Nostrand Reinhold, 1983. Provides information about designers, pilots, and planes that successively pushed official airspeeds higher.

Reithmaier, L. H. *Mach 1 and Beyond: The Illustrated Guide to High-Speed Flight*. New York: McGraw-Hill, 1994. Written for the nontechnical reader, this guide covers high-speed aerodynamics, flight principles, gas turbine jets, and other engineering challenges of both subsonic and supersonic flight.

Sweetman, Bill. *High-Speed Flight*. London: Jane's, 1983. An excellent illustrated history of high-speed flight, from the pioneer era to the early space era. The technical problems encountered and their solutions are well described.

See also: Concorde; Glenn H. Curtiss; Jimmy Doolittle; Hypersonic aircraft; Jet engines; Mach number; Military flight; Propellers; Rocket propulsion; Alberto Santos-Dumont; Sound barrier; Supersonic aircraft; Wing designs; Wright brothers; X planes; Chuck Yeager

Hijacking

Definition: The act of commandeering an aircraft in flight by means of force or violence.

Significance: Beginning in the late 1960's, air piracy became a major technique of world terrorism. The rise in hijacking incidents led to increases in airport security and air traffic control.

Scope

Aviation security is a major concern, even though hijackings and terrorist acts against civil aviation declined from their height in 1969. Hijacking first became a serious problem for the United States in the late 1960's and early 1970's, when the majority of forcibly diverted flights were directed to Cuba. Air piracy events initiated stricter airport security provisions in the United States with the passage of 14 CFR Part 107, amended in December, 1972. The number of U.S.-registered aircraft hijacked per year fell dramatically from a peak of forty in 1969 to one in 1973. After initiating regulations increasing airport security in the early 1970's, the United States passed Public Law 93-366, the Air Transportation Security Act of 1974. At the international level, the International Civil Aviation Organization (ICAO) adopted Annex 17, Safeguarding International Civil Aviation Against Acts of Unlawful Interference, which became applicable in February, 1975. The number of hijackings briefly remained low, with two in 1976, but subsequently increased.

From January, 1977, to July, 1979, there were seventy-eight air carrier hijackings worldwide, twenty-four of which were of U.S. aircraft. The United States' share steadily increased from 16.6 percent of all hijackings in 1977, to 32 percent of those in 1978, to 47.8 percent of those in the first half of 1979; this two-and-one-half-year period saw more hijackings than the total occurring between 1972 and 1977. All these occurred while a record of more than 18,000 firearms confiscated at airport screening points and 6,400 related arrests showed the effectiveness of new airline passenger screening procedures. In the twenty-four U.S. hijackings that occurred during this period where the hijackers were processed through passenger screening, none actually had a real weapon or high explosive.

In 1980, twenty-one U.S.-registered airplanes were hijacked. In 1981 and 1982, there were fewer than ten hijackings each year, but in a sharp increase, eighteen occurred in 1983. Additional security measures were taken, followed once again by the steady decline. From 1984 to 1987, there were fewer than five hijackings per year, and only two in 1988.

At the end of the twentieth century, the vulnerability of civil aviation to the different forms of terrorist hijacking action was still a major concern. The geographic areas of

Trade Center, collapsing both of the center's towers. Another was crashed into the Pentagon, in Washington, D.C., collapsing part of that building. A fourth airplane crashed outside of Pittsburgh, Pennsylvania when passengers confronted the hijackers. In all, more than three thousand people died. Although no terrorist group immediately claimed responsibility for the crashes, all evidence pointed to the al-Qaeda terrorist network headed by Saudi billionaire and Islamic fundamentalist Osama bin Laden.

Who Hijacks and Why

Developing a profile of the typical hijacker and understanding the motivation for such an act provides the basis for trained observation to identify and deal with potential hijackers. One set of classifications identifies rational, psychological, or cultural hijackers. Another set of classifications determines whether hijackers are motivated by money, politics, or religion. A rational but dishonest thief with a financial motivation may be swayed by patient discussion, leading to a nonviolent conclusion to the extortion attempt. Both political and religious fanatics hold the greatest threat for an unsatisfactory outcome.

Criminal motives were a factor in 68 percent of the hijackings of U.S. airplanes from 1984 to 1988. Thirteen of the nineteen involved simple extortion, demands for the release of certain incarcerated prisoners, political asylum or repatriation, or flight from criminal prosecution. Of these thirteen, seven activists demanded to be repatriated back to Cuba. The next largest group, four of the nineteen, were determined by judicial authority to be mentally incompetent. Political terrorism accounted for 11 percent of the events between 1984 and 1988.

The hijackers were almost uniformly male; only one of them was a female. Three of the nineteen cases involved more than one hijacker. It was worrying that 47 percent of the hijackers had undergone preboard screening. Although the hijackers claimed to have knives, guns, explosives, incendiary devices, or a combination of these weapons in their possession, the claimed items were verified in only three of the nineteen instances.

The second of two hijacked airplanes heads straight into the South Tower of the World Trade Center in New York City on September 11, 2001. The simultaneous hijacking of four planes, of which one other was crashed into the Pentagon in Washington, D.C., and another crashed in western Pennsylvania, marked a renewal of hijacking terrorism after a period of relative quiet. (AP/Wide World Photos)

greatest danger were Europe, the Middle East, and Central America. Within the United States, the anti-Castro and the Croatian and Serbian groups were most active. Although hijacking posed a serious threat to civil aviation throughout the world, terrorist activity was curtailed greatly in South America (the location of the first hijacking in aviation history), primarily due to successful paramilitary security, albeit at the expense of significant civil liberties.

On the morning of September 11, 2001, in what was immediately termed the worst act of terrorism in U.S. history, four commercial jetliners were hijacked by teams of terrorists and crashed into significant American buildings. Two airplanes were flown into New York City's World

The incidents of September 11, 2001, demonstrated the deadly evolution of hijackings. The nineteen terrorists, all men, were willing to die for their cause and to kill thousands in the process. No political demands were made.

Hijackings Outside the United States

Cases of foreign registry hijackings had the same decreasing frequency from a high in 1970. A total of seventy-four foreign-registered aircraft were hijacked from 1984 through 1988. One notable difference, however, was the prolonged duration of threat in terrorist hijackings. A significant example occurred in 1988. On April 5, Kuwaiti Airways Flight 422, en route from Bangkok to Kuwait, was seized. At least seven Middle Eastern men were involved, although the exact number was not verified. They demanded that the Kuwaiti government release seventeen other terrorists incarcerated for the 1983 bombing of government facilities as well as the U.S. and French embassies in Kuwait. The aircraft was diverted to Mashad, Iran, then to Larnaca, Cyprus, and Algiers, Algeria, over a sixteen-day period. Two Kuwaiti passengers were killed. It is believed that the hijackers were well-trained, organized individuals, conscious of the value of manipulating media coverage of the event.

Other motives in foreign cases vary from individuals fleeing authoritarian regimes or law enforcement agencies, to the mentally unstable, to people searching for better economic conditions. One person even sought the reunification of China through hijacking. The most popular area in the world for hijack activity was the Middle East (twenty-six of seventy-four hijackings), followed by Europe (twelve), and Latin America (nine).

With the outbreak of the Gulf War, many individuals feared there would be a widespread outbreak of terrorist crimes. For the first time ever, the entire U.S. National Airspace System was elevated to a Level 4 security status. Previously, the National Contingency Plan was not in effect, nor had its different security levels been established. Tightened security under the plan includes increasing law enforcement officer patrols, allowing only ticketed passengers and employees into boarding areas, eliminating curbside check-in, and denying passenger access to checked luggage. At O'Hare and Dallas/Fort Worth airports, all newspaper vending machines, trash receptacles, and ashtrays were even removed from the terminals. Companies warned their employees to take extra precautions, advising people to take nonstop flights from origin to destination and to avoid certain destinations altogether. Certain airlines known to be the focus of terrorists were to be avoided. Some companies canceled all but the most essential travel. Corporate and private business jets in the United States became popular as companies searched for travel options. Unfortunately, most airports had no budget for extended periods of sustained, high-level security measures and personnel.

Terrorism by definition is "the systematic use of terror, especially as a means of coercion." Unfortunately, effective terrorists want to make big headlines, which can be quickly accomplished when many people are killed or injured or held on an airplane for days. No matter how strict the security measures, it is probable that any terrorist could get a weapon into any airport, anywhere. There are no X-ray machines or any other means of detecting weapons at the entrances to the public areas of airports. Roving police officers have their attention focused on illegally parked vehicles at the curb, on vehicles trying to get to the curb, or on other distractions. Most people around the world share an unspoken but common assumption that hijacking cannot happen to them. This assumption may be unduly optimistic, but in the meantime, cautious security checks continue in an attempt to protect air travelers from hijackings and other acts of terrorism.

Although incidents of terrorism and bomb threats in aviation are few and far between, at the turn of the twenty-first century, threats of terrorism in the muslim world placed airlines and airports on a high state of alert from the Middle East to Europe as well as North America. The events of 2001 showed that the U.S. mainland was a very credible target as well. Iraq and Afghanistan became new breeding grounds for terrorist groups from the Middle East, who have often found hijacking to be an effective terrorist tool.

In December, 1999, Kashmiri hijackers commandeered a plane en route from Kathmandu, Nepal, to New Delhi, India, flying the plane to Amritsar, India; Lahore, Pakistan; Dubai, United Arab Emirates; and finally to Kandahar, Afghanistan. They demanded the release of political prisoners held in India, and killed one passenger who did not comply with their orders quickly enough. The other 154 passengers were eventually released after negotiation, but the hijackers' difficulty in finding a location where they could stop to negotiate illustrates the effectiveness of international treaties against hijacking and the reason why hijacking has become a less effective terrorist tool. Unfortunately, since it is no longer easy to hold a planeload of passengers hostage in order to make a political point, terrorists have turned their energies simply to bombing planes out of the sky or to crashing them, resulting in much higher death rates for passengers caught up in political turmoil.

Security Measures

On December 21, 1988, Pan American Flight 103 exploded over Lockerbie, Scotland, killing 270 people on the plane and 11 others on the ground. Investigation revealed that a plastic explosive, hidden in a portable radio in baggage in the cargo hold, had ripped the jet apart. The placement of the plastic explosive was linked to activities of the Abu Nidal group.

In response to findings of lax airport security leading up to the bombing of Pan American Flight 103, the General Accounting Office (GAO) testified in front of the Presidential Commission on Aviation Security. Four areas of major deficiency were outlined during testimony: passenger screening, airport security controls, security inspections, and airline training requirements for security personal, especially better training standards for overseas security personal. Furthermore, it was suggested that accountability for and oversight of airport security were made especially difficult by the division of responsibility among different organizations. The Federal Aviation Administration (FAA), despite its regulatory role, is not responsible for airport security in any direct way. This contrasts with the state of affairs in Europe, where even though security standards differ among countries, it is a common practice for governments, in their role of overseeing all aspects of aviation, to hire, staff, and operate airport security programs and equipment.

Firearms and other prohibited items continue to be found in large numbers at screening checkpoints. Of thirty-one attempts to hijack scheduled air carriers, none resulted from real firearms or explosive devices passing undetected through screening. In eleven cases, the hijackers either forced their way aboard or in another fashion avoided the normal passenger screening. In fifteen cases, the hijackers said that they had deadly weapons when in fact they had no weapons at all. However, the events of September 11, 2001, showed that knives can be equally dangerous. The hijackers killed crew and passengers with box cutters smuggled on board. As a result, knives of any length were banned on flights.

One security problem is unauthorized access to sensitive areas. Following the crash of a Pacific Southwest Airlines (PSA) flight in California on December 7, 1987, investigators found that there had been a breach of security screening when a former employee used one of six invalid airline photo-identity cards to bypass the passenger screening station at Los Angeles International Airport. He showed the ID card, smuggled a pistol aboard the plane, and shot the flight crew in an act of murder-suicide.

The incident pointed out some of the shortcomings of existing security procedures: poor accounting of identification badges, the need for increased security over points of access to aircraft, and lack of any method to identify and track personnel moving into and out of secured areas. A number of measures, including computer-based electronic card access control systems, eye retina scanners, digitized images or fingerprints, "voiceprints" and closed-circuit television cameras have been implemented to prevent unauthorized persons, including potential hijackers, from gaining access to aircraft. However, the FAA has made slow progress toward certification and installation of the advanced bomb detection equipment at U.S. airports.

In general, efforts to enhance security systems only occur after some specific incident attributable to lax security has occurred. One such reactive response to the Lockerbie tragedy was the FAA's research into and employment of thermal neutron analysis (TNA) explosive detection systems at air terminals. The FAA is also interested in the X-ray computed tomography (CT) scanner as a second sensor to back up the TNA system. Another system receiving the attention of the FAA is the high-speed backscatter X-ray system, with automatic explosives screening capability, that can search for plastic explosives concealed in luggage. The system has been installed at Honolulu International, Los Angeles International, San Francisco International, and John F. Kennedy airports by Japan Airline Company.

The implementation of the March, 1979, revised federal aviation regulation (FAR) Part 107 governing airport security included the training of law enforcement officers in support of airport security programs and gathering explosives-detection K9 teams. The revision also provided that in certain instances, law enforcement officers supporting the passenger screening system can patrol in the public areas of terminals away from the screening checkpoints, thereby enabling them to provide broader deterrence to criminal acts of violence, while maintaining the capability of responding quickly to any need at the passenger screening points.

The revised rule also contained a total prohibition against unauthorized carriage of a firearm, explosive or incendiary device by persons when entering sterile areas or presenting themselves for inspection at established passenger-screening points. Prior to the revision, only the actual carriage of unauthorized weapons aboard an aircraft was prohibited by the FARs. The revised rule provides for a civil penalty of up to $1,000 and is intended to complement existing federal or local criminal sanctions. This revision strengthens the ability to deter hijackings by keeping weapons off airplanes. Security measures cost money, however, and airport operators are critical of the FAA mandating new programs without providing any funding mechanism for them. The costs of anti-hijacking measures must be passed along to consumers in the form of taxes added to the price of air travel tickets.

International Cooperation

The Bonn Declaration on Hijacking (1978) brought together seven heads of state who jointly committed to intensifying efforts to combat terrorism. The Declaration announced that when a country refuses to extradite or prosecute those who have hijacked an aircraft or if the country does not return the aircraft, the seven nations would initiate action to cease all flights to that country, to halt all incoming flights from that country or any country by airlines of the country concerned. Seven hijackings met the criteria that are covered by the Bonn Declaration.

ICAO, at its first European regional security seminar in Paris, contributed to the enhancement of civil aviation security and improved cooperation between states on a regional basis, including extensive programs to provide technical aid and training to African states.

At a meeting in Quito, Ecuador, in 1979, representatives from all North, Central, and South American states dedicated themselves to ensuring that civil aviation security requirements were diligently carried out. They all supported the International Criminal Police Organization (INTERPOL) General Assembly's resolution to encourage governments to prevent the use of their territories for criminal activity related to interference with civil aviation or as a refuge to avoid criminal prosecution for such acts.

William B. Rourke

Bibliography

Abeyratne, Ruwantissa I. R. *Aviation Security: Legal and Regulatory Aspects*. Aldershot, England: Ashgate, 1998. Covers the legal aspects of hijacking.

Choi, Jin-Tai. *Aviation Terrorism: Historical Survey, Perspectives, and Responses*. New York: St. Martin's Press, 1994. Looks at hijacking within the historical perspective of various forms of aerial terrorism.

Gero, David. *Flights of Terror: Aerial Hijacking and Sabotage Since 1930*. London: Haynes, 1997. A thorough summary of hijackings in the twentieth century.

Wallis, Rodney. *Combating Air Terrorism*. Sterling, Va.: Brassey's, 1998. Focuses on measures being taken to combat hijacking and other terrorist acts.

See also: Air carriers; Airport security; Commercial flight; Emergency procedures; Federal Aviation Administration; Gulf War; Safety issues; Terrorism

Hindenburg

Also known as: *Luftschiff* Zeppelin 129 (LZ-129)
Date: From March 4, 1936, to May 6, 1937
Definition: The largest rigid lighter-than-air passenger transport vehicle ever constructed.
Significance: Dirigibles were becoming an important means of overseas transportation when the *Hindenburg* exploded while docking at Lakehurst, New Jersey, eliminating any hope that this means of transoceanic travel might become widespread.

Germany and the Development of Dirigibles

Lighter-than-air flight began in Europe as early as 1783, when a cloth balloon filled with hot air carried several animals aloft in France. By 1898, European aviation pioneer Alberto Santos-Dumont had fashioned a cylindrical balloon that flew over Paris and the surrounding countryside powered by a motorcycle engine and steered by a rudder. This vehicle, however, carried only one person. By 1900, Count Ferdinand von Zeppelin had built a huge oblong aircraft with a cloth-covered steel frame inside of which were large bags of hydrogen that lifted the vehicle into the air. Several such aircraft, built by Zeppelin's company, Luftschiffbau Zeppelin, were built and were used to carry passengers on sightseeing trips across Germany.

In 1909, the world's first passenger airline, Deutsche Luftschiffahrts Aktien-Gesellschaft (Delag), was established. Its lighter-than-air fleet, consisting of the *Schwaben*, the *Victoria-Luise*, and the *Sachsen*, carried 37,250 passengers on sixteen hundred flights. During their 3,200 hours aloft, the airships covered more than 100,000 accident-free miles.

During World War I (1914-1918), the Germans used dirigibles for reconnaissance and for bombing missions over London. During the following decade, many civilian uses were found for dirigibles. Arctic explorer Roald Amundsen bought a dirigible, in which he flew over the North Pole, traveling the 3,180 miles from Spitsbergen, Norway, to Teller, Alaska, in about 71 hours.

By 1929, Germany had built the *Graf Zeppelin*, which carried twenty passengers on the first nonstop flight around the world. This feat marked the beginning of regular overseas passenger travel in lighter-than-air craft. At this time, it took at least five days to cross the Atlantic Ocean by steamship, and crossings were often rough during storms. In contrast, a dirigible, averaging 80 miles per hour, could make the transatlantic crossing in two and one-half days, floating like a cloud above turbulent seas.

When Adolf Hitler came to power in Germany during the mid-1930's, political storm clouds gathered over Europe. Hitler accomplished a tactical victory by luring the 1936 Olympic Games to Berlin. He conceived the idea of building the largest dirigible in the world, to be flown over the Olympic stadium during the games.

The project, referred to simply as *LZ-129*, was completed quickly. An 804-foot rigid frame of steel was covered with a superstrong, hand-stitched cotton fabric, and the ship's interior amenities were refined to the point that it unquestionably offered the most luxurious means of crossing the Atlantic. On March 4, 1936, German aeronaut Hugo Eckener took *LZ-129* on its maiden flight.

As Eckener hovered over Munich, the city's mayor radioed to ask him the name of the ship. He unhesitatingly responded with the name *Hindenburg*, after German field marshal and former president of Germany's Weimar Republic Paul von Hindenburg, who had died two years earlier. Joseph Goebbels, Germany's minister of propaganda, reprimanded Eckener severely for presuming to name the ship without authorization, telling him that the Reich had been planning to call it the *Adolf Hitler*. A change could not be made gracefully after Eckener's public statement, so the ship continued to be called the *Hindenburg*.

The *Hindenburg*'s Amenities

The luxurious *Hindenburg* was three and one-half times the length of a Boeing 747 and about the same length as the steamship *Titanic*. It was outfitted with extremely lightweight furniture, including a 397-pound aluminum piano. It had a lounge, a writing room, a smoking room, and a dining room, whose tables were set with exquisite floral arrangements, silver, and china. Lavish meals prepared by superb chefs issued forth from its kitchens. Banks of windows along the bottom portion of the aircraft provided dramatic vantage points from which to view the scene below.

The *Hindenburg*'s staterooms were small but efficient, with bunk beds and foldout tables and sinks. Originally the ship could accommodate fifty passengers, but with the success of the 1936 season, during which every stateroom was usually filled, the ship was modified to serve seventy-five passengers. The new staterooms, unlike the old ones, had windows that offered spectacular views.

The May 3, 1937, flight of the *Hindenburg* carried thirty-six passengers and a crew of sixty-one. Those who were traveling alone had staterooms to themselves. Above the passenger-crew areas of the ship were cavernous spaces that could carry up to 100 tons of cargo. These spaces contained bags of hydrogen, required to lift the craft, and water, used for ballast.

Because hydrogen is a highly explosive substance, every precaution was taken to prevent the hydrogen on board from being ignited accidentally. Crew and passengers wore slippers with felt soles. Matches and cigarette lighters were confiscated and later returned to debarking passengers. The smoking room contained only one lighter, secured by a chain, and the room was tightly sealed so that no sparks could escape.

Helium, another gas, which is not explosive, would have lifted the craft as well as hydrogen. Hydrogen, however, took up less space, permitting the *Hindenburg* to carry a larger payload. In addition, the United States, a major supplier of helium, was reluctant to sell this substance to Germany as it moved increasingly toward fascism.

The *Hindenburg*'s Fateful Landing

On Monday, May 3, 1937, the *Hindenburg* drifted from its moorings in Frankfurt at 7:30 P.M. to begin its first flight of the season from Germany to the United States. Although it had made ten trips to New York in 1936, in winter, when the North Atlantic was stormy, the *Hindenburg* flew the Frankfurt-to-Rio de Janiero route instead, resuming its North Atlantic flights when the weather improved. Eighteen flights to the United States were scheduled for 1937.

The *Hindenburg*'s May 3 flight was to have taken about thirty-six hours, with touchdown at Lakehurst, New Jersey, outside New York City, scheduled for the morning of Thursday, May 6. Headwinds across the Atlantic delayed the ship's arrival. By the time it flew over New York City, it was nearly twelve hours late.

The weather was bad, so even though the aircraft flew over Lakehurst, it did not land immediately. Rather, it flew down the coast toward Atlantic City, New Jersey, before circling back for its landing at Lakehurst, where it was awaited by a ground crew and people who had come to meet arriving family and friends.

As the ship inched toward its metal mooring at about 7:30 P.M., it dumped some of its water ballast to slow its descent, dousing some of the ground crew below. Those on the ground looked up at the gleaming ship with rapt expressions. Suddenly a thunderous noise shook the area, and the observers' expressions turned from joy to horror, as the ship trembled violently with reverberating explosions. As the hydrogen quickly ignited, fireballs engulfed the ship.

Chaos ruled as people on board, many with their clothing and hair on fire, jumped from the craft to the ground 100 feet below. Others, such as cabin boy Werner Franz, who, two weeks short of his fifteenth birthday, was the *Hindenburg*'s youngest crew member, were trapped. As

This photograph of the Hindenburg *on fire as it attempted to land at Lakehurst, New Jersey on May 6, 1937, is among the most dramatic pictures ever taken of an air disaster in progress.* (AP/Wide World Photos)

fire rolled toward Franz from two directions, his situation seemed hopeless. Suddenly a ballast tank ruptured, immersing him in 2 tons of water. Soaking wet, Franz jumped from the inferno onto the ground, emerging with only minor injuries. He arrived home in Germany on May 22, his birthday.

In all, twenty-two of the *Hindenburg*'s crew of sixty-one died in the disaster, including Captain Ernst Lehmann who, although badly burned, had returned to the inferno in an attempt to rescue trapped passengers and crew. Twenty-three of the thirty-six passengers survived, although a number of them were severely injured.

Possible Causes of the Disaster

Following the *Hindenburg*'s destruction, speculation about its causes was widespread. Certainly the hydrogen used to lift the craft, once ignited, exploded to create a fire of great intensity. However, what caused the hydrogen to ignite remained a mystery.

Some experts believed that as the aircraft had flown through the electrical storms that had raged along its course, static electricity had collected on its exterior, so that when it made contact with its metal mooring, sparks flew and ignited the hydrogen, small quantities of which could already have been leaking. The U.S. Department of Commerce established a commission to probe into the cause of the explosion, but no firm conclusion was forthcoming from that commission. Among the possible causes mentioned were a ball of lightning, demon protons, static electricity, and St. Elmo's fire, a discharge of atmospheric electricity that commonly collects on aircraft flying in thunderstorms. However, eyewitnesses verified that the fire started inside the ship; if any of these possibilities been valid, the fire would have begun on the outside.

Given the strained relations between the United States and Hitler's Germany, the U.S. government wanted to prevent the disaster from escalating into an international incident. The official finding of the committee identified the disaster's cause as St. Elmo's fire, although in all of aviation history, no similar incident had ever been recorded.

In Germany, General Hermann Göring ordered the German commission investigating the explosion to "discover nothing." He officially declared the event an act of God, foreclosing further investigation.

Conspiracy Theories

Accidents such as the explosion of the *Hindenburg* often spawn conspiracy theories, which are sometimes given serious consideration. One cannot forget that Adolf Hitler, in promoting the development of the *Hindenburg*, sought to bring favorable attention both to Germany and to his despotic regime, in only its second year when the airship was conceived.

Germany had already planned to build other transoceanic dirigibles, and those opposed to Hitler did not want Germany to fulfill this dream. The destruction of the largest dirigible in the world would thwart plans for expanding Germany's lighter-than-air passenger service and would be a great personal blow to the country's dictator. Further, one must remember that threats had been made against the *Hindenburg*. Not long before its ill-fated trip, a bomb had been found in the dining salon of the *Graf Zeppelin* and was removed before it exploded.

Some conspiracy theorists noted that one of the passengers on board the *Hindenburg* had been Joseph Spah, a German who had fled the country as Hilter was coming to power, and who was an outspoken opponent of the Nazi government. Spah had been observed in restricted areas and explained his presence there by saying that he had wanted to visit his dog, who was being carried in the ship's hold.

Those doubting the conspiracy theories pointed out that if a passenger or crew member had sought to destroy the *Hindenburg* by planting a bomb somewhere aboard, that person would have had to die in the explosion. The counterargument to this objection is that a time bomb might have been hidden somewhere in the craft's vast superstructure with the intention of destroying the ship after it had landed. Because the *Hindenburg* arrived twelve hours behind schedule, such a bomb might have detonated just as the dirigible was landing.

R. Baird Shuman

Bibliography

Archbold, Rick, et al. *Hindenburg: An Illustrated History*. New York: Warner, 1994. Filled with startling photographs, this oversized volume offers shocking, mute testimony to the extent of the *Hindenburg* disaster.

Mooney, Michael Macdonald. *The Hindenburg*. New York: Dodd, Mead, 1972. A detailed account of the disaster, well written and accurate. A personalized view with strong human interest elements.

Morrison, Herbert. "The *Hindenburg* Aflame." In *Mine Eyes Have Seen: A First Person History of Events That Shaped America*, edited by Richard Goldstein. New York: Simon & Schuster, 1997. A brief, lively account of the disaster and an enticing read.

Tanaka, Shelley. *The Disaster of the Hindenburg*. New York: Scholastic, 1993. Excellently illustrated and engagingly written for teen audiences, this book should also prove useful to adult readers.

See also: Dirigibles; Lighter-than-air craft; Transatlantic flight; Ferdinand von Zeppelin

History of human flight

Definition: A series of developments that have allowed people to travel through the air in manufactured aircraft.

Significance: Since the earliest recorded history, people dreamed of flying, often ascribing the power to mythical gods. The airplane changed the world as has no other invention before or since by conquering the problem of distance.

Early Scientific Theories

Seventeenth century English physicist Sir Issac Newton postulated that heavier-than-air flight was impossible. Newtonian physics concluded that the resistance encountered by a wing would require an even heavier engine, which in turn would require an even larger wing, which would require an even heavier engine, and so on, in a circuitous conundrum.

The history of the science of human flight arguably began in 1680, when Italian physicist Giovanni Alfonso Borelli definitively proved that humans could not fly under their own power, because their pectoral muscles were simply too weak to support flight, regardless of the wing structures one might employ. That evidence should have ended tower jumping and flapping wing contraptions, but it did not. Some persisted, even into the twentieth century, in their preoccupation with the impossible. Others searched for less fatal alternatives, turning from flapping to floating.

343

Hot-Air and Hydrogen Balloons

An artist captured the supposed earliest recorded hot-air balloon demonstration, which was a small model, sent briefly aloft in 1709. Scientifically studying and documenting their efforts with pubic demonstrations, French brothers Joseph-Michel and Jacques-Étienne Montgolfier achieved the first true hot-air balloon ascents. On June 4, 1783, near Lyon, France, they demonstrated for the public their uncrewed aerostat, a huge linen bag lined with paper, 100 feet in circumference, which rose 6,000 feet aloft when a straw-fed fire heated the air inside the bag.

The Montgolfiers were not alone, however, in their quest for the sky. A series of scientific discoveries followed, and in 1766, hydrogen was discovered to be one-fourteenth the weight of air. French physicist Jacques-Alexander-César Charles created his own version of the aerostat, crafting a rubber-coated silk balloon filled with hydrogen, which he publicly demonstrated on August 24, 1783, before a large crowd which included the American diplomat and inventor Benjamin Franklin.

During this period, the field of aviation experienced many pioneering firsts. In a demonstration before French king Louis XVI and his wife Marie-Antoinette at Versailles in September, 1783, the Montgolfiers sent aloft aviation's first living voyagers: a rooster, a sheep, and a duck. The first crewed balloon flight came on October 15, 1783, with volunteer Jean-François Pilâtre de Rozier, a young doctor, on board. The original plan had been to send aloft two criminals from prison, in case they did not come down alive. However, Pilâtre de Rozier insisted on taking the place of the prisoners. On November 21, 1783, he and the marquis François d'Arlandes flew untethered across Paris. On December 1, 1783, the first crewed hydrogen balloon ascended with Charles and a passenger. After a lengthy two-hour, 27-mile flight, Charles set down, left off his passenger, and made a second flight, at sunset. With one less person aboard, the balloon rose to 9,000 feet, and Charles became the first person to see the sun set twice in one day.

With these first successes also came tragedy. The first to fly was also the first to die. Pilâtre de Rozier, in attempting to cross the English Channel on June 15, 1785, combined the hot-air-and-hydrogen balloon technology, putting a fire under a hydrogen balloon. The flight lasted only four minutes before exploding and killing its pilot.

Military use for the balloon was not far behind, starting a familiar sequence which would be repeated throughout history. In June, 1793, the French Republican government put observers in tethered balloons to report on enemy movements. In April, 1794, the French formed the first balloon corps, used in several European campaigns but disbanded by Napoleon in 1802.

Powered Flight

The matter of balloon steering remained unresolved until the twentieth century, when the elongated steerable dirigible was developed. At about the same time, the first powered airplane was invented. These near-simultaneous achievements were not serendipitous. Both enterprises depended on the same thing to succeed: a suitable engine to power the aircraft.

Although early engines were problematic, they held great promise. In 1876, German engineer Nikolaus August Otto designed and built the world's first practical internal combustion engine to use liquid petrol as fuel. In 1885, simultaneously and independently, German engineers Gottlieb Daimler and Carl Benz built the first lightweight, high-speed petrol engines.

Gliders and Winged Flight

Although Orville and Wilbur Wright's secret to success in achieving the first powered flight was the engine they designed and built themselves, the two brothers researched, designed, tested, and built the plane, propellers, and control surfaces and structures that ultimately helped them to succeed. They systematically and scientifically studied the work of early glider pioneers, most notably that of the British Sir George Cayley, known as the father of aeronautics.

In 1804, Cayley had built the first known heavier-than-air flying model. Over the next fifty years, he built three full-scale gliders capable of flight with a passenger on board. In 1871, the wind tunnel was invented to enable the aerodynamic study of scale models. The Wrights perfected their own wind tunnel and used it systematically to study and perfect their wing and propeller designs. Their scientific approach enabled them to succeed where others had failed.

Another glider great, the German aviation pioneer Otto Lilienthal, developed and flew controllable gliders, working from 1891 until his death in 1896 while attempting a powered glide. He tested his gliders by leaping from an enormous hill he had built near Berlin. The Wrights, too, began by experimenting with gliders.

Still others would play a role in the Wright's story by disseminating information. Octave Chanute was a French-American engineer credited with building the first bridge across the Missouri River and the stockyards in Chicago and Kansas City. Bored with engineering for trains and livestock, he turned his attention to aeronautics. In 1894 he published *Progress in Flying Machines*, which collected and summarized the information humans had learned to date about heavier-than-air flying machines. On May 13, 1900, Wilbur Wright wrote to Chanute to introduce himself and inquire about available information that would assist the Wrights' experimentation.

The Wrights had learned of Chanute after having written the Smithsonian Institution seeking information on flying. They learned that Samuel Pierpont Langley, the director of the Smithsonian, was experimenting with heavier-than-air flight. Langley had received the first federal government contracts to build a powered human-carrying plane, but both his attempts, with planes launched from atop a houseboat in the Potomac River, were failures. He gave up in disappointment, most of his calculations proven embarrassingly incorrect when, one week later, he was beaten by the Wrights in the race to fly.

The Wright Brothers' Achievement

It is almost impossible to overstate the significance of the Wrights' accomplishment. Through careful study and diligent testing, they unlocked the secret to controlled flight. By wing warping, or twisting, they could cause the plane to turn. This mechanism was the forerunner of the aileron on modern planes. The Wrights systematically studied aspect ratios, comparing the wing's length to its width, and devising tables to decide on the most suitable wing sizes and shapes. They researched propellers in their wind tunnels, understanding that the propeller was a rotary wing with forward lift. They defeated torque by using two propellers rotating in opposite directions, connected to sprockets by a bicycle chain. When they could find no satisfactory engine, they designed and built their own.

At their testing grounds at Kitty Hawk, North Carolina, on December 17, 1903, at 10:35 A.M., the Wright brothers made their first flight, with Orville at the controls, and Wilbur running alongside him. Orville had positioned a camera before the flight, and John T. Daniels, a volunteer helper who had run up from the Kill Devil Hill Life Saving Station, snapped the picture of the first powered, sustained flight by humankind. The Wrights made four flights that day. The longest, with Wilbur at the controls, lasted 59 seconds and covered 852 feet.

In many ways the most important part of the history of flight was over on the day it began. The scant one hundred years in the history of human flight show astonishing discovery and achievement, but in reality, much remains exactly as it was researched and recorded in the Wrights' early records. In the next two years, the Wrights built more airplanes and made more discoveries about piloting them: how to control, turn, and avoid stalls. In January, 1906, the Wrights offered to sell their plane to the U.S. War Department, which declined. In 1907, they took their plane to Europe, seeking in vain to find a buyer overseas. The Wrights left their airplane stored in a shed in Europe and returned, dejected, to Dayton.

In 1908, however, the British Army acquired the Wrights' aeroplane number 1 and the U.S. Army agreed to pay the Wrights $25,000 for one of their airplanes. A French group agreed to pay $100,000. Wilbur went to France, got the plane out of the shed and upgraded it with some recent advancements.

To fulfill the U.S. government contract, Orville went to Fort Myer to test-fly the airplanes. Tragedy struck on the last day of the test flights, and a twenty-six-year-old lieutenant, Thomas Selfridge, became the first person to lose his life in an airplane accident.

Thereafter, the aviation firsts came in rapid succession. In 1909, French aviator Louis Blériot flew across the English Channel in a self-built monoplane. The public's fascination with aviation was fueled by air meets that occurred on both sides of the Atlantic Ocean. By 1910, there were nighttime takeoffs, makeshift lighted beacons and runways, stunt flying, and the first takeoff from a ship deck. The next few years brought ship-deck landings, the first U.S. transcontinental flights, the crossing of the Mediterranean and the establishment of the British Royal Flying Corps. With heavy initial losses and little early success, the U.S. Signal Corps was also established.

Airplanes as Warplanes

On June 28, 1914, Europe was thrown into World War I. At the start of the war, there were 1,200 German planes, and 1,000 French and British planes. On April 6, 1917, the United States entered World War I, and a U.S. military aviation section was established. Although 1,000 men enlisted, fewer than 250 planes were amassed.

Fighter planes and their pilots would earn fame and affection during World War I. Eddie Rickenbacker of Columbus, Ohio, who later helped found Eastern Air Lines, was the top U.S. ace, and also flew for France with the U.S. volunteer group, the Lafayette Escadrille. General William "Billy" Mitchell, returned home in 1919 from his European service advocating an independent U.S. air power. He predicted the attack on Pearl Harbor decades before its occurrence and forced the U.S. government to examine what had happened to money appropriated by Congress for World War I fighter planes that were never delivered. Justice Department investigations and Congressional hearings were held, but eventually Congress tired of the issue and agreed not to pursue the matter further.

Aviation in the Interwar Years

After the war was over, airplane travel offered a way around the war's destruction and devastation, and, in combination with ground transportation, allowed access to far-flung colonial outposts. European governments directly subsidized the development of commercial air carriers, such as KLM, Lufthansa, British Airways, and Air France.

The U.S. government, in contrast, opposed direct subsidies for the development of commercial air carriers, but instead used U.S. airmail contracts to establish and subsidize the aviation industry. In 1925, air mail was privatized, and wealthy American industrialists snapped up the first contracts. As aircraft improvements were made and more reliable engines were developed, navigational aids helped to make flying a more certain venture. In 1926, government regulation and certification of pilots, aircraft, air traffic rules, maps, weather reports, and accident investigation aided the private air carriers by improving the safety, efficiency, economics, and reputation of flying.

American fliers and planes soon established their worldwide dominance in the field of aviation. The first around-the-world flight was accomplished by Douglas Aircraft World Cruisers, manufactured in Santa Monica, California. Four Cruisers departed Seattle, Washington, on April 6, 1924, and two Cruisers returned to the same spot 27,553 miles and 175 days later, on September 28. Seven years later, a similar feat was accomplished in just eight days, when American aviator Wiley Post circumnavigated the globe.

In May, 1927, Charles A. Lindbergh, flying from New York to Paris, became the first pilot to make a solo transatlantic crossing. He was immediately lauded as a hero and remains among the most famous fliers in history. Lindbergh would go on to devote his life to the promotion of both civil and military aviation. In 1932, Amelia Earhart crossed the Atlantic solo, and fame followed her flight. She was lost in 1937, attempting to circumnavigate the globe via the 27,000-mile equator route.

The record-setting flights of the 1920's and 1930's bear witness to the fact that during this period, planes were undergoing dramatic technical improvements. No airplane before or since has captivated the world, or its aircraft sales, as did the Douglas DC-3. Still the most successful transport plane ever, with 10,926 manufactured in the United States, and perhaps as many as 5,000 more manufactured overseas by other countries, the twin-engine DC-3, also known as the Gooney Bird, Dakota, or Skytrain, along with the DC-4, also known as the Skymaster, with double the DC-3's engines, passenger capacity, and range, revolutionized air transportation.

Alternate Methods of Flight

Other methods of human flight rose, or fell, in the 1920's and 1930's. In 1926, American physicist Robert H. Goddard demonstrated the liquid fuel rocket. In 1936, the first truly successful helicopter, the Focke-Wulf, was developed in Germany. In 1937, British engineer Sir Frank Whittle established the world's first turbojet engine development program. Zeppelin airships, two and one-half times the length of a football field, were first launched in 1909 and began commercial service in 1911. Zeppelins provided the world's first passenger airline service. On May 6, 1937, the world's largest airship, the hydrogen-filled *Hindenberg*, exploded while approaching moorings in New Jersey, after completing a trip from Germany. Although lives had been lost in zeppelin travel until the *Hindenberg* disaster, the loss of the airship, captured on film and rebroadcast worldwide, ended the era of the airship, a scant thirty years into its history. Today, the sight of a helium-filled blimp overhead is a rare occurrence usually confined to the airspace over sporting events.

World War II

As the 1930's drew to a close, war again loomed in Europe and Asia. In 1932, Japan employed aircraft carriers in conflicts with China. In 1935, Italy used air forces to invade Ethiopia. In 1936, the nation sent air forces to aid General Francisco Franco in the Spanish Civil War, as did Germany, which had sent troops to Italy for secret pilot training. By 1938, Germany had reached wartime levels of airplane production. The Soviet Union sent planes to Spain to help defend against Franco's forces. In 1939, the Soviet Union aided China against Japan, as did the United States, with its American Volunteer Group, also known as the Flying Tigers.

On September 1, 1939, German chancellor Adolf Hitler invaded Poland. The Luftwaffe, the German air force, struck the Polish airfields, taking out most of Poland's planes. In 1940, Denmark, the Netherlands, Belgium, and France fell to the Germans. Beginning on September 7, 1940, Hitler's Luftwaffe commenced nightly bombing of London. Aided in part by radar warning stations, London and Britain held, and Hitler turned his attention elsewhere when he failed to achieve control of the air in the Battle of Britain. In 1941, Hitler invaded the Soviet Union. Although the Soviets suffered significant casualties and the loss of 8,000 planes, the German planes could not reach the Soviet aircraft factories, and the Soviets kept building.

In the United States, airplane production had been dramatically increasing throughout the late 1930's. In 1938, airplane production was increased to 10,000 units per year.

On December 7, 1941, the Japanese attacked Pearl Harbor, Hawaii, much as Billy Mitchell had predicted. In rapid succession, the Philippines, Hong Kong, Singapore, Malaya, the Dutch East Indies, Borneo, and Burma fell to the Japanese. In 1942, American bomber groups were deployed over Tokyo, Europe, and Africa. In 1943, the Eighth Air Force began attacks on Germany, and the Fifteenth Air Force began attacks on Italy. By 1944, U.S. aircraft manufacturers had produced 96,318 planes in one year. On May 7, 1945, Germany surrendered, even though it had developed formidable new weapons in the V-1 pilotless bomber jet and the V-2 missile, with a 2,000-pound warhead, a range of 220 miles, and a speed of up to 3,600 miles per hour.

Meanwhile, the air war raged on in the Pacific. The United States continued its strategic bombing of Japan with B-29 aircraft. The threat posed by Japanese kamikaze suicide bombers increased, as it surfaced that Japan intended to use the majority of its remaining planes as kamikazes. The decision was made to use the atomic bomb on Japan. On August 6, 1945, the first bomb was dropped on the city of Hiroshima, and a second was dropped on Nagasaki on August 9. Within six days, Japan had surrendered.

Berlin Airlift

After World War II, Germany was literally divided in two. East Germany was walled off by the Soviet Union and placed under a Communist government. West Germany was free and protected by U.S. forces. Landlocked within East Germany was the city of Berlin, half of which was not under Communist control and was protected by the U.S. and its allies. In 1948 and 1949, the United States airlifted food and supplies into Berlin, using Douglas C-47 and C-54 aircraft, in what was at the time the largest humanitarian effort in history.

An Independent U.S. Air Force

Following World War II, the United States altered its development and use of military aircraft. In 1947, the Army Air Corps became the newest branch of the armed forces, and the U.S. Air Force and the Central Intelligence Agency (CIA) were created. These two acts were not independent. The CIA, the Air Force, and private aerospace contractors worked together to develop new aircraft and intelligence technologies. One such facility, Lockheed Corporation's secret development division was dubbed the "Skunk Works," and its projects were so classified that they did not appear even in federal budgets. In 1947, a military plane broke the sound barrier.

The Cold War

Although World War II had ended, the Cold War took its place. A handful of the world's most powerful nations possessed the capability to make and deploy nuclear weapons. The United States and the Soviet Union, former World War II allies, both developed intercontinental ballistic missiles (ICBMs) capable of attacking the other nation when launched from home soil. The deterrent effect of these weapons was called mutual assured destruction (MAD). The destructive capabilities and the distrust between the two superpowers spurred the space race, as well as military actions in other parts of the world.

The Korean War

On June 25, 1950, Communist North Korea crossed the thirty-eighth parallel, invading free South Korea. The Soviet Union aided North Korea, and the United States helped to defend South Korea. November, 1950, saw the world's first all-jet air battle between a Soviet MiG and a U.S. F-80 Shooting Star. Later, the U.S. F-86 Sabre jet would prove an even tougher opponent against the MiGs. On July 27, 1953, an uneasy armistice was signed, but difficulties persisted, and U.S. forces continued to help defend the peace.

The Jet Age

In the 1950's civil aviation also entered the jet age. In May, 1952, the British De Havilland Comet commenced passenger service. Soon after entering service, three such planes seemingly came apart in midflight. By April, 1954, the plane was grounded, and the American Douglas DC-8 and the Boeing 707 came to dominate the world's jet passenger airline market, giving their manufacturers the lead in the industry for years, until a European consortium was formed in 1970 to manufacture the Airbus aircraft.

The Space Age

The Soviet Union led the early space race, with a series of firsts. In 1957, the Soviet Union sent Sputnik, the world's first Earth-orbiting satellite, into space. In 1961, the Soviet cosmonaut Yuri Gagarin became the first human in space with his Earth-orbiting mission Vostok 1. The United States followed shortly thereafter with Alan Shepard, Virgil "Gus" Grissom, and John Glenn.

History of human flight

In the early 1960's international attention and tensions were also riveted by the work of American spy planes when the Soviets shot down an American U-2 plane and captured its pilot, Gary Powers, and spy plane photographs revealed Soviet movement to put missiles on Cuba, within range of the United States.

The Vietnam War
Events in Southeast Asia during the 1950's and 1960's involved the United States in another war and again tested the nation's air power. While trying to stabilize a tenuous political situation between North and South Vietnam, the United States was drawn into a police action that would occupy two presidents and divide the American people. The Vietnam War was called the first television war, with fighting broadcast on the nightly news.

Memorable Events in Flight
Many people claim there are events in history that are so important that every person who was alive and sentient can remember exactly where they were and what they were doing when it happened. One such event was the assassination of President John F. Kennedy on November 22, 1963. Another three involve human flight. On July 20, 1969, the *Eagle* lunar landing craft set down on the surface of Moon, where U.S. astronauts Neil Armstrong and Edwin "Buzz" Aldrin left footprints and an American flag. Another such event is the January 28, 1986, explosion of the space shuttle *Challenger*, which killed seven astronauts, including Christa McAuliffe, the first teacher in space. The third day is September 11, 2001, when four hijackings resulted in the deaths of almost five thousand people at the World Trade Center and the Pentagon.

Operation Desert Storm
By 1991, when Americans would watch another war on television, aviation had evolved significantly from the time of the Vietnam War. During the Gulf War, missile-mounted cameras delivered photographic images while delivering bombs with exactitude measurable in inches, without risking American fliers. Global Positioning System (GPS) satellites had been placed in orbit and delivered with inexpensive handheld units target exactitude. One-half million American military personnel and the armament and equipment to support them were delivered to the other side of the world. The war was over within days. For the first time since the invention of the airplane, there was a war with no aces.

Highway in the Sky
The technology revealed in Operation Desert Storm helped to revolutionize the world of civilian aviation throughout the late twentieth century. The U.S. air traffic control (ATC) system had been pinning its hopes on a new microwave landing system, which was scrapped in favor of the astonishingly accurate GPS system. Computer flight control and navigation technology was adapted for affordable installation in small general aviation and personal aircraft, delivering military precision and failsafe computer systems for private pilots.

The ability to wage war without legions of pilots convinced the U.S. Joint Chiefs of Staff that the military should develop uninhabited aerial vehicles (UAVs) for both intelligence and weapons delivery. Lightweight and quiet jet engines and lightweight but strong composite flight structures were developed for the job. The military was not alone in realizing the value to human flight of such engines and materials.

In 1977, one of the oldest obstacles to human flight was finally overcome, when *Gossamer Condor*, powered by pedals, made the first human-powered flight. Its designer had worked with extremely lightweight but strong materials, as had Jeana Yeager and Dick Rutan in piloting the *Voyager*, which in 1986 became the first plane to make a nonstop transglobal flight without refueling. The 1903 Wright *Flyer* and the 1988 *Voyager* sit side by side at the National Air and Space Museum, awaiting the next addition in the history of human flight.

Mary Fackler Schiavo

Bibliography
Boyne, Walter, ed. *The Smithsonian Book of Flight*. New York: Smithsonian Books, Orion Books, 1987. The history of flight in narrative and color photographs.

Josephy, Alvin, ed. *The American Heritage History of Flight*. New York: American Heritage, Simon & Schuster, 1962. The history of flight with letters and writings of those making history interspersed with the narrative and photos.

Taylor, John, and Kenneth Munson. *History of Aviation*. New York: Crown, 1976. A lavishly illustrated and lengthy book with detailed information about a wealth of aviation subjects.

See also: Air carriers; Apollo Program; Balloons; Commercial flight; Gulf War; *Hindenburg*; Human-powered flight; Korean War; Lighter-than-air craft; Manufacturers; Military flight; Billy Mitchell; Montgolfier brothers; Propellers; Burt Rutan; Space shuttle; Spaceflight; Uninhabited Aerial Vehicles; Vietnam War; Wing designs; World War I; World War II; Wright brothers; Wright *Flyer*

Hornet

Also known as: F/A-18, XF-17 Cobra

Date: First flight of XF-17 Cobra, 1974; first flight of F/A-18A, 1983; first flight of F/A-18C, 1987; first flight of F/A-18E, 1995

Definition: A fighter and attack aircraft that represents one of the first truly multirole military aircraft.

Significance: The Hornet represents the cornerstone of current and future U.S. Navy and Marine Corps air power.

Development

One of the most successful combat aircraft in history, the F/A-18 Hornet finds its orgins in the failure of another aircraft, its precursor, the Cobra. Designed by the Northrop Corporation in the late 1960's, the Cobra was a lightweight, multimission aircraft offered to the air forces of smaller nations that could not afford large numbers of separately dedicated fighter and attack aircraft.

Although the Cobra was a capable aircraft, it found no takers. However, an opportunity emerged in the early 1970's, when the U.S. Air Force solicited proposals for a lightweight fighter design. Air Force fighters of the early 1960's, such as the F-4 Phantom II, relied on long-range missiles as their primary armament. During the Vietnam War, however, the Air Force found itself engaging smaller, more agile Soviet-built fighters in close-combat situations, in which the pilots of the U.S. aircraft could not use their missiles and had difficulty outmaneuvering their smaller adversaries.

The purpose of the new aircraft design search was to reverse the trend of increasingly larger and more expensive aircraft. The Air Force planned to build hundreds of the lightweight fighters to counter the Soviet threat to Western Europe at the height of the Cold War. In January, 1972, the Air Force opened the Lightweight Fighter Program (LFP) by soliciting design bids from various aircraft producers. Northrop responded with an updated version of the Cobra, labeled the YF-17. A year later, the Air Force selected the YF-17 and an offering from General Dynamics, the YF-16, for prototype production, and both aircraft flew in 1974.

The two designs had significant differences. The Northrop aircraft featured two smaller engines with twin vertical tails, whereas the General Dynamics craft had a single large engine and a single tail fin. The YF-16 carried a limited armament of short-range air-to-air missiles and an internal 20-millimeter cannon. In comparison, the YF-17 carried the same weaponry, but also featured advanced radar capable of guiding medium-range air-to-air missiles. Despite meeting all of the flight requirements and possessing a greater range of weapons, the YF-17 lost the competition to the less expensive YF-16 in 1975.

This defeat was not the end of the Cobra, however. By 1975, the U.S. Navy had opened its Carrier Fighter and Attack, Experimental (VFAX) competition to find a new strike fighter for its aircraft carriers. The new Navy aircraft, in replacing two different aircraft, would have to perform multiple tasks in limited carrier deck space. The Navy wanted the new airplane to replace the F-4 Phantom II, an air-defense fighter with a secondary attack capability, and the A-7 Corsair II, a dedicated light attack aircraft. Northrop gained the upper hand in the VFAX competition by teaming with McDonnell Douglas Corporation, a company with a long history of building carrier aircraft for the Navy. Northrop and McDonnell Douglas adapted the original land-based Cobra design into a that of a carrier-based strike fighter, adopting the new designation XF-18 Hornet to signify the emergence of a new plane from the XF-17 Cobra. With McDonnell Douglas now acting as the lead company in the aircraft's development, the Navy selected the XF-18 Hornet as its VFAX winner in 1976. Final design work proceeded, and the single-seat F/A-18A and two-seat F/A-18B became operational in 1983.

The redesigned Hornet immediately proved its worth. The Navy had originally intended to produce separate versions of the Hornet in F-18 fighter and A-18 attack models. The advanced radar originally installed for the LFP, however, proved capable of handling both missions, and separate variants never emerged. As a multimission aircraft, the Hornet became the only airplane with the F/A designation, symbolizing its dual role of air defense and attack.

In 1987, the Navy took delivery of its first improved Hornets, the single-seat F/A-18C and the two-seat F/A-18D, with provisions for Maverick air-to-surface missiles, AMRAAM air-to-air missiles, and advanced avionics for night flying. The popularity of the Hornet eventually led the Navy's precision-flying team, the Blue Angels, to adopt the agile aircraft in 1986. The Hornet's multimission capability attracted several other buyers; the U.S. Marine Corps replaced its F-4 Phantoms, A-4 Skyhawks, and A-6 Intruders with the Hornet. The Hornet is also employed by the air forces of Australia, Canada, Finland, Kuwait, Malaysia, Spain, and Switzerland.

Use

The Hornet F/A-18 boasts an excellent combat record. It first entered combat in 1986, when the United States

F/A-18 Hornet Characteristics

	F/A-18C, F/A-18D	F/A-18E, F/A-18F
Primary Function	Multirole attack and fighter aircraft	Multirole attack and fighter aircraft
Builder	McDonnell Douglas (prime), Northrop (major subcontractor)	McDonnell Douglas
Unit Cost	$24 million	$35 million
Propulsion	Two F404-GE-402 enhanced performance turbofan engines	Two F414-GE-400 turbofan engines
Thrust per Engine (pounds static thrust)	17,700	22,000
Length (feet)	56	60.3
Height (feet)	15.3	16
Maximum Takeoff Gross Weight (pounds)	51,900	66,000
Wingspan (feet)	40.4	44.9
Ceiling (feet)	50,000+	50,000+
Speed	Mach 1.7+	Mach 1.8+
Crew	C model, 1; D model, 2	E model, 1; F model, 2
Armament	One M61A1/A2 Vulcan 20-millimeter cannon	One M61A1/A2 Vulcan 20-millimeter cannon
External Payload	AIM 9 Sidewinder, AIM 7 Sparrow, AIM-120 AMRAAM, Harpoon, HARM, Shrike, SLAM, SLAM-ER, Walleye, and Maverick missiles; Joint Stand-Off Weapon; Joint Direct Attack Munition; various general-purpose bombs, mines, and rockets	AIM 9 Sidewinder, AIM 7 Sparrow, AIM-120 AMRAAM, Harpoon, HARM, Shrike, SLAM, SLAM-ER, Walleye, and Maverick missiles; Joint Stand-Off Weapon; Joint Direct Attack Munition; various general-purpose bombs, mines, and rockets
Date Deployed	November, 1978 (first flight)	December, 1995 (first flight)

Source: Data taken from (www.chinfo.navy.mil/navpalib/factfile/aircraft/air-fa18.html), November 6, 2001.

bombed the North African country of Libya in retaliation for that nation's support of terrorist organizations and the bombing deaths of U.S. citizens. In support of the air raids, Hornets from the USS *Coral Sea* destroyed Libyan air defense sites with HARM antiradar missiles.

Hornets also participated in Operation Desert Storm, the 1990-1991 military campaing to end Iraqi occupation of its neighboring nation, Kuwait. In this conflict, the Hornet's flexibility proved to be its biggest asset. F/A-18's destroyed Iraqi patrol boats that threatened Allied ships with antiship missiles, provided air defense for coalition forces, and bombed Iraqi targets in support of the ground offensive. The best example of the F/A-18's flexibility during the Gulf War happened when two Hornets on a bombing mission came under attack from two Iraqi fighters. Without dropping their bombs, the Hornet pilots switched their radars to air defense mode, shot down the Iraqi aircraft, switched their radars back to ground attack, and finished their bombing run.

The Hornet continues to receive upgrades that will keep it in service for years to come. In 1995, the prototype F/A-18E Super Hornet made its first flight. Designed to replace U.S. Navy A-6 Intruders and F-14 Tomcats, the Super Hornet is 25 percent larger than earlier F/A-18's, with a corresponding increase in capability.

Steven J. Ramold

Bibliography

Drendel, Lou. *F/A-18 Hornet in Action*. Carrollton, Tex.: Squadron, 1993. A study of the F/A-18, from its F-17 origins to its combat in the Gulf War, featuring many photographs.

Gandt, Robert L. *Bogeys and Bandits: The Making of a Fighter Pilot*. New York: Penguin, 1998. A description of U.S. Navy fighter pilot training, from recruitment to assignment to an active F/A-18 squadron.

Jenkins, Dennis R. *F/A-18 Hornet: A Navy Success Story*. New York: McGraw-Hill, 2000. Details the development of the F/A-18 as a best-case example of the Pentagon's weapons-systems acquisition process.

Kelly, Orr. *Hornet: The Inside Story of the F/A-18*. Shrewsbury, England: Airlife, 1991. A brief summary of the F/A-18's career, complete with photographs of various Hornet models from all the nations flying the aircraft.

See also: Air force, U.S.; Aircraft carriers; Eagle; Fighter pilots; Gulf War; Marine pilots, U.S.; McDonnell Douglas; Navy pilots, U.S.; Tomcat; Vietnam War

Hot-air balloons

Date: First crewed free flight on November 21, 1783
Definition: Large round inflatable sacks filled with hot air that rise above the ground, towing compartments for passengers or cargo.
Significance: The hot-air balloon ushered in the age of human flight by providing a means for people to leave the earth and rise to significant heights for sustained periods. This lighter-than-air craft also proved that air was still breathable and life sustaining at higher altitudes.

Early History

Hot-air balloons inaugurated the concept of human flight. The hot-air balloon proved for the first time that a human being could survive at some height above the earth. This was a notable scientific achievement, since prior to the advent of balloons many people had no clear understanding of how high the breathable atmosphere extended. With the advent of the balloon, the dream of leaving the confines of the earth was realized. This was the dawn of a new era, the preamble to the space age.

Two French brothers, Joseph-Michel and Jacques-Étienne Montgolfier, invented the hot-air balloon in 1783. Their inspiration was the observation that a paper bag placed over an indoor smoking fire rose in the air. As a test, they lined a large cloth bag with paper and caused it to rise by filling it with black smoke and hot air from an outdoor straw fire. Later, the Montgolfiers sent animals aloft first on tethered balloons and then on a free flight in order to prove that the animals could survive above the earth. They succeeded: The animals lived. After the free flight, King Louis XVI of France was persuaded to allow the required permission for humans to attempt a test flight. With approval, two other Frenchmen, Jean-François Pilâtre de Rozier and the Marquis François-Laurent d'Arlandes, made the first human free-flight balloon ascent on November 21, 1783. In a 70-foot-high, 46-foot-diameter Montgolfier balloon, they flew for 25 minutes, traveling for several miles over the city of Paris. The balloon carried its own grated fire pot, to which the pilots frequently added straw. Although the pilots had to extinguish small fires when parts of the balloon's flimsy material ignited from sparks, they landed safely. This flight was witnessed by thousands of Parisians. The second human free-flight balloon ascension was made by Professor Jacques Alexandre César Charles and a passenger on December 1, 1783, in a hydrogen-filled balloon.

Hydrogen-filled balloons, filled with dangerously combustible gas, nevertheless had the advantage of requiring only one-third the gas volume of hot-air balloons for the same buoyancy. The larger hot-air balloons were more difficult to handle and transport. The risk of balloon material igniting from the sparks of open fires made them hazardous, and smoke from the fire choked the riders. Flight time was limited by the fuel supply. In contrast, the hydrogen balloon was well suited to long-term scientific and military observation. Its gas was not expelled until a descent was desired. For these reasons, hot-air balloons became rare during the years between 1800 and 1960, while hydrogen types flourished.

Twentieth Century

A rebirth of hot-air ballooning occurred on October 10, 1960, in Bruning, Nebraska, when an American, Ed Yost, performed a free-flight test in his prototype balloon. His

351

new design featured a polyurethane-coated nylon envelope and a propane-powered burner. This system was much safer and more rugged than that of the previous era. In 1963, Yost and a partner, Don Piccard, traveled to Britain and made the first English Channel crossing by hot-air balloon.

By the 1970's, hot-air balloon manufacturers had flourished in the United States, Britain, and France. A hot-air balloon could be obtained for the price of an expensive motorcycle, thus bringing it within the budget of many sports enthusiasts. Many balloonists started businesses offering one-hour chartered flights for one hundred dollars.

High cost and adventurous record-breaking attempts also continued in the twentieth century. Bertrand Piccard and Brian Jones achieved the first nonstop circumnavigation of the globe in March, 1999, in a combination hot-air-and-helium balloon. They launched their *Breitling Orbiter 3* from Switzerland, traveled around the world in twenty days, and landed in Egypt.

Construction

The main parts of a modern hot-air balloon are the envelope, the burner-fuel system, and the basket. The envelope is the bag, or air sack, containing hot air. It is constructed of pieces of fabric, usually nylon. Each slice of fabric, called a gore, consists of panels and stretches from the top to the bottom of the balloon. Forming the gores in specific dimensions determines the overall shape of the balloon. Round, oblong, and special shapes such as those of a piggy bank, a soda can, and even Mickey Mouse have been constructed, often for advertising.

The envelope top, or crown, is constructed with a parachute valve, a piece of fabric in the shape of a parachute. It is attached in such a manner that a section can be pulled away when a pilot pulls a connected cord. This action releases some of the hot air through the top of the balloon, reduces the overall inside air temperature, and causes the balloon to descend. At the base, which is open, there is usually a short, cylindrical fabric section called the skirt. It is coated with fire-resistant material, because it is close to the flame. The burner is mounted in a frame attached between the basket and the skirt.

Propane from a tank is ignited by the burner's pilot light. An on-off valve allows the pilot to control fuel flow. The amount of fuel available determines the amount of time the balloon can stay aloft. Baskets, which usually hold from two to five people in addition to propane fuel tanks, are still made of wicker because the shock-absorbent material helps provide a soft landing for passengers and pilots.

Use

In the United States, hot-air balloons must be registered with the Federal Aviation Administration (FAA). Pilots are certified in one of three classes: student, private, or commercial. Hot-air balloons lift off by inflating their containing envelope with heated air. Because hot air expands, the heated air becomes lighter than the ambient, cooler surrounding air, which pushes upward against the air bag and provides the lift necessary for flight. Within the envelope, the heated, lighter air rises and displaces the cooler, heavier air, which descends.

Prior to launch, the pilot checks weather conditions for local winds and any possible storm indications. Storms are hazardous for several reasons: Lightning strikes can electrocute people and damage the balloon; rain, hail, or snow can cause damage, present visibility problems, and make the balloon heavier; and high wind makes launching and landing dangerous. To check the weather conditions, a pilot can either consult a weather service or go to the launch site and send up a small party-size helium balloon. From the balloon's changing position as it ascends, the pilot can gauge both the speed and the direction of the wind.

Because the air inside the envelope of a hot-air balloon is lighter than the air outside, the relative pressure is upward, and air does not pour out of the open-ended base. To prepare for launching, the deflated envelope is laid out on the ground, then the gas-fired burner is posi-

---

Milestones in Hot-Air Ballooning

November 21, 1783: De Rozier and d'Arlandes make the first crewed free flight, in Paris, France, in a Montgolfier hot-air balloon.

June 15, 1785: De Rozier and a companion fall to their deaths after a hybrid hot-air-and-hydrogen balloon ignites over the English Channel, becoming hot-air ballooning's first fatalities.

1800-1960: Hot-air ballooning experiences a low-activity period as hydrogren-filled balloons increase in popularity.

October 10, 1960: Ed Yost, of Bruning, Nebraska, reintroduces a newly designed hot-air balloon, initiating a renaissance in hot-air ballooning.

January 17, 1991: Richard Branson and Per Lindstrand make the first hot-air transpacific flight, in the largest hot-air balloon flown.

March 20, 1999: Bertrand Piccard and Brian Jones make the first nonstop global circumnavigation, in a hybrid hot-air and helium balloon.

tioned to force heated air into the envelope opening. Another method uses a powerful fan to initially provide a partial cold-air inflation. The balloon, as it inflates, gradually rises from horizontal to vertical. The balloon basket is anchored to prevent a gust of wind from blowing the balloon away prior to launch. The ground crew also holds the basket down until pilot and passengers are ready to launch.

Once the balloon is fully inflated, more lift can be generated by continuing to heat the air within it. When the lift of the heated air is greater than the total weight of the balloon, basket, equipment, and occupants, the balloon rises. Just prior to this point, all tie-lines are released, and the crew releases the basket. The pilot fires the burner again, and the balloon lifts off. Whenever the burner is turned off, the air in the bag gradually cools, and the balloon slowly descends. Neither the heating nor the cooling causes an instant effect. There is a thermal time lag, usually of a half-minute or more, due to the large amount of air to heat or cool. To maintain one particular altitude, the pilot periodically turns the burner on and off. If the pilot is skilled, the balloon will neither rise nor fall to any appreciable degree during this operation. In addition to keeping the burner off, the pilot can also cause a descent by momentarily opening the parachute valve and allowing some of the hot air to escape.

Because a hot-air balloon has no propulsion system, the horizontal direction and speed of the balloon are determined by the prevailing winds. Riding with the wind, passengers feel no wind except for gusts. Winds generally blow in different directions at different altitudes. The pilot seeks out the desired wind to carry the balloon in the desired direction.

There is an upper limit to balloon ascension, even if the burner is left on continuously. As elevation above the ground increases, the air becomes thinner. Eventually, the air becomes so thin that it provides no further lift. The pilot uses an onboard altimeter to determine the balloon's altitude and a variometer to indicate the rate of ascent or descent. A Global Positioning System (GPS) device can be used to obtain a readout on the balloon's latitude, longitude, and elevation.

Normally, the pilot tries to land in a large, flat, open area, such as a field, meadow, flatland, or desert, with no nearby obstructions, such as power lines, telephone poles, trees, or fences. In the case of a no-wind landing, the touchdown can be very gentle. If there is wind, the basket will drag along the ground until stopped by friction. After the basket has stopped, the pilot can fully open the parachute valve, causing the balloon to collapse completely. The ground crew tracks the balloon's path in a recovery vehicle and meets it at the landing site.

Festivals

There are thousands of hot-air balloon pilots worldwide, and periodic balloon festivals are held in many countries. These festivals usually feature competitions and mass ascensions, in which as many as five hundred balloons float in the air at the same time. The annual October festival in Albuquerque, New Mexico, is one of the largest festivals, with more than 850 balloons aloft in cooperative weather.

Robert J. Wells

Bibliography

Cowl, Clayton T., et al. "Factors Associated with Fatalities and Injuries from Hot-Air Balloon Crashes." *Journal of the American Medical Association* 279, no. 13 (April, 1998). Summarizes data collected by the Civil Aeronautics Board and the National Transportation Safety Board covering the years from 1964 to 1995, with causes and types of injuries and deaths due to crashes.

Heppenheimer, T. A. *A Brief History of Flight: From Balloons to Mach 3 and Beyond.* New York: Wiley, 2001. An overview of the important developments in aeronautical history, including the contributions of the Montgolfier brothers.

Scott, Phil. *The Shoulders of Giants: A History of Human Flight to 1919.* Reading, Mass.: Addison-Wesley, 1995. An in-depth account of the balloon flights of the Montgolfier brothers.

Wirth, Dick. *Ballooning: The Complete Guide to Riding the Wind.* New York: Random House, 1980. Focuses on all types of hot-air balloons, from 1783 to 1980, with ample sketches and more than 120 color photographs.

See also: Balloons; Blimps; Buoyant aircraft; Dirigibles; History of human flight; Lighter-than-air craft; Montgolfier brothers

Hovercraft

- **Also known as:** Air cushion vehicles, Surface effect ships
- **Definition:** Vessels that float above the surface of the water on a cushion of air.
- **Significance:** Hovercraft have allowed aircraft vessels to operate at very high speeds and become fully amphibious.

Hovercraft

Background

Humans have sailed ships since the beginning of recorded history. These ships have always been designed and built based on the ancient mathematician Archimedes's principle of displacement. More recently, using eighteenth century Swiss mathematician Daniel Bernoulli's principle of dynamic lift, humans learned to build vessels that lift out of the water and fly above it.

A vessel that flies over the surface of the water is interesting for a number of reasons, the first of which is the concept of displacement. A ship floating in water displaces, or pushes aside, a weight of water equal to its own weight. This is Archimedes's principle. If the displacement is reduced by flying the vessel above the water, the drag, or the friction acting against the vessel's hull to slow it down, is reduced. Secondly, if the drag is reduced by reducing displacement, the speed can be increased dramatically using the same horsepower. Most conventional floating vessels have a top speed of 35 to 40 miles per hour. Hovercraft have a top speed of 100 to 150 miles per hour. A final advantage to flying over water is that hovercraft can be fully amphibious. That is, they can travel over land as easily as they travel over water.

History

The earliest experiments with hovercraft were undertaken in 1716 by Emanuel Swedenborg, a Swedish designer and philosopher. Swedenborg designed and built a vessel that looked somewhat like an upside-down dinghy. It had a cockpit in the center with air scoop openings on either side. These scoops were rotated by the operator, and air forced under the vessel lifted it above the water's surface. The problem with the design was that the horsepower required to maintain the lift was greater than the operator could create.

The first successful operation of a hovercraft was made by another Swede, Hans Dineson. Dineson built a vessel with rigid sidewalls and a flexible skirt both fore and aft, or front and back. By 1916, Austrian engineer Dagobert Müller von Thomamuhl had built another rigid sidewall hovercraft torpedo boat that was capable of a speed of 40 miles per hour.

Over the next half-century, many other designers and builders experimented with hovercraft and other types of "flying" vessels. In 1959, Christopher Cockerell tested his vessel. This vessel not only floated on a cushion of air, as many others had done, but it also used air jets, rather than fans, to maintain this air cushion. These air jets reduced the leakage from the vessel and increased the height of clearance from the sea. The first full-scale hovercraft was built by Saunders-Roe in England and christened the *SR.N1*. The vessel made its maiden voyage from Calais, France, to Dover, England, on the morning of July 25, 1959. This date was chosen to commemorate French aeronautics pioneer Louis Blériot's epic cross-Channel flight in a heavier-than-air craft fifty years earlier.

Another Englishman, C. H. Latimer-Needham, added skirts to Cockerell's invention in 1961. This adjustment dramatically increased the height of the vessel above the water. The increase in the depth of the vessel's air cushion allowed it to function in much rougher waters.

Hovercraft Design

Vehicles that either ride above the surface of the water or are partially lifted above the water's surface by a cushion of air have been called by many names by their various designers and builders. Although "hovercraft" is certainly one of the most familiar of these names, the vehicles are also known as air-cushion vehicles (ACVs), trapped-air-cushion vehicles (TACs), captured-air-bubble vehicles (CABs), ground-effect machines (GEMs), surface-effect vessels (SEVs), and surface-effect ships (SESs). In all cases, the design of the hovercraft follows a few basic principles. First, since air is 815 times less dense than water, it is easier to push something through the air than through the water. Second, increasing the amount of the hull that is lifted out of the water decreases the amount of drag the vehicle experiences and increases the speed of the vessel.

Hovercraft, or ACVs, are lifted out of the water in one of two ways: by either static or dynamic lift. Hovercraft are said to be aerostatic or aerodynamic. "Aerostatic" means they can be lifted, generally by fans, even when they are not moving. "Aerodynamic" means that the hovercraft's forward motion creates the lift. These vessels settle back to the surface when their forward motion is stopped.

Aerostatic vessels have developed in two different ways. The first of these is through use of the plenum chamber. The plenum chamber is the large area under the hovercraft that contains the air cushion. Fans push large volumes of air down into this area. Skirting around the edge of the vessel helps contain the cushion of air under the vessel. These vessels are designed so that a large amount of air escapes around the bottom of the skirt and helps to lift the vessel clear of the water.

The second type of aerostatic hovercraft is the annular jet type, such as that designed and built by Cockerell in 1959. In the annular jet type hovercraft, the inner skirt and the outer skirt are pinched together at the base, and this pinching creates a jet of air. These jets are focused inward

The hovercraft flies very low and at very high speeds over a surface, allowing it to be truly amphibious. (AP/Wide World Photos)

and downward around the edges of the vessel. In this way, less air from the cushion is lost and greater lift can be generated with the same power.

Aerodynamic hovercraft depend on their forward motion to create enough lift for the vessel to rise clear of the water's surface. There are two types of aerodynamic vessels. The first of these is the ram-wing design. As the name implies, the speed of the vessel forces, or rams, air under the hull, lifting the vessel clear of the water's surface. At slow speed or when stopped, the vessels float in the water, only lifting as they accelerate. Many of these vessels use rigid sidewalls to contain or focus the airflow under the hull when moving.

The second type of aerodynamic vessel is the wing-in-ground type, also sometimes called ground-effect vessels. The Soviets built a class of this type of vessel, called Ekranoplan, for their military. In ground-effect vessels, the surface of the sea and the underside of the vessel create a tunnel in which air is trapped, lifting the vessel clear of the water's surface. These vessels also usually have rigid sidewalls to support the air cushion.

Skirting

In 1961, when skirts began to be added to hovercraft, a number of things occurred. First, the skirt deepened the air cushion, so the vessels rose higher out of the water. Second, drag was reduced by lifting the vessel, so speeds increased using the same amount of horsepower. Finally, the skirt reduced the size of vessel required to operate in rough water by 75 percent, because the skirt effectively lifted the vessel above the waves rather than running through them.

Skirts are of two types. The first is the flexible skirt, resembling large rubber inner tubes that extend down from the sides and ends of the vessel. Even though this skirt extends all the way around the vessel, it is usually made up of more than one piece and contains the cushion of air. Side sections and front and rear sections are placed very close together to appear as one piece. The skirt on a vessel is designed so that its depth is twice the significant, or average, wave height for the area in which the hovercraft is to be used. In this way, the waves do not wash over the vessel when it is moving. Some vessel designs contain not only a flexible outer skirt, but also smaller skirts within the larger one. These inner skirts are called petticoats. In this way, the air cushion can be maintained even in rough sea conditions.

The second type of skirting is rigid. These are often called sidewalls. Vessels with this type of skirting generally have flexible "finger" skirts at the front and back of the vessel and along the vessel's rigid sidewalls. The sidewalls are constructed of the same metals as the hull of the vessels, whereas the fingers are of the same rubber as the flexible skirts.

Propulsion and Lifting Systems

Hovercraft are different than other types of seaborne vessels in that they need two different types of power systems. One system creates the lift required to form the cushion of air under the vessel. The other system is used to develop the thrust to drive the vessel through or over the water.

Propulsion systems for most types of hovercraft involve propellers driving the vessel over the water. These propellers are driven by gas-turbine or diesel engines. A small percentage (10 percent) of hovercraft, mainly surface-effect ships (SESs), are driven by water jets that extend down from the rigid sidewalls. Such vessels can be problematic in very rough seas, although water jets control the steering of the vessel better than do the propellers.

Lifting systems involve pushing a very large volume of air under the vessel to create a cushion. The simplest type are the axial fans, in which the air moves in the same direction as the axis of the fan. This system works well for smaller vessels and vessels that do not require a high-pressure air cushion. The other type of fan is a centrifugal fan, in which the air is thrown out at 90-degree right angles to the axis of the fan. Centrifugal fans appear to work better in larger vessels, in which higher pressures are needed and fans may be spaced along the length of the vessel.

On some types of vessels, side thrusters are used for maneuvering at slower speeds. At speeds of less than 15 miles per hour, the cushion fans can release small amounts of air out of the side of the vessel, causing it to turn. These are called "puff ports" or "thrust ports." At higher speeds, however, these ports are ineffective.

Application of Design

Hovercraft, or ACV, designs have been adapted by a variety of users in different areas over the years. One of the first groups to exploit the application of hovercraft design was the military. Hovercraft were fast, maneuverable, and completely amphibious. They could be made small in size and armed as patrol boats or gun boats. They could be used in coastal areas, swamps, and even over open ground. They could be adapted and made larger to carry people and equipment ashore from naval vessels lying offshore.

The civilian adaptation of the hovercraft concept was no less effective or diverse. The most widely advertised uses of hovercraft were as passenger and vehicle ferries in congested urban areas. The ferries that cross the English Channel, large vessels carrying both passengers and vehicles, have for a number of years been successful on several routes.

An interesting use of hovercraft is in areas of sensitive terrain. Hovercraft are used in the Arctic over frozen tundra, over frozen ocean surface, or on frozen rivers. They are also used in swamp or marsh areas or on beachfronts where sand may be too soft for other types of vehicles. Recently, they have been used for heavy lifting of industrial equipment such as oil-field or mining equipment. Of course, no vehicle that travels at great speeds can escape the sporting enthusiast. Groups have developed that race different types of hovercraft depending on size, horsepower, and the skill of the driver.

Robert J. Stewart

Bibliography

Blunden, Alan. *The Hovercraft.* Loughborough, England: Ladybird, 1985. An illustrated reference for children detailing the workings of hovercraft.

Cagle, Malcolm W. Rear Admiral. *Flying Ships: Hovercraft and Hydrofoils.* New York: Dodd, Mead, 1970. A well-written explanation of the design and operation of hovercraft and hydrofoils. The author traces not only the history and uses of military hovercraft, but also hovercraft racing and personal uses.

Croome, Angela. *Hover Craft.* 4th ed. London: Hodder and Stoughton, 1984. A history of hovercraft with a helpful index.

McLeavy, Roy. *Hovercraft and Hydrofoils.* New York: ARCO, 1977. A well-illustrated discussion of the development of hovercraft, with helpful color photographs and drawings and a glossary.

See also: Forces of flight; Jet engines; Military flight; Propellers; Propulsion

Howard R. Hughes

Date: Born on December 24, 1905, in Houston, Texas; died on April 5, 1976, in an airplane en route from Acapulco, Mexico, to Houston, Texas

Definition: Pioneer aviator, aircraft designer, builder, and multimillionaire.

Significance: A world-class pilot and aircraft designer, Hughes is known, in aviation, for building and flying the *Spruce Goose*, by far the largest aircraft of its day and for founding the Hughes Aircraft Corporation.

Howard R. Hughes was born into wealth in 1905, attended private schools in his youth, and later studied at both Rice University and the California Institute of Technology. He first flew in an airplane when he was fourteen years old. Upon the death of both of his parents in his late teens, he inherited $871,000 and the Hughes Tool Company, which held the patent on the most widely used well-drilling bit in the world. Hughes left school to operate the company, but his interests were not limited by that business.

From 1926 through 1932, Hughes was active in the production of motion pictures, became a pilot, and founded the Hughes Aircraft Company, where he designed, built, and flew airplanes. In 1935, in a plane of his own design, he set a world speed record of 352.39 miles per hour and followed that with transcontinental records in 1936 and 1937. Following his record-breaking around-the-world flight in 1938, he was treated to a ticker-tape parade in New York City. By 1938, he held nearly every major aviation award. For his flying accomplishments he won the Harmon Trophy in 1938, the Collier Trophy in 1939, the Octave Chanute Award in 1940, and a Congressional Medal in 1941.

By 1939, Hughes had placed the Hughes Aircraft Company at the forefront of design in experimental military airplanes. During World War II, his company was a major defense contractor. Hughes designed the eight-engine *Spruce Goose*, a large plywood seaplane contracted as a troop carrier in 1942. Its only flight was piloted by Hughes in 1947. Hughes's successes placed him among the top three most wealthy Americans.

At the war's end, Hughes reentered the Hollywood scene and controlled RKO Studios from 1948 through 1955. Throughout the 1950's, he concentrated on expanding his business empire, and by the 1960's, he was a billionaire. He owned the controlling stock in Trans World Airlines until he was forced to sell out in 1966. Hughes had suffered a nervous breakdown in 1944 and had been critically injured in a 1946 air crash, after which he developed an addiction to morphine that led to other dependencies. Always an eccentric, he went into seclusion in 1950, becoming a reclusive shell of a person living in a rented hotel room in Las Vegas, Nevada. Almost nothing is known of this period of his life. Hughes was elected into the Aviation Hall of Fame in 1973. He died in 1976 on board a plane traveling from Acapulco, Mexico, to Houston, Texas, where he was to receive medical treatment.

Kenneth H. Brown

Bibliography
Barton, Charles. *Howard Hughes and His Flying Boat*. 2d ed. Vienna, Va.: Charles Barton, 1998. The story of the building of the *Spruce Goose* and the controversies surrounding it.
Brown, Peter Harry, and Pat H. Broeske. *Howard Hughes: The Untold Story*. Collingdale, Pa.: Diane, 2000. Uses posthumous source material to document the life of this brilliant eccentric.
Maguglin, Robert O. *Howard Hughes: His Achievements and Legacy*. Carpinteria, Calif.: Sunrise, 1988. A highly cited source, this is the "standard" biography of Hughes and extensively covers his involvement in aviation.

See also: Manufacturers; Military flight; Record flights; *Spruce Goose*; Trans World Airlines; Transcontinental flight

Human-powered flight

Definition: Sustained, level flight powered solely through the use of human muscle.
Significance: The earliest attempts at human flight were powered by the pilot's own activity. Although non-human engines proved to be the key to viable aircraft, experimental human-powered craft continued to be built into the twenty-first century. These craft were often the products of university students and professors or enthusiastic amateurs, spurred on as much by the intellectual challenge as by the stimulus of monetary prizes.

Although it will never be an efficient mode of transportation, human-powered flight satisfies an innate human desire to emulate the freedom of birds. Unfortunately, using arms to flap attached wings cannot generate adequate lift and propulsion, as bird wings do, but well-conditioned athletes can maintain fractional horsepower outputs for long periods of time using their legs, and this, in the late twentieth century, led to a series of remarkably long, controlled flights over both land and water. The earliest truly successful flights were made by entrepreneurs in response to monetary prizes. Unfortunately, it does not appear that the resulting aircraft are practical flying machines for the vast majority of fliers and homebuilders, requiring too much muscle power and being far too large, too fragile, too expensive and too vulnerable to being upset by atmospheric turbulence.

Human-powered flight

The earliest seekers of human-powered flight were the tower and bridge jumpers, dating from at least 1000 C.E. Stability and control, as well as wing-flapping propulsion, were always in question, although some glides were at least partially successful. The key insight, as it was for motor-powered human flight, was to separate lift and propulsion: use fixed wings for lift and an engine and a propeller for propulsion. Monetary prizes eventually stimulated gifted teams of designers and enthusiasts and they have transformed the almost universal dreams of human-powered flight into reality.

The first prize offered for human-powered flight, the Prix Peugeot of 1912, was won in Paris in 1921 by bicycling champion Gabriel Poulain and his *Aviette* when he flew 40 feet in a straight line, using biplane wings attached to a bicycle to glide forward after he abruptly increased his wing angle to lift him into the air. By 1937, a 154-pound German bicycle racer, who was able to generate a momentary power output of 1.3 horsepower, had upped the straight-line distance to almost 0.5 miles using a 75-pound sailplanelike airplane, called *Mufli*, with a pedal-powered propeller.

The Kremer Prize

Late-blooming enthusiasm for human-powered flight in England resulted in seven men forming the Cranfield Man-Powered Aircraft Committee in 1957. Industrialist and philanthropist Henry Kremer was then inspired, in 1959, to offer a £5,000 prize for the first British human-powered aircraft that could take off and fly a figure-eight course between two turning points not less than 0.5 miles apart and fly over a 10-foot height marker at the beginning and end of the flight. In response, three postgraduate students of Southampton University formed SUMPAC (for Southampton University Man-Powered Air Craft) and made the first British human-powered flight of 50 feet in 1961. But SUMPAC was unable to exceed 2,000 feet in flight length and could not turn more than about 80 degrees.

A second effort, backed by the famous De Havilland Aircraft Company, flew about 3,000 feet at an average height of over 6 feet in 1962 in *Puffin*, creating a world record that was to stand for ten years, but the craft could not be turned more than about 80 degrees. The distance record, still a British record, was made in 1972 by John Potter with a 3,513-foot flight in *Jupiter*. Meanwhile, Professor Hidemasa Kimura of Nihon University was working with his students, and in 1966 their *Linnet* made Japan's first human-powered flight; the flight was only 49 feet in length but this began a long-term commitment to human-powered aircraft. By 1977 their *Stork B* had established a new world record of 6,869.75 feet in a flight of over four minutes and was a strong contender for the Kremer Prize.

By 1967, the Kremer Prize for a figure-eight human-powered flight had been doubled and opened to entrants from any country. Then, in 1973, with still no winner in sight, Henry Kremer raised the award to £50,000 (about $129,000 at that time), the largest prize in the history of aviation.

The human-powered movement was very slow to reach the United States. Finally, in 1973, Professor Eugene Covert and students at the Massachusetts Institute of Technology (MIT) built a two-person biplane named *Burd*, which apparently never even left the ground under its own power. Credit for the first human-powered flight in the United States is therefore given to Joseph Zinno, retired from the U.S. Air Force, for his 77-foot flight in 1976 in *Olympian ZB-1*, which he had designed, built, and flown.

MacCready's Success

It was in that same year of 1976 that fifty-one-year-old Californian Paul MacCready decided that he knew how to design a human-powered aircraft that could win the Kremer Prize. He had impressive credentials for the challenge. As a teenager, MacCready was a Junior National Champion in model airplanes; at the age of sixteen, he soloed a Piper Cub; in 1947, he graduated from Yale with a degree in physics; in 1948 and 1949, he was the National Soaring Champion; in 1952, he received a doctorate in aeronautics from California Institute of Technology; in 1957, he decided to go into business for himself, eventually forming AeroVironment in 1971 to solve energy and environmental problems.

MacCready's initial design was inspired by observations of soaring birds and the Rogallo hang glider. He realized that the low power output from a human meant that the airplane had to have a very large wing area (around 1,000 square feet) and have a very high aspect ratio (a large span of about 100 feet with a chord of only about 10 feet) in order to minimize lift-induced drag. The drag of the required bracing wires for an extremely light, fragile aircraft with these huge dimensions would be acceptable if flight speeds and flight altitudes were very low. The structure would have to be designed to be easily repaired, the same rule practiced by the Wright brothers. Aerodynamicist Peter Lissaman convinced MacCready that a canard surface had to be added to his wing for pitch stability. Turning the aircraft was a major hurdle, because the outer wing always wanted to stall; wing warping and a rolling front (canard) surface eventually solved this problem.

MacCready thought it would take six weeks to win the prize; it took a year. Flight control, weather, power, and structural problems kept cropping up. Finally, on August 23, 1997, the Kremer Prize was won by MacCready's team with an official flight time of 6 minutes, 22.5 seconds. Their huge airplane, the *Gossamer Condor*, weighed 70 pounds and the pilot and engine, bicycle racer Bryan Allen, weighed 137 pounds. On September 22 of that year, Maude Oldershaw piloted the *Gossamer Condor*. It is interesting to note that all of the principal members of the team were model aircraft builders; many were also hang-glider enthusiasts. The *Gossamer Condor* is now the property of the National Air and Space Museum in Washington, D.C.

Crossing the English Channel

Retired British Rear Admiral Nicholas Goodhart had developed a huge (138-foot wingspan) twin-powered airplane, *Manflier*, for the Kremer Prize and, beaten to the prize, he suggested that the next great project should be a human-powered flight across the English Channel. Henry Kremer responded with a doubled award of £100,000 for the first such successful human-powered flight. It would require remaining in the air for more than one hour.

MacCready quickly rose to the new challenge with a new, lighter, stronger, more streamlined design, the *Gossamer Albatross*, using high-technology materials (carbon fiber-reinforced plastic, DuPont Kevlar, and a new, super-thin DuPont Mylar for the covering), a new cruise prop designed by aerodynamicist Eugene Larabee of MIT, and new cockpit instrumentation, including a Polaroid sonar altimeter. By June, 1978, guided in his rigorous physical training by physiologist Joseph Mastropaolo, Allen was able to generate 0.31 horsepower for 2.5 hours, enough time, MacCready thought, to make a successful flight. However, two months later, the warp control jammed and *Gossamer Albatross* suffered the worst crash of the program, although the pilot was only bruised. Some eight months later, on April 25, 1979, Allen flew a record flight of over one hour and the decision was made to go to England and try for the prize. After weeks of waiting on the English coast for suitable weather, at 5:51 A.M. on June 12, 1979, pilot/power plant Allen lifted off from England. Slowed by a headwind, out of his crucial water supply, and cockpit instrumentation out of battery power, Allen felt at four different times that he would have to give up the effort. Somehow, fighting cramping legs and nearing exhaustion, he struggled on and, at 7:40 A.M., touched down lightly in France, winning the second large Kremer Prize for the team. He had flown *Gossamer Albatross* 22.25 miles in 2 hours, 49 minutes (an average speed over the water of less than 8 miles per hour).

The Langford Group

Meanwhile, in 1978, the MIT Model Rocket Society, led by student John Langford, decided to see if they could get the hangar-evicted MIT *Burd* to fly with the addition of two 1.5-horsepower model airplane engines. The attempt failed, but the society pledged to build something that would fly by springtime, a craft that would compete for Kremer's Channel prize. The society's *Chrysalis* made its first flight on June 5, 1979, just one week before Allen won the English Channel prize. They had built a real flying machine, however, one that ended up being flown by more than forty-five pilots before the end of the summer.

Two years later, Langford had returned to MIT as a graduate student and led an effort to win a new Kremer prize, this one for flying around a 1,500 meter (4,185 feet) course in less than three minutes, requiring a speed of 21 miles per hour. Energy storage before takeoff was allowed. The group's *Monarch* won the $33,000 prize on May 11, 1984, narrowly beating MacCready's latest effort. Inspired, the Langford team vowed to pursue the "ultimate" human flight challenge: to emulate the fabled flight of the exiled Daedalus and son Icarus from the island of Crete to Greece. Thus began a four-year effort that ended up requiring more than $1 million worth of corporate and institutional sponsorship.

Key members of the team included builder Juan Cruz, Mark Drela (completing a thesis on low-speed aerodynamics), physiologist Ethan Nadel, and a group of highly trained and conditioned superathletes, as well as leader Langford. The result was a plane that weighed 70 pounds without pilot, power plant, or fuel, 29 feet in length, with a wingspan of 112 feet, and with a cruising airspeed of 15 miles per hour. On April 23, 1988, piloted and powered by a Greek bicycle champion racer, Kanellos Kanellopoulos, they flew their *Daedalus* the more than 70 miles from Crete over the sea to Santorini in about four hours, breaking up just 90 feet off shore when the craft encountered a strong headwind with turbulent air.

The next frontier in human-powered flight appears to be the helicopter. In 1980, a prize of $25,000 was offered by the American Helicopter Society for the first human-powered helicopter that could hover for a full minute, rising to at least 10 feet above the ground at some point during that period. Successful hovers have so far not exceeded about 24 seconds and the height requirement appears to be even more difficult.

W. N. Hubin

Bibliography

Allen, Bryan. "Winged Victory of *Gossamer Albatross*." *National Geographic*, November, 1979, 640-651. The 26-year-old biologist/pilot/bicycle racer/who pedaled the *Albatross* across the English Channel describes his flight in this picture essay.

Dorsey, Gary. *The Fullness of Wings: The Making of a New Daedalus*. New York: Viking, 1990. A well-written account of the efforts of the team led by John Langford and associated with the Massachusetts Institute of Technology. The contributions of members of the team and their interpersonal conflicts are well covered.

Grosser, Morton. *Gossamer Odyssey: The Triumph of Human-Powered Flight*. Boston: Houghton Mifflin, 1981. The author presents an engaging, blow-by-blow discussion of the successful efforts of the team lead by Paul MacCready to make the first significant human-powered flights. Also covers the contributions of the many hang-glider and model-airplane enthusiasts who made it possible, as well as the history of previous human-powered flight efforts.

Langford, John S. "Triumph of *Daedalus*." *National Geographic*, August, 1988, 191-199. The manager and spark plug for the re-creation of the flight of Icarus uses pictures and text to tell the story of their success to a large audience. A video was also made and shown on public television.

Long, Michael E. "Flight of the *Gossamer Condor*." *National Geographic*, January, 1978, 131-140. An easily accessed description of the problems and successes of the winner of the first Kremer Prize for human-powered flight and the driven, inventive people who made it possible. An acclaimed documentary video was also made by Ben Shedd.

See also: Aerodynamics; Airplanes; Experimental aircraft; Forces of flight; Helicopters; Ultralight aircraft; Wing designs

Hypersonic aircraft

Definition: Aircraft capable of flying at speeds greater than five times the speed of sound.
Significance: Flight at hypersonic speeds is required to efficiently reach space and return from it. Aircraft flying at hypersonic speeds encounter several problems in addition to those encountered at lower speeds, including extremely high temperatures and pressures, as well as the need for control systems which react to disturbances extremely quickly.

Applications

Although they are advertised as being able to circle the globe in less than four hours, hypersonic aircraft do not offer much promise to weary airline passengers in the near future. Most applications of hypersonic aircraft are either in the context of warfare or spaceflight. With the exception of the terminal stage of certain missiles, hypersonic flight is conducted exclusively at very high altitudes, where the air density and pressure are a fraction of their values at sea level.

In space, any controlled maneuver requires the expenditure of fuel, whereas inside the atmosphere, aerodynamic forces can be used by deflecting control surfaces. Because the speed required for Earth orbit at low altitudes is approximately 18,000 miles per hour, spacecraft reenter the atmosphere at extremely high Mach numbers, ranging typically from 25 on the space shuttle to over 36 on the Apollo capsules. In reentry flight, the craft spends only a few minutes at hypersonic speed before decelerating to supersonic speeds, which allow more controlled maneuvering and gliding to selected landing sites.

During ascent into space, modern hypersonic aircraft ride on rocket boosters, spending the shortest possible time in the dense lower regions of the atmosphere. This situation will have to change when aircraft use air-breathing engines for propulsion at hypersonic speeds. Air-breathing engines take the oxygen needed for combustion from the atmosphere, reducing the amount lifted from the ground. The advantage of mastering this technology may be easily seen. In a hydrogen-oxygen propulsion system, which is the most efficient known means of chemical propulsion, 89 percent of the total weight of fuel and oxidizer is oxygen. However, air-breathing hypersonic flight poses several difficult problems.

Features of Hypersonic Flows

The air flowing around a vehicle moving at hypersonic speeds has several interesting features. In front of the vehicle nose stands an extremely strong shock wave. This shock is like the blast wave from an explosion, heating the air enough to make oxygen and nitrogen molecules vibrate at high frequencies, dissociate into atoms, radiate large amounts of heat, and even ionize. The air becomes compressed to values as high as ten to one hundred times its normal density, and the extremely high pressure imposes very high loads on the vehicle. Over the upper surface of the vehicle, the air accelerates to supersonic speeds, and the density and temperature fall so quickly that the dissociated air does not have time to recombine. Around the vehicle, shock waves lie very close to the surface. Air friction heats the surface and increases the drag on the vehicle. Within a thin layer, the flow changes properties through a very large range. The reliable design of such vehicles is extremely difficult, because accurate, full-scale aerodynamic prediction is difficult and expensive, and approximate methods do not provide enough accuracy.

Refining the prediction methods through experimentation is also not easy because of the sheer difficulty of conducting flow experiments under hypersonic conditions. Hypersonic wind tunnels require extreme pressures, temperatures, and flow rates and can operate under steady conditions only for milliseconds. In the early 1990's, when President Ronald Reagan's National AeroSpace Plane initiative resumed the development of technology for hypersonic flight, the total experience of wind-tunnel testing at hypersonic speeds from all tests conducted to that date was estimated to be less than one second.

Early Hypersonic Flights

The inherent difficulties of hypersonic travel have not prevented the development of hypersonic vehicles. In 1933, German rocket expert Eugen Sänger published his concept for an "antipodal bomber" (antipodes are two points on opposite sides of the earth), a crewed hypersonic glider launched on a large rocket that would deliver bombs to distant targets across the globe, by skipping in and out of the atmosphere. This project was canceled in 1942.

In February, 1949, the U.S. Army launched the V-2 WAC Corporal rocket from the White Sands Missile Range in New Mexico. The rocket reached a speed of 3,500 miles per hour and an altitude of 100 miles before the WAC Corporal stage ignited and reached an altitude of 244 miles. The vehicle reentered the atmosphere at a speed of more than 5,000 miles per hour.

On April 12, 1961, Soviet flight major Yuri Gagarin returned to Earth after an orbital flight during which he traveled at hypersonic speeds that charred the surface of his spherical space capsule. Since then, rockets with or without human crew have routinely flown in the hypersonic regime.

The X-15 Program

The first hypersonic research airplane, which used aerodynamic lift to stay aloft, was the North American X-15, developed by the National Aeronautics and Space Administration (NASA). Air-launched from a B-52 bomber, the X-15 first flew on June 8, 1959. It was 50.75 feet long with a wingspan of 22.25 feet. Its Thiokol XLR-99 throttleable rocket engine burned a mixture of anhydrous ammonia and liquid oxygen to reach Mach 6. By the end of August, 1963, the X-15 piloted by NASA's Joseph A. Walker had reached a record altitude of 354,200 feet.

X-15 flight tests revealed a number of interesting facts about hypersonic flight, including the existence of turbulent hypersonic boundary layers, and that turbulent heating rates were lower than predicted by theory, but that hot spots developed on the surface, causing material failures. The flights demonstrated piloted transition from aerodynamic to reaction controls and back again, including hypersonic/supersonic reentry at angles of attack up to 26 degrees and glide to precise landings.

The third X-15, which set a number of records, was lost, along with its pilot, Michael J. Adams, on November 15, 1967. The program was canceled after this fatal accident.

Air-Breathing Propulsion

The X-15A-2 vehicle was designed to pursue the idea of hypersonic flight using an air-breathing engine instead of a rocket. The plan was to test a ramjet engine using supersonic combustion, although it was never flight-tested. The challenges of hypersonic air-breathing propulsion were numerous, but two fundamental problems dominated.

First, theoretical research showed that drag is incurred when a supersonic flow is slowed down to subsonic speeds, as through a shock, and when heat is added to a flow at a high Mach number. At low supersonic speeds, the drag due to the shock is less than the drag that would be incurred if heat were added to a supersonic flow. Thus, ramjet engines for flight at less than Mach 4 use shocks to slow the flow to subsonic speeds before adding heat by burning fuel in the combustion chamber of the ramjet engine. At speeds above Mach 4, it is more efficient to add heat at supersonic speeds than it is to slow down the flow to subsonic conditions.

Second, in supersonic combustion there is an extremely short time available in which to add fuel, mix it with the air moving at supersonic speed, and complete the combustion before the flow exits the engine. The X-30, dubbed the National AeroSpace Plane, was built to develop supersonic combustion ramjets, or scramjets. In the 1990's, this program was canceled without any test flights.

NASA's Langley Research Center at the turn of the millennium described a program called Hyper X to study hypersonics technology at speeds from Mach 5 to Mach 10. The NASA/Boeing X-43 was designed to study scramjet-powered flight at speeds from Mach 6 to Mach 10, following launch using a Pegasus booster rocket from a

The X-15, shown here with pilot Neil Armstrong, was the first hypersonic aircraft developed by the United States. (NASA)

B-52 over the Pacific Ocean. Released at 20,000 feet, the 12-foot-long X-43 was designed to be accelerated by the rocket to a speed of Mach 6 and an altitude of 90,000 feet. The scramjet engine was designed to operate for seven to ten seconds, accelerating the X-43 to a speed of Mach 10. The engine had an oval-shaped air intake and burned hydrogen with air in a copper combustion chamber at supersonic speeds. Lacking landing gear, the vehicle was designed to transmit data before expending its energy and falling into the ocean.

Lifting Bodies

The U.S. Air Force and NASA have continued to study hypersonic lifting bodies for hypersonic reentry. The X-20 Dyna-Soar hypersonic boost glide vehicle was designed to launch into orbit on a Titan III solid-fuel rocket, reenter the atmosphere, and glide at hypersonic speeds to deliver a nuclear weapon. However, the Dyna-Soar was shelved without ever flying.

The X-23 lifting body flew in 1966, demonstrating maneuvering during reentry. The X-24A and X-24B craft investigated low-speed characteristics of lifting bodies. The NASA/Boeing X-37, part of NASA's Hyper X program, investigates technologies for orbit-on-demand, including hypersonic glide reentry. The vehicle, built by Boeing Phantom Works, is 27.5 feet long, with a wingspan of 15 feet, a weight of about 6 tons, and a payload bay 7 feet long and 4 feet in diameter. The Boeing X-40 maneuverable spaceplane integrated technology demonstrator is a predecessor to planned vehicles for flight at Mach 16 up to 300,000 feet, sending 1,000 to 3,000 pounds of payload into orbit for military missions.

In the 1990's, the X-38 crew return vehicle (CRV) extended the work on the X-23 and X-24, in the development of a lifting body that would be attached to the International Space Station (ISS) as an emergency escape system. Separated from the ISS using rocket thrusters and able to carry an incapacitated crew of up to seven, the X-38 was to navigate using the Global Positioning System (GPS) and glide through hypersonic reentry at angles of attack of up to 38 degrees, with the heating taken by thermal tiles on the vehicle. Following supersonic maneuvering using flaperons, the X-38 would deploy first parachutes and then a large parafoil. An on-board automatic control system would guide the parafoil-suspended X-38 to a soft landing into the wind. In 2001, the X-38 project was canceled, but a parallel project conducted by the French and the European Space Agency aimed to develop a reusable crew taxi or crew rescue vehicle.

NASA's space shuttle uses aerodynamic lift at high angles of attack and hypersonic speeds of up to Mach 25 during its reentry and descent into the atmosphere. It uses heat-shield tiles to protect critical parts of the fuselage and the wings during reentry. By using aerodynamic lift in the upper atmosphere, the shuttle stays at high altitudes, where the air is much thinner, until much of its orbital kinetic energy has been dissipated before sinking into the denser parts of the atmosphere and gliding to a runway landing.

Other Reusable Hypersonic Spaceplanes

The NASA/Lockheed Martin X-33 reusable launch vehicle, a smaller predecessor of the Lockheed VentureStar concept, tested the idea of achieving single-stage boost to low-Earth orbit using ultra-lightweight composite fuel and oxidizer tanks and a rocket engine that used an "aerospike" external expansion nozzle. The X-33 was canceled in 2001, along with the launch-on-demand, glide-to-landing NASA/Orbital Sciences X-34 vehicle.

The Buran (Snowstorm) Soviet space shuttle had its first orbital flight in November, 1988, on an Energia booster. It circled Earth twice between 247 and 256 kilometers above the surface before reentering and landing at Tyuratum. The French-European Hermes spaceplane project was conceived as a mini-shuttle, carrying four to six crew members and 4,500 kilograms of cargo into orbit atop an Ariane-5 booster. The project was canceled in 1992 but may have been replaced by the continuing European Space Agency (ESA) crew rescue vehicle project.

Hypersonic air-breathing vehicle designs including a scramjet engine were reported to have been tested in the 1990's by Russia on top of a surface-to-air missile and by the Indian Space Research Organization using a solid rocket booster. The Japanese Hope-X space shuttle and the British horizontal takeoff and landing (HOTOL) concepts do not appear to have progressed beyond small-scale wind-tunnel models. As of mid-2001, there was no reusable hypersonic aerodynamic vehicle in operation other than NASA's space shuttle.

Wave-Rider Concepts

Aircraft configurations optimized for aerodynamic flight at hypersonic speeds are generally thin and flat, with a highly swept fuselage and short wings. At hypersonic cruise, the upper surface of the vehicle stays essentially parallel to the flight direction, minimizing the disturbance to the flow there. The oblique shock formed under the vehicle stays very close to the slanted surface, providing a lifting cushion of high pressure. Such vehicles are called hypersonic waveriders. Waverider configurations generally exhibit rudders and elevator-aileron combinations (elevons) as primary control surfaces. Tip flaps improve lift-to-drag ratio and rudder effectiveness. Such vehicles are unstable in pitch, like many modern fighter planes, and require fly-by-wire, stability-augmented computer control. Concepts for reducing the shock drag and heating at the nose include the Russian idea of injecting ionized gas jets into the shock, and the American idea of ionizing the gas ahead using plasma or laser beams.

Narayanan M. Komerath

Bibliography

Miller, Jay. *The X-Planes: X-1 to X-29*. Specialty Press, 1983. A history of the experimental aircraft programs of NASA and its predecessor, the National Advisory Committee for Aeronautics (NACA), with good coverage of the X-15 program and many illustrations of successful and unsuccessful concepts.

Smith, Terry. "The Dyna-Soar X-20: A Historical Overview." *Quest* 3, no. 4 (Winter, 1994): 13-18. An article on the lifting-body program that has gained new relevance with the advent of CRVs and hypersonic guided weapons, developed by NASA, the U.S. Air Force, and the ESA.

See also: Air Force, U.S.; Forces of flight; Yuri Gagarin; High-speed flight; Mach number; Military flight; National Aeronautics and Space Administration; Rocket propulsion; Sound barrier; Spaceflight; Supersonic aircraft; X planes

Iberia Airlines

Also known as: Iberia, Compania Mercantil Anonima Iberia

Definition: Spain's largest international carrier and one of the world's major carriers.

Significance: A large global carrier with a consolidated position in its domestic and regional market as well as the Europe-Latin America market.

History

Iberia, in full Compania Mercantil Anonima Iberia, or Iberia Commercial Limited-liability Company, is a major airline headquartered in Madrid, Spain. In its current incarnation, Iberia was originally state-owned and created by law on June 7, 1940. As such, it was given rights to the air transport of persons and cargo within Spain. It took control of a privately owned airline established in 1937, which in turn had revived the name of a company called Iberia Compania Aerea de Tranportes, founded June 28, 1927. As of December 14, 1927, that airline began a regular service between Madrid and Barcelona. King Alfonso XIII was a passenger on the inaugural flight, made in one of the new company's three Rohrbach-Roland aircraft. The current name of the airline was adopted September 5, 1941. Based on its original date of operations (1927), Iberia is one of the world's oldest scheduled airlines. Between 1927 and 1939, Iberia's service was entirely within Spain (including Majorca). Its longest route, established in 1937, was from Vitoria in northern Spain to Tetuán in Spanish Morocco, with stops in Burgos, Salamanca, Cáceres, and Seville. It also provided services linking Santiago de Compostela with Salamanca and Valladolid. Madrid-Seville flights were added in 1939.

Iberia became an international airline in 1939 when it began regular services between Madrid and Lisbon. In 1946, Iberia began a service connecting Madrid with London and Rome. That same year, it became the first airline to fly between Europe and South America, using a DC-4 to cover the Madrid-Buenos Aires route. Shortly afterward it added regular flights to Havana, Caracas, Puerto Rico, Mexico City, Rio de Janeiro, and New York. In the 1960's, Iberia joined the jet age, replacing its Super Constellations with DC-8's on the Madrid-New York route. This both shortened the duration of the flights and added seat capacity and passenger comfort. The arrival in 1970 of the first wide-bodied aircraft, the Boeing 747, consolidated Iberia's competitive position. Iberia also acquired Boeing 727's for its domestic routes, including the busy Madrid-Barcelona shuttle launched in 1974, as well as new DC-10's to replace its turboprop fleet.

New maintenance facilities were built at the La Muñoza site near Madrid's Barajas Airport and the company joined the international aircraft maintenance consortium, Atlas. Iberia's technicians were trained to maintain the latest aircraft in its own fleet and those of other airlines. Iberia's fleet includes the Boeing 747, Boeing 767, Boeing 757, Boeing 727, Boeing 737, McDonnell Douglas (Boeing) DC-9, McDonnell Douglas (Boeing) MD-87 and MD-88, McDonnell Douglas (Boeing) DC-8 Cargo, Airbus A340, A300, A321, A320, and A319, Canadair CRJ 200, Aerospatiale ATR72, and Fokker F-50. On the company's fiftieth anniversary in 1977, the Iberia corporate logotype was changed and its fleet was given the new look. Iberia became a founding partner of the computerized European ticket reservations system Amadeus, embarked on a major fleet replacement program, and set up a new air freight company and the regional airlines that now make up the Iberia Group.

Organization and Network

Iberia is the head of a group that encompasses three other carriers. Two of these airlines are subsidiaries (Binter Canarias and Binter Mediterráneo) and one a franchise (Iberia Regional/Air Nostrum). The trend toward market globalization in the airline industry led Iberia to join the oneworld Alliance on September 1, 1999. Along with the Star Alliance, oneworld Alliance is one of the two major international alliances with a global scope. Iberia's partnership with American Airlines and British Airways, along with its membership in the oneworld Alliance, enhanced its competitive position in the global market. In addition to American Airlines, British Airways, and Iberia, oneworld members include Aer Lingus, Cathay Pacific, Finnair, Lan Chile, and Qantas. Alliance members cooperate in schedules and routes to create a seamless global network. As its membership attests, oneworld covers the entire globe.

In 2001, the Iberia Group flew to ninety-nine destinations in forty-two countries. With a fleet of more than two

> ### Events in Iberia History
>
> **1927:** Iberia is formed and begins regular service between Madrid and Barcelona, Spain.
> **1939:** Iberia makes its first international flight, from Madrid and Lisbon, Portugal.
> **1944:** The airline is nationalized and expands its route network.
> **1946:** Iberia begins service to London and Rome and becomes the first airline to fly between Europe and South America, establishing a route from Madrid to Buenos Aires.
> **1960's:** The airline takes delivery of its first jet-powered aircraft, the DC-8, which flies the Madrid-to-New York route.
> **1970:** The airline takes delivery of its first wide-body aircraft, a Boeing 747 jumbojet.
> **1980's:** Iberia is a founding partner of Amadeus, a computerized ticket reservations system.
> **1999:** Iberia joins the oneworld Alliance, a global network of cooperating airlines.

hundred aircraft, it offers an average of nine hundred daily flights. In 1999, Iberia carried 26 million passengers and 220,000 tons of freight. The number of its destinations, the frequency of its flights, and its market share make Iberia the leader of the Spanish market and the airline with the most comprehensive network for travel between Europe and Latin America.

Iberia has an experienced air-maintenance operation, servicing not only its own fleet but also those of other airlines. Iberia is also Spain's leading handling company, supplying ground services to aircraft and passengers in all of Spain's domestic airports on behalf of some 220 airlines and charter companies. In 1999, it provided such services to a total of 428,000 aircraft and 79 million passengers. Iberia is a founder and 18.28 percent partner in Amadeus, one of the world's major computerized air ticket reservation systems. With Gate Gourmet, a leading in-flight catering company, it is the co-owner of Iberswiss, which prepares almost 11 million meal trays per year. As a partner in the tour operator companies Viva Tours and Tiempo Libre, Iberia is actively involved in the holiday travel package business, and through its Cacesa subsidiary it provides urgent freight and courier services.

Triantafyllos G. Flouris

Bibliography

Groenewege, Adrianus D. *The Compendium of International Civil Aviation.* 2d ed. Geneva, Switzerland: International Air Transport Association, 1999. A comprehensive directory of the major players in international civil aviation, with insightful and detailed articles.

Weimer, Kent J. ed. *Aviation Week and Space Technology: World Aviation Directory.* New York: McGraw Hill, 2000. An excellent introductory guide on all global companies involved in the aviation business. The information is very basic but very essential as a first introduction to each company.

See also: Air carriers; American Airlines; British Airways

Icing

Definition: Accumulation of frozen moisture on an aircraft.
Significance: The buildup of ice on an aircraft poses a serious hazard by interfering with the aircraft's lift and causing additional drag and weight.

Dangers

When an aircraft encounters freezing temperatures and visible moisture, icing, the accumulation of frozen moisture, is possible. Although icing is a serious hazard to the safety of any flight, light aircraft are particularly susceptible to aircraft icing, as such craft have few, if any, anti-icing or deicing systems. Icing can destroy an aircraft's ability to create lift and engine power when ice builds up on the structure and within the engine-induction system.

Types of Icing

There are two types of aircraft icing, structural and induction. Structural ice may form on aircraft lifting surfaces, such as the wing and horizontal stabilizer, and on the windshield and protruding devices, such as the propellers, engine air intakes, antennas, struts, and landing gear. Ice adds additional weight to the aircraft. More critical, though, is the additional drag that the ice causes by disrupting the smooth flow of air over the lift-producing surfaces. Moderate to severe accumulations of structural ice can greatly affect aircraft controllability. Both wind-tunnel and flight tests have proven that ice accumulations no thicker or rougher than a piece of coarse sandpaper can reduce lift by 30 percent and increase drag by as much as 40 percent.

Structural icing may be present as rime, clear, or mixed ice. Rime ice has a rough, milky-white appearance. Rime ice forms when relatively small drops of moisture strike freezing aircraft surfaces and adhere to the surface rapidly.

The milky white appearance is caused by the presence of air trapped in the rapidly freezing ice. Deicing systems are generally effective in removing rime ice, because rime ice is less tenacious than other forms of ice.

Clear ice forms when large drops of moisture strike aircraft surfaces and freeze at a slower rate. The slower freezing process displaces air from the accreting ice, allowing the formation of a clear, very tenacious coating of ice on the aircraft's surfaces. Because of the lack of aeration in the ice, clear ice is difficult to remove and quite heavy. Mixed ice is a combination of rime and clear ice and exhibits characteristics of both.

Induction icing can reduce engine performance and may result in complete engine stoppage. Aircraft equipped with carburetors may experience ice buildup in a restricted air passage, called a venturi, that is located in the carburetor. An increase in air velocity and a resultant decrease in pressure within the venturi results in a reduction in air temperature. This lowering of air temperature creates the potential for moisture within the air to freeze and create ice accumulations along the sides of the venturi. The ice buildup reduces the flow of air and fuel through the venturi, resulting in decreased engine performance. In severe instances, ice may completely occlude the venturi, resulting in complete loss of engine power. In the case of aircraft equipped with fuel-injection systems, ice can accumulate in air intakes, reducing the flow of air to the engine. Ice occluding engine air intakes can cause reductions in available engine power as well as complete engine failure.

Formation of Ice

Although all clouds are the manifestation of water in its gaseous state, the moisture content of clouds can vary greatly. Very-cold-winter states such as Montana, North Dakota, and Minnesota often have relatively dry clouds. In contrast, states such as Pennsylvania and New York often produce very wet winter clouds that, when temperatures drop below freezing, have a high potential for icing. Clouds with temperatures at or just below the freezing point, 32 degrees Fahrenheit, or 0 degrees Celsius, are the

The accumulation of ice on the exterior structures of an aircraft can affect a plane's lift and drag. NASA has conducted extensive research on icing in its icing research tunnel at the Glenn Research Center. (NASA)

most likely to result in aircraft icing. Moisture in air that is well below the freezing point is already frozen and therefore will not adhere to aircraft. Wind can move moisture-laden air between regions. Wind moving across large bodies of water, such as oceans or the Great Lakes, will result in greater moisture content within the air. Mountains can cause a lifting phenomenon that may force moisture-laden air upward in the atmosphere where the natural temperature lapse rate cools the surrounding air to the freezing point.

Areas of low-pressure and fronts are the greatest producers of ice. Although in some instances, isolated airmass instabilities may also produce sufficient moisture and temperatures capable of producing ice-generating conditions.

Freezing rain and drizzle are the most hazardous ice-producing conditions. Freezing rain occurs when temperature inversions exist. Rain falling from clouds in warmer air aloft begins to freeze as it enters freezing air at lower altitudes. Freezing rain and drizzle can produce severe ice accumulations that rapidly overwhelm the ice-shedding capabilities of even the best anti-icing and deicing equipment.

Predicting Ice

In the United States, the U.S. National Weather Service (NWS) is the government agency responsible for weather forecasting. Utilizing NWS and other weather forecasting sources, the Federal Aviation Administration (FAA) disseminates weather information to the aviation community through a network of Flight Service Stations (FSS). FSS specialists provide comprehensive weather briefings to pilots. These briefings are usually conducted over the telephone but may also be accomplished in person at the Flight Service Station. Pilots may also obtain icing and other weather information on the Direct User Access Terminal System (DUATS), utilizing a personal computer and Internet connection. Graphic weather charts available to FSS specialists and DUATS users include predictions of areas of potential icing. In addition, special meteorological notices called AIRMETS and SIGMETS are issued when potentially hazardous icing conditions exist. These notices provide pilots with an additional warning of potential icing. Pilots experiencing icing conditions report these conditions to the nearest FSS. Pilot reports (PIREPS) are usually conveyed directly to FSS specialists via the aircraft radio. PIREPS are an important component of the weather reporting system, because they describe actual conditions and not merely forecasts.

Alan S. Frazier

Bibliography

Dondzila, Kathy, and John Steuernagle, eds. *Aircraft Icing*. Frederick, Md.: Aircraft Owners and Pilots Association Air Safety Foundation, 1999. An excellent safety pamphlet addressing all aspects of aircraft icing.

Peters, Lestor. *Aviation Weather*. Englewood, Colo.: Jeppesen-Sanderson, 1998. A comprehensive overview of meteorology, including basic and advanced weather theory as well as interpretation of weather observations and forecasts.

Schlachter, Kathleen. *Aviation Weather Services AC 00-45E*. Oklahoma City, Okla.: Federal Aviation Administration, 1999. The official Federal Aviation Administration guide to coded weather observations and forecasts.

Willits, Pat, ed. *Private Pilot Manual*. Englewood, Colo.: Jeppesen Sanderson, 1997. An excellent basic flight training text with two chapters devoted to meteorology and the interpretation of weather data.

See also: Accident investigation; Airplanes; Federal Aviation Authority; National Transportation Safety Board; Safety issues; Weather conditions

Insects

Definition: A small invertebrate animal that has a segmented body, six legs, and two or four wings.
Significance: Due to their unique flight environment and small size, insects have evolved ingenious flight mechanisms to generate lift.

Background

A popular anecdote relates that in the 1930's a student of German aerodynamicist Ludwig Prandtl was asked by a biologist at a dinner party to estimate the lift of a bumblebee. To make this estimate, techniques similar to those commonly used to predict the lift of aircraft wings were used. To the surprise of the dinner guests, the results suggested that bumblebees should not be able to fly, although this is obviously not the case.

Insects are, in fact, the most accomplished of flying animals, with unsurpassed flying abilities. Insects can hover, fly backward, and even perform somersaults. Because insects are small in size and their wings typically move at relatively low speeds, the air through which an insect flies has the same relative feel as syrup to a human.

An important parameter in aerodynamics is the Reynolds number, which relates the motion of the air to its viscosity, where the viscosity is a measure of the stickiness of the air. Thus, for air, a low Reynolds number flow generally indicates that the airspeed is low, and the effects of viscosity are significant. As insects move their wings at comparatively low speed, they fly at very low Reynolds numbers. Few airfoils, or shapes of wings in profile, are capable of creating lift efficiently at the Reynolds numbers of an insect wing in flight or hover.

To circumvent the problem of flying at very low Reynolds numbers, insects have developed sophisticated flight mechanisms for developing lift, mechanisms of which engineers in the 1930's were unaware. This is one of the reasons for the problems with the analysis by Prandtl's student. From the 1970's to the 1990's, a clearer picture of insect flight techniques developed, based on the data from numerous comprehensive experimental studies and some computer-based numerical analysis.

Flight Basics

A wing in steady flight, such that its speed and angle of attack, or the angle of the wing to the oncoming airstream, are unchanging, develops lift due to the air flowing smoothly over its surfaces, and being deflected downward. This type of lift is called attached flow lift. An aircraft wing can also develop lift from the formation of a tornado-like vortex above the wing surface. Such leading edge vortices can clearly be seen above the wings of aircraft, such as the Concorde, at takeoff or landing on humid days. The vortex tends to pull up the wing, thereby increasing its lift. This type of lift is called vortex lift. An aircraft can use both attached flow lift and vortex lift, such that the two lift values can be added together.

Due to viscosity on the wing's surface, the speed of the air is zero. This represents a condition referred to as the no-slip condition. However, at some distance above the wing's surface, the airspeed reaches that which would occur if the flow had no viscosity. The region between the surface and this point is referred to as the boundary layer. The nature and behavior of this boundary layer has a significant impact on the ability of a wing to develop lift at very low Reynolds numbers. The boundary layer can either be laminar, turbulent, or transitional from laminar to turbulent. A laminar boundary layer is composed of air moving in orderly lines. A turbulent boundary layer is composed of air moving close to the airfoil surface in swirling motions. A laminar boundary layer is prone to separate from the airfoil surface far more easily than a turbulent boundary layer. At the very low Reynolds numbers at which insects fly, the boundary layer over their wings is always laminar. This causes the air to separate very easily over their wings, with the result that it is difficult for insects to develop enough attached flow lift to support their weight. However, for some insects, even if the boundary layer did not separate, the attached flow lift developed by the insect wing would still not be sufficient to support the insect's weight. It is thus necessary for insects to use other lift mechanisms, such as vortex lift, to create enough lift to stay aloft and maneuver.

Insect Flight Apparatus

An insect wing is composed of a thin membrane, which uses veins to provide strength. The wings of insects reflect the largest differences between the different insect orders. Some insects have two wings, and others four, but they all use similar flying techniques. Several insects, such as houseflies, originally had four wings. However, evolutionary development modified the two hind wings into small stumps, or halteres, which stabilize the housefly. Some insects with four wings, such as the dragonfly, beat their front and rear wings out of phase, meaning that the two sets of wings do not move forward and backward simultaneously. Other insects that also have four wings, such as butterflies, beat the front and back wings in phase, so both sets of wings flap effectively as a single set of wings.

To create the flapping motion, insects can use either of two muscle systems, direct or indirect. Direct muscles are attached to the wings and the bottom of the insect's thorax. Separate muscles are used to raise and lower the wings. To use a flapping system with direct muscles, the insect's brain must continually tell the flight muscles to relax and contract. Generally, insects that use direct muscles for flight cannot beat their wings very quickly because the brain has to coordinate the two sets of flight muscles for the insect to fly successfully. Indirect muscles are not directly attached to the wings. The indirect muscles consist of dorsoventral muscles, which connect to the top and bottom of the thorax, and the longitudinal muscles that run from the front to the back of the insect's thorax. The insect's wings are connected to the thorax by hinges. By alternating the contraction of the two muscle sets, the thorax of the insect begins to vibrate. The wings, attached to the thorax, begin to flap, with a contraction of the dorsoventricular muscles moving the wings upward. Contraction of the longitudinal muscles pulls the wings down.

One advantage of an indirect muscle system is that the insect's wings can beat at very high frequencies, up to 1,000 times per second for a gnat. Flies typically beat their wings approximately two hundred times per second, whereas beetles may beat them about eighty times per second, and butterflies about thirty times per second. The major advantage of indirect muscles, though, is that they require fewer instructions from the insect's brain than do direct muscles. Once the muscles are rhythmically contracting, they no longer need instructions from the brain. Houseflies use an indirect muscle system, whereas locusts use a direct muscle system. Insects using an indirect muscle system are far better fliers than those using a direct muscle system; the latter often appear clumsy in flight.

Insect Flight Techniques

Meticulous experiments performed in the 1990's clarified the methods that insects use to develop lift in the potentially unfavorable environment in which they fly. Experiments by Cambridge University zoologist Charles Ellington and colleagues showed that insects use attached flow lift as well as vortex lift, similar to the lift developed over highly swept wings such as those of the Concorde or numerous fighter aircraft. Computer simulation of the flow over a large moth, the hawkmoth, showed similar results.

Insects generally move their wings in a pattern that may resemble a figure eight or some variant of it. The plane in which the wings are moved backward and forward is the so-called stroke plane. A wing stroke begins with the wings almost touching above the insect's body. The front of the wing is rotated down rapidly, and the wing is accelerated downward; this is the downstroke. For most insects, the wings are rotated through approximately 120 degrees in the stroke plane. The boundary layer, the thin layer of air adjacent to the wing surface that is affected by viscosity, separates from the wing surface at the front of the wing, and no longer conforms smoothly to the wing's surface. Due to the motion of the insect wing, this boundary layer forms a tornado-like vortex above the wing. The vortex has the effect of increasing the lift of the insect's wing by causing vortex lift to develop.

At the beginning and end of the insect's wing stroke, the wing is rotated or flipped rapidly. Through careful timing of the point at which the wing is flipped, the insect is able to develop extra lift by causing the air over its upper surface to effectively speed up and that on the lower surface to slow down. This lift is similar to that developed by a spinning tennis ball. Some insects may also move their wings in such a fashion that they move through the wake, or energized air left behind by the previous wing cycle. As the insect wing moves through the air, air that comes into contact with the wing is set in motion and may begin to rotate. This air can then increase the lift of the wing if the motion of the wing is correct. For many insects, the angle of the stroke plane to the insect's body is essentially fixed. Thus, for the insect to change from hovering to forward flight, it rotates its body, so that the force from the wings will generate both some lift to support its weight as well as some thrust to propel it forward. Generally, insects generate most of the lift to support their weight on the downstroke, where the wings are moved from above to below the insect's body. The duration of the downstroke is also typically twice as long as the upstroke.

Another flight technique, referred to as the clap-and-fling technique by scientist Torkel Weis-Fogh, is used by some smaller insects such as Chalcid wasps. Initially, the insect's wings are positioned above the body with the wings touching, as may be seen when a butterfly is at rest. The insect then rapidly draws the front, or anterior, edges of its wings apart, and then rotates the two wings down. The advantage of such a flight method is that both wings instantly develop maximum lift. Normally, when a stationary wing is initially accelerated, it takes some time for the lift developed by the wing to reach its final steady value. However, the clap and fling represents a brilliant biological adaptation for circumventing the reasons for delay. Presumably, due to wear on the wings from continual colliding, few insects actually use the clap and fling.

Lance Wayne Traub

Bibliography

Dickinson, M. H., F. O. Lehmann, and S. P. Sane. "Wing Rotation and the Aerodynamic Basis of Insect Flight." *Science* 284 (1999): 1954-1960. A thorough paper giving detailed, if somewhat technical, explanations of the flight mechanisms used by flies.

Dudley, R. *The Biomechanics of Insect Flight: Form, Function, Evolution*. Princeton, N.J.: Princeton University Press, 1999. An exceptionally thorough compendium of information relating to insect flight, with an exhaustive reference list.

Ellington, C. P., C. van den Berg, A. P. Willmott, and A. L. R. Thomas. "Leading Edge Vortices in Insect Flight." *Nature* 384 (1996): 626-630. A clear description of the leading-edge vortices that develop over insect wings and their importance to the overall flight of insects.

Weis-Fogh, T. "Quick Estimates of Flight Fitness in Hovering Animals, Including Novel Mechanisms for Lift Production." *Journal of Experimental Biology* 59 (1973): 169-230. A groundbreaking paper on insect flight that remains an excellent source of information on insect flight mechanisms, with considerable experimental data pertaining to various insects.

See also: Aerodynamics; Animal flight; Bats; Birds; Forces of flight; Ludwig Prandtl

Instrumentation

Definition: Gages and instruments used by the pilot to monitor the condition of an aircraft and the condition of flight.

Significance: Instrumentation contributes to flight safety and the usability of aircraft. Without instruments, aircraft would be able to fly only for short periods on sunny days.

History

The earliest aircraft had no instruments at all. Pilots controlled the airplane and the engine using their senses of sight, hearing, and touch. As airplanes grew more complex, pilots needed more instruments to control the planes and monitor the engines. In addition, pilots required instruments to help them navigate and to maintain control of the aircraft in fog or clouds.

The first instruments installed in aircraft monitored the crafts' engines and fuel. By World War I (1914-1918), aircraft had compasses, inclinometers, and simple altimeters to help pilots navigate and maintain control.

In 1928, Paul Kollsman invented the first sensitive altimeter. A year later, on September 24, 1929, Army lieutenant James H. "Jimmy" Doolittle, using Kollsman's altimeter and other instruments, demonstrated that an aircraft could be successfully controlled by reference to instruments alone. With a safety pilot in the forward cockpit, Doolittle climbed into the rear cockpit and covered it so he could not see out. Then he took off, flew a 15-mile triangular course, and landed. For the first time, an aircraft had been flown by reference to instruments alone. Although engineers improved instrument accuracy and reliability, the basic design of flight instruments remained the same from the 1930's to the 1960's.

During the 1960's and 1970's, as the transistor and, later, the integrated circuit came into general usage, instruments began to change dramatically. The instrument could be mounted away from the cockpit, and the information could be displayed on a simple indicator. In the 1980's, as microprocessors came into general usage, the indicators could be replaced with cathode ray tubes and liquid crystal displays.

Magnetic Compass

The most basic instrument used for navigation is the magnetic compass. The magnetic compass uses two small magnets attached to a floating compass card inside a container filled with kerosene. These magnets point toward the earth's magnetic north pole. The compass card has letters and numbers printed on it that allow the pilot to determine the direction of flight. The movement of the airplane during flight causes the magnetic compass to swing back and forth. This limits the pilot's ability to determine flight direction with precision.

Pitot-Static Flight Instruments

The static system is designed to measure the ambient air pressure surrounding the aircraft. A static port consisting of small holes drilled through the side of the aircraft is connected to tubing that leads to the pressure-sensing instruments. The pitot tube is usually a cylindrical device with a hole at one end, installed so that the end with the hole faces forward. The other end is connected to a hose that leads to airspeed sensing instruments. With this arrangement, as the aircraft moves forward, it will create a positive air pressure within the pitot tube. Used together, the pitot tube, the static port, and the hoses associated with each are known as the pitot-static system.

Three flight instruments are based on measuring air pressure and are connected to the pitot-static system. These are known as pitot-static instruments and, in general, need no external power source.

Airspeed Indicator. The airspeed indicator is connected through hoses to both the pitot tube and the static port. The basic function of the airspeed indicator is to compare air pressure caused by aircraft movement to ambient air pressure. Within the instrument, a small set of bellows connects to the hose leading to the pitot tube. The bellows are also mechanically connected through gears and springs to a needle on the face of the airspeed indicator. The case of the instrument is connected to the hose leading to the static port. As the aircraft moves through the air, the pressure in the pitot tube inflates the bellows. As the bellows expand, the needle will move to indicate airspeed. Airspeed indicators can be calibrated in nautical miles per hour (knots), miles per hour, or both.

Altimeter. The altimeter is connected through hoses to the static port. The basic function of this instrument is to measure barometric air pressure. If a tube is placed into a mercury reservoir, the atmospheric pressure will force the mercury up into the tube. Measuring the length of tubing filled with mercury will give an indication of the atmospheric pressure. At sea level, the length of tube filled will be approximately 29.92 inches of mercury. At 20,000 feet, the length would only be 13.75 inches of mercury. This pressure is commonly known as barometric pressure.

Inside the altimeter is a sealed pressure capsule connected to needles on a dial calibrated in feet of altitude. As the aircraft climbs skyward, the capsule expands, causing the needles to indicate an altitude above sea level. The altimeter is only accurate when the pilot sets the altimeter for the local barometric pressure. For example, before takeoff, the pilot gets a weather report that indicates the local barometric pressure and then enters the pressure into the altimeter. Once entered, the altimeter will read the field elevation, or altitude above sea level.

Vertical Speed Indicator. The vertical speed indicator is connected through hoses to the static port. The function of this instrument is to measure the rate of altitude change. Inside the vertical speed indicator is a pressure capsule with a calibrated leak. This capsule is connected to a needle on the face of the instrument. As the aircraft increases or decreases in altitude, the capsule will expand or contract, and air will either leak in or out of the capsule, causing the needle to indicate the rate of either climb or descent.

Gyroscopic Flight Instruments

The gyroscopic instruments work on the principle that a spinning wheel will remain rigid in space. The gyroscopic instruments are constructed around a spinning wheel called a gyroscope. Once spinning, the gyroscope will remain rigid; therefore, it is mounted on special devices called gimbals. The gimbals allow the aircraft to move freely around the rigid gyroscope. Gyroscopic instruments are different from pitot-static instruments in that they require a power source. These instruments may be either air or electrically powered.

Directional Gyro. Unlike the magnetic compass, the directional gyro remains stable in spite of aircraft movement. The gimbal of the directional gyro connects to a circular compass card. A number or letter under a lubber line at the top of the instrument indicates the direction in which the aircraft is pointed.

Attitude Gyro. This instrument is also known as the artificial horizon, or attitude indicator. Two gimbals within the attitude gyro are connected to a horizon-reference arm. Using two gimbals allows the aircraft to move freely in all directions around the rigid gyroscope. The reference arm rotates right and left and moves up and down. When the gyroscope is spinning and rigid in space, the horizon reference bar will remain level. As the airplane climbs, descends, or banks, the pilot can compare the position of the reference bar to an airplane symbol and bank index on the face of the instrument. In this manner, the pilot can then determine the attitude of the aircraft relative to the horizon.

Rate Gyros. There are two different types of rate gyros, the turn and slip indicator, and the turn and bank indicator. Both types feature an inclinometer on the face of the instrument that indicates whether or not the aircraft is sliding sideways. A sideways slide is known as either a slip or a skid.

The turn and slip indicator uses a gyroscope in a horizontally mounted gimbal connected to a needle in the face of the instrument. As the aircraft turns, the gimbal rotates and forces the needle to the left or right, depending on the direction of the turn. The faster the turn, the greater the deflection of the needle. In a turn and bank indicator, also known as a turn coordinator, the gimbal is mounted at an angle and connected to a symbolic airplane on the instrument face. This instrument senses both bank rate and turn rate.

Engine Instruments

All aircraft are equipped with a tachometer. A tachometer measures the rotation speed of the engine in revolutions per minute or in percent of maximum. In piston-powered aircraft, the tachometer may also include an hour meter to measure the time that the engine has been running. In helicopters, the tachometer will have two needles, one to measure engine speed and the other to measure rotor speed. Jet-powered aircraft have two tachometers labeled N_1 and N_2. The N_1 tachometer measures the speed of the low-pressure compressor, and the N_2 tachometer measures the speed of the high-pressure compressor.

Oil temperature and pressure gauges are also found on all aircraft. Many piston-powered aircraft are cooled by a combination of air and oil. By monitoring the oil temperature, the pilot can determine if the engine is operating within its proper temperature range. All engines are lubricated with oil, and the oil pressure gauge alerts the pilot to any changes in oil pressure that would indicate an engine problem.

Many aircraft are equipped with an exhaust-gas temperature gauge. This instrument measures the temperature of the exhaust gases, and pilots use this instrument to monitor the efficiency of the engine.

Piston-powered aircraft may be equipped with a manifold pressure gauge. This instrument is similar in construction to, yet less sensitive than, an altimeter. The manifold pressure gauge measures the air pressure within the intake manifold. For aircraft equipped with constant-speed propellers, this instrument is the only reliable way to measure the power output of the engine.

Jet engines will have instruments that measure pressure at both the low and high pressure compressors. These pressure gauges allow the pilot to monitor the performance of the engine.

Systems Instruments

Pilots monitor the condition of the electrical system in the aircraft by using an ammeter. Ammeters measure electrical current flow in amperes. Some aircraft also have a voltmeter. The voltmeter measures electrical potential in volts. By monitoring these instruments, the pilot can determine whether the battery is charging or discharging and whether the generator is working properly.

All aircraft are equipped with fuel quantity indicators, the equivalent of a fuel gauge in an automobile. Since many aircraft have more than one fuel tank, there may be more than one fuel gauge. In some cases, a single gauge can be used with a selector switch so that the pilot must measure fuel quantity one tank at a time.

Some aircraft are equipped with fuel flow gauges. These instruments monitor the rate at which the engine or engines are using fuel. Pilots use these gauges to monitor the condition of the engines and to plan when fuel stops will be necessary.

Electronic Flight Instrumentation System

Electronic flight instrumentation systems (EFIS) can be used in place of every instrument except the magnetic compass. By nature, instruments with no moving parts are more reliable than their mechanical counterparts. Various techniques are used to replace the mechanical components of an instrument. For example, by using accelerometers coupled to microprocessors, engineers can duplicate the operation of the gyroscope. In addition, a laser beam shining through a ring of optic fiber can duplicate the operation of a mechanical accelerometer.

By using technology similar to computers and televisions, information can be displayed on cathode ray tubes or liquid crystal displays. In most EFIS designs, all of the flight instrument information is exhibited on one or two displays, while navigation, engine, and other information will be shown on other displays.

EFIS-equipped aircraft may a have special engine monitoring system called the engine indicating and crew alerting system (EICAS). With EICAS, engine data are not all displayed continuously. During normal operation, only a minimum amount of information is displayed. If a malfunction occurs, important information will appear automatically on the electronic display.

Thomas Inman

Bibliography

Brown, Carl A. *A History of Aviation*. 2d ed. Daytona Beach, Fla.: Embry-Riddle Aeronautical University, 1980. A well-illustrated book that covers the history of flight from ancient times to the space age.

Cessna Pilot Center. *Manual of Flight*. Denver, Colo.: Jeppesen, 1982. Part of Cessna's integrated flight training system for pilots seeking their private pilot license.

Eismin, Thomas K. *Aircraft Electricity and Electronics*. 5th ed. Westerville, Ohio: Glencoe, 1994. A beginner's text starting with the fundamentals of electricity and ending with electric instruments and autoflight systems.

Helfrick, Albert. *Principles of Avionics*. Leesburg, Va.: Avionics Communications, 2000. A very complete avionics text that includes history.

Jeppesen Sanderson. *Instrument Rating Manual*. 7th ed. Englewood, Colo.: Jeppesen Sanderson, 1993. A textbook designed to assist pilots to prepare to add an instrument rating to their pilot license.

Treager, Irwin E. *Aircraft Gas Turbine Engine Technology*. 3d ed. Westerville, Ohio: Glencoe, 1996. Written for the aircraft maintenance technician, with a comprehensive view of gas turbine engine technology.

See also: Airplanes; Avionics; Cockpit; Flight control systems; Guidance systems; Pilots and copilots; Training and education

J

Japan Airlines

Definition: Japan Airlines is part of a privately owned Japanese travel corporation. The airline serves both a large domestic market and a network of international routes.

Significance: Japan Airlines is Asia's largest airline.

History

Japan's major international airline began shortly after World War II, when the country was recovering economically and was beginning to see opportunities to participate in the newly aligned world. In 1951, Japan Air Lines was formed as a privately owned company. Its first flights were domestic, achieved by leasing both aircraft (Martin 202's) and crews from Northwest Airlines, which served Japan from North America.

In the following year, Japan Air Lines had acquired its own aircraft and trained its own crews and had become a major element in Japan's internal transportation system. In 1953, the Japanese government acquired 50 percent of the company and became an owner and controller for the next thirty-four years. During this time the company was considered a government-sponsored air carrier.

Japan Air Lines achieved its ambition of becoming an international carrier in 1954, when it introduced its first foreign destination, San Francisco. As the decade continued, the airline added other international routes, with accelerated growth beginning in 1960 when jet service with DC-8's was introduced. Polar flights to Europe (London, Paris, and Copenhagen) and westward lower-latitude flights to Europe (Rome, Frankfurt, and London via Karāchi and Cairo) constituted a truly global pattern. When the United States finally allowed Japan Air Lines to cross it with flights from the West Coast to New York and on to Europe, it became officially an "around-the-world" airline.

A noteworthy introduction occurred in 1974 when the airline began flights to and from the People's Republic of China. Historians list this event as one of the important opening steps between Communist China and the West. Japan Air Lines flights provided a channel of travel, communication, and commerce where one was greatly needed.

In 1987, the Japanese government divested itself of its share (then 34 percent) in the company, which became again a private corporation. Ownership is traded on the stock exchange and majority stockholders are primarily Japanese banks and insurance companies.

Two years later, the company underwent a reorganization, the most visible aspect being a change in its name from Japan Air Lines to Japan Airlines. During the last decades of the twentieth century, the corporation expanded its business into other travel and related companies, including subsidiary airlines, hotels, and even rapid surface travel concepts. By the year 2000, Japan Airlines was carrying over 30 million passengers and 1 million tons of cargo per year. It had become Asia's largest airline. By that year, revenues of the airline part of the corporation had reached a level of just over $10 billion.

Routes

At the beginning of the twenty-first century, Japan Airlines routes served seventy-eight different cities in a total of twenty-nine countries and territories, and, through code-sharing agreements with other airlines, its routes included eighty additional cities in the United States. The majority of its primary destinations are in Japan, where the schedules include twenty-three cities. It directly serves twelve U.S. airports. Its worldwide routes include polar routes to Europe, around-the-world service via the United States, extensive Asian service especially to China, and one South American city, São Paulo, Brazil.

Within Japan, the airline shows an unusual pattern of service. In most countries, especially physically small countries such as Japan, domestic airlines use small, short-haul aircraft. Japan Airlines, however, serves Japanese cities with wide-body craft, including many Boeing 747's. In fact, Boeing developed the 747SR (short range) and the 747SR-SUD (short range, stretched upper deck) largely because of Japan Airlines' domestic needs. To support these routes, Japan Airlines has eighteen thousand employees and operates 112 offices worldwide.

Fleet

Japan Airlines has an unusually top-heavy fleet, with the largest number of Boeing 747's of any airline in the world. In 2001, it was flying eighty 747's, including seven different versions of that airplane. These made up the bulk of its fleet of 135 planes. Of the remainder, most were also jumbojets (including the 767, which, although smaller than the 747 and the 777, qualifies as a jumbojet because of its intercontinental capability). There were only twelve smaller jets, including Boeing 737's and MD-11's.

Most JAL aircraft are painted in traditional, businesslike colors, a white body with the circular JAL logo, formed by the body and wings of a *tsuru* (crane), on the tail and the letters JAL on the fuselage. However, the company introduced fancier colors for special routes in the 1990's. The domestic 737's, for instance, are each named for a different flower and sport pictures of their flower on their sides. The 777's are called "star jets" and the name of a bright star with a picture of its constellation is shown on each plane's fuselage. Planes used for resort destinations, such as Hawaii, Guam, and Saipan, are called *Reso'cha* and are decorated with elaborate pictures of tropical flowers and birds.

Subsidiaries

The airline expanded and diversified in the last decades of the twentieth century and now is connected with approximately three hundred subsidiaries and affiliates, including a hotel chain (Nikko Hotels International), subsidiary airlines (such as Japan Asian Airways) and tour and resort operations. In addition to these attempts to enhance revenue, the company has also engaged in environmental activities, including a program of monitoring the carbon dioxide content in the stratosphere using equipment installed on its intercontinental jet planes on normally scheduled flights. It sponsors international cultural and sports events, such as the Otobutai concerts, remarkable musical events that combine traditional Japanese music performances with music from the West, all performed in one of the historic castles of Kyoto.

Paul Hodge

Bibliography

Bullock, F. *Pacific Glory: Airlines of the Great Ocean.* Osceola, Wis.: Motorbooks International, 1999. A comprehensive and heavily illustrated look at the airlines that serve the Pacific rim countries.

Doganis, R. *The Airline Business in the Twenty-first Century.* London: Routledge, 2001. A technical look at the future of the airline industry and the new problems and opportunities that are likely to arise.

Hanlon, J., and P. Hanlon. *Global Airlines: Competition in a Transnational Industry.* Woburn, Mass.: Butterworth-Heinemann, 1999. A detailed economic analysis of the strategies of international airlines.

See also: Air carriers; Boeing; Jumbojets; Northwest Airlines; 707 plane family; Transglobal flight

Jennys

Also known as: Curtiss Jennys, JN-2, JN-3, JN-4, JN-4C, JN-4D, JN-4H
Date: First JN design built in 1914; JN-4D introduced in June, 1917
Definition: The most important U.S.-designed and-built airplane of the World War I era.
Significance: Thousands of American, British, and Canadian army pilots were trained in Jennys, and after the war, the readily available airplane served in the United States as a trainer and a barnstorming exhibition plane at county fairs and farmers' fields. It was also the first plane officially to carry airmail in the United States.

Evolution of the JN Series

"Jenny" was the affectionate nickname given to any of several models of the Curtiss JN series of aircraft by thousands of U.S. and British flight cadets who learned to fly between 1915 and the early 1920's. The JN aircraft design resulted from a 1914 request from the British government for a trainer aircraft for its army pilots.

By 1914, aeronautical pioneer Glenn H. Curtiss had established the largest aircraft manufacturing company in the United States, although most of his airplanes were sold either to the U.S. Navy or to European governments to avoid entanglement in his patent battles with the Wright brothers. Prior to the JN aircraft, most of Curtiss's landplane designs had used pusher propellers, which Curtiss believed gave the pilot better visibility, but, in response to an Army request, he developed a tractor design with the propeller in front. The initial design, termed the "J" model aircraft, was developed by B. Douglas Thomas, an engineer whom Curtiss hired from the Sopwith Company of England. The best elements of this design were combined with the best of Curtiss's "N" aircraft designs to give the "JN" designation.

The aircraft evolved from the JN-2, which had two wings of equal span, into the JN-3 and the JN-4, which had slightly staggered (offset front-to-back) wings with the upper wing of greater span than the lower wing. Also departing from earlier Curtiss designs, the Jenny had flaplike ailerons built into the trailing edges of its upper wings rather than small winglike ailerons suspended between the

This squadron of Jennys, based in New Mexico, was used in a campaign against Pancho Villa in 1916. (The Institute of Texas Cultures, courtesy Kirk McManus Collection, Aeroflax Inc.)

wings' tips. To avoid the hotly contested Wright patent on lateral control, `which the Wrights claimed included ailerons, the Curtiss planes were built without ailerons and shipped to England, where ailerons made by another Curtiss company in Canada were added.

World War I

The British loved the Jenny, calling it the perfect trainer, and more orders followed, leading Curtiss to build many in Canada, where the JN-4C became known as the Canuck. When the United States entered World War I, it also chose the JN-4 as its trainer, deciding to use European-designed planes for fighters and bombers. Over eight thousand of these various JN-4 versions were built as trainers, and hundreds more were built for private purchasers. Almost three thousand JN-4D versions, powered by the famed 90-horsepower Curtiss OX-5 engine, were built for the U.S. Army and others. The JN-4D cruised at 60 miles per hour, had a top speed of 75 miles per hour, and had a ceiling altitude of 6,500 feet. The basic JN-4D weighed 1,390 pounds and could carry 530 pounds of fuel, people, and baggage or mail. It had a 43.65-foot wingspan along its upper wing and a total wing area of 352 square feet. It was 27.33 feet long. The JN-4H, with a larger 150-horsepower Hispano-Suiza engine, boasted a slightly higher speed and was purchased in quantity later in the war by the U.S. Army. It was used for training well into the 1920's. Curtiss also built a Navy version of the JN-4 with floats, designated N-9H.

After World War I

The end of the conflict in Europe brought thousands of former Army pilots home with a yearning to keep flying. They were joined by other young men and women who were excited about learning to fly, but opportunities for civilians to fly for a living were very limited. Unlike in Europe, no airlines existed in the United States, and the fledgling U.S. airmail service was being flown by Army pilots in Jennys. However, surplus Jennys were plentiful and inexpensive, and many were purchased by flight schools and groups of pilots who formed exhibition teams traveling the country giving airplane rides and barnstorming.

The absence of any regulations for flying in the United States enabled almost anyone with an airplane, regardless of pilot ability or airplane state of repair, to offer rides for a few dollars or to do stunt flying at county fairs or at farms on the outskirts of small towns. The Aero Club of America did issue pilot's licenses, but neither the U.S. government nor most states required licensure or registration of any kind. Indeed, part of the thrill of going to a barnstorming exhibition was the anticipation of a crash, and it was fortunate that the limited speeds of the Jenny and similar planes enabled pilots to survive many accidents with only broken bones. Many young people of the era earned their flight training by working on the Curtiss OX-5 engine, by repairing the JN-4 airframe, and sometimes even by signing on as wing-walkers, who hung onto a Jenny's wings and struts by their arms and legs as the plane flew over cheering local crowds.

The Jenny truly opened up the world of aviation to Americans, giving many an insatiable taste for flying. It did more to awaken the nation to the thrills and promises of aviation than any other airplane of its time. Many Jennys survive today in private and museum collections, and if one is fortunate, he or she might catch one flying an exhibition of antique aircraft.

James F. Marchman III

Bibliography

Christy, Joe. *American Aviation: An Illustrated History*. Blue Ridge Summit, Pa.: Tab Books, 1987. A well-organized, thorough, and profusely illustrated review of aviation in America from the nineteenth century through the space age.

Donald, David, ed. *The Complete Encyclopedia of World Aircraft*. New York: Barnes & Noble Books, 1997. An outstanding source of photos, drawings, and statistics on almost every airplane ever built anywhere in the world.

Roseberry, C. R. *Glenn Curtiss: Pioneer of Flight*. Syracuse, N.Y.: Syracuse University Press, 1991. The definitive biography of Curtiss and an excellent source of information on the origins of early Curtiss aircraft.

See also: Airmail delivery; Barnstorming; Glenn H. Curtiss; Pilots and copilots; Training and education; Wing-walking; World War I

Jet engines

Definition: An internal combustion engine that converts the chemical energy of fuel into mechanical energy in the form of thrust by the high-speed exhaust gases leaving the engine nozzle.

Significance: Fundamentally, a jet engine is a gas turbine. Gas turbines are used widely to generate electricity in power stations, to power boats, trains, military tanks, and to drive gas pipeline compressors. It is as a jet engine, however, that the gas turbine has had its greatest industrial impact.

Description

The jet engine consists of several components: a compressor, a combustion chamber, a turbine, and an exhaust system. At the front of the jet engine is the compressor, driven by a shaft connected to the turbine. The compressor takes in air from the atmosphere and compresses it to produce high-pressure air. The air then enters the combustion chamber, where jet fuel is injected in fine droplets. Combustion occurs with ignition, and the hot gases exit the combustion chamber and enter the turbine, downstream of the combustion chamber. The hot gases leave the turbine through the exhaust system, exiting at high speed from the jet engine nozzle and propelling forward both the jet engine and the aircraft attached to it. The principle behind this propulsion is described by Newton's third law of motion, which states that for every action there is a reaction equal in magnitude and opposite in direction. Jet propulsion is the movement of a small mass of gas at a very high velocity, whereas in a propeller plane, the propeller moves a large mass of air at low velocity.

History

The first patent for the modern gas turbine was granted in 1930 in England to Sir Frank Whittle, whose design led to the W-l turbojet engine with a centrifugal compressor. Simultaneously yet independently, German engineer Hans P. von Ohain also obtained a patent for a turbojet engine less than five years after Whittle had received his patent. Von Ohain's engine also had a centrifugal compressor, whereas another German design, by Ernst Heinkel, had an axial compressor. A plane with von Ohain's He-S3b engine made its test flight on August 27, 1939. Two years later, on April 12, 1941, a plane with Whittle's turbojet engine was tested.

By the 1940's, German turbojet engine prototypes had adopted the axial compressor, whereas British models all used the centrifugal compressor. By 1943, the two main turbojet engines were Germany's Junkers Jumo 004 and Britain's Rolls-Royce Welland. In the United States, General Electric Company engineers modified the Whittle engine and produced an American version called the I engine. In October, 1942, the I engine had its first test flight in the Bell P-59A.

During World War II, scientists from both Allied and Axis countries worked feverishly to design and test the jet engine. By 1946, several countries had successfully developed turbojet engines. In the United States, General Electric built the I-16 and the I-40. In England, Rolls-Royce built the Welland I, the Derwent I, and the Nene. In Germany, Junkers manufactured the Jumo 004-4.

By the 1950's, the turbojet had been applied to civilian aviation. Early passenger jets included the De Havilland Comet I, which first flew in 1952 but was withdrawn from service two years later because of fatal accidents. By 1954, the United States had successfully tested its Boeing 707 passenger jet, with regular flights commencing four years later. After adopting the jet engine, commercial aviation quickly developed into an international business, with most countries operating their own national airlines. International jet aircraft industries manufacture many types of planes: wide-body models that can carry hundreds of passengers; supersonic planes that can fly at Mach 2; aircraft that are capable of vertical takeoffs and landings (VTOL); and military jet aircraft that can take off and land on the deck of an aircraft carrier.

The gas-turbine engine that powers all jet aircraft is, however, basically the same engine that was designed by Sir Frank Whittle in 1930. It consists of a compressor, combustion chamber, turbine, and exhaust system. There are four major manufacturers of jet engines: Société Nationale de Construction de Moteurs Aeronautiques (SNECMA) in France, Rolls-Royce in the United Kingdom, and Pratt & Whitney and General Electric in the United States.

Components

Compressor. The purpose of the compressor is to increase the pressure of the gas. In the compressor, atmospheric air is pressurized to typically ten to forty times the inlet pressure, and consequently the temperature of the air rises to between 200 and 550 degrees Celsius. The ideal gas law states the proportionality of the pressure and temperature of gases. The two basic types of compressors are the centrifugal-flow compressor and the axial-flow compressor.

The centrifugal-flow compressor, preferred for smaller engines, is a simpler device that uses an impeller, or rotor, to accelerate the intake air and a diffuser to raise the pressure of the air. The axial-flow compressor is favored for most engine designs, because it is capable of increasing the overall pressure ratio. The axial-flow compressor uses rotors fitted to many differently sized discs to accelerate the intake air and stationary blades, known as stators, to diffuse the air until its pressure rises to the correct value.

The type of compressor used in an engine affects the engine's exterior appearance: An engine with a centrifugal compressor usually has a larger front area than an engine with an axial compressor. An engine with an axial compressor is longer and has a smaller diameter than an engine with a centrifugal compressor.

Combustion Chamber. In the combustion chamber, jet fuel, typically kerosene, is injected in fine droplets to allow for fast evaporation and subsequent mixing with the hot, compressed air. The compressed air is used for combustion, which occurs with ignition; the hot pressurized gases then reach temperatures of 1,800 to 2,000 degrees Celsius. To protect the combustion chamber walls from these high temperatures, some of the intake air, routed from the compressor, is used to cool the combustion chamber walls.

The three types of combustion chambers are the multiple chamber, annular chamber, and can-annular chamber. The multiple chamber, with individual chambers, or flame tubes, arranged radially, is used on engines with centrifugal compressors and early axial-flow compressor engines. The annular chamber has one annular flame tube with an inner and outer casing. The can-annular chamber combines characteristics of the multiple chamber and the annular chamber and has several flame tubes in one casing.

Turbine. In an aircraft engine, the sole function of the turbine, which is downstream of the combustion chamber, is to power the compressor. Similar to the compressor, the turbine has several large discs, though typically not as many as the compressor, fitted with many blades. Gases at temperatures between 850 and 17,000 Celsius exit the combustion chamber and enter the turbine. The hot gases impact the turbine blades, causing the discs carrying them to rotate at high speeds, averaging 10,000 revolutions per minute. The discs are mounted on a shaft that is connected at the other end to the compressor discs. The turbine blades are usually made of nickel alloys, because these materials are both strong and able to withstand the high temperatures within the turbine. The blades are fitted with many small holes through which cool air is forced to prevent the blades from melting.

Exhaust System. The jet engine's exhaust system is configured so as to maximize the thrust of the engine. The exhaust system consists of a nozzle and may also include a thrust reverser and an afterburner.

In a basic exhaust system, the hot gases leaving the turbine are discharged through a propelling nozzle at a velocity that provides thrust. In VTOL aircraft, the nozzle swivels vertically so the aircraft can move up and down.

The thrust reverser enables the aircraft to slow down and stop more quickly upon landing, allowing the aircraft to land on shorter runways without relying solely on braking devices. Thrust reversal quite simply reverses the direction of exhaust gases to decelerate the aircraft. The two main thrust reversal methods use either clamshell-type deflector doors or bucket-type deflector doors on a retractable ejector.

Afterburner. An afterburner is used in some aircraft, such as supersonic jets (SSTs), including the Concorde and military aircraft, that need to reach high speeds in a short time. Unburned oxygen from the jet engine's exhaust system flows into an afterburner, where more fuel is injected into the hot gases to augment the thrust of the engine. The temperature of the exhaust gases increases, thereby increasing the gas velocity and the thrust of the engine. This additional thrust allows for acceleration to supersonic speeds or for faster takeoffs to accommodate combat situations or the shorter runways of aircraft carriers.

Types of Jet Engines

The basic types of jet engines are the turbojet, turbofan, turboprop, and turboshaft. Turbojet and turbofan engines are called reaction engines, because they derive their power from the reaction to the momentum of the exhaust gases. The turboprop and turboshaft engines, however, utilize the momentum of the exhaust gases to drive a power turbine that, in turn, drives either a propeller or an output shaft.

Turbojet. The turbojet was the first jet engine type to be invented and flown. In a turbojet, all of the intake air passes through the compressor and is burned in the combustion chamber. The hot gases pass through the turbine and are then expelled through the exhaust nozzle to provide the thrust required to propel the engine and the aircraft attached to it forward. Examples of the turbojet appear in both civilian and military aircraft, including the Olympus 593 in the Concorde SST.

Turbofan. By the end of the twentieth century, the turbofan had become the most popular choice for aircraft propulsion in both civilian and military aircraft. In a turbofan engine, a large fan is placed at the front of the compressor of the jet engine. The amount of intake air is increased up to ten times. Most of this cool intake air either bypasses the compressor, combustion chamber, and turbine and exits the fan nozzle separately, as in separate-flow turbofans, or gets mixed with the turbine exhaust and exits through a common nozzle, as in the mixed-flow turbofan.

Afterburners in turbofan engines are equipped with a mixer to mix the cooler bypass air with the hot exhaust gases, thus allowing an easier burning of the bypassed air. Turbofan engines are characterized by their bypass ratio, which is the mass flow rate, in pounds per second, of air going through the fan divided by the mass flow rate of air going through the compressor. Low-bypass engines have ratios of up to two; medium-bypass engines have ratios from two to four, and high-bypass engines have ratios from five to eight. Ultrahigh-bypass engines have bypass ratios from nine to fifteen or higher. The highest bypass ratios, although providing high propulsion efficiency, likewise involve large, heavy components.

The advantage of the turbofan is its greater thrust on the same amount of fuel, which results in more efficient propulsion, lower noise levels, and an improved fuel consumption. Turbofan jet engines power all modern commercial aircraft, such as the Boeing 747; business jets, such as the Gulfstream IV; and most military airplanes, such as the F-18. Future turbofans may combine various bypass features. For example, the variable-cycle engine (VCE) would have both high-bypass and low-bypass features. Such an engine would be designed for planes that travel at subsonic and supersonic speeds. The VCE would operate by a valve that would control the bypass stream, either increasing it for subsonic speeds or decreasing it for supersonic speeds.

Turboprop. A turboprop engine is a turbojet engine with an extra turbine, called a power turbine, that drives a propeller. In the turboprop engine, the jet exhaust has little or no thrust. Planes powered by turboprop engines typically fly at lower altitudes and reach speeds up to 400 miles per hour (640 kilometers per hour). An example of the turboprop engine is the Rolls-Royce DART in the British Aerospace 748 and the Fokker F-27.

Turboshaft. A turboshaft is a turboprop engine without the propeller. The power turbine is instead attached to a gearbox or to a shaft. One or more turboshaft engines are used on helicopters to power the rotors. The turboshaft engine has industrial applications, such as in power stations, and marine applications, such as in hovercrafts.

Jet Engine Pollution

Because it is an internal combustion engine whose exhaust gases flow directly into the environment, a jet engine is a serious source of air pollution. Because of its high level of noise, its also causes noise pollution.

Air Pollution. Air pollution results from the combustion process of the gas-turbine engine. Jet-engine emissions, including carbon dioxide, carbon monoxide, hydrocarbons, and nitrogen oxide gas, contribute to both the greenhouse effect and atmospheric ozone depletion. They also endanger the health of people especially near airports.

Some regard aircraft transportation as more polluting than any other type of transportation, including the automobile. Generally, older aircraft are greater polluters than newer aircraft. The turbofan and bypass turbofan engines in particular use less fuel and therefore pollute less. A new MD-90 is about 50 percent more economical than a DC-9 or a DC-10, because the newer plane uses less fuel. Nevertheless, studies show that per passenger, an airplane uses twice as much fuel per passenger than does a car with three passengers, when the car drives the distance a jet travels in one hour (770 kilometers).

Airplane fuel consumption could be improved by eliminating various classes of cabins in the aircraft. Business- and first-class cabins seat fewer passengers, thereby reducing the overall fuel efficiency of the aircraft. If a reduction in carbon dioxide aviation emissions is to be realized, older aircraft must be replaced with newer ones that have more fuel-efficient engines. The most environmentally friendly aircraft include the B-777 and B-767. Carbon monoxide is contained in the combustion exhaust fumes. Both carbon monoxide and hydrocarbon emissions occur at the highest rates when airplanes idle their engines on runways, where often twenty planes are lined up waiting for takeoff. Airplanes pollute hundreds of times more when idling than when flying.

Nitrogen dioxide emissions contribute to acid-rain formation. The emission of hydrocarbons, especially radical ones, contribute to ozone formation. In terms of these emissions, the new high-bypass turbofan jet engines pollute much less than older turbofan and turbojet engines. Sulfur dioxide emissions also contribute to acid-rain formation. Nitrogen oxides have a possible role in ozone depletion, and its reduction can only be effected by less air traffic in general.

Noise Pollution. Noise is measured on a logarithmic scale in decibels, a unit of audio power. The decibel range is from zero decibels to about 160 decibels. A normal conversation takes place at about 40 decibels, and a noise level of 90 decibels would make it impossible to hear a normal conversation. The noise from a nearby jet takeoff is about 110 decibels. The main source of jet-engine noise is the propulsion system and the resultant noises generated by both internal and external processes.

In early turbojet engines, the noise occurred behind the exhaust nozzles when the hot exhaust gases mixed with the cool atmospheric gas. The high-bypass turbofan engines alleviated this noise problem.

Nevertheless, noise issues continue with the fan noise and core noise in high-bypass turbofan engines. Fan noise can be either broadband, discrete tone, or multiple tone, depending on whether the tip speed of the fan rotor blades is subsonic or supersonic. Core noise includes the noise from the rotation of the compressor, the noise from the turbulence generated in the combustion chamber, and the noise from the turbine.

Aircraft noise is regulated by federal rules that become increasingly stringent with time. Aircraft are classified as either stage one, for very noisy, 1960's-era jetliners; stage two, for moderately noisy, 1970's-era jetliners; or stage three, for more quiet, modern aircraft. Beginning in the year 2000, only stage-three aircraft may operate in the United States and Europe. Supersonic commercial aircraft, such as the Concorde, operate under different regulations and are only allowed to take off and land at certain airports because of the noise they make during takeoff.

To reduce external noise, the exhaust stream velocity may be decreased by flying jets that have a turbofan engine with a bypass ratio of five or higher. Such engines reduce exhaust noise considerably. With lower levels of external noise, internal noises are more audible.

To reduce internal noise, the fan tip speed can be decreased, although this would result in the necessity of more compressor stages, therefore resulting in a heavier engine. More spacing between the rotor and stator would also lessen the noise, but the larger spaces would require a larger engine.

Said Elghobashi

Bibliography

Bathie, William W. *Fundamentals of Gas Turbines*. New York: John Wiley & Sons, 1984. A thorough history of the gas turbine, with sections on thermodynamics, fluid mechanics, combustion, component matching, and environmental impacts and a detailed section on jet engine noise.

Cohen, H., G. F. C. Rogers, and H. I. H. Saravanamuttoo. *Gas Turbine Theory*. Essex, England: Addison-Wesley Longman, 1996. A detailed explanation of how the different components of a gas turbine work, with graphs and equations and prediction of performance of a gas turbine.

Kerrebrock, Jack L. *Aircraft Engines and Gas Turbines*. Cambridge, Mass.: MIT Press, 1992. An explanation of the thermodynamic cycles of the different types of jet engines, component design, component matching, and aircraft engine noise.

Rolls-Royce. *The Jet Engine*. 5th ed. Derby, England: Author, 1996. An excellent overview of the subject, with emphasis on the turbojet engine and featuring easy-to-understand charts and diagrams.

See also: Engine designs; Jumbojets; Propulsion; Ramjets; Turbojets and turbofans; Turboprops

Jet packs

Definition: Propellant packs used for individual flight, rather than for aircraft.

Significance: Jet packs, originally conceived for use in terrestrial battle, have become of major importance in providing for the safety of astronauts during space walks.

Rocket Belts

The jet pack is a device to allow a single person to fly without being enclosed in an aircraft. Jet packs first came to public attention during the opening ceremonies of the 1984 Summer Olympic Games in Los Angeles, California. The jet pack itself attaches to a regular backpack.

The inventor of the first practical jet pack, or rocket belt, was Wendell F. Moore. In the early 1950's, Moore was an engineer at Bell Aerosystems and worked on the concept of small, light system mounted on a person's back, that could be worn into battle. The idea had first been proposed by the Germans, who had been working on it at the end of World War II. However, Moore found very few people at Bell willing to fly the jet pack more than once or twice. Fortunately, Moore's nineteen-year-old neighbor, William P. Suitor, had watched him working on the project in his backyard and was eager to fly the rocket belt. Suitor was hired by Bell in 1964 to work with its designers and engineers to learn to fly the new aircraft, at first on tethers, then in free flight. Suitor became known as the "Rocket Man."

The rocket belt or jet pack used a hydrogen peroxide reaction rocket engine. The engine has a tank of compressed liquid nitrogen that pushes hydrogen peroxide out of two other tanks into a reaction chamber, a box with silver screens coated with samarium nitrate. This box reacts to the hydrogen peroxide, in turn creating a high-pressure steam that propels the belt as it flows out of the flight nozzles. The steam is so hot that it renders the jet pack not only quite dangerous but also loud, emitting a screaming sound. Nevertheless, the pack handles amazingly well.

In addition to the original Bell rocket belt, there is the RB2000, designed by Brad Barker, Joe Wright, Larry Stanley, and Doug Malewicki. These men used the basic principle and design of the original Bell model but managed to increase the flight time from 20 to 30 seconds. Various improvements, such as the use of new materials that can withstand higher temperature, have led to a lighter belt. The importance of such a belt is its ability to carry more propellant while still being comfortable for the pilot. Nonetheless, 30 seconds is the most one can expect to fly with the belt. In order for the jet pack to be really practical, it will be necessary to develop tiny jet engines to power it, which can be used in concert with the lightweight hydrogen peroxide rockets for fast takeoff, higher altitude, and longer flights.

Given its early promise, it is surprising that jet-pack technology failed to make an impact on personal transportation during the late twentieth century. There are hopes that the twenty-first century will finally see it achieve its promise as a viable means for personal travel.

Jet packs have not proved practical for daily transport, but they often add a touch of excitement to festive occasions such as the Rio de Janeiro carnival samba parade. (AP/Wide World Photos)

Jet Packs in Space

Jet packs, once purely science fiction, are now part of the standard equipment of astronauts. The pack is a device fitted with pressurized metal containers that let out jets of gas, worn by astronauts on their backs to enable them to move around in space outside a spacecraft. The National Aeronautics and Space Administration (NASA) has introduced a new version of the jet pack called Simplified Aid for Extravehicular Activity Rescue (SAFER). This pack is a backup for the traditional tether that attaches the astronaut to the spacecraft. It is intended as an extra precaution for astronauts working outside space vehicles. The jet pack is also useful as a rescue device for astronauts who work outside spaceships. This pack was first tested in 1994 during a flight of the space shuttle *Discovery*. Astronauts Mark Lee and Carl Meade were the first to test the jet pack in space on September 16, 1994.

The pack weighs 80 pounds and carries 3 pounds of nitrogen propellant. There are twenty-four 1-inch-long thrusters, four to each side of a cube. Astronauts use a joystick fastened to the chest of the spacesuit to control their maneuvers. After astronauts right themselves, the packs enable them to get back to their vehicles at a maximum rate of 10 feet per second, or just over 6 miles per hour. The average speed, however, is closer to 1 mile per hour. There is little time for hesitation, since the packs only hold thirteen minutes of propellant fuel.

SAFER maneuvers much more easily than the previous 340-pound pack last used in 1984, the Manned Maneuvering Unit (MMU). Unlike the MMU, the new jet pack is worn during routine space walks. The astronaut can use various combinations of the jets to control pitches and rolls. The jet pack, which is rather boxy in shape, clips onto the regular backpack. There is a liquid crystal display allowing the astronaut to monitor information about fuel and battery power. There is also a computer in the pack to control the deployment of jets to stabilize the falling astronaut.

The development of SAFER has given greater credibility to the jet pack. Extravehicular activity emergencies are an astronaut's worst nightmare. SAFER provides the astronaut a good chance to get back to the vehicle even in a worst-case emergency scenario. The first test of the jet packs was a success. However, two subsequent trials revealed problems. In 1997, the jet thrusters of Scott Parazynski's pack failed to fire. In 1998, Jerry Ross's pack burned his nitrogen gas at a higher rate than expected. These problems led NASA to conduct rigorous ground tests to locate and solve the problems. Astronauts compare jet packs to parachutes: pieces of equipment that they hope never to use, but that are reassuring to have available.

Frank A. Salamone

Bibliography

Hecht, Jeff. "Finding Your Way Back Home." *New Scientist* 168, no. 2262 (October 28, 2000): 16. The use of SAFER, a jet pack for astronauts.

Kiernan, Vincent. "How Not to Get Lost in Space." *New Scientist* 143 (September 24, 1994): 7. A detailed discussion of SAFER.

"Put Your Faith in Engineering." *Discover* 15 (December, 1994): 22. A discussion of the jet pack.

Wolf, Jaime. "Canceled Flight." *The New York Times Magazine*, June 11, 2000, 36. More details on astronauts and the jet pack.

See also: Astronauts and cosmonauts; National Aeronautics and Space Administration, Propulsion; Spaceflight

Jet Propulsion Laboratory

Definition: The primary National Aeronautics and Space Administration (NASA) site for control and operations of U.S. lunar and interplanetary missions.

Significance: Almost all U.S. lunar and planetary missions have been controlled from the Jet Propulsion Laboratory (JPL) since it was transferred to NASA's control. Prior to that time, many of the United States' early developments in rocketry and missiles took place at JPL. JPL is also responsible for NASA's Deep Space Network of tracking and telemetry stations.

The Early Years

The Jet Propulsion Laboratory, located in Pasadena, California, evolved from a project in rocket propulsion that began in the early 1930's. During that time, one of the leading organizations in aeronautics study and research was the Guggenheim Aeronautical Laboratory at the California Institute of Technology (GALCIT), directed by Dr. Theodore von Kármán, also in Pasadena. In 1936, graduate student Frank J. Malina successfully approached von Kármán with a proposal to write his doctoral dissertation on rocket propulsion and high-altitude sounding rockets. This early work in rocket propulsion attracted the attention of two local rocket enthusiasts, John Parsons and Ed Forman. Together, the four men worked through the theories of rocket propulsion and designed a rocket engine, with some insights gained from a meeting with rocket pioneer Robert H. Goddard.

Because no safe campus facilities were available at which to test the rocket engine, Malina, Parsons, and Forman drove to an isolated site a few miles from the California Institute of Technology (Caltech) in the Arroyo Seco wilderness area. Although their first few tests were unsuccessful, the men eventually developed a working rocket engine. Their early successes with rocket engines gained the group facilities on the Caltech campus in which to continue their work.

In 1938, GALCIT was awarded a grant to study the possibility of using rockets to assist U.S. Army Air Corps aircraft on takeoff from short runways. A much larger grant from the National Academy of Sciences was awarded in 1939 to continue the jet-assisted takeoff (JATO) rocket work, signaling the beginnings of a significant shift for GALCIT's rocket project, from research for sounding rockets to research for military applications. In 1943, von Kármán produced a report, together with Malina and Qian Xuesen, on rocket research at GALCIT and proposed a significant expansion of rocket research, including a proposal to construct missiles capable of carrying explosive warheads and investigations of ramjet engines. This report contained the first usage of the term Jet Propulsion Laboratory to describe the GALCIT rocket facilities that had been constructed for the JATO work.

Though the laboratory's research was focused primarily on rocket propulsion technology, von Kármán chose the name Jet Propulsion Laboratory over Rocket Propulsion Laboratory. There may have been several reasons for this choice. Because rockets propel themselves through jets of gas, the term "jet propulsion" is more general than "rocket propulsion" and technically more accurate. Furthermore, by not limiting the scope of the laboratory to rocket research, von Kármán was leaving the door open for the laboratory to continue the original GALCIT work in other fields of aeronautical research. In addition, many military minds may have mentally associated the term "rocket" with fireworks. Jet propulsion was a new technical term that would more readily have caught their attention. Finally, due to the preponderance of poorly written science fiction about rockets and rocket ships and the negative publicity many amateur rocket enthusiasts had garnered, the term "rocket" had come to carry an unfavorable connotation, which von Kármán may have been trying to avoid.

The Army Years
In 1944, the Army authorized a $1,600,000 grant to construct a major research and development facility for rocketry and guided missile research operated under contract by Caltech. The new facility was officially named the Jet Propulsion Laboratory, GALCIT. The new JPL was charged with the mission of carrying forth several separate areas of research: rocket engine research, underwater solid-fueled missiles, ramjet research, and long-range heavy missile research, most of which had been mentioned in von Kármán's proposal the year before. At about this time, von Kármán left both Caltech and JPL, and the directorship of the now-official Jet Propulsion Laboratory fell to his former graduate student, Dr. Frank Malina.

To measure performance of their rockets, JPL's engineers and scientists developed radio telemetry techniques to monitor their missiles in flight. Telemetry is data transmitted from a remote location by radio signals. To track its missiles, JPL also developed a series of ground radio and radar stations. By 1945, JPL had launched rockets from White Sands, New Mexico, to altitudes of nearly 30 miles. The JPL team eventually developed the technology for two-way radio control of the rockets. In 1947, JPL launched the Bumper-Wac rocket, which first carried an American payload to the edge of space.

By the late 1940's, JPL had developed the Corporal missile, the United States' first operational surface-to-surface missile. By the early 1950's, researchers at JPL had designed the first solid-fueled antiaircraft missiles. In 1954, JPL proposed Project Orbiter, which would use a Redstone rocket as a first stage and either Loki or Sergeant rockets as upper stages, to put an artificial satellite into orbit around the earth by as early as 1957. The project was rejected. In October, 1957, however, the Soviet Union placed its Sputnik satellite into orbit. After Sputnik, JPL was given the go-ahead on its orbital project. Redstone would provide the missile, but JPL would design the payload and upper stage of the rocket to put the satellite into orbit. JPL would also handle tracking of the satellite. Finally, on January 31, 1958, the United States launched JPL's satellite, which was named Explorer 1.

With Explorer 1, JPL had once again shifted its emphasis, which now focused on the electronics and communications involved in fabricating a satellite rather than on the rocket used to launch the satellite. Following Explorer 1, JPL, under the Army's supervision, was responsible for the development and operation of several other uncrewed Explorer spacecraft.

The NASA Years
Prior to launch of Explorer 1, several different government agencies were involved in space-related activities. It was

deemed advantageous, however, to put all space-related activities except for certain military applications, under one civilian agency's jurisdiction. Thus, on October 1, 1958, the National Aeronautics and Space Administration (NASA) was created. On December 3, 1958, JPL was transferred from the jurisdiction of the Army to that of NASA but would continue to be operated by Caltech, under contract with NASA. The role of JPL under NASA would be primarily one of satellite and space probe design and operations. Although JPL was responsible for the Deep Space 1 spacecraft, which successfully tested an ion-drive propulsion engine, very little rocket propulsion work continued at JPL after this time.

NASA continued the expansion programs at JPL's Pasadena site that had begun under the Army's administration. Additional scientists and engineers were hired, and new facilities were built, so that JPL came to be situated on 177 acres of land near where von Kármán's team had done its original rocket propulsion experiments. Although under NASA, the Jet Propulsion Laboratory ceased research in jet or rocket propulsion, its original name remains in use.

By the year 2001, JPL had been responsible for nearly 60 spacecraft missions, as well as numerous payloads flown on space shuttle missions. Although a few of these missions failed to perform as expected or were lost due to launch vehicle or spacecraft failures, most missions were successful. Several JPL missions, such as the Voyager missions to the outer solar system, many of the Mariner missions to the inner planets, the Galileo mission to Jupiter, the Magellan mission to Venus, and the Viking missions to Mars, have enjoyed spectacular successes. Under NASA, JPL has achieved dominance in the field of lunar and planetary exploration, having successfully handled missions to every planet in the solar system except for Pluto, as well as missions to several asteroids. Although studies of Earth were largely carried out by other NASA centers, JPL has also played a key role in several missions studying the planet Earth.

The Deep Space Network

When Explorer 1 was to be placed into orbit in 1958, scientists immediately realized that there would be difficulty monitoring it. As the earth turned beneath the satellite, the groundtrack, or location on the surface of the earth underneath the spacecraft, would shift to the west with each orbit and not all of the orbits would pass over the United States. The satellite would be overhead in the United States only for a short period of each orbit that did pass over the United States. To track and monitor the satellite, therefore, JPL was responsible for deploying portable radio tracking equipment to several sites around the world. Two other Explorer spacecraft were successfully launched, and two more were lost during launch vehicle failure, before JPL was transferred from the Army to NASA. All these satellites needed remote facilities for tracking, telemetry, and control. The original equipment and sites used for Explorer 1 would suffice for the later missions, so that new facilities for each mission would not have to be built and deployed. This decision paved the way, however, for more permanent tracking and telemetry stations.

After JPL was transferred to NASA, a decision was made to build permanent tracking and telemetry stations to support the large number of planned space missions, both crewed and uncrewed. These stations formed the backbone of the Deep Space Network (DSN), operated for NASA by JPL. The core of the DSN is composed of three large communications complexes located near Madrid, Spain, near Canberra, Australia, and at Goldstone, in California's Mojave Desert. These sites are located nearly 120 degrees apart on the earth's surface and thus can provide whole-sky coverage. Nearly any portion of the sky is above the horizon from at least one of the DSN sites. Each site has several antennas for telemetry and two-way communications with spacecraft.

Because many of NASA's space probes have traveled a long way from Earth, the signals from these space probes have become increasingly weak. The DSN has located at each site a 230-foot diameter parabolic dish, forming one of the most sensitive and powerful telecommunications systems on Earth. Also located at each site are 112-foot-diameter, high-efficiency dishes for use with slightly stronger signals. Each site also holds 85-foot-diameter dishes on mounts designed to track satellites in fast-moving orbits near Earth. Each site also holds a 36-foot-diameter dish, each of which can be linked together with those of the other sites for astronomical use in a technique known as long-baseline interferometry.

Other Projects

Although JPL is known primarily for its roles in the early years of American rocket research and in the design and control of NASA spacecraft, JPL has also been involved in several other noteworthy projects. Many of these projects are natural spin-offs and extensions of the technologies that were developed for uncrewed spacecraft operations. JPL has played an important role in the study of solar energy as an alternate source of energy. JPL has also worked to develop an airborne, infrared fire-spotting system for the U.S. Forest Service. JPL has been involved in the advancement of robotics and automation and the development of miniature sensors and instrumentation. To deal with the enormous volume of data returning from space probes, JPL has also developed new, more powerful computer technologies, many of which have found their way into everyday non-space-related applications.

Raymond D. Benge, Jr.

Bibliography

Anderson, Frank W., Jr. *Orders of Magnitude: A History of NACA and NASA, 1915-1980.* 2d ed. Washington, D.C.: Government Printing Office, 1981. A history the U.S. space agency, including uncrewed space exploration.

Jet Propulsion Laboratory. *Deep Space Network.* Pasadena, Calif.: Author, 2000. This pamphlet, part of the NASA Facts series, describes the facilities and operations of NASA's Deep Space Network.

_____. *Jet Propulsion Laboratory.* Pasadena, Calif.: Author, 2000. This pamphlet, part of the NASA Facts series, describes JPL's history and many of the missions operated by the laboratory.

Koppes, Clayton R. *JPL and the American Space Program.* New Haven, Conn.: Yale University Press, 1982. A very thorough and well-researched history of the Jet Propulsion Laboratory.

See also: Aeronautics; Aerospace industry, U.S.; Robert H. Goddard; Jet engines; National Aeronautics and Space Administration; Orbiting; Propulsion; Ramjets; Rocket propulsion; Rockets; Satellites; Spaceflight

Amy Johnson

Date: Born on July 1, 1903, in Kingston upon Hull, Yorkshire, England; died January 5, 1941, in Thames estuary, London, England
Definition: Pioneering female pilot, considered by many to be the British equivalent of Amelia Earhart.
Significance: In the early years of aviation, Johnson held many long-distance flying records and was the first woman to fly solo from London to Australia.

Amy Johnson earned a bachelor of arts degree in economics from the University of Sheffield in 1926. Despite her education, she found it difficult to find suitable employment in an era when few women worked outside the home. She reluctantly accepted a secretarial position and instead chose to challenge herself through hobbies.

One of those hobbies was the relatively new field of aviation. During the winter of 1928-1929, Johnson learned to fly at the London Aeroplane Club. She earned private and commercial pilot's licenses and was qualified as a navigator. She was also the first woman in England to be certified as a ground engineer.

Determined to find an area in which women could compete equally with men, Johnson focused her attention on distance flying. She planned a solo flight from England to Australia, with the intention of beating the previous record of sixteen days, held by Bert Hinkler. With the support of her father, a successful merchant, and financial backing from Lord Wakefield, Johnson purchased a used De Havilland DH-60G Gipsy Moth. She named the open-cockpit biplane *Jason,* after the trademark for her family business.

Johnson set off from Croydon, a suburb of London, on May 5, 1930, making her first stop in Karachi, India, and breaking the record for that distance by two days. Bad weather and damage from a landing near Rangoon delayed her progress, however, and she landed in Darwin, Australia, on May 24, 1930, after 11,000 miles and nineteen and one-half days in the air. Although Johnson did not break the record, she did gain fame as the first woman to fly solo from London to Australia. She was nicknamed "Queen of the Air" by the British press and named a Commander of the Order of the British Empire.

More records followed. In July, 1931, Johnson and copilot Jack Humphreys set the England-to-Japan record. They followed with record-breaking flights from England to Capetown in 1932. In 1932, Johnson married leading British pilot and long-distance flier Jim Mollison, with whom she attempted an around-the-world flight. They crashed in Connecticut, however, and were divorced in 1938.

In 1939, at the start of World War II, Johnson joined the Air Transport Auxiliary (ATA), a pool of experienced pilots ineligible for duty in the Royal Air Force (RAF) who ferried planes from factories to bases. While flying a mission from Blackpool to Oxford, Johnson was caught in a storm and blown off course. Her plane ran out of fuel and she was forced to ditch into the Thames Estuary. Although observers spotted a parachute, her body was never recovered, and Johnson was presumed drowned. After her death, a song, "Amy, Wonderful Amy," was written in her honor.

P. S. Ramsey

Bibliography

Cadogan, Mary. *Women with Wings: Female Flyers in Fact and Fiction.* Chicago: Academy Chicago, 1992. Pro-

files of a wide variety of women in aviation, from eighteenth century balloonists to twentieth century astronauts.
Grey, Elizabeth. *Winged Victory: The Story of Amy Johnson.* Boston: Houghton Mifflin, 1966. A biography of pioneer female pilot Amy Johnson.
Welch, Rosanne. *Encyclopedia of Women in Aviation and Space.* Santa Barbara, Calif.: ABC-Clio, 1998. A reference work containing a broad overview of women's roles in the fields of aviation and space.

See also: Military flight; Record flights; Women and flight; World War II

Johnson Space Center

Also known as: Lyndon B. Johnson Space Center
Date: Established September 19, 1961; began operations March 1, 1962
Definition: The principal facility for oversight and operations of crewed spaceflight by the National Aeronautics and Space Administration (NASA).
Significance: The Johnson Space Center (JSC) has been responsible for astronaut training, crewed spacecraft development, and control of all U.S. crewed space missions in flight since 1965. JSC is also the site of the primary control center for the International Space Station (ISS) and is the location of the Lunar Receiving Laboratory, which studies Moon rocks and meteorites.

History

As early as 1957, engineers and scientists at the Langley Aeronautical Laboratory at Hampton, Virginia, were collaborating on the possibility of crewed exploration of space. With the United States rapidly increasing the number of planned space missions, the National Aeronautics and Space Administration (NASA) was created on October 1, 1958, to coordinate the rapidly expanding U.S. space program and to consolidate the various space projects under one civilian agency. Realizing that crewed space missions would be much more complex and challenging than uncrewed missions, on November 4, 1958, NASA created a special task force, called the Space Task Group (STG), to deal with the issues of crewed spaceflight. The STG was based at Langley but was charged with oversight of the crewed spaceflight. STG's first crewed space program was Project Mercury. In May of 1959, STG was made one of six departments of the newly formed Goddard Space Flight Center, in Greenbelt, Maryland. Because of STG's rapid growth during this period, however, STG never physically moved to Goddard. On March 1, 1961, STG was made an independent entity within NASA.

On May 25, 1961, President John F. Kennedy made public a challenge and a goal for NASA to send a crewed mission to the Moon. This was an enormous jump from Project Mercury, and it required a major expansion of the roles, duties, and personnel associated with the STG. With the expansion of the STG to such levels, NASA administrator James Webb created the Office of Manned Space Flight, a special NASA division that included STG. One of the first goals of the new Office of Manned Space Flight was to secure a location for a new NASA center dedicated to crewed space missions. Cape Canaveral, NASA's primary launch facility, was also a military missile test facility, and the Langley site was not fully suitable for expansion to include all of the facilities envisioned for the new center.

The selection of a permanent site for the new NASA center near Houston, Texas, was not without contention. Many NASA personnel wanted the new center to be either in California, near the Jet Propulsion Laboratory, or in Florida, near the launch facilities. Most of the STG team at Langley preferred establishing a facility adjacent to or near Langley. Pressure from then-vice president Lyndon B. Johnson and Speaker of the House Sam Rayburn, both of Texas, together with several influential Texas legislators, caused NASA to consider a more centrally located site. Longtime associates of Johnson at Humble Oil finally helped the Houston site to win NASA's favor. Humble Oil donated 1,000 acres of land to Rice University in Houston, with the stipulation that the land be made available to NASA. Although land costs were not a major issue, it would not have been prudent for NASA to turn down the offer of free land for the center, especially in light of the political pressure placed upon the agency to locate a major NASA center in Texas.

Thus, on September 19, 1961, NASA announced that the new center would be located on the outskirts of Clear Lake City, a suburb of Houston. On November 1, 1961, the new NASA installation became officially designated the Manned Spacecraft Center (MSC), at which time the STG ceased to exist as a separate entity and was absorbed into the new center. Some operations began at once in leased office spaces in the Houston area, and, on March 1, 1962, Robert Gilruth, director of the new MSC and former head of the STG, moved his headquarters to Houston, officially making the MSC an operational NASA center. MSC was formally opened in February, 1964.

Construction on Mission Control began soon after the Houston site was selected, and MSC's Mission Control served as the backup command center for the Gemini 2 and Gemini 3 missions, the first crewed Gemini missions. Beginning with the Gemini 4 mission in June of 1965, Mission Control in Houston has acted as the principal mission-command center for all U.S. crewed space missions.

Astronaut training facilities were constructed at MSC to prepare the astronauts for the conditions that they would face in space travel. Spacecraft were designed and tested at MSC, and the Lunar Receiving Laboratory was constructed to house and study the Moon rocks returned to Earth by the Apollo astronauts. Nearly adjacent to MSC was Ellington Air Force Base, later renamed Ellington Field after it was decommissioned by the Air Force, where training aircraft were kept for the astronauts. On February 17, 1973, the Manned Space Flight Center was formally renamed the Lyndon B. Johnson Space Center (JSC) in recognition of the late President Lyndon B. Johnson, his role in the Houston site's selection, and his support for crewed spaceflight.

Mission Control

The Mission Control Center (MCC) is the part of JSC with which the public is most familiar. Mission Control occupies a prominent building, designated Building 30, near the center of JSC. On the first floor of the MCC, advanced computer systems analyze the telemetry data collected during crewed space missions. The most visible part of the MCC is the Flight Control Room (FCR). There are actually several FCRs in the MCC. Nearly identical FCRs exist on the second and third floors, with the third floor FCR used primarily for military missions. Down the hall from the primary space shuttle FCR is a slightly different FCR used for the International Space Station (ISS) operations. The FCR consists of rows of flight-control consoles facing a large display at the front of the room. Each flight-control position has computer screens and other readouts, and the controller at that position is responsible for monitoring a specific part of the mission. The lead flight control position is that of the flight director, who is ultimately responsible for all decisions related to the mission. Although the FCRs are the most publicly visible part of the MCC, they are only a small part of Mission Control. Each flight-control position is assisted by a team of engineers and technicians, many of whom work in small rooms adjacent to the FCR.

Training Systems

To prepare astronauts for the various situations to be encountered in spaceflight, numerous training facilities were built at the Johnson Space Center and at nearby Ellington Field. Some of these facilities, such as a large centrifuge built to simulate the high accelerations experienced on liftoff, were built for the Gemini and Apollo missions and were later dismantled to make room for space shuttle training systems. Other training systems include mock-ups of the various spacecraft used in crewed spaceflight. The mock-ups were used as simulators to train astronauts to deal with various situations that they would encounter in space travel. The space shuttle simulators are still used.

A Space Environment Simulation Laboratory (SESL) was constructed at MSC/JSC. The SESL consists of several chambers that are designed to reproduce the environment experienced by astronauts and equipment in space. The atmospheric pressure within the chambers can be reduced to that of a vacuum, and high intensity lamps and other electromagnetic radiation sources can be used to simulate the radiation environment in space. These chambers were used to test spacecraft, equipment, and space suits. The SESL can also be used to train astronauts to deal with the difficulties faced by such harsh environments.

To simulate the near-weightless conditions of spaceflight, JSC constructed a Neutral Buoyancy Training Facility (NBTF) at Ellington Field. The NBTF consists primarily of a very large tank of water. Astronauts wearing space suits and equipment are weighted to have a buoyancy equal to their weight. This simulation of weightlessness gives astronauts a chance to practice working and handling equipment in such an environment. A smaller but similar facility, the Weightless Environment Training Facility (WETF), where the centrifuge used to operate, was constructed in the early days of the space shuttle program.

Aircraft Operations

The Johnson Space Center operates several aircraft from Ellington Field. Some of these aircraft are used for astronaut training, and others are used in support of JSC's mission as lead NASA center for crewed spaceflight operations. One of JSC's training aircraft is a KC-135A transport aircraft, known as the "Vomit Comet," which flies parabolic arcs that yield a few seconds of near-zero-gravity environment inside the aircraft. The KC-135A is used to train astronauts and perform experiments at very low gravity in a manner far superior to that of the NBTF. Unfortunately, it is unable to maintain a low-gravity environment for more than a few seconds at a time, so many parabolic arcs are needed per flight.

Many of the astronauts act as pilots for their spacecraft. These astronauts must keep current in flight training. JSC maintains T-38 jet trainers at Ellington to allow the astronauts to train in high-performance aircraft. Furthermore, at least one of the T-38 trainers is fitted with control systems that mimic the very sluggish and difficult flight controls of the space shuttle. Pilot astronauts can use this trainer to practice the maneuvers needed to pilot the space shuttle to a safe landing.

In addition to the training aircraft at Ellington, JSC also is the home to a very large turboprop cargo aircraft called the Super Guppy. This aircraft has a cargo bay 25 feet tall, 25 feet wide, and 111 feet long. It is used to transport large pieces of equipment, such as ISS components. A similar aircraft, nicknamed the Pregnant Guppy, carried components of the Saturn rockets used in the Apollo missions.

Lunar Receiving Laboratory

In 1967, construction began on a special laboratory at MSC designed to handle the Moon rocks expected to be brought back to Earth by the Apollo astronauts. Not knowing at the time whether the Moon had any indigenous life, NASA constructed the laboratory with special safeguards designed to prevent any cross-contamination of the Moon rocks with the Earth environment. Although it was soon determined that there is no life on the Moon, this sterile laboratory environment permits researchers the opportunity to analyze Moon rocks without accidentally contaminating them with Earth material. Although the last Moon mission returned to Earth on December 19, 1972, NASA maintains the Lunar Receiving Laboratory as a repository for the precious Moon rocks brought back to Earth. Facilities were constructed at the laboratory to analyze the geological properties of the Moon rocks and to study any life-forms that may exist in them.

Because the Lunar Receiving Laboratory was designed to study Moon rocks without contaminating them with Earth material, it was natural for scientists to think of using the same laboratory to study meteorites found on Earth. Numerous meteorites found during the late 1970's and 1980's were sent to JSC's Lunar Receiving Laboratory for study. Among these meteorites, one called ALH-84001 created a great deal of excitement when researchers at JSC, working with scientists at Stanford University, announced in 1996 that ALH-84001 appeared to be a piece of the planet Mars thrown loose during a giant meteorite impact on that planet long ago. Furthermore, these researchers announced findings that indicated that this meteorite may contain fossil remains of Martian life. These findings remain in doubt, but it is clear that the unique facilities of the Lunar Receiving Laboratory present an ideal location to study extraterrestrial samples.

Raymond D. Benge, Jr.

Bibliography

Bilstein, Roger E. *Stages to Saturn: A Technological History of the Apollo/Saturn Launch Vehicles.* Washington, D.C.: Government Printing Office, 1996. A history of the development of the Saturn rockets, with some information on support activities at JSC.

Dethloff, Henry C. *Suddenly Tomorrow Came: A History of the Johnson Space Center.* Washington, D.C.: Government Printing Office, 1993. A very thorough and readable account of the history of operations at JSC from its founding until 1993.

Johnson Space Center. *Mission Control Center.* Houston, Tex.: Johnson Space Center, 1993. A NASA Fact Sheet with information on the layout, organization, and operations of JSC's Mission Control.

Shepard, Alan, and Deke Slayton. *Moon Shot: The Inside Story of America's Race to the Moon.* Atlanta, Ga.: Turner, 1994. A narrative from the astronauts' point of view of crewed spaceflight and the associated training for space missions, with a chapter on the selection of Houston as the site of the MSC.

See also: Apollo Program; Crewed spaceflight; National Aeronautics and Space Administration; Space shuttle; Spaceflight; "Vomit Comet"

Jumbojets

Definition: The term jumbojet was coined to refer to the Boeing 747, and by extension, to any wide-bodied plane that seats five hundred or more passengers.

Significance: Jumbojet planes carry more passengers per flight, reducing costs and providing more efficiency for airlines.

The Jumbojet has been so popular that the U.S. Post Office recently put it on a 33-cent stamp in the Celebrate the Century series, honoring the most significant people, places, events, and trends of the 1970's. Once airlines discovered that jets were significantly cheaper to operate per passenger mile than even the most efficient piston-engine planes, it was only a matter of time before jumbojets came on the market. The first jumbojet was the Boeing 747, capable of carrying five hundred passengers. However, most

747's were designed for about four hundred passengers, allowing room for mail, freight, and baggage. The 747's inaugural commercial flight was made in 1970.

The Boeing 747 has four jet engines and reaches a cruising speed of 550 miles per hour. Other manufacturers soon produced their own versions of wide-body jumbojets. McDonnell Douglas built the DC-10, a three-engine plane. McDonnell Douglas later modified this design to produce the MD-11. Lockheed had its own jumbojet, the L-1011 TriStar, which is no longer produced. Airbus Industrie produced the A300 twinjet wide-body.

The 1980's witnessed changes in jumbojets. McDonnell Douglas manufactured the MD-80 series of twin-engine jets, while Boeing introduced the 757 and 767 twinjets. The 757 was a narrow-body jet, complementing the wide-body 767. Meanwhile, Airbus introduced the A310 twinjet and its own narrow-body A320. The A320 twin was unique, featuring a sidestick controller for pilots, replacing the typical control columns and wheels. Airbus also came out with the A330, a larger twin-engine, and the A340 four-engine plane, designed for longer flights. Airbus plans to manufacture superjumbos that will carry more than 550 passengers.

Other manufacturers also have plans to build larger jumbos. Boeing's 777 wide-body jumbo currently holds up to four hundred passengers. Boeing purchased McDonnell Douglas in 1997, and in 1999 revealed plans to expand the 747 to hold up to 524 passengers.

History

In the early 1960's, Douglas, Lockheed, and Boeing were in competition for a U.S. Air Force contract for an order of a new heavy cargo jet. The Lockheed Galaxy was the Air Force's choice. However, even though Boeing lost the contract, the company put its experience to good use in a project to build a new civil aircraft. This aircraft would have a huge passenger capacity, made possible by General Electric and Pratt & Whitney's new engine. Boeing engineers built the fuselage as one long tube, including an upper flight deck. The new plane would have a maximum of five hundred passengers in rows of ten seats (divided into set of three, four, and three). The 747 became popularly known by its nickname, the "jumbojet."

The jumbojet was revolutionary in many ways. Its wing concept was different from that of other planes. It was the first civil plane to have four huge, powerful engines such as the Pratt & Whitney JT9D, which were needed to power an airplane with a weight of nearly 335 tons.

On February 9, 1969, the 747 made its maiden voyage. Twenty-six airlines had ordered the 747. Pan American was the first airline to make a commercial flight with the jumbojet, on a New York-to-London flight on January 22, 1970. The success of the first 747's led to the development of new engines by Pratt & Whitney, as well as General Electric and Rolls-Royce. On October 11, 1970, the first 747-200 flew. The 747-200 weighed about 378 tons and sported a larger fuel capacity. There is a version for passengers, the 747-200B, and one for cargo, the 747-200F. The 747-200C can be converted to passenger or cargo use. The 747-200 had 650 units delivered, easily the most successful jumbojet.

Boeing wanted a shorter version of the 747 and in 1973 produced the 747SP (Special Performance). It was a challenge to the Lockheed TriStar and the Douglas DC-10. The 747SP can fly very long distances. Furthermore, 90 percent of the parts used in the 747SP are the same as those used in the 747-200. It has a higher tail than the 200, as well as a longer elevator unit. Boeing manufactured forty-four 747SP's. From a shorter plane, Boeing turned to a larger one, the 747-300. It had a stretched upper deck that could seat sixty-nine passengers. Ninety of these planes were manufactured. The first of this series flew commercially on October 5, 1982.

The next of the 747's was the 747-400. It had a new wing design and new fuselage material as well as a two-pilot glass cockpit. These features made the 747-400 the most advanced and economic jumbojet. Its new engines allow the 747-400 to carry over 394 tons. It also has both cargo and the convertible models.

Other Jumbojets

McDonnell Douglas decided to improve its DC-10, and in the 1960's produced the longer DC-10-60. It was able to seat up to four hundred passengers. The DC-10-60 was supposed to have better engines and a better wing performance. However, it had more accidents than Douglas was comfortable with, and the company decided not to produce any new versions of the DC-10.

In 1981, McDonnell Douglas began trying various winglets and better engines on DC-10's. These proved sound, and in 1984, McDonnell Douglas debuted the MD-11. The first version, the MD-11X-10, was the same size as the DC-10. However, it had more powerful engines and a higher gross weight. In July, 1985, McDonnell Douglas released its passenger version. The standard version has a two-pilot cockpit, is longer than the DC-10, and has a 28 percent longer range. Nevertheless, it is a more economical plane; expenses are about 31 percent less. The MD-11 was a success. There are three versions available, a passenger, cargo, and convertible. The passenger version can hold up to 405 passengers and has a range about 7,000 miles.

In 1996, McDonnell Douglas manufactured the MD-11ER. This version has longer range and larger tanks than previous versions. Boeing's takeover of McDonnell Douglas in 1997 means that no further MD-11's will be produced after current orders are filled.

Airbus Industrie, a European consortium founded by France and West Germany in 1970, is the largest European producer of large jets. They shared the goal of Hawker Siddley, sponsored by the British government, to develop, construct, and market a European short- and medium-range airliner. The first Airbuses to be certified for flight in Europe and the United States were the A300-B1 and the A300-B2, in 1974. The first commercial A300-B2 had a takeoff weight of 138 tons and was sold mainly to European airlines, particularly Air France and Lufthansa.

Eastern Air Lines ordered thirty-eight A300-B4's, which had a higher takeoff weight and greater fuel capacity than did previous models, as well as optimized flaps. This was Airbus's medium- and long-range airplane. After the Airbus A310 made its successful debut, Airbus added new features: a two-pilot cockpit, improved wing design, and nonmetallic structures, creating the A300-600, which made its first flight in 1983. The A300-600 has the same cockpit as the A310-300, and both aircraft can be operated with the same type rating. However, the A300-600 has a stronger engine and a higher fuel capacity, for long-range flights, and the usual freighter and convertible versions. Its shape has led to it being nicknamed the Beluga.

Freight Carrying

Jumbojets are increasingly turning their efforts toward the hauling of freight. Boeing has turned more toward the freight or mixed use of its 747. The success of even Airbus's proposed superjumbo may depend on its ability to haul freight. In fact, Airbus has secured orders from Federal Express and others for freighter versions of its superjumbojet.

There is speculation that smaller widebodies, such as Boeing's 777 and 767 and Airbus' A330 and A340, eventually will fill the market for jumbojets. The reason for this move to smaller jumbos is that passenger routes are fragmenting as passengers' travel preferences shift toward fre-

The new Airbus A380 double-decker jumbojet can hold 555 passengers. (AP/Wide World Photos)

quent nonstop flights between cities and away from hub-to-hub trips. The shorter flights use smaller aircraft, while the longer flights are most efficient for the jumbojets.

This preference is not a problem in the cargo business. The economies of scale favor large hubs from which cargo can be sorted and dispatched, a situation that favors the largest possible planes. Airbus's proposed superjumbojet, for example, would be able to carry 150 tons of freight, compared with the 747's 120 tons.

The Future of the Jumbojet

Although there were many innovations in jet travel in the 1960's, no jetliner has yet matched the impact of the original jumbojet, the Boeing 747. At that time, there was increasing danger from crowded skies, which was averted through the use of more powerful engines. The 747 is still the world's largest commercial jetliner. With nearly 1,200 delivered, the 747 is the best-selling twin-aisle jet in the industry. The 747's longevity and popularity are based on its unbeatable low seat-mile costs, flexibility, long-range dominance, and unmatched comfort. During its lifetime, the 747 worldwide fleet has logged more than 50 million flight hours, 12 million flights and 20 billion miles, enough to make 42,000 trips to the Moon and back. The 747 is capable of carrying up to 568 passengers, depending on the model and its interior configuration. The 747-400, the only model in production in 2001, entered commercial service in 1989 and has sold more than any other 747 version.

The jumbojet is moving into the age of the superjumbojet with not only increased size but also increased range. The first jumbojet engines have been greatly improved upon in later models. Their range has expanded to over 8,000 miles. The next increase will be in its size.

Boeing, however, has stated that it will not build a successor to the 747. It has yielded the market for large jets to Airbus and its A380. Boeing will instead develop its Sonic Cruiser, a jet that can fly faster and farther than commercial jets currently flying. Except for the Concorde, no commercial jet flies significantly faster than 550 miles per hour, the 707's cruising speed. Boeing says its new sonic cruiser will fly at 648 miles per hour. It will also be more economical. Thus, the company that pioneered the jumbojet appears to be taking another direction. Airbus says that its new A380 has chased Boeing from the field.

Frank A. Salamone

Bibliography

Endres, Gunter. *McDonnell Douglas DC-10*. Osceola, Wis.: Motorbooks International, 1998. A well-illustrated history of the DC-10, including history, production, and coverage of its crashes.

Irving, Clive. *Wide-body: The Triumph of the 747*. New York: William Morrow, 1993. A behind-the-scenes account of the development of the first jumbojet.

Norris, Guy, and Mark Wagner. *Boeing 747: Design and Development Since 1969*. Osceola, Wis.: Motorbooks International, 1997. A well-illustrated history of the 747 since its inception.

Tennekes, Hank. *The Simple Science of Flight: From Insects to Jumbojets*. Cambridge, Mass.: MIT Press, 1996. An overview of the development of flight, including the importance of the jumbojet.

See also: Air carriers; Airbus; Airline industry, U.S.; Airplanes; Boeing; Lockheed Martin; McDonnell Douglas; Manufacturers; 707 plane family

K

Kamikaze missions

Date: From 1944 to 1945

Definition: Aerial suicide attacks waged by Japanese pilots against Allied forces as Japan faced catastrophic defeat in World War II.

Significance: Kamikaze missions inflicted high losses upon Allied naval forces and convinced Americans of Japan's overwhelming desire to avoid defeat.

Background

Tales of suicidal acts of bravery and extremely dangerous missions are found in many nations' war histories and heroic legends. During the Battle of Midway (1942) in World War II (1939-1945), American torpedo bomber pilots pressed on with their attacks despite impossible odds and severe losses. However, various religious, social, and military influences led Japan at World War II's end to conduct a sustained attack campaign that obviously entailed the attackers' deaths.

For the Japanese, mixed religious influences had bred their extreme reverence for one's lord and ancestors, strong allegiance to one's family and emperor, and a desire not to bring shame upon one's family or country. According to Japanese tradition, both life and death with honor guaranteed a godly standing in the afterlife.

The rise of militarism in early twentieth century Japan engendered a widespread embrace of the Bushido code of conduct espoused by the samurai warrior class. The Bushido code emphasized a profound sense of loyalty and honor, that would extend even to suicide if defeat or disgrace loomed.

Wartime Influence

In June, 1944, defeat directly confronted the Japanese, as the Americans crushed its naval, land, and air forces during the Marianas Islands invasion and the accompanying naval battle in the Philippine Sea. Japanese air losses were so severe they prompted U.S. Navy fighter pilots to nickname the battle the "Marianas Turkey Shoot." Stuck with increasingly inferior planes and unable to replace fallen pilots, Japanese military leaders explored other means of averting defeat and shame. Despite some opposition, lower-ranking officers had already suggested that, given inevitable high losses, crashing an airplane or other craft into an American ship would be a relatively inexpensive trade of one person, or at most, a few people, for an entire enemy vessel. Advocates felt this "body-crashing" tactic would also openly demonstrate superior Japanese willpower. In early October, 1944, Japanese rear admiral Masafumi Arima crashed a bomber into and damaged the aircraft carrier USS *Franklin*. His act signalled an apparent sanction by higher command and galvanized further action.

First Organized Attacks

In mid-October, 1944, as American landings in the Philippine Islands appeared likely, the swashbuckling, air-power-minded Vice Admiral Takijiro Onishi assumed command of part of Japan's land-based air defenses there. Hoping to support the Japanese fleet as it attempted a desperate counterattack, he pushed for the creation of the first suicide air groups. Composed entirely of volunteers, they embraced the battle nickname "kamikaze," meaning "divine wind," recalling the typhoons that had saved Japan from Mongol invasion in the thirteenth century.

The Japanese did not make many kamikaze attacks during the ensuing Battle of Leyte Gulf (1944), but they seriously damaged several ships and sank one small aircraft carrier, providing one bright spot in their otherwise overwhelming naval defeat. Thus, with their navy practically destroyed, and their overall war situation growing more dire, Japanese leaders expanded the kamikaze effort from an extraordinary battle tactic to a full-fledged campaign.

After Leyte Gulf, Japan fielded a variety of suicide units. The Japanese navy produced midget submarines that functioned as human-guided torpedoes. Both the army and navy deployed small boats carrying bombs to thwart amphibious landings. Although these sea-based efforts yielded some success, kamikaze air attacks were by far more productive.

Air Campaigns

As the Americans commenced amphibious landings at Leyte Gulf and further north on Mindoro Island through the end of 1944, the Japanese intensified their aerial kamikaze operation. The U.S. landings required that many American ships remain stationary offshore, thus easing the

A Japanese kamikaze pilot swoops over a U.S. warship during the Battle of Leyte Gulf in October, 1944. (AP/Wide World Photos)

kamikazes task. Smaller, less heavily armored ships such as transports, destroyers, minesweepers, and escort aircraft carriers were especially vulnerable. Kamikazes damaged and sank several ships during this time, but the effort eliminated Admiral Onishi's air force.

When the Americans and their allies commenced landings at Luzon Island's Lingayen Gulf in January, 1945, the remaining Japanese air units on the Philippine Islands commenced almost continual kamikaze attacks that sank or damaged dozens of ships until almost no Japanese planes were left. As the Americans advanced closer to Japan, other air units eagerly assumed the kamikaze role. Forming a new kamikaze outfit on Taiwan, Admiral Onishi directed attacks that crippled a few carriers and destroyers operating nearby. Suicide planes disabled the aircraft carrier USS *Saratoga* and sank an escort carrier just prior to the February, 1945, landings on Iwo Jima. Because Japanese fighter planes had difficulty shooting down B-29 bombers raiding Japan, individual pilots conducted ramming attacks.

The most spectacular kamikaze assault occurred during the Battle of Okinawa (1945). Under the command of Vice Admiral Matome Ugacki, southern Japan-based kamikaze units not only attacked ships involved in the Okinawa landing, but also attempted a raid on the U.S. naval anchorage at Ulithi, an atoll island group east of the Philippines. From March through June, 1945, successive waves of massed kamikaze attacks, known as *kikusui*, or "floating chrysanthemum," for spiritual purity, exacted a fearful toll. More than twenty U.S. ships were sunk and an equal number were severely damaged. However, the kamikaze threat was dissipated before the war ended by U.S. air raids on kamikaze bases and by the obvious operating cost of the kamikaze raids themselves. Although their own surrender later preempted an invasion of their homeland, the Japanese husbanded resources for a kamikaze campaign against it. On the war's last day, Admiral Ugaki died in a failed kamikaze mission, and Admiral Onishi committed suicide.

Pilots and Planes

One reason for Japan's conservation of resources for an expected invasion of its homeland was an increasing lack of trained fliers. Japanese leaders embraced the kamikaze strategy in part because relatively unskilled pilots could be used. Up until the Okinawa fighting, Japanese pilots willfully sacrificed themselves to national adoration. However, the continued loss of pilots required ever more replacements. This relentless operational toll spurred more aggressive recruiting, and Japanese army aviation units eventually drafted nonvolunteers to fly kamikaze missions. However, a desire to avoid shaming one's peers, family, and emperor amid Japan's desperate situation ensured deliberate sacrifice by all, including conscripts.

Although Japan's fuel and aircraft construction problems hindered the kamikaze effort somewhat, kamikaze planes needed only to crash into their target, therefore the shortages had less effect than they might have in a conventional air campaign. Although the Japanese kamikazes used many types of airplane, such as twin-engine bombers, dive-bombers, trainers, and even seaplanes, they most often used the venerable Mitsubishi Zero fighter. Kamikaze planes usually carried bombs for extra destructive effect.

The Japanese created a specially designed suicide plane, the Okha, or Cherry Blossom, which the Americans nicknamed "Baka," or "Crazy." Launched from a bomber plane's belly, the Okha's small rockets initially propelled it for a high-speed glide, with target impact detonating a warhead in its nose. Okhas and their "Thunder God" pilots achieved moderate success, but often their bomber carriers were shot down before they reached the Okhas' fifteen-mile range.

Tactics

Kamikaze units carefully considered their tactics. Reconnaissance planes located American ships and helped guide the kamikazes, who favored traveling in formations in order to mass their overall attack. Experienced fighter pilots escorted the formations to provide navigational assistance, protection, and after-action reports. Given strong American defenses, kamikaze formations sometimes snuck toward their targets by following American carrier planes returning home. Additionally, attacks from land, as during the Lingayen Gulf amphibious operations, allowed kamikazes a better element of surprise than did attacks from the sea, as at Okinawa. Kamikazes preferred twilight attacks, in which low visibility hindered the defenders target spotting, although it could also hinder the kamikazes as well.

Once in the target area, the formations split up for individual attacks. Kamikaze forces would have liked to mass their attacks against their prized targets, aircraft carriers. However, a combination of too few kamikazes, too many carriers, and too strong air defenses often prevented this strategy. Kamikazes apparently picked the best vessels available as they encountered swarming fighters and a hail of defensive fire. During the Okinawa campaign, for example, destroyers on the U.S. fleet's defensive perimeter were popular targets.

The kamikazes preferred either high-altitude, steep-dive attacks, or very low target runs culminating in a pop-up climbing maneuver that went into a steep dive. Sometimes, they quickly shifted away from one ship to strike another one nearby. In order to maximize damage, they tried to hit aircraft carrier elevators and ships' superstructures. Some even strafed their targets during their final approach. For all this effort, however, the mission's inexorable attrition degraded tactical sophistication as more inexperienced pilots became kamikazes.

Defenses

Intense kamikaze assaults such as those at Lingayen Gulf and Okinawa shook Allied sailors who had never experienced this type of warfare and understood that the only way to prevent being hit was to destroy a kamikaze plane outright. Lesser-caliber guns that scored well against conventional attacks failed to stop a determined kamikaze, and concentrated barrage fire by guns of 5-inch caliber or greater was a better solution. However, even small-caliber guns had some effect as long as gunners led their target and sustained fire.

The United States used airplanes against the kamikazes; fighters intercepted them and bombers attacked kamikaze airfields. One reason kamikazes attacked the destroyers on the outer perimeter of the Okinawa invasion fleet was that these ships controlled the interceptor fighters. Kamikaze formations, with their inferior planes and their pilots' inexperience and resolve to press on toward their targets, were decimated by the Americans. Indeed, U.S. Navy fighter aces such as Commander Eugene Valencia achieved impressive aerial victory tallies during the Okinawa fighting. Airfield attacks eased the kamikaze scourge at Lingayen Gulf and Okinawa.

Damage-control strengths, such as the Americans' water fog firefighting technique, also saved stricken ships. The aircraft carrier USS *Bunker Hill* endured an attack that killed four hundred crew members. British carriers with armored flight decks better withstood kamikaze hits than their unarmored American counterparts. Finally, many ships survived because kamikazes hit their upper superstructures instead of their hulls, nearer to the waterline. Kamikazes also lacked the mass and velocity of a well-directed heavy shell or properly released bomb.

Overall Air Campaign Results

Kamikaze air attacks were costly to both sides. Although kamikaze missions took many Allied ships and sailors, they also required the attackers' self-destruction. For a loss of nearly 4,000 aircrew, over 3,000 kamikaze sorties scored roughly 360 hits on about 350 different boats and ships. Of these, fifty-six sank, including three small escort carriers, seventeen destroyers, and dozens of transports. Eight large aircraft carriers, five smaller carriers, and six battleships were among the many vessels whose damage required at least some time away from combat. Total human casualty estimates vary, but the Okinawa kamikaze campaign alone resulted in the deaths of approximately 3,000 U.S. Navy sailors.

For all the havoc wreaked by kamikazes, the United States possessed the resources to overcome it. Further, kamikaze attacks incurred an assured depletion of Japan's own air forces. As the statistics show, kamikazes more frequently crashed or were shot down than achieved their objectives. Still, they confronted Americans with an unprecedented level of commitment that at times adversely affected American sailors' morale. This commitment may have seemed foolhardy to the Allies, but it served as a human model for late-twentieth century mechanical "smart" weapons. It also convinced Americans that an invasion of Japan would involve heavy casualties.

Douglas Campbell

Bibliography

Hoyt, Edwin. *Japan's War: The Great Pacific Conflict, 1853 to 1952.* New York: Da Capo Press, 1986. A nice historical overview of Japanese militarism and warfare philosophies.

_____. *The Last Kamikaze*. Westport, Conn.: Praeger, 1993. A biography of the honor-bound admiral who led the Okinawa kamikaze air campaign.

Inoguchi, Rikhei, Tadashi Nakajima, and Roger Pineau. *The Divine Wind*. Annapolis, Md.: Naval Institute Press, 1958. A valuable classic, in which two kamikaze unit leaders tell their story, focusing primarily upon Admiral Onishi's efforts.

Millot, Bernard. *Divine Thunder*. Translated by Lowell Blair. New York: McCall, 1971. A good short survey of the overall kamikaze effort.

Naito, Hatsuho. *Thunder Gods*. Translated by Boye De Menthe. Tokyo: Kodansha International, 1989. The Okha units' human side, including the stresses and internal frictions that sometimes shook the pilots' attitudes toward their mission and leaders.

Seno, Sadao, Denis Warner, and Peggy Warner. *The Sacred Warriors*. New York: Van Nostrand Reinhold, 1982. A very good detailed survey of the kamikaze campaign from both American and Japanese perspectives.

See also: Aircraft carriers; Fighter pilots; Navy pilots, U.S.; Pearl Harbor, Hawaii, bombing; Superfortress; World War II

Kennedy Space Center

Date: Established on March 7, 1962
Definition: The primary launch facility for the National Aeronautics and Space Administration.
Significance: All crewed spaceflights currently launch from the Kennedy Space Center. Additionally, KSC coordinates NASA missions launched from the adjacent Cape Canaveral Air Force Station.

History

After World War II, the United States began serious development of long-range missiles. Work to extend the range of missiles quickly encountered a major public safety issue. Missiles fired from existing test sites would have to fly over populated areas. Early missiles were inherently unsafe and unreliable, so civilian overflight was deemed unacceptable. A coastal or island launch facility was considered ideal, since flights over unpopulated ocean would result in minimal civilian risk. Many sites were considered. Soon, however, the Cape Canaveral area of Florida became the choice for most of the large missile tests. Cape Canaveral prominently juts out from Florida's eastern coastline. This provides a large margin for safety if a missile were suddenly to go off course. Furthermore, the area around the cape was marshy and had a low civilian population density. Despite its relative isolation, major roads, rail lines, and port facilities were nearby, so logistics were less of a difficulty at the Cape Canaveral site than many others suggested.

Limited tests were conducted in the Cape Canaveral area as early as 1947, but full-scale missile tests began in earnest in July, 1950. Missiles and rockets have been fired from Cape Canaveral ever since. The Cape Canaveral site began in 1940 as the Banana River Naval Air Station. The site was transferred to the Air Force in 1950 and renamed the Patrick Air Force Base. The launch facilities were designated the Atlantic Missile Range and the Missile Firing Laboratory. The launch facilities are now part of the Cape Canaveral Air Force Station, associated with the Patrick Air Force Base, under the jurisdiction of the Forty-fifth Space Wing.

Most early missiles, and nearly all intercontinental ballistic missiles (ICBMs), were tested at the Cape Canaveral launch facilities. Working under the principle promoted by Wernher von Braun, the chief missile designer in the United States, each launch facility was built for a different type of missile. Fueling equipment, servicing equipment, and a service tower, called a gantry, were all built specifically for each rocket. Furthermore, control systems for each rocket were housed near the launch pad in a reinforced concrete bunker called a blockhouse. Missiles and rockets were generally assembled at the launch site, so each launch complex required vehicle assembly equipment. Each launch complex received a numerical designation, based on the order of its construction.

When the United States made the decision to send humans into space, it made sense to use the facilities at Cape Canaveral to launch the rockets carrying the astronauts. Launch Complexes 5 and 6 served as the launch sites for the first U.S. crewed spacecraft, the Mercury/Redstone flights. With the decision to go forward with the Apollo Program, Launch Complexes 34 and 37 were constructed to test the Saturn I rockets.

Launch Operations Center Establishment

Two key factors played a role in the creation of a separate launch facility for the crewed spaceflight program. One of these factors was a Department of Defense study in April, 1960, in which the Atlantic Missile Range was described as being nearly saturated with launch facilities. Additional facilities could not be built on site without the safety hazard of overflying other launch facilities. A second factor was the directive associated with the National Aeronautics and Space Act of 1958, in which a separate civilian space organization, the National Aeronautics and Space Administration (NASA), was created and dedicated to the peaceful exploration of space. While NASA continued to use Department of Defense facilities at Cape Canaveral for the Gemini missions and early Apollo tests using the Saturn I rocket, various government officials felt strongly that NASA should have its own launch facilities.

In selecting a launch site for the rockets used for the Apollo Program, NASA was faced with several considerations. The farther south the launch site was located, the easier it would be to launch a spacecraft into an equatorial orbit around Earth. Furthermore, a launch site from which spacecraft could be launched in an easterly direction would enable the rocket to use Earth's eastward rotation to assist in achieving the necessary velocity for Earth orbit. Numerous sites were studied, including several Pacific islands as well as barrier islands off Georgia and Texas. Ultimately, the logistic capabilities, together with the need to use some of the tracking systems of the Atlantic Missile Range, led NASA to a site adjacent to the Cape Canaveral Air Force Station (CCAFS). Shortly after the selection of the Cape Canaveral site, NASA acquired over 111,000 acres on Merritt Island, just northwest of CCAFS. On March 7, 1962, NASA made the Launch Operations Center a separate NASA field center, and was made the controlling entity for the new Merritt Island Launch Area on January 17, 1963. The launch area was designated Launch Complex 39. On November 29, 1963, the Launch Operations Center was renamed the John F. Kennedy Space Center (KSC) in honor of the assassinated president a mere week after his death. Cape Canaveral was also renamed Cape Kennedy at this time, but in 1973 the state of Florida changed the name back to Cape Canaveral. KSC headquarters moved to Merritt Island on July 26, 1965, and KSC became a fully functioning space center.

Though a separate facility, KSC continued use of launch complexes constructed at CCAFS for launches of uncrewed missions until 1990. During 1989 and 1990, control over uncrewed launches shifted from KSC to the Air Force and to rocket manufacturers. Most of the uncrewed NASA missions, however, are still launched from CCAFS, and payload processing often occurs at KSC, though the launch itself is no longer under KSC direct control.

Launch Complex 39

The heart of KSC is Launch Complex 39, designed initially for the Saturn V rockets, but adapted for use with the space shuttle. Launch Complex 39 has two virtually identical launch pads, 39-A and 39-B. Earlier rockets were generally assembled at the launch pad, fueled, and then launched. Such an approach was fine for the smaller rockets. However, the time needed to assemble the massive rockets needed for lunar missions would require a launch pad to be tied up for many months. Additionally, the corrosive, salty ocean spray and the potential for tropical storms at Cape Canaveral made a spacecraft exposed on the launch pad susceptible to damage. Launch Complexes 34 and 37 at CCAFS had louvers on a mobile service structure to protect the spacecraft. The Moon rockets would be too large, however, for that approach to protecting them. Additionally, with pads tied up for months, it was projected that NASA would need up to several dozen launch pads. A better, less expensive approach was needed.

The solution was to build a Vehicle Assembly Building (VAB) a safe distance from the launch pad. The rocket would be assembled in the VAB while sitting on a Mobile Launch Platform (MLP) which would then be transported to the launch pad when the craft was completed. Three MLPs were constructed. A Mobile Service Structure (MSS) was used with the Saturn V rockets to prepare them for launch. The MSS was removed prior to launch, and the gantry at launch was part of the MLP. The MLP system was redesigned for the space shuttle without the large gantry. A Fixed Service Structure (FSS) is now built at each launch pad, which contains orbiter crew access and umbilical arms for fueling the space shuttle. Attached to the FSS is a Rotating Service Structure (RSS) that swings into position to cover the orbiter while it is on the launch pad, permitting access and servicing of the payload bay. A system of flame deflectors and trenches channels rocket exhaust away from the rocket as it takes off.

Vehicle Assembly Building

To protect the Saturn V during assembly, and to promote a faster launch pad turn around, the Vehicle Assembly Building was constructed. The VAB, one of the largest buildings ever built, covers 8 acres of land, and measures 716 feet long, 518 feet wide, and 525 feet tall. It consists of four high bays and a low bay. The high bays were originally used to assemble the Saturn V. Two bays are now used to mate the space shuttle orbiter with the solid rockets and the external fuel tank. The other two bays are used for external tank checkout and storage, solid-rocket contingency handling, and orbiter contingency storage. The low bay is used for engine maintenance shops and as a storage area for certain solid-rocket aerodynamic parts.

Launch Control Center

Advances in electronics technology by the time of the Apollo Program meant that launch control no longer needed to be housed in a blockhouse adjacent to the launch pad. Thus, KSC's launches are directed from the Launch Control Center (LCC) located over three miles away from the launch pads. The LCC is a multilevel building containing offices, computers, and data analysis equipment on the first three levels. Offices and conference rooms are on the fourth level. The third level contains the firing rooms, where launches are directed. Two firing rooms are fully operational and can be used to direct launches. The other two are used for software development and analysis and for data and engineering analysis. Controllers have a view of the launch pads from large windows at one end of the firing rooms. Large, heavy steel shutters are designed to close rapidly to protect the windows in the event of a catastrophic accident at the launch pad.

Shuttle Landing Facility

The Shuttle Landing Facility (SLF) is essentially an airport-like facility for the space shuttle. Its main feature is a 15,000-foot-long, 300-foot-wide runway on which the space shuttle can land upon returning from orbit. Adjacent to the runway is a Recovery Staging Area where a convoy of recovery vehicles can wait for the shuttle to land. These vehicles extract the poisonous fuels from the shuttle and make sure that there are no poisonous vapors in the area prior to crew egress. Also adjacent to the runway is the Orbiter Processing Facility (OPF), where the orbiter can be serviced. The OPF has facilities to mate or remove the orbiter from the back of a modified Boeing 747 used as a transport between NASA facilities.

Transporters

To carry various components and equipment from place to place within the facility, KSC has a variety of transporters. Most have special functions, such a solid-rocket transporter, an orbiter transporter, or a payload-canister transporter. The most impressive, however, are the two oldest transporters used, the crawler transporters (CTs). The CTs, originally designed to carry the MLP from the VAB to the launch pads carrying the Saturn V, now carry the MLP with a space shuttle on board to the launch pad. Moving at about one mile per hour, the CT is 131 feet long and 113 feet wide, and carries loads as heavy as 12 million pounds. The crawler is able to deliver the MLP to its proper position to within 2 inches precision. Each crawler is able to travel about 35 feet per gallon of diesel fuel.

The Future

As the United States' spaceport, KSC is looking ahead to the next-generation launch vehicle that will replace the space shuttle. The modular design of Launch Complex 39 permits great flexibility in adapting to new launch vehicles. Unlike previous launch complexes that generally became obsolete along with the rocket that they were originally designed for, Launch Complex 39 was readily adapted from Saturn V operations to space shuttle operations. Thus, it is expected that similar adaptations would be possible for most of the foreseeable designs of launch vehicles in the coming decades.

Raymond D. Benge, Jr.

Bibliography

Benson, Charles D., and William Barnaby Faherty. *Moonport: A History of Apollo Launch Facilities and Operations*. NASA SP-4204. Washington, D.C.: Government Printing Office, 1978. A very thorough history of KSC through the Apollo Program.

Kennedy Space Center. *The Kennedy Space Center Story*. Kennedy Space Center, Fla.: Author, 1974. A very good overview of the origins of KSC.

_____. *KSC Transporters*. Kennedy Space Center, Fla.: Author, 2000. A short pamphlet in the NASA Facts series about the unique KSC crawler/transporters.

_____. *Launch Complex 39 Pads A and B*. Kennedy Space Center, Fla.: Author, 1999. A short pamphlet in the NASA Facts series about the major launch facilities at KSC.

National Aeronautics and Space Administration. *America's Spaceport: John F. Kennedy Space Center*. Washington, D.C.: Government Printing Office, 1994. A short but informative pamphlet about KSC.

See also: Air Force, U.S.; Apollo Program; Wernher von Braun; Crewed spaceflight; Mercury project; Missiles; National Aeronautics and Space Administration; Rockets; Saturn rockets; Space shuttle; Spaceflight

Kites

Definition: A heavier-than-air, flexible, fabric structure or lightweight, covered frame flown at the end of a long line.

Significance: As the first heavier-than-air device to fly, the kite has contributed to humans' understanding of flight. Over a long and rich history, the kite has in-

The Wright brothers first tested their gliders by flying them as kites before experimenting with engines. Here Orville and Wilbur Wright fly a glider in September, 1900. (Hulton Archive)

grained itself in the folklore, religion, celebration, military, art, science, sport, and recreation of many cultures.

History and Evolution

Kites have played a special role in the folklore, legend, art, recreation, and religious ceremony of many cultures. As the first heavier-than-air flight vehicle, the kite also has been used in science and military applications.

The first documented evidence suggests kites originated in China more than 2,500 years ago. Originally constructed from bamboo and silk, kites became more widespread with the development of inexpensive paper in the second century C.E. Buddhist missionaries most likely introduced the kite to Japan and Korea, from where it spread to Indonesia and the Malay Peninsula. By the year 700, kites had been introduced to the Middle East and were used in recreation and in a sport known as "fighting kites." The explorer Marco Polo noted seeing both kite flying and crewed kites in thirteenth century Asia. Through trade routes, kites reached Europe in the early Middle Ages and were brought to the United States from both Europe and Asia.

Military Uses

Over its long history, kites have been used by militaries around the world to signal, carry messages and food to troops, to carry out crewed aerial observations, and for rescue. About 200 B.C.E., a Chinese general attached a humming device to a kite. When it was flown overhead at night, the enemy, believing the sounds came from evil spirits preparing to attack, fled. Another Chinese general used a kite to measure the distance between his troops and an enemy palace. Early Japanese prints depict archers carried by large kites.

In the mid- to late 1800's, kites were used by the British military. In 1897, a young officer, Captain B. F. S. Baden-Powell, built a 36-foot kite to be used for crewed aerial observations over enemy territory. Baden-Powell also developed a series of tandem kites. In 1901, Samuel F. Cody patented a kite system for crewed observations; the system included a basket which could support the weight of a person. Although further major developments in crewed kite flight were stunted by the introduction of crewed powered flight by the Wright brothers in 1903, the Germans used crewed aerial observation kites from submarines in World War I and World War II.

Science

Kites have been used in scientific investigations of climate and weather, aerodynamics, and electricity. In 1752, statesman and inventor Benjamin Franklin used a kite for his famous investigation into the nature of electrical charges in clouds. Kites have been used in climatic and meteorological studies. The U.S. Weather Bureau has used large box-type kites flown on piano wire that have reached altitudes over 31,000 feet. A variety of meteorological instruments, such as thermometers, anemometers, and barometers, have been attached to kites to investigate temperature, wind speed, and pressure differences at different altitudes.

Sir George Cayley, who developed the first practical glider, flew those gliders as kites. Alexander Graham Bell, the inventor of the telephone, used kites to study weather and to understand flight. He developed the tetrahedral cell, a strong, light-framed kite capable of supporting a person in the air. Early aviation pioneers such as Otto Lilienthal, Octave Chanute and the Wright brothers used kites to experiment with and learn about forces, stability, and control. The Wright's early airplane attempts were flown as kites.

Cultural Importance

Throughout many centuries and cultures, kites have been used in recreation, religious ceremony, celebration, hunting and fishing, sports, and as art. Throughout the world, kite festivals are held annually. These events educate participants and teach kite building and flying, as well as providing an exciting recreational activity.

From the time of the kite's invention, early Chinese drawings depict elegantly sculptured and beautifully decorated kites. Some cultures have used kites to communicate with spirits or gods. In Thailand, kites have been used to ask the gods for good weather and crops. In some cultures, kites are associated with good luck. It is believed when the line of the kite is cut, the kite takes away bad luck or evil spirits. In Japan, one form of kite, called a windsock, is made in the shape of a carp fish, which symbolizes the strength and will to overcome great obstacles. In ancient Rome, windsock banners designed to look like dragons were used for military and religious purposes. Koreans fly kites to announce the birth of a child. European hunters used kites to flush birds from bushes. In the Solomon Islands, kites have been used in fishing.

In the late 1990's, a new extreme sport, kite boarding, was introduced in Europe and spread rapidly throughout the world. Large, harnessed kites pull individuals on boards, similar to surf boards, across water or even snow. At the highest competitive level, professional athletes perform exciting acrobatics with these kites.

Kite Flight

Kites, like other flight vehicles, have different shapes, sizes, and components based on the mission or type of work the kite will perform. Although the variations are endless, basic forms include flat, bowed, box, cellular, and semirigid or nonrigid (soft fabric shape). Regardless of the shape, for a kite to fly, the aerodynamic forces of lift, drag, and the kite's weight must be balanced. The movement of air across the kite's surfaces provides the pressure to balance the kite's forces. Extensions to the kite, such as tails, drogue cups, or cones, add stability and balance to the kite.

Jani Macari Pallis

Bibliography

Wiley, Jack, and Suzanne L. Cheatle. *Dynamic Kites*. 2d ed. Blue Ridge Summit, Pa.: Tab Books, 1988. This book describes the basic aerodynamics of kites with extensive information regarding the design, materials, and construction of a wide range of kites.

Thomas, Bill, *The Complete World of Kites*. Philadelphia: J. B. Lippincott, 1977. Very through and comprehensive treatment of the history and uses of kites throughout many cultures.

Morgan, Paul, and Helene Morgan. *The Ultimate Kite Book*. New York: Simon & Schuster, 1992. Beautifully illustrated and photographed, this book reviews the history of kites and clearly describes the technical differences between the wide variety of modern kites.

See also: Aerodynamics; Octave Chanute; Forces of flight; Heavier-than-air craft; History of human flight; Wright brothers

KLM

Also known as: KLM Royal Dutch Airlines, Koninklijke Luchtvaart Maatschappij, N. V.

Date: Founded and incorporated in the Netherlands on October 7, 1919

Definition: One of the world's first scheduled international airlines.

Significance: As the oldest continously operating scheduled airline, Koninklijke Luchtvaart Maatschappij (KLM) is the national flag carrier of the Netherlands. With its partner airlines, it serves more than 150 destinations in seventy countries on six continents.

Origins

In 1919, the young Dutch military aviator Albert Plesman founded KLM with support from both industry and government to establish the national airline for the Netherlands. From its early beginnings, KLM had strong government assistance. The Kingdom of the Netherlands had granted the fledgling aviation enterprise the right to bear the "Royal" title as part of its designation. Actual government participation in the company has varied over the years from a majority shareholder position in the early days to about a 14 percent stake in 2001.

Routes and Expansion

KLM began scheduled service on May 17, 1920, with flights between Amsterdam and London. Four years later, the airline initiated its first intercontinental flights to Indonesia, one of the Dutch colonies. From that point on, KLM's route structure expanded steadily until World War II, when all regular flight operations were suspended. During the German occupation of the Netherlands, the KLM headquarters was moved to Indonesia, and only a few unscheduled flights took place.

After the war, scheduled service resumed, and in May of 1946, KLM opened transatlantic services to the United States. During the decades that followed, new services were added to North and South America, Asia, Africa, and some parts of the Caribbean. After airline deregulation in the United States (1978) and initial efforts toward liberalization in Europe, KLM management began to concentrate on establishing partnerships to expand the KLM network. By 2000, KLM and its national and international partners operated a route network connecting about 150 cities in more than seventy countries on six continents.

Fleet and Safety

KLM entered service with a chartered De Havilland DH-16 in 1920. With government support, the KLM fleet grew steadily. Until World War II, the carrier operated aircraft predominantly manufactured by the Dutch company Fokker. After the war, the KLM fleet was rebuilt, mainly with American Douglas and Lockheed aircraft. In 2000, KLM expanded its fleet from 68 aircraft in 1946 to more than 120 airliners, including aircraft owned by its immediate partners. At the beginning of the twenty-first century, KLM's fleet consists mostly of Boeing aircraft, such as the 737 and the 747.

During the decades following World War II, KLM lost several Douglas and Lockheed aircraft in air crashes. Especially notable was KLM's involvement in the world's most deadly aviation accident, the collision of a KLM B-747 and a Pan Am B-747 on March 27, 1977, on a foggy runway at Tenerife Airport, Canary Islands. In the ensuing carnage, 583 people were killed, and nearly all of the survivors were injured to a significant degree.

Following this collision, KLM's safety record improved significantly. In the period from 1978 to 2000, the company lost only one aircraft, a Saab 340, belonging to KLM Cityhopper, the KLM regional carrier. One crewmember and two passengers were killed in that crash.

Company Strategy and Alliances

Beginning in the late 1970's, KLM's management decided to diversify the company to manage the cyclical nature of the airline industry. Hotel chains, technical services, and management consulting became part of the overall busi-

---

Events in KLM History

1919: The Koninklijke Luchtvaart Maatschappij (KLM) is incorporated in The Hague, Netherlands.

1920: First scheduled KLM flight is made from London to Amsterdam.

1924: Scheduled flights begin between Amsterdam and the Dutch colonies in Indonesia.

1946: KLM begins transatlantic services to New York.

1959: The first jet aircraft, a DC-8, enters service at KLM.

1969: The first widebody aircraft, a Boeing 747, is introduced at KLM.

1977: KLM 747 collides with a Pan Am 747 on a runway at Tenerife Airport, Canary Islands, resulting in one of the worst air disasters in history, with 583 causalities.

1989: KLM acquires an equity stake in Northwest Airlines.

1997: KLM sells participation in NWA but maintains a long-term joint-venture agreement.

1998: KLM establishes far-reaching alliance with Alitalia, which it terminates the following year.

2001: KLM continues the search to become a major partner in a worldwide alliance.

ness activities at KLM. Other Dutch carriers, Martinair and Transavia Airlines, also became part of the overall KLM organization. By 2000, KLM's subsidiaries included the regional carrier KLM Cityhopper, KLM UK, Transavia, and Martinair. Main divisions included KLM Cargo and KLM Systems Services.

When air transportation liberalization efforts got underway in Europe in the 1990's, KLM decided to aggressively develop its hub in Amsterdam by establishing partnerships and alliances with numerous other airlines that would feed traffic into Schiphol Airport, KLM's home base. However, faced with the limited growth capabilities at its hub, KLM began to pursue a multihub system in the late 1990's to guarantee its growth potential into the new millenium.

One of the initial KLM alliances was with Northwest Airlines of the United States. KLM acquired a significant stake in this carrier in 1989 but later sold its equity position at a profit in 1997. KLM and Northwest remained global partners and signed a long-term joint venture agreement that same year. In 1998, KLM established another highly publicized alliance, with Alitalia, the national flag carrier of Italy. Unfortunately, the conditions of the agreement were not met, and KLM management decided to terminate the partnership. Challenges that continue to face KLM include competition on the transatlantic routes from American megacarriers, low-cost Far East carriers expanding their global reach, and integrators with one-stop-shopping freight services. To meet these challenges, KLM management decided to position the carrier as a potential partner in a worldwide airline alliance.

Willem J. Homan

Bibliography

"Airline of the Year." *Air Transport World*, February, 1998, 39-40. A description of the annual achievement award presented by *Air Transport World* in recognition of excellence in the airline industry.

Dienel, Hans-Liudger, and Peter Lyth, eds. *Flying the Flag: European Commercial Air Transport Since 1945*. New York: St. Martin's Press, 1998. An analysis of seven European flag carriers and their prosperity in the new age of globalization in the airline industry.

Hengi, Bi. *Airlines Worldwide*. 3d ed. Leicester, England: Midland, 2001. An excellent review of essential data on more than 350 airlines worldwide, with an overview of the different aircraft fleets.

Toy, Stewart, et al. "Flying High." *Business Week*, February 27, 1995, 90-91. An excellent overview of KLM's emerging global strategy and its partnership with Northwest Airlines during the early 1990's.

See also: Accident investigation; Air carriers; Alitalia; Fokker aircraft; Northwest Airlines; Runway collisions; Safety issues

Korean Air

Also known as: Korean Air Lines
Date: Beginning in 1962
Definition: A leading South Korean airline.
Significance: Although Korean Air is South Korea's flagship carrier, the company has also been plagued by several serious air disasters, including a famous incident in which a commercial airliner was shot down over Soviet airspace, killing all 269 people on board.

History and Fleet

In 1962, the South Korean government established a new airline to replace the former national carrier, Korean National Airlines. Korean Air Lines (KAL), as the fledgling company was then known, began to offer domestic flights and international flights to Hong Kong and China on Boeing 707's. Seven years later, the Hanjin Transport Group acquired the airline from the government and began to

---

Events in Korean Air Lines History

1962: The South Korean government establishes a new national carrier to replace the former carrier, Korean National Airlines.
1969: The Hanjin Group takes over operation of the government-owned Korean Air Lines (KAL).
1973: KAL begins using Boeing 747's on Pacific routes to Japan and the United States and inaugurates its first European route, to Paris.
1983: Straying off course, KAL flight 007 flies into Soviet airspace and is shot down by a Soviet fighter. All 269 people on board are killed.
1987: A bomb planted on a KAL 747 explodes in midair, and the plane crashes into the sea off Burma, killing all 115 people on board.
1997: A KAL flight crashes into a Guam hillside, killing 228 of the 254 people on board.
2000: KAL takes delivery of seventeen new aircraft, including Next Generation Boeing 737-800's and 777's, with further acquisition plans for the following year.

make changes, launching international flights to Japan and Southeast Asia. In 1973, KAL began to use Boeing 747's on their Pacific Ocean routes to Tokyo and the United States. The company also inaugurated KAL's first European route, a service to Paris, using the aging 707 aircraft. In 1984, the company shortened its name to Korean Air and unveiled a new look for its fleet: All the aircraft were repainted a sky blue color on top. Two years later, Korean Air began supplementing its fleet of Boeing 747's with McDonnell Douglas MD-11's. As the airline's passenger traffic has grown, the MD-11s are now used mainly in cargo operations. The airline's passenger fleet is now primarily composed of Boeing and Airbus aircraft, including Boeing 737's, 747's, and 777's and Airbus A330's.

Safety Record

Korean Air has been dogged by its safety record. One of Korean Air's most notable disasters happened on the night of September 1, 1983. Korean Air Lines Flight 007 took off from Anchorage, Alaska, on its way to Seoul, South Korea. The flight plan called for the flight to follow the northernmost international air traffic lane between Alaska and Japan, called R20. Instead, the flight deviated more than 200 miles to the northwest, flying over Soviet airspace.

Along R20, there are seven waypoints. After passing each of these waypoints, flights are supposed to check in with air traffic control and estimate their distance to the next waypoint. Throughout the flight, the jet reported as if it were on course, following the international air traffic lane well south of Soviet territory. However, the jet actually flew over sensitive Soviet military installations on the Kamchatka Peninsula and Sakhalin Island.

As the jet flew over the Kamchatka Peninsula, the Soviet Air Defense Forces monitored the flight's progress. Soviet fighters were scrambled over Kamchatka but were unable to intercept the plane before it passed back into international airspace on the other side of the peninsula. The plane continued on a southeastern course that took it straight over Sakhalin Island. Over Sakhalin, Soviet Air Defense Forces deployed at least four and as many as six Soviet interceptor planes. At 18:26 Greenwich mean time (GMT), one of the interceptor planes fired on KAL 007 and reported, "The target is destroyed."

Explanations for KAL 007

In the wake of the tragedy, analysts tried to account for the plane's deviation from its flight path, advancing four main sets of hypotheses. The first hypothesis suggested that the jet strayed due to causes beyond the control of the plane's flight crew. Scenarios involving equipment malfunction, crew incapacitation, or hijacking fall into this category. At first, Korean Air Lines officials suggested that a passenger's onboard use of a personal computer somehow could have interfered with the navigational equipment.

A second hypothesis proposed that innocent human error was to blame. Seymour Hersh's *The Target Is Destroyed: What Really Happened to Flight 007 and What America Knew About It* (1986) makes a strong argument that the flight engineer made an error of 10 degrees when initially programming the navigational system. Plotting the flight with a heading of longitude 139 degrees west, instead of longitude 149 degrees west, closely approximates the flight's actual path.

A third explanation posits that the crew deliberately flew into Soviet airspace, possibly to save time and fuel, or to fulfill a dare, or out of a misguided sense of adventure. Some commentators have noted that most Korean Air pilots, including KAL 007 pilot Captain Chun Byung In, are former South Korean air force pilots, who are trained to take risks. Most other airlines employ civilian pilots, who are specifically trained not to take risks.

The last hypothesis, and the Soviet Union's explanation for its actions, is that Flight 007 was conducting intelligence missions for the U.S. government. It should be noted that during 1983, the United States routinely flew missions in the area to gather intelligence about possible Soviet missile tests. Although many writers have produced cogent arguments to support each of these explanations, it is impossible to say with any certainty which of these hypotheses is correct.

Other Notable Disasters

Korean Air has suffered other incidents. On August 6, 1997, a Korean Air flight crashed into a hillside in Guam, killing 228 of the 254 people on board. A navigational aid called a glide slope was not working that day. The crew did not understand that the glide slope was out of service and descended below the approach profile, striking the hillside, about 3 miles short of the runway. It has been suggested that the pilot's English was not good enough to understand that the glide slope was unusable.

On March 15, 1999, a McDonnell Douglas MD-82 overran the runway at Pohang, South Korea. The accident occurred on the plane's second attempt to land in high winds and poor visibility. The aircraft broke into several pieces; fortunately, none of the 156 people aboard was killed.

Alexandra Ferry

Bibliography

Dallin, Alexander. *Black Box: KAL 007 and the Super-*

powers. Berkeley: University of California Press, 1985. An account of the downing of KAL Flight 007, focusing on the role the U.S. and Soviet superpowers played in the tragedy.

Hersh, Seymour M. *The Target Is Destroyed: What Really Happened to Flight 007 and What America Knew About It*. New York: Random House, 1986. An account of the ill-fated KAL Flight 007 that argues for navigational error as a factor in the incident.

Johnson, R. W. *Shootdown: Flight 007 and the American Connection*. New York: Viking Penguin, 1986. An account of the KAL Flight 007 incident that holds the flight was actually on an American surveillance mission over the Soviet Union.

See also: Accident investigation; Air carriers; Airbus; Boeing; McDonnell Douglas; Safety issues

Korean War

Date: From June 25, 1950, to July 27, 1953
Definition: War between U.S.-led U.N. forces supporting South Korea against Soviet-supported Communist Chinese and North Korean forces.
Significance: As the first jet-age war, the Korean conflict affirmed air power's decisive importance in modern warfare, but its conditions undid some air power expectations.

Overview

After World War II, the Korean Peninsula was divided into two countries, the Republic of Korea (ROK), supported by the United States, in the south, and the Democratic People's Republic of Korea (DPRK), with Soviet and Chinese backing, in the north. After Communist North Korea invaded South Korea on June 25, 1950, the United States led a U.N. effort to help South Korea repel the assault, supplying the vast majority of U.N. forces. At first, neither the United Nations nor the South Koreans were prepared for the North Korean onslaught, but desperate fighting enabled them to retain some of the southeastern peninsula near Pusan during the summer of 1950. The Americans' September 15, 1950, Inchon Landing, combined with a breakout from Pusan, helped the South Koreans to rout the North Koreans that autumn.

The United Nations then resolved to destroy the North Korean Army and to reunite Korea under its sponsorship. However, China, threatened by U.S. aggression in Asia, attacked U.N. forces in late autumn, 1950, forcing their lengthy retreat back into South Korea. The United Nations counterattacked in early spring, 1951, and had stabilized the lines near the prewar boundary by summer. The two sides entered protracted negotiations as their forces fought for limited advantage. The July 27, 1953, armistice terminated active hostilities.

Air Forces

Both sides in the Korean War fought for limited objectives, and the superpowers were concerned with defense needs elsewhere in their worldwide face-off. Thus, neither side fully committed its air forces to this fight. Also, the war occurred during a transition period in air warfare technology.

Thus, World War II-vintage, propeller-driven fighters, such as the Soviet Yak-9 and U.S. P-51 Mustang, did much of the early fighting for the respective sides. Other propeller planes, such as the A-1, Corsair, and British Sea Fury, also provided excellent service as attack planes throughout the war. Because the Americans did not commit their frontline strategic bombers to Korea, World War II-era B-29's accomplished most of the United Nations' long-range heavy bombing tasks. U.S. transport planes were mostly propeller-driven holdovers from the last war. The Communists even used P0-2 biplanes to fly nighttime nuisance attacks, nicknamed "Bedcheck Charlies," against U.N. forces.

Simultaneously, the Korean War introduced jets to air combat. U.S. F-80's and F-9F Panthers were among the straight-wing, subsonic jets that mostly flew attack missions. The most noteworthy jet development occurred with the appearance of the Soviet-built Mikoyan-Gurevich MiG-15. This swept-wing, transonic fighter seriously threatened the U.N. air effort until the Americans quickly fielded a counterpart, the F-86 Sabre jet. Jets such as the U.S. F-94 Starfire and F-3D Skyknight also served as radar-equipped night fighters.

The Korean War also witnessed the first extensive use of helicopters. These early, underpowered, piston-engine models flew light logistics missions. However, they also demonstrated impressive utility for rescue missions and covert operations.

Air War Conduct

The war's limited scope precluded nuclear weapons usage by both sides. Also, the combatant air arms attacked targets only in Korea, not Communist targets in the Soviet Union and China, or U.S. targets in Japan. Both sides thus emphasized tactical air combat, though each remained wary of the other's capacity to escalate the air war, and with it, the war itself.

At the war's start, U.S. fighters quickly vanquished the inexperienced North Korean Air Force, thus allowing attack planes to maul the North Korean Army's supply lines. These interdiction air raids, along with close air support (CAS) missions against frontline troops, were major factors in repelling the Communist invasion.

U.N. air forces pulverized North Korean transportation links during the autumn, 1950, U.N. advance. As they entered the war, the Chinese introduced the MiG-15, flown by Chinese and Soviet pilots, to check this effort. They failed partly because of the MiG's short range and partly because F-86 pilots were better trained. Although U.N. air raids destroyed Communist air bases in North Korea, MiG-15's could still fly from their safe havens in China and harrass U.N. planes in far northeast Korea, nicknamed "MiG Alley." The Chinese did have bombers, but they kept them only as an in-place air raid threat.

Air power was important in stopping the late-1950 Chinese advance. On two occasions, U.N. CAS and air supply saved large units surrounded by Communist armies. As the battle lines stabilized and truce talks stalemated, U.N. leaders approved several U.S. Air Force-led attempts to interdict the Communist supply lines. These interdictions inflicted serious damage and kept many troops and supplies from the front, but they did not compel capitulation or even perceptibly affect the truce talks. The Communists were

Korean War, 1950-1953

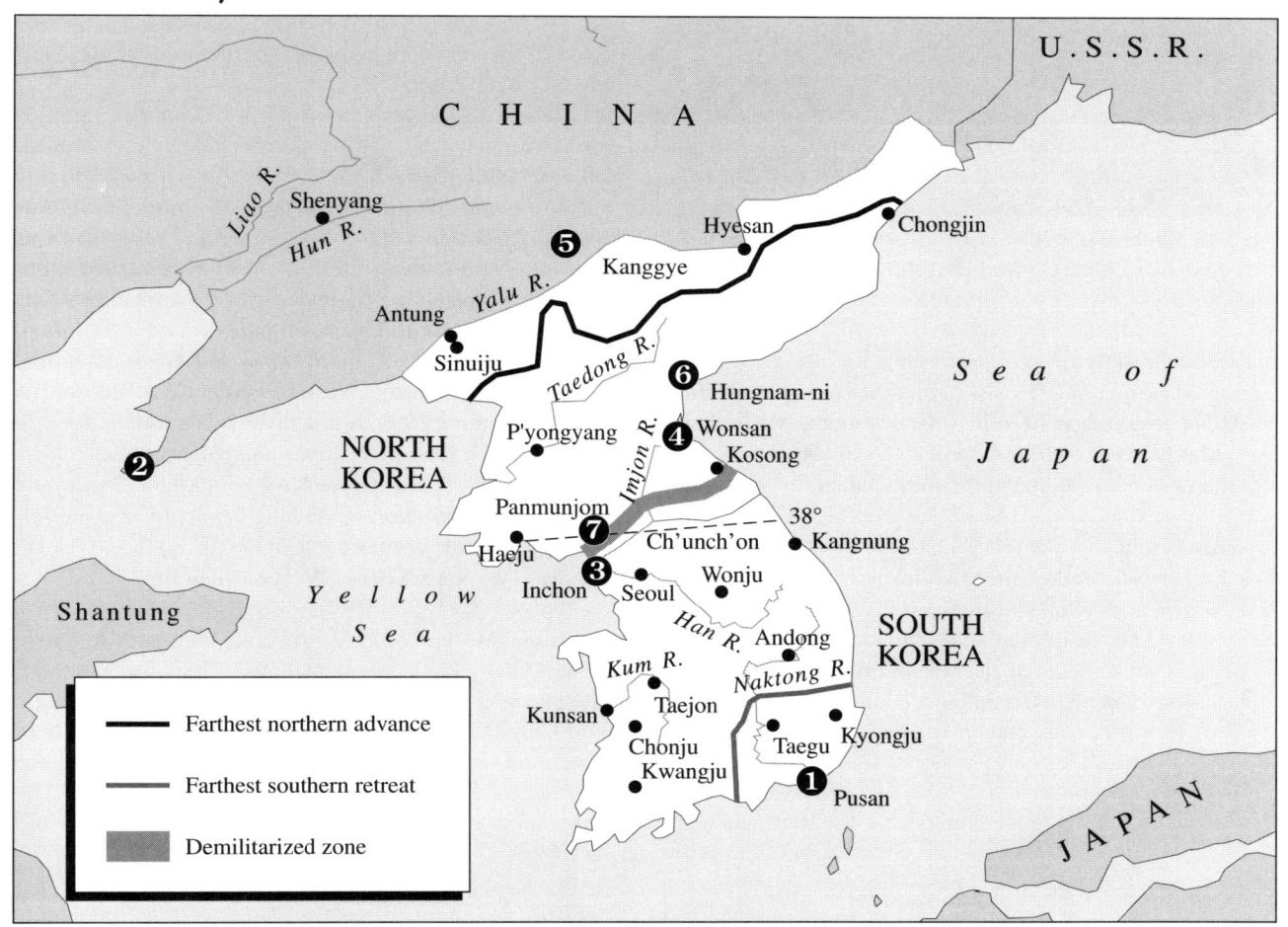

(1) Main U.N. base. (2) Russian-Chinese naval installation. (3) Sept. 15, 1950, U.N. forces land. (4) Oct. 8, 1950, U.N. forces land. (5) Nov. 26, 1950, Chinese attack. (6) Dec. 9, 1950, U.N. forces evacuate. (7) July 27, 1953, armistice signed.

The F-86 Sabre jet was deployed in the Korean War to counter the Soviet MiG-15 fighter. (AP/Wide World Photos)

masters of primitive improvisation, and because both sides attempted no major offensives, interdiction's true effect could not be assessed. More dramatic were the MiG Alley air battles between F-86's and MiG-15's, in which U.S. pilots increasingly dominated their opponents.

Air War Results

The Korean War ended after the death of Soviet dictator Josef Stalin and a veiled American threat to use nuclear weapons. U.N. aerial successes probably helped convince the Communists of the war's futility, but the later interdiction campaigns remained controversial because they did not meet their proponents' claims. Indeed, the war demonstrated that not all post-World War II conflicts would be decided exclusively by nuclear bombing campaigns by or conventional interdiction, as some air power advocates asserted.

Instead, the Korean War revealed an ever-widening air warfare spectrum. Per the air power ideal, jet fighters remained necessary to achieve air superiority, and heavy bombers and attack planes remained decisive with behind-the-lines attacks. However, in Korea, tactical missions such as CAS rose in importance. Aircraft carrier-based planes were especially valuable early in the war, when battle conditions eliminated land bases. The performance of helicopters did not match that of airplanes, but their utility showed great promise for future conflicts. Although U.S. leaders saw Korea as an aberration, they encountered similar conditions in the Vietnam War.

Douglas Campbell

Bibliography

Crane, Conrad. *American Airpower Strategy in Korea, 1950-1953*. Lawrence: University Press of Kansas, 2000. A well-documented work discussing the American air campaign's successes and shortcomings.

Futrell, Robert. *The United States Air Force in Korea, 1950-1953*. Reprint. Washington, D.C.: Office of Air Force History, 1996. A lengthy presentation of the U.S. Air Force's Korean War role and perspectives.

Hallion, Richard. *The Naval Air War in Korea*. Baltimore: Nautical & Aviation Publishing Company of America, 1986. A nicely written account of American and British naval aviation's Korean War contribution.

See also: Air Force, U.S.; Aircraft carriers; Bombers; Fighter pilots; Helicopters; Military flight; Superfortress; Vietnam War

Landing gear

Definition: Equipment that supports an aircraft on the ground, allows it to maneuver between runways and parking places, and supports the aircraft during takeoffs and landings.

Significance: Landing gear allows aircraft to move effectively around the surface and provides for safe takeoffs and landings.

Purpose

The weight of an airplane in flight is supported by the lift force on its wings. However, the airplane must pass through two transitional stages: takeoff, when the airplane leaves the ground, and landing, when it returns to the ground. The demands upon the landing gear during takeoffs differ from those during landings. During takeoffs, the airplane may accelerate to a speed of more than 140 miles per hour in a runway distance of less than 5,000 feet. Should the pilot stop the airplane during its takeoff run, the tires and brakes must sustain heavy mechanical friction loads without failure. During a routine takeoff, the landing gear must not only support the airplane but also respond to the pilot's directional commands. During landing, the wheels must absorb the descent speed of the airplane as it makes contact with the runway. The tires, on first contact with the runway, spin to a rotational speed that matches the airplane's landing speed. The brakes contained in the landing gear must then bring the airplane to a stop.

In the routine landing of heavy commercial airplanes, reverse thrust is obtained from the engines, whether propeller or jet. However, in an emergency, the brakes must be capable of stopping the airplane without any engine assistance.

Purpose

Airplanes have landing gear for three reasons: to maneuver the airplane along the ground, to support and control the direction of the airplane during takeoff until the lift on the wings is able to support the weight of the airplane, and to support the weight of the airplane during landing as the wings gradually lose lift. The wheels and the connecting structure must be able to absorb the vertical or descending speed of the airplane at the instant of touchdown. During the critical landing phase, the pilot must have sufficient skill to keep the descent rate within a small enough magnitude to prevent damage to the landing gear and the rest of the airplane. During takeoff and landing, the pilot must be able to control the airplane during both routine conditions and emergency conditions, such as tire blowouts.

Airplanes that operate from an aircraft carrier must have very strong and resilient landing gear. The relative velocity between the wheels and carrier deck might be much higher than that experienced by a land-based airplane and the course is not entirely under the control of the pilot.

In addition to the requirements of landing, takeoff, and ground maneuvering, some landing gear must be retracted into the airplane's wings or fuselage. Except for low-performance general aviation airplanes, retractable landing gear is a feature of nearly all modern airplanes. The reason for retracting the landing gear is to reduce aerodynamic drag that would otherwise be caused by the extended gear.

Because the space in either the wings or fuselage is limited, there is an incentive to limit the diameter of the wheels. To meet the airplane's takeoff, landing, and maneuvering requirements, the tire pressure can be as high as 200 pounds per square inch for typical military airplanes; the tires in commercial airplanes might be as high as 140 pounds per square inch. An important part of the design of an airplane's landing gear is the selection of the proper tire, and a significant part of the routine maintenance of an airplane is the regular inspection and replacement of tires.

Types of Landing Gear

The most obvious part of the landing gear is where and how the wheels are attached to the airplane. There are many common arrangements. In the so-called conventional arrangement, two main wheels are placed near the front of the airplane and well ahead of the airplane's center of gravity. A much smaller tail wheel is placed at the rear, just under the elevator. For the first four decades of powered flight, nearly all airplanes, both civil and military, used this arrangement. Except in some limited-production aerobatic, sport, or homebuilt airplanes, this wheel arrangement is no longer in use. The increasingly inappropriate term "conventional" has been replaced by the more descriptive term "tail-dragger."

Landing gear supports the plane on the ground, absorbs friction, and provides maneuverability during takeoff and landing. (NASA)

The tricycle arrangement has become the most common form of landing gear. In the tricycle gear, there is a wheel and strut placed forward, with the main wheel of the tail-dragger moved back past the center of gravity of the airplane. The tail-dragger arrangement, nevertheless, has certain advantages over the tricycle arrangement, one of which is that the presence of two rather than three wheels means less drag in flight. The tail-dragger arrangement also provides for better propeller clearance when the aircraft is on the ground. Because the tail-dragger lands at a higher angle relative to the wind, it can use more lift in the wing and consequently land at a lower speed and therefore require a shorter runway. Because of its lower landing speed, the tail-dragger might be better suited to rough-field landings.

The tail-dragger's disadvantage is the location of the center of gravity behind the main wheels, an inherently unstable condition. Unless quickly corrected, the response of a tail-dragger to a slight side motion, or drift, at landing is the ground loop, a maneuver in which the airplane turns suddenly to one side, rolling the airplane to touch down the opposite wingtip. Damage to airplane from a ground-loop can include a crushed wingtip or a collapsed landing gear. The tail-dragger pilot must have sufficient skill to keep the airplane completely aligned with the runway during landings, even at low speeds.

The advantage of the tricycle gear, used in most airplanes except heavily loaded transport aircraft or sailplanes, is the reduced likelihood of ground loops, as the center of gravity is ahead of the two main wheels. In addition, the pilot has better visibility on the ground. The cabin floor is horizontal on the ground, facilitating the loading of passengers and cargo.

The bicycle, or tandem-wheel, arrangement is a specialized arrangement occasionally used on military airplanes and common on sailplanes. The advantage is the reduced weight of a third wheel. Weight reduction is especially critical on aircraft intended for vertical takeoff, such as the Harrier jet.

Large transport airplanes often employ multiple-wheel arrangements to distribute the weight of the aircraft on the runway. The C-5A aircraft has a double wheel at the nose. In the rear, there are four sets of double bogies. A bogie is wheel arrangement in which the wheels are mounted one at each of the four corners of a cart. The center of the cart is strut-connected to the airplane.

Conclusion

An airplane's landing gear permits it to take off, land, and maneuver on the ground. The landing gear also allows control of the airplane during the critical landing and take-off operations and provides brake force as needed in emergency conditions. Although there are several types of landing gear arrangements depending upon the performance and weight of the airplane, the tricycle landing gear remains the most common.

Bibliography

Raymer, Daniel P. *Aircraft Design: A Conceptual Approach*. 3d ed. Reston, Va.: American Institute of Aeronautics and Astronautics, 1999. A comprehensive and up-to-date book on the design of airplanes directed at the engineering student, with many sections where the discussion is without complex mathematics. Chapter 11 on landing-gear design and implementation requires little more than high-school algebra.

Stinton, Darrel, *The Design of the Airplane*. New York: Van Nostrand-Reinhold, 1985. An excellent introduction to landing-gear design, especially for general aviation airplanes.

Taylor, John W. R. *The Lore of Flight*. New York: Crescent Books, 1974. A massive, well-illustrated, oversized book featuring nontechnical descriptions of airplanes and spacecraft, and covering controls and cockpit instruments.

See also: Airplanes; Flight control systems; Landing procedures; Pilots and copilots; Taxiing procedures

Landing procedures

Definition: Steps which, when followed, achieve the safe return of an aircraft from the sky to the surface.
Significance: Landings, an essential part of flight, allow little room for error, because speed, ground proximity, winds, and momentum must all be balanced for reasons of safety and economy.

Background

A common aviation joke attests that although takeoffs are optional, landings are mandatory. Although landings may seem effortless to nonpilots, landing procedures comprise a large portion of any student pilot's flight training. As student pilots become more comfortable and proficient at landings, however, they may treat them more lightly. The first aviators, who had no teachers, had to learn how to fly through trial and error. Some early fliers could commit their attention only to getting airborne and allowed landings to take care of themselves, often with tragic consequences. Landing procedures have an obvious purpose: to return the aircraft and its passengers safely to the surface. The first generation of pilots seemed happy to walk away after just about any landing.

Orville and Wilbur Wright equipped their first *Flyer* with skids instead of wheels, expecting the sands at Kitty Hawk, North Carolina, to intervene and soften the blow of the first landings and the area's average 16-mile-per-hour winds to allow the *Flyer* to touch down as slowly as possible. Fortunately, the brothers had gained previous landing experience with gliders designed similarly to their *Flyer*. However, the powered *Flyer* differed from the Wrights' earlier kites and gliders not only in its engine and propellers but also in its substantial pair of skids, which traversed the machine's length. Later versions of the *Flyer* repositioned the pilot from a prone to a seated position and strengthened the landing skids and their supports. Wheels remained absent from Wright airplanes until 1910, when the U.S. Army's purchase demanded specific modifications.

Pilots and designers learned quickly that landing was to be as new a science as was flight itself. At first, there were as many designs and combinations of skids and wheels as there were airplanes. For example, although the Wright brothers did not add wheels to the *Flyer* design until 1910, in 1909, Louis Blériot used two main wheels on a single axle under the engine and equipped his airplane with a non-steerable tailwheel. In the same year, the Antoinette airplane was built, with two main wheels behind the engine, a spoon-shaped skid poking ahead of the main wheels, and another skid beneath the tail. These skids absorbed the shock of landings performed by inexperienced pilots.

Landing Fields

Early aviators used landing fields that were, as their name implies, open fields, in which pilots could point their airplanes directly into the prevailing winds. This orientation ensured that each landing could be made directly into the wind, for early airplanes' controls were usually too weak or

Landing procedures

unbalanced to permit reliable crosswind landings. Crosswind landing capabilities are essential in modern airplanes, because runways long ago replaced landing fields. Whenever winds blow cleanly down the runway's length, crosswinds pose no challenge. The greater the wind's angle to a runway's centerline, the more skill a pilot must demonstrate to make a safe landing. Much of the reason for this difficulty is because airplanes in flight move about the concentration of mass that pilots call the center of gravity. If an airplane could be held off the ground by a cable attached at its center of gravity, it would remain balanced, with both wings and nose level. As runways became more prevalent after the 1930's, pilots had to develop techniques to prevent any crosswinds from pushing on their airplanes' vertical stabilizers. As an airplane slows after landing, side winds hit the vertical stabilizer, much as they fill the sail of a boat. More force concentrates on the tail, as the wind pushes against the entire airplane, and the tail moves downwind, as the nose swings in the opposite direction. As the airplane slows, the crosswind's force can become great enough that the rudder can no longer overcome it, causing the pilot to lose control and forcing the airplane off the runway. Crosswind landing techniques emerged to counter this threat.

Landing Techniques

The earliest and most basic landing technique involves the pilot crabbing the airplane into the wind until just a moment before touchdown. At the split second before the tires contact the runway, the pilot straightens the nose relative to the runway using the rudder. This technique causes the airplane's wheels to touch the surface with little sideload but requires that the airplane be stopped quickly. Because so many early airplanes were tailwheel types, quick stops were not always possible. Many airplanes ran off the runway, or ground-looped. However, the technique found wide acceptance on broad grass runways. From the 1950's on, more costly, and, therefore, more narrow, paved runways became the norm. Landing accidents increased, not because pavement was a more difficult landing medium to master, but because crosswind techniques on pavement required a crisper, more certain control technique.

In the days before airplanes had landing flaps, pilots could lose altitude quickly and safely by slipping, a technique wherein the pilot lowers one wing and keeps the airplane from turning by using the opposite rudder. The same technique, refined by a pilot's delicate touch, worked well to land an airplane in a strong crosswind. By lowering the wing into the wind, a pilot could use the airplane's lift to maintain position on a runway's centerline. Touching down on the upwind wheel allowed pilots to maintain directional control by using the rudder. An airplane's fuselage, no longer streamlined into the wind, provided welcome aerodynamic drag to slow the airplane quickly, so the moment between the flight controls losing effectiveness and the airplane slowing to the point that most crosswinds would not push the tail became minimum.

The point at which a wind becomes too strong to allow a proficient pilot to land safely is called the maximum crosswind component of the airplane's performance envelope. At end of the twentieth century, the U.S. Federal Aviation Administration (FAA) recognized only the slip-to-landing crosswind technique. Straightening the nose at the last moment required too unreliable a sense of timing and was simply less safe than the slip-to-landing technique.

The particular technique that a pilot uses to land an aircraft depends on several things, including the airplane's landing gear, the length of the runway, and the runway's surface. The three basic landing techniques are the normal landing, the soft-field landing, and the short-field landing.

Normal Landings. Pilots elect to make normal landings when the available runway length allows plenty of room, there are no obstructions to approach, and the runway surface is smooth, hard, and dry. Practiced normal landings appear effortless to observers but require much skill and judgment on the part of the pilot. Student pilots normally begin their flight training with normal landings, the simplest of landing techniques.

In normal landings, pilots must align their airplanes with the runway centerline and, maintaining an appropriate airspeed, plan a stable approach path to the runway. Airspeed control is critical during all types of landings, because the goal is always to touch down with as little downward motion as possible in order to prevent damage to the landing gear. The second critical part of landing is airspeed control. If the airspeed is too slow on approach, the pilot may lose control of the airplane. If the airspeed is too fast, the pilot may not be able to touch down at the appropriate point, using up too much runway and damaging the airplanes at the end of the runway.

Soft-Field Landings. Soft-field landings require a high degree of pilot awareness, because the pilot essentially handles the controls as if to keep the airplane flying until the wings simply stop producing enough lift for flight. This procedure must be timed so that all of the aircraft's wheels touch the runway surface at the same moment. After the wheels touch, the pilot must apply just enough power to reduce the nosewheel's pressure on the runway by applying back pressure on the stick, or yoke, by pulling the stick forward with very light hand pressure. The pilot continues to apply back pressure until the airplane slows so much that the weight of the nose finally rests fully on the rolling nosewheel.

Because there are so many types of runway surfaces, pilots must use extreme care and near-faultless judgment to analyze and properly land on a soft field. Pilots must avoid portions of the runway that might damage their airplanes. Obstacles such as broken concrete, badly eroded asphalt, snow packed to iceberg hardness, or windborne debris can contaminate a landing field. Special caution is also essential on grass or dirt runways after a rain. Muddy surfaces can stop an airplane so suddenly as to flip the airplane over.

Short-Field Landings. Pilots use the short-field landing technique when a runway is shorter than normal. Short-field landings demand skill and practice, because they require pilots to touch down on or near a specific point at the lowest safe airspeed. After all wheels have made contact with the surface, pilots must apply heavy braking to stop the airplane in the shortest distance. Successful short-field landings require a pilot's heavy reliance on the pilot's skill and judgment. Student pilots practice short-field landings throughout most of their training, and their flight instructors emphasize them with increasing frequency as students approach their practical test. Airspeed control, pitch attitude control, and power control blend together through the pilot's hand in a ballet of momentum management that ends in a thrilling dissipation of energy.

U.S. Navy pilots are, in effect, making short-field landings when they land on aircraft carriers. They rely on shipboard signal officers, who manually signal essential corrections, as they concentrate on lighted approach-slope aids. A properly flown approach to the short field of an aircraft carrier results in the airplane's tailhook grabbing a landing cable, which slows the airplane violently but certainly on a pitching, rolling runway. A civilian pilot has only the airplane's brakes and flap retraction to stop the airplane on the runway after the pilot's visual judgment places the airplane on its touchdown point.

Regardless of the type of landing a pilot selects, consistency is the key to success. Pilots attain and maintain consistency by keeping in practice. U.S. regulations have long required pilots to have landed at least three times within the ninety days preceding a flight carrying passengers.

Landings have fulfilled aviators, met schedules, thrilled passengers, and even saddened those experiencing flight's end. Aviation has inspired poets in most of its aspects, but landings have received rare poetic treatment. In 1956, F. Pratt Green recounted his emotion at the moment of landing, and of exiting the airplane to meet loved ones at the fence in his five-part poem "Return to Earth."

Odd, then, that to alight on a runway
was to die another death. Required
to declare our love, we found nothing
to say to those who at barriers waited
to embrace us. Our return to earth,
we felt, was to be mourned, not fêted.

David R. Wilkerson

Bibliography

Roberts, Joseph, and Paul Briand, eds. *The Sound of Wings: Readings for the Air Age.* New York: Henry Holt, 1957. A collection of prose and poetry covering the history of aviation from its inception to the rocket age.

Taylor, John, ed. *The Lore of Flight.* New York: Mallard Press, 1990. A thorough and informative historical overview of most aspects of aviation, including landing-gear design development. Profusely illustrated with line and color drawings and photographs.

Wright, Orville. *How We Invented the Airplane.* Reprint. New York: Dover, 1988. An unabridged republication of the 1953 work edited by Fred C. Kelly and written in 1920 by Orville Wright. Illustrated with photos discovered up to 1988.

See also: Aircraft carriers; Airplanes; Airports; Landing gear; Pilots and copilots; Runway collisions; Takeoff procedures; Training and education; Wright brothers; Wright *Flyer*

Samuel Pierpont Langley

Date: Born on August 22, 1834, in Roxbury, Massachusetts; died on February 27, 1906, in Aiken, South Carolina

Definition: Late nineteenth century American scientist who made important contributions to aerodynamics, astrophysics, and meteorology.

Significance: Through pioneering research in aerodynamics, Langley established the principles of flight and demonstrated the practicability of mechanical flight with self-propelled heavier-than-air machines, building a steam-powered model aircraft that flew in 1896 and a gasoline-powered aircraft that flew in 1901.

Born in 1834, Samuel Pierpont Langley concluded his formal education upon graduation from Boston High School. He then worked for several architectural firms while pursuing his passion for building telescopes. The latter skill led to several academic appointments, culminating in 1867 with a post at Western University in Pittsburgh, Pennsylvania, where for twenty years Langley taught and was the director of the Allegheny Observatory. Langley made landmark contributions to the study of sunspots and invented the bolometer, a device to measure infinitesimal temperature variations across the light spectrum. In 1881, he led an expedition to Mount Whitney, California, to measure the amount of heat received from the Sun by Earth's atmosphere, a partially successful effort that resulted in the unit of measure named after him.

Langley's study of aerodynamics began shortly before his appointment in 1887 as secretary of the Smithsonian Institution, a position he held until his death. Throughout the early 1890's, Langley built successive models of what he called "aerodromes," uncrewed flying machines driven by gasoline-fueled, steam-powered engines. He launched his aerodromes from a track atop a houseboat on the Potomac River near Quantico, Virginia. On May 6, 1896, his 16-foot-long aerodrome model number 5 was catapulted out and flew for 90 seconds over a range of 3,000 feet. This epochal event marked what was arguably the first sustained flight of a heavier-than-air craft.

Although Langley intended to set aside aeronautical work after that success, he was persuaded by President William McKinley to develop a crewed craft in 1898. When European firms could not supply a suitable engine, Langley's assistant, Charles Manly, built a light but powerful internal combustion engine. In 1901, an uncrewed aerodrome model using such an engine became the first gasoline-powered vehicle to fly. A houseboat rigged with a cumbersome 85-foot-long track on its roof served as the launch for the 850-pound crewed machine, which Manly piloted. When it was launched on October 7, 1903, 40 miles south of Washington, D.C., it became caught in the launch mechanism and plunged overboard. A similarly disastrous second launch was attempted nearer the city on December 8, 1903. Nine days later, Orville and Wilbur Wright, operating independently of Langley and without government aid, made a successful flight at Kitty Hawk, North Carolina. Langley, discouraged by his failures, died of a stroke on February 27, 1906.

Langley's successor at the Smithsonian, Dr. Charles Walcott, in 1914 enlisted aviation pioneer Glenn H. Curtiss to reconstruct the 1903 Langley machine and launch it from pontoons. The effort was successful, but the revisions made by Curtiss as well as Curtiss's own financial interest in undermining the Wright brothers' aircraft patents, leave open the question whether Langley's original craft might have flown had it not been for his unfortunate launch mechanism.

David M. Rooney

Bibliography
Berliner, Don. *Aviation: Reaching for the Sky*. Minneapolis: Oliver Press, 1997. Contains a chapter on Langley and the aerodrom, while chapters on other aviation pioneers provide context for his aeronautical research. Includes technical details and a selected list of Langley's publications.
Crouch, Tom D. *A Dream of Wings: Americans and the Airplane, 1875-1905*. New York: Norton, 1981. Covers developments in American aviation, including several chapters on Langley. This work is the most complete research on Langley's aeronautical contributions and includes an extensive bibliography.
Vaeth, J. Gordon. *Langley: Man of Science and Flight*. New York: Ronald Press, 1966. Short but complete biography of Langley written for nonspecialists. Includes a short bibliographical essay on sources.

See also: Aerodynamics; Glenn H. Curtiss; Heavier-than-air craft; History of human flight; Wright brothers; Wright *Flyer*

Learjets

Date: First production Learjet flew in October, 1963
Definition: The first successful small-business jets.
Significance: The Learjet, with its combination of attractive styling and high power, quickly became the industry standard in small business jets and dominated the business jet market for many years.

The Need for Business Jets
Prior to the development of business jets, options for business air travelers were varied but limited. For corporate travel, corporations could purchase their own small, propeller-driven aircraft, modify full-sized commercial airliners, charter full-sized aircraft, or book regular passenger seats on commercial airliners. The use of full-size aircraft often entailed more expense than could be justified by the number of people flying, and the use of small, propeller-driven aircraft lacked the range, speed, and comfort provided by commercial airliners. Flying on regularly scheduled commercial flights also meant that corporate travelers had to adjust their schedules to match those of the airlines.

Business jets filled a niche that had been unfulfilled by these various options. They were small enough to be affordable, yet large enough to provide amenities, such as galley kitchens and onboard restrooms, that small general aviation aircraft could not. They had cruising ranges and speeds to rival those of full-sized airliners. Perhaps most importantly, business jets provided flexibility: Corporate officers could now fly anywhere at any time.

Lear Jet Corporation

The Learjet was developed by William Powell Lear, a pioneering figure in the airline industry. Born in Hannibal, Missouri, in 1902, Lear left high school before graduating and lied about his age to enlist in the U.S. Navy at the age of sixteen. He learned basic electronic skills while serving in World War I. As an inventor and entrepreneur, Lear built a successful corporation specializing in avionics systems. His wide-ranging inventions included the first successful car radio and the eight-track audio cassette player.

Some of Lear's innovations, particularly in electronics and avionics, became integral components of larger technological systems. His development of the automatic pilot in the 1930's, for example, revolutionized aviation. Often Lear's success as an innovator and entrepreneur was based not on his ability to invent totally new devices, but instead on his genius at recognizing new possibilities for existing technologies and on his ability to market his innovations.

In the late 1950's, Lear founded the Swiss American Aviation Corporation (SAAC) to design and manufacture corporate jet aircraft. By 1963, he had moved the company from Switzerland to Wichita, Kansas, and renamed it the Lear Jet Corporation. Like many successful entrepreneurs, he had a knack for envisioning the market for a product before there was such a market. This was certainly the case with the Learjet. Although industry analysts were intially skeptical about the Learjet's business prospects, for several years after Learjet production began, demand outpaced supply. Although the original market had been corporate travelers, buyers soon included celebrities for whom ownership of a Learjet had become a necessary status symbol.

The biggest challenge faced by Lear and his design team in building the Learjet was to develop an airframe that was strong enough to withstand the forces created by jet engines, that could incorporate a passenger cabin with sufficient headroom to qualify as a desirable travel option, and that could be small and light enough to be economically feasible. The airframe, engines, and other components all had to be integrated carefully into a complete aircraft system. Lear knew the potential market existed for a business jet, but he could not simply scale down an existing full-sized commercial airliner. Instead, Lear looked to the military for inspiration, incorporating many of the features of the P-16, a small fighter-bomber used by the Swiss Air Force.

The resulting aircraft combined sophisticated good looks with speed and power. The first Learjet, the Model 23, carried seven passengers and made its first flight on October 7, 1964. Powered by two General Electric CJ610-4 turbojet engines, it had an effective range of 1,875 miles and a top speed of 564 miles per hour. Learjet produced and sold approximately one hundred Model 23's before introducing the Model 24 in 1966.

In 1969, Lear resigned from the board of Lear Jet Industries, and the company merged with Gates Aviation to become Corporation Gates Learjet. Learjet changed corporate ownership several times before becoming part of Bombardier, a Canadian corporation, in 1990. Learjets continue to be built in Wichita, Kansas, and the Learjet Model 45 was introduced in 1995. The Model 45, powered by two Allied Signal TFE 731-20 turbofan engines with 3,500 pounds of thrust each, accommodates a two-person crew and up to nine passengers.

Nancy Farm Mannikko

Bibliography

Boesen, Victor. *They Said It Couldn't Be Done: The Incredible Story of Bill Lear.* Garden City, N.Y.: Doubleday, 1971. A biography of the man who created the Learjet.

Porter, Donald J. *Learjet: The World's Executive Aircraft.* Blue Ridge Summit, Pa.: Tab Books, 1990. The story of the Lear's business jets.

Rashke, Richard. *Stormy Genius: The Life of Aviation's Maverick, Bill Lear.* Boston: Houghton Mifflin, 1985. A biography detailing the life and career of William P. Lear.

Szurovy, Geza. *Learjets.* Osceola, Wis.: Motorbooks International, 1996. A descriptive book about Learjets.

See also: Airplanes; Corporate and private jets; Jet engines; Manufacturers

Leonardo da Vinci

Date: Born on April 15, 1452, in Vinci, Tuscany, Italy; died on May 2, 1519 at Cloux Château, Amboise, France

Leonardo da Vinci

Definition: The first person to design flying machines and a parachute.

Significance: Leonardo da Vinci drew up plans for several fanciful human-powered flying machines and a heliocopter-like airscrew. He also sketched a potentially practical pyramidal parachute.

Leonardo da Vinci is best known as the painter of the *Mona Lisa* (1503). Owing to the enormous breadth and range of his talents and interests, he is considered the original Renaissance man. Among his interests was an obsession with flying machines.

Although da Vinci was given a good education for a boy from a small Tuscan town in Renaissance Italy, he was never a scholar and cheerfully acknowledged the accusation of critics that he was "a man without learning." He wrote well but, being left-handed, he also developed for his notes an idiosyncratic and almost indecipherable mirror-image style of writing that ran right to left with the letters also reversed left to right. He never published these personal notes and sketches. On his death, his papers were willed to his apprentice and friend Francesco Melzi, who kept them for about fifty years. On Melzi's death, the collection was sold and scattered.

For all these reasons, da Vinci's work had little impact on developments in science and technology. Nonetheless, his sketches of flying machines were recognized well before the era of workable flying machines. Da Vinci favored flapping wings powered by the combined efforts of arms and legs because he recognized the impossibility of flight powered by human arms alone. His early preference for "bat wings" faded as articulation problems became clear. An intensive study of bird flight left him uncertain of how to coordinate the timing of wing motions with the powering arm and leg motions. Although he spent some thirty years studying flight, none of his designs seem to have led to actual models or trials.

The weaknesses of human power were fully apparent to later pioneers of flight, as were the deficiencies of flapping wings. Hence, da Vinci's designs made no contribution to the details of realistic flying machines. Although Octave Chanute suggested the wing warping of the Wright brothers was an extension of Leonardo's plans, the Wrights explicitly denied the connection. Da Vinci's only confirmed

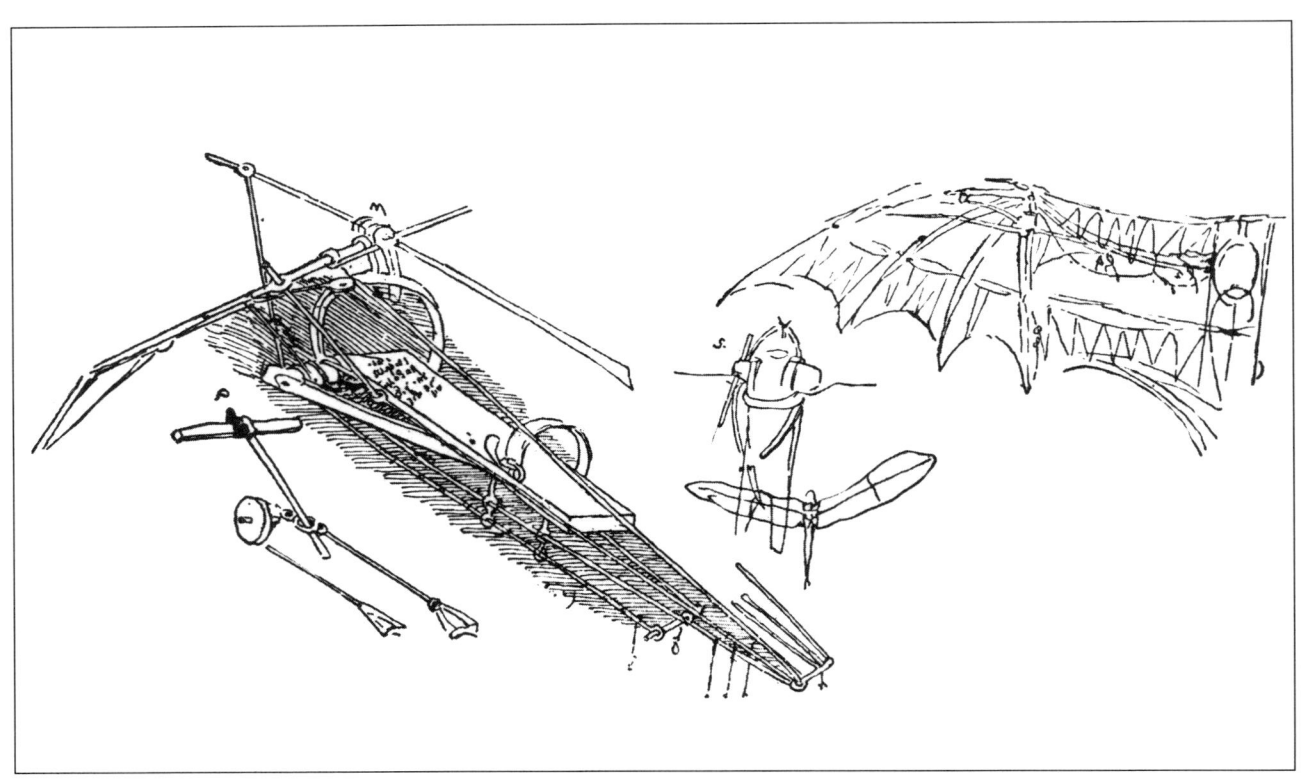

Leonardo da Vinci sketched designs for heavier-than-air craft five centuries before the technology existed to put his plans to practical use. (Hulton Archive)

contribution to actual flight was as a stimulator and encourager of the dream.

It is also doubtful that da Vinci's airscrew design, which might at least have made a good toy, had any direct influence on the development of helicopters. On the other hand, working parachutes dating from the late eighteenth century may have been inspired by Leonardo's design.

John A. Cramer

Bibliography

Ackerman, James S. "Leonardo da Vinci: Art in Science." *Daedalus* 127 (Winter, 1998): 207. The author discusses the interaction of science and art as it relates to the works of da Vinci. He includes details on the history of science and on da Vinci's scientific observations.

Hunt, Ivor B. "Leonardo da Vinci: Pioneer in Aviation." In *Men in the Air*, edited by Brandt Aymar. New York: Crown, 1990. Contains sketches and translations of da Vinci's notes with insightful comments.

Kemp, Martin, Jane Roberts, and Philip Steadman. *Leonardo da Vinci.* New Haven, Conn.: Yale University Press,1989. The Flying Machines section has a good discussion of the development of da Vinci's thought with drawings and photographs of a model machine.

See also: Aerodynamics; Octave Chanute; Helicopters; History of human flight; Human-powered flight; Parachutes; Wing designs; Wright brothers

Lighter-than-air craft

Definition: Craft that float in the sky because of lighter-than-air (LTA) gas, including both balloons that float with the winds and dirigibles that can propel themselves and direct their course.

Significance: Although LTA craft have been supplanted by heavier-than-air (HTA) for most tasks, many techniques and technologies later adopted for HTA were developed with LTA craft. LTA craft provide a number of niche functions, such as weather sampling, advertising, telecommunications repeaters, high-altitude science platforms, and heavy-cargo transporters.

Design Principles

A balloon is a fabric container for LTA gas that allows the balloon to float. Usually, a balloon also lifts a payload (often called a gondola) hanging beneath the balloon. A dirigible, which is a shortened form of the term "dirigible balloon" (meaning directable balloon), has one or more balloons plus the propulsion system and payload. Balloons and dirigibles are called LTA craft to compare them with airplanes and helicopters, which are heavier-than-air (HTA) craft that stay in the sky because of the application of some form of propulsion.

Buoyancy is the key factor for LTA craft. Archimedes (287-212 B.C.E.) derived the principle stating that a body immersed in a fluid is buoyed up by a force equal to the weight of the displaced fluid. The LTA uses gases including warmed air (which has expanded and is thus lighter than the surrounding air) or gases with densities less than air.

Two low-density gases widely used to provide buoyancy are hydrogen and helium. Typically, hydrogen lifts 60 pounds per thousand cubic feet. Helium lifts 14 percent less (53 rather than 60 pounds) per thousand cubic feet, but helium has the major safety advantage that it does not burn, while hydrogen can ignite explosively.

Unfortunately, helium was not available until the 1920's, and even then the United States government (which had most of the world's supply) was slow to allow exports. Consequently, most LTA craft until the late 1930's flew with hydrogen, and there were many catastrophic fires.

Hot air gets only 17 to 20 pounds of lift per thousand cubic feet, about one third that of hydrogen. Thus, hot-air balloons must be three times larger to lift the same payload, which makes hot-air dirigibles very inefficient. However, for balloons, the lesser complexity and cost of avoiding hydrogen or helium is a major advantage.

Heating air for buoyancy is usually done by burning propane or kerosene. Heat is constantly drained away at the surface of the balloon, so hot-air balloons require frequent firings of their burners. Consequently, they tend to have shorter range than balloons using low-density gas. However, the rapid changes in the buoyancy of hot-air balloons do allow their pilots to ascend or descend to catch different winds and thus get some control of their craft's direction.

LTA craft pilots can decrease buoyancy to drop lower or land by valving out some of the lifting gas. They can increase buoyancy by dropping ballast (water, sand, or other material carried along for dropping as needed). In extreme conditions, balloonists have dropped everything in the gondola and even the gondola itself.

There are several more-sophisticated methods of modifying buoyancy, particularly for craft on long-duration and/or high-altitude flights, where warmth during the day causes the craft to rise too high and cold at night causes it to sink too low. Shiny upper surfaces, reflecting sunlight that would cause the balloon to expand and rise too high, and transparent lower surfaces, absorbing infrared radiation (heat waves) from the ground at night, often help. The Rozier balloon has a hot-air balloon, providing buoyancy variation, beneath a low-density gas balloon, providing endurance.

Conversely, superpressure balloons maintain buoyancy by having an envelope strong enough to keep the same volume even if the gas inside them expands. This comes at a cost of additional weight compared to zero-pressure balloons, which expand and contract with changes in surrounding pressure.

Another aspect of buoyancy is that the density and pressure of the surrounding air decreases with altitude. Hence, there is less lift available per unit volume, so LTA craft must be larger to carry a given payload to higher altitudes. Consequently, LTA craft with heavy payloads tend to be limited to low altitudes of a few thousand feet. For higher altitudes, designers can compensate for decreased lift per unit volume by using lighter payloads, such as remotely controlled instruments to operate the craft instead of people.

Light materials are vital for LTA construction. The best material for the early balloons was light, strong, and expensive silk. By the mid-twentieth century, synthetic materials, such as polyester and polyethylene-coated nylon, improved on silk's performance at a lower price. By the beginning of the twenty-first century, composites of a number of synthetic materials allowed even greater strength and lighter weight. Similarly, the electrolytic process for purifying aluminum, invented in 1886, allowed structures light enough to fly dirigible structures and pressurized gondolas carried by balloons. Composites in the late twentieth and early twenty-first centuries allowed all of these structures to become lighter still.

Dirigibles are of three types: nonrigid, a streamlined balloon with the car and engines below; semirigid, the same with a strengthening keel below so the craft can be larger; and rigid, an enclosed structure holding any number of gas bags so the size can be very large.

History of LTA Flight

In 1782 and 1783, Joseph-Michel and Jacques-Étienne Montgolfier, two French brothers, flew hot-air balloons with animals as their first aeronauts. On November 21, 1783, they were ready for a human crew. Their pilot, Jean-François Pilâtre de Rozier, and another man flew over Paris for twenty-five minutes while desperately stoking their lifting fire and sponging out fires in their rigging caused by sparks from the lifting fire.

Only a few days later, on December 1, 1783, Jacques-Alexander-César Charles, of the French Academy, flew a hydrogen balloon. The flight illustrated the advantages of hydrogen balloons over hot air. Because hydrogen is more buoyant than hot air, the balloon could be one-third the size of a comparable hot-air balloon. Rather than just twenty-five minutes, Charles flew for two-and-a-half hours, dropped off his passenger at sunset, and then rose high enough to be the first person to see the sun set twice in one day.

Shortly thereafter, balloonists began attempting not just to fly, but to go places. Jean-Pierre Blanchard, another Frenchman, and John Jeffries, an American, were the first aeronauts to fly across the English Channel to France on January 7, 1785. However, their flight illustrated the major problem of balloons as transportation. They had to drop all their cargo to reach land, and their destination could be only roughly planned—they could have no more specific intention than to land somewhere in France. That vagueness increased as balloonists made longer flights. Inventors tried vainly for decades to make their balloons steerable, but they always failed because engines powerful enough to move a craft against strong winds were too heavy to be lifted.

Still, balloon flights in the nineteenth century supplied entertainment, scientific data, and observation data for armies. Balloon rides and balloon-borne fireworks were connected with most major celebrations. For scientists, balloonists discovered that the atmosphere grew thinner and cooler with increased altitude but that the magnetic field retained its strength. For armies, tethered balloons allowed observers to see several miles beyond the enemy's lines. Such balloons were first used during the French Revolution in 1793, and again in the American Civil War (1861-1865). By the end of the nineteenth century, observation balloons were in wide use.

Dirigibles, Balloons, and Their Competition

As with HTA aircraft, dirigibles only became practical when light and powerful internal combustion engines were developed. On September 20, 1898, Brazilian Alberto Santos-Dumont first used a 3.5-horsepower, 66-pound motor to propel himself and *Number 1*, an 82-foot nonrigid craft with 64,000 cubic feet of gas volume, around Paris. Santos-Dumont made steady improvements over the next several years, inspiring many other nonrigids.

> ### Events in the History of Lighter-Than-Air Craft
>
> **1782-1783:** Joseph-Michel and Jacques-Étienne Montgolfier fly hot-air balloons with animals as their first aeronauts.
>
> **1793:** French armies use tethered balloons to see several miles beyond enemy lines during the French Revolution.
>
> **1861-1865:** Balloons are used for observation of enemy positions during the American Civil War.
>
> **1870-1871:** The French use observation balloons during the Franco-Prussian War.
>
> **1899-1902:** The British use balloons and kites for observation purposes during the Boer War.
>
> **1900:** The first zeppelin is built.
>
> **1904-1905:** During the Russo-Japanese War, the role of balloons leads to later military systems for employing aircraft for reconnaisance and artillery spotting.
>
> **1920's-1930's:** The U.S. government, which controls most of the world's supply of helium, operates four rigids for long-range reconnaissance.
>
> **May 6, 1937:** The hydrogen-filled German airship *Hindenburg* explodes at Lakehurst, New Jersey, convincing the public that large dirigibles are unsafe.

Meanwhile, in Germany, Count Ferdinand von Zeppelin built a large rigid dirigible, *Luftschiff Zeppelin Number 1* or *LZ-1*, which translates as "airship number one." It was 420 feet long and 42 feet in diameter, with a gas volume of 460,000 cubic feet, sixty times greater than Santos-Dumont's *Number 1*. The *LZ-1*, which first flew in July, 1900, had seventeen separate gas cells held together by an aluminum framework and covered with fabric. After ten more years of work, von Zeppelin had dirigibles in commercial service carrying sightseeing passengers and mail.

With the beginning of World War I, rigid dirigibles did well at first, staging the first long-range bombing attacks in 1915. However, airplane technology rapidly improved, and pilots found the rigids to be large, slow, highly flammable targets. Likewise, airplanes replaced observation balloons because the airplanes could cover more territory and also attack targets. The only dirigibles successful throughout the war were nonrigids used to guard convoys against submarines.

Still, the long flights by rigid dirigibles during the war suggested that intercontinental passenger service, or even flying warships, might develop. All these dreams eventually crashed. France abandoned large rigids when the *Dixmude* exploded in 1923. Great Britain abandoned large rigids when the *R-101* crashed and burned in 1924.

In the 1920's and 1930's, the U.S. government operated four rigids as military ships intended for long-range reconnaissance. Two of the airships, the *Akron* and *Macon*, carried their own fighter planes for defense. Because the United States had most of the world's helium supply and used helium for its LTA gas, none of these craft exploded. However, three of them were lost in storms, and the United States abandoned the giant rigids after the third, the *Macon*, went down in a storm at sea in 1935.

The Lufftschiffbau Zeppelin company in Germany had the best safety record because it had built more than a hundred rigids and had thoroughly worked out the design details. In 1928, the company's *Graf Zeppelin* began a commercial flight life that circled the world, made regular flights to Brazil and North America, made an Arctic expedition, and flew one million miles before being retired.

The last and greatest rigid was the *Hindenburg*: 803 feet long and 135 feet in diameter. Its seven million cubic feet of gas allowed it to carry fifty passengers and sixty crew in absolute luxury at a speed of 84 miles per hour and a range of 11,000 miles.

Unfortunately, the Luftschiffbau Zeppelin company still flew with hydrogen, and the doped-cloth skin was also quite flammable. Lightning, leaking gas, or anti-Nazi sabotage caused the *Hindenburg* to catch fire while preparing to land at Lakehurst, New Jersey, on May 6, 1937. Within one minute, the craft was destroyed, and filmed footage of the event convinced the public that large dirigibles were unsafe.

That left only nonrigids, which were again a major part of antisubmarine warfare in World War II. However, they were retired in the 1950's when helicopters provided the same hovering capability with greater dash capability and easier storage. In the last third of the twentieth century, the few working nonrigid dirigibles were limited to flying advertising billboards and carrying television cameras for overhead views of sporting events. The only new application came in the 1990's, when tethered balloons returned to service as aerostats, providing platforms at altitudes as high as ten to fifteen thousand feet for radar stations and communications repeater stations.

Balloons fared better than dirigibles. Development of small radio transmitters combined with remotely operating weather instruments made possible balloon-borne radiosondes to report temperature, pressure, and relative humidity. Angle data from antennas tracking the radiosondes yielded wind speed and direction at different heights. Use of radiosonde balloons continued into the twenty-first century, helping predict weather, plot sky conditions for aircraft, and fire artillery more accurately.

Larger balloons have carried science payloads and human crews to high altitudes for decades because they can reach altitudes as high as 30 miles, which airplanes cannot reach, carrying large payloads that would not fit in an airplane fuselage. From the 1930's through the early 1960's, balloons were the frontier of human-crewed aviation that led to higher flights by HTA craft and eventually to space capsules.

The greatest problem at high altitudes is low pressure, which Swiss balloonist Auguste Piccard surmounted with a pressurized cabin, essentially the first space capsule, and he suggested similar pressurized cabins for high-flying transports. On May 27, 1931, Piccard and an assistant reached 51,793 feet (9.8 miles), making them the first to reach the stratosphere. More importantly, they discovered that cosmic rays increased with altitude, proving that they came from somewhere in space rather than the other suggested source, radioactivity within the earth. Such flights carried personnel and instruments to steadily greater heights and developed many technologies that were later used in the space race. In fact, on May 4, 1961, the American Stratolab V balloon reached an altitude of 113,700 feet (21.5 miles) with an open gondola so the two pilots could test space suits in near-space conditions for the Mercury orbital-flight program.

After the 1960's, scientific balloon flights using improved robotic instrumentation allowed balloons to shed the weight of the balloonists and their life-support gear. In the closing decades of the twentieth century, astronomic balloon-borne instruments conducted sky surveys in a number of frequency bands that cannot penetrate the lower atmosphere and provided valuable weather data from the lower stratosphere.

By the late twentieth century, advances in fabrics allowed the U.S. National Aeronautics and Space Administration (NASA) to begin replacing zero-pressure balloons with superpressure balloons, which do not need to vent excess helium when warmed by the sun and which consequently can fly for weeks or months. By the early twenty-first century, NASA had begun flying large superpressure balloons with several-ton payloads in a program called the Ultra Long Duration Balloon (ULDB).

Ballooning for Fun and Adventure

Although the aviation frontier passed ballooning by, a balloon ride is still a beautiful and awe-inspiring experience. A panoramic view floats by below and sounds from the ground float up to balloonists.

This was a rare experience until the renaissance of hot-air ballooning, started by American Edward Yost. While developing high-altitude balloons for the United States government in the 1950's, Yost realized that polyethylene-coated nylon is a lighter, less flammable material than that used in the Montgolfiers' balloons. He used an acetylene welding torch as a less labor-intensive source of hot air than the Montgolfiers used. After some development, such as replacing the welding torch with a propane burner, Yost made the first modern hot-air balloon launch from Bruning, Nebraska, on October 10, 1960.

Beginning in the 1960's, the new hot-air balloons radically reduced the cost and complexity of supplying buoyant gas. Thus were born ballooning clubs, competitions, and tour services. Also, for advertising, hot-air balloons have flown in shapes varying from spark plugs to human faces, and even a mansion.

For more ambitious flying, Yost's hot-air technology (plus lightweight insulating material lining the gasbag, and helium) made the Rozier balloon practical for long-distance flights. Varying the amount of heat in the inner balloon provides altitude control for hunting favorable winds. That capability, along with worldwide weather reports, made balloon flights possible across the Atlantic and then the Pacific Oceans. In March, 1999, another Piccard, Auguste's grandson Bertrand, and Brian Jones spent twenty days flying 30,000 miles to make a complete circumnavigation of the globe.

For astronomical and meteorological observations, balloons are still a much cheaper alternative to spacecraft, with shorter turnaround times and without the vibration and acceleration of a rocket launch.

Dirigible Economics and Prospects

By the beginning of the twenty-first century, dirigibles were enjoying a resurgence in several niche markets. However, dirigibles will probably never recover aviation primacy from HTA's for several reasons.

First there is a massive investment cost for building and developing dirigibles. Several factors make dirigibles more efficient as size increases. In particular, lifting volume increases by the cube while surface volume (and thus drag) only increases by the square. However, the large size makes the design and building of a dirigible as expensive as that of a ship. Large size also reduces the number of units made, so dirigibles have less chance to go down the learning curve toward lower costs and improved designs than HTA craft, which are typically made by the hundreds or thousands.

Second, hangar costs are high. Dirigibles are kept inflated because their helium lifting gas is expensive and would require too much time and effort to pump back into tanks. However, inflated dirigibles can easily be swept off their parking area by winds. Consequently, dirigibles must have their own special hangars rather than be casually parked on runways, as airplanes are.

Third, dirigibles are vulnerable to and limited by bad weather. The giant buoyant structures can be seized by freak gusts of wind on takeoff and landing, and they are more vulnerable than airplanes to icing. Zeppelin passenger flights were not scheduled in winter. In the sky, dirigibles are so large that winds may pull them in different directions and destroy them, as happened to the U.S. *Shenandoah*, *Akron*, and *Macon*. Moreover, unless specially designed for high altitude, dirigibles cannot readily climb above storms as jet-propelled airplanes can.

Fourth, due to the drag from the great size per unit mass of cargo, dirigibles are significantly slower than HTA competition. At best, they can obtain half the speed of propeller-driven planes and a fifth that of jets. Thus, a jet with one fifth of the cargo capacity of a dirigible can deliver the same cumulative mass of cargo. This longer time makes dirigibles uncompetitive in the passenger market.

Still, dirigibles have potential for certain markets because they can run quietly, run smoothly, linger for long periods, carry heavy and awkwardly large payloads, and land without runways. Lighter and more fireproof materials have increased these advantages. The number of advertising dirigibles increased steadily beginning in the 1980's. At the start of the twenty-first century, the Zeppelin Company was marketing sightseeing semirigids a third the size of the *Hindenburg*. CargoLifter in Berlin was designing a cargo-carrying rigid larger than the *Hindenburg*.

Meanwhile, an entirely new concept was being developed: dirigibles in the lower stratosphere serving as high-altitude platforms. Such platforms could serve many functions of communications satellites and astronomical satellites at a fraction of the cost. However, as with most LTA tasks, there is competition from airplanes.

Roger V. Carlson

Bibliography

Cross, Wilbur. *Disaster at the Pole*. New York: Lyons Press, 2000. Contains technical details and a great historical account of the airship *Italia*'s gallant attempt to do science at the North Pole; the disaster; and finally, the political backlash in Italy against dirigibles.

Hutheesing, Nikhil. "Airship Internet." *Forbes* 59, no. 9 (May 5, 1997): 170-171. Describes Skyship International's dirigible-borne telecommunications repeating stations; applies to all airborne telecommunications stations.

Kunzig, Robert. "Dirigibles on the Rise." *Discover* 21, no. 11 (November, 2000): 92-99. Describes the new dirigible enterprises that were being developed as the twentieth century ended, including new passenger craft and heavy-cargo lifters.

Piccard, Bertrand, and Brian Jones. *Around the World in Twenty Days*. New York: John Wiley & Sons, 1999. The two authors (one the grandson of Auguste Piccard) describe the adventures and mechanics of their successful round-the-world balloon flight in March, 1999. Their account highlights the challenges of all balloon flights and the technological advances that permitted their success.

Ryan, Craig. *The Pre-Astronauts: Manned Ballooning on the Threshold of Space*. Annapolis, Md.: Naval Institute Press, 1995. Describes the lives spent and the lives lost working at progressively higher altitudes developing equipment that was later used in spaceflight.

Smith, I. Steve, Jr., and James A. Cutts. "Floating in Space." *Scientific American* 281, no. 5 (November, 1999): 132-139. Describes the scientific uses of super-pressure balloons at high altitudes.

See also: Balloons; Blimps; Dirigibles; Experimental aircraft; Goodyear blimp; Heavier-than-air craft; *Hindenburg*; Hot-air balloons; National Aeronautics and Space Administration; Auguste Piccard; Alberto Santos-Dumont; Ferdinand von Zeppelin

Otto Lilienthal

Date: Born on May 23, 1848, in Anklam, Prussia (now in Germany); died on August 10, 1896, in Berlin, Germany

Definition: An aviation pioneer and creative genius who was the first man to build and fly a successful heavier-than-air flying machine.

Significance: Lilienthal was the first person to prove that flight could be achieved and sustained with the cambered, or curved surface, airfoil wing. He built and successfully flew a number of heavier-than-air flying machines before anyone else in history had done so.

Otto Lilienthal flies in his glider from a hill near Berlin in 1896, the same year in which he died in a glider crash. (Hulton Archive)

Otto Lilienthal's passion to fly blossomed early in his life. Although there was no formal science of aviation during Lilienthal's youth, there is evidence that Lilienthal studied birds in grammar school. At the age of twenty-five, Lilienthal joined the Aeronautical Society of Great Britain, where he gave his first lecture about the theory of avian flight. He then began systematic experiments and tests with models and kites on the force of air on human-made wings. No mere tinkerer, he was an accomplished engineer, with his own business engineering boilers and steam engines. He obtained a patent for a mining machine, the first of his twenty patents, four of which were aviation patents.

Lilienthal's ongoing experiments and studies culminated, in 1891, with his building his first heavier-than-air flying machine, which flew for a distance of 80 feet. This machine would be described today as a hang glider. Over the next five years, he built a total of eighteen flying machines and made more than two thousand sustained and replicable flights.

In 1892, Lilienthal built a new glider with improved flight characteristics. The following year, he built a flight station near his home, where he made a number of flights with distances of up to 800 feet. Lilienthal not only designed, engineered, and built a machine that could fly, but he also taught himself to fly it.

Although Lilienthal's flying machines were difficult to control and to turn, they did accomplish sustained flight. His outstanding contribution to the science of flight was the cambered, or curved surface, wing. This wing form, with a rounded top surface and a concave or flat underside, produces the lift needed to make an airplane fly and is still used today on most airplanes.

By 1895, Lilienthal's flight accomplishments were widely reported, and Lilienthal was visited by flight enthusiasts from many different countries. He corresponded with and shared his ideas with other aviation pioneers, such as Octave Chanute and Orville and Wilbur Wright. He generously published and shared the results of his aviation theories and experiments.

On August 9, 1896, at the age of forty-eight, Lilienthal crashed while flying one of his machines and died the next day. He is famous for the following quotation, "To invent an airplane is nothing. To build one is something. But to fly is everything." Lilienthal was a creative genius whose ingenuity, observations, engineering, and daring laid the cornerstone for the development of aviation.

Mary Ann Turney and Robert Maxant

Bibliography

Combs, H., and M. Caidin. *Kill Devil Hill*. Boston: Houghton Mifflin, 1979. A very readable study of the Wright brothers that also explains the principles behind aviation.

Lilienthal, Otto. *Birdflight as the Basis for Aviation: A Contribution Towards a System of Aviation*. Translated by A. W. Isenthal. Hummelstown, Pa.: Markowski, 2001. An unabridged facsimile reprint of Lilienthal's 1889 work, including original illustrations.

National Air and Space Museum. *Otto Lilienthal and Octave Chanute: Pioneers of Gliding*. Washington, D.C.: Author, 1980. A publication by the Smithsonian Institution, National Air and Space Museum on the early years of flight research.

See also: Airfoils; Octave Chanute; Heavier-than-air craft; History of human flight; Wing designs; Wright brothers

Charles A. Lindbergh

Date: Born on February 4, 1902, in Detroit, Michigan; died on August 26, 1974, in Hana, Maui, Hawaii

Definition: A pioneer of early aviation, who became the first aviator to fly an airplane nonstop from New York to Paris.

Significance: While Lindbergh's 1927 New York-to-Paris flight made him a national and worldwide hero, he was more than another flier who set a record. In the forty-seven years between the flight and his death, he contributed significantly to civil and military aviation, scientific research, and conservation.

Early Life

Charles Augustus Lindbergh, whose family moved about a great deal, was raised more by his mother, Evangeline Land Lindbergh, than by his father, Charles August Lindbergh, who served in the U.S. House of Representatives from 1907 until 1917. During his precollege years, Lindbergh, an unimpressive student, attended eleven schools. He showed considerable mechanical ability, however, and was entranced by automobiles, motorcycles, and especially airplanes.

Interest in Flying

Lindbergh first saw an airplane in 1910, when a single-engine aircraft flew at treetop level up the river alongside the Minnesota farm where his family was living. From that time forward, Lindbergh thought of little but flying. He wanted to study aeronautical engineering in college, but no universities offered such programs. Finishing high school in 1918, he farmed for two years before entering the University of Wisconsin to study civil engineering. By 1920, he owned an Excelsior motorcycle, on which he rode to Lincoln, Nebraska, in 1922 when, bored by his studies, he dropped out of the university to attend flying school. Although the school closed before he earned his pilot's license, he knew by then that he wanted to spend his life flying.

Lindbergh apprenticed as a mechanic to a barnstorming pilot. He earned the nickname "Daredevil Lindbergh" by walking on the wings of the planes piloted by his boss, dazzling and delighting the assembled throngs below. By 1923, he was able to pilot planes himself. He traded his motorcycle for a war-surplus airplane, a Curtiss Jenny, in which he barnstormed on his own until, determined to perfect his skills as a pilot, he joined the U.S. Army Air Service Reserve in 1924.

In 1925, the U.S. Postal Service inaugurated airmail service to the Midwest, and Lindbergh became one of its earliest pilots, flying between St. Louis and Chicago, a treacherous route because of its severe winter weather. Twice Lindbergh had to parachute from his plane. While flying this route, Lindbergh learned that an affluent Frenchman, Raymond Orteig, was offering a $25,000 prize to the first person to fly nonstop from New York to Paris. Seven people had attempted this feat and failed. Lindbergh immediately began to work toward winning the prize. He designed a plane, the *Spirit of St. Louis*, to be built by Ryan Airlines in San Diego with funding from both Lindbergh and a group of St. Louis businessmen.

Charles Lindbergh poses with the Spirit of St. Louis *before taking off on his solo transatlantic flight in 1927.* (AP/Wide World Photos)

Setting Records

Those who had failed to fly nonstop across the Atlantic Ocean had attempted the flight in dual-engine planes. Lindbergh designed a single-engine plane that would conserve weight. An enormous fuel tank occupied the area from the engine to the pilot's seat, totally blocking forward vision. A periscope was installed on the left window to overcome this problem. The plane carried 450 gallons of fuel, which so impeded its takeoffs that it barely cleared trees at the ends of runways.

After battling eight days of bad weather conditions that made a takeoff impossible, Lindbergh finally was ready to fly out of New York's Roosevelt Field on May 20, 1927, taking off at 7:52 A.M. To minimize weight, he carried only five sandwiches and a quart of water. He further lightened the plane by having no radio or parachute aboard.

Lindbergh flew the great circle route over Cape Cod, Nova Scotia, Newfoundland, and, after the long Atlantic crossing, Ireland, England, and France. The most hazardous leg of the flight, the crossing of the Atlantic, occurred at night. Ice formed on the wings shortly after Lindbergh passed Newfoundland. Fortunately, it soon dissipated. Lindbergh's chief battle now was against sleep. He would doze off and then quickly be jarred into wakefulness, realizing he was flying off course.

The *Spirit of St. Louis* flew through rain while passing over the southern tip of Ireland, but as the plane approached southern England, the weather cleared. The weather over Cherbourg, France, was so good that Lindbergh finally took a first bite from one of his sandwiches. He followed the Seine to Paris's Le Bourget Airfield where he landed on May 21 at 10:22 P.M., having flown more than 3,500 miles in 33.5 hours. Cheering crowds greeted him, and Raymond Orteig later awarded him the promised $25,000 prize.

Once home, the bashful Lindbergh was lionized. He was given a ticker-tape parade down New York City's Broadway. He became a roving international goodwill ambassador for the United States. In the course of these travels, he met Anne Spencer Morrow, the daughter of the U.S. ambassador to Mexico, whom he married in 1929.

The Down Years

Celebrity perplexed the ever-reticent Lindbergh. He tried increasingly to evade public notice. He and his wife traveled throughout the world and became ardent conservationists. Their first son, Charles Augustus, Jr., born in 1930, was kidnapped and murdered in 1932. In 1935, the Lindberghs, longing for privacy, relocated to England, where Lindbergh worked with Dr. Alexis Carrel to develop an early heart pump machine for use in open-heart surgery.

In Lindbergh's later years, his pro-Nazi, anti-Semitic sentiments were condemned by his once-adoring public. He gradually withdrew from public life, spending many of his remaining years at his favorite home in Hana, on the island of Maui, Hawaii, where he died of cancer in 1974.

R. Baird Shuman

Bibliography

Blythe, Randolph. *Charles Lindbergh*. New York: Franklin Watts, 1990. A brief yet accurate account aimed at juvenile readers.

Davis, Kenneth S. *The Hero*. Garden City, N.Y.: Doubleday, 1959. A splendid assessment of the role the mass media played in shaping Lindbergh.

Giblin, James Cross. *Charles A. Lindbergh: A Human Hero*. New York: Clarion, 1997. A thorough account aimed at adolescent readers, but useful as well to general readers. Profuse illustrations.

Lindbergh, Reeve. "Charles Lindbergh." In *People of the Century*. New York: Simon & Schuster, 1999. A brief, personal account by Lindbergh's son.

See also: Airline industry, U.S.; Airmail delivery; Barnstorming; Jennys; Military flight; Record flights; *Spirit of St. Louis*; Transatlantic flight

Lockheed Martin

Definition: Aerospace company formed by the 1996 merger of Lockheed and Martin.
Significance: Lockheed was founded in 1916 and became a leader in the American aerospace industry. The smaller Martin company was founded in 1912 and eventually focused on space travel.

Early Years

Lockheed was originally founded by brothers Allan and Malcolm Loughead in 1916. The Loughead brothers had broken into the aircraft manufacturing business three years earlier when they constructed a seaplane under the auspices of their Alco Hydro-Aeroplane company in San Francisco. The Loughead Model G seaplane carried visitors to the Panama-Pacific Exposition over San Francisco Bay at a cost of $10 per person. The company folded when the exposition ended, and the Loughead brothers decided to move to sunnier Los Angeles, where they formed the Loughead Aircraft Manufacturing Company.

During World War I, the company built two patrol bombers for the U.S. Navy, but these did not lead to additional orders. The Loughead brothers then decided to capitalize on the popularity of aviation in the United States by building a sport airplane for the masses. The program produced an aircraft known as the S-1. The S-1 was a technological breakthrough, but a commercial disaster. The U.S. government dumped thousands of war surplus aircraft into the market and Loughead did not sell a single S-1. The Loughead Aircraft Manufacturing Company went out of business in 1920.

Six years later, Allan Loughead and his former employee Jack Northrop decided to begin manufacturing airplanes again. They incorporated the Lockheed Aircraft Company in December, 1926. Irritated by mispronunciation of his name, Allan Loughead decided to use the phonetic spelling for his new company. The company immediately began work on a planed designed by Jack Northrop. Lockheed dubbed the aircraft the Vega, starting a tradition at Lockheed of naming planes for celestial phenomena.

Charles A. Lindbergh's solo flight across the Atlantic in 1927 sparked widespread interest in aviation and the Vega quickly became a popular aircraft. The first well-known Vega pilot, George Hearst, Jr., disappeared during a race from San Francisco to Honolulu, but this did not spoil the Vega's reputation. Australian George Hubert Wilkins bought the fourth Vega, and he and his pilot, Ben Eilson, used the plane to become the first men to fly over the North Pole on April 15, 1928. Famous American aviator Wiley Post and his navigator flew the Vega around the world in 8 days and 16 hours in 1931. Two years later, Post made the same journey solo in 7 days, 19 hours. Post also flew the plane to an unofficial altitude record of 55,000 feet in 1935.

The success of the Vega created a great deal of interest in Lockheed, and in 1929, the company accepted a buyout offer from the Detroit Aircraft Company. Allan Loughead opposed the sale, but the company's board of directors did not agree. Bitter at this defeat, Loughead resigned and, despite repeated attempts, never established another viable aircraft or manufacturer. At the same time, Jack Northrop also left Lockheed to form the Avion Corporation, which later became the Northrop Corporation.

The Lockheed company continued on as part of Detroit Aircraft's "General Motors of the Air" and produced three more notable aircraft before World War II. The Sirius immediately became famous when Charles A. Lindbergh bought the first model. He and his wife Anne Morrow Lindbergh used the plane in 1930 for a number of well-publicized flights over the North Pacific and North Atlantic. Lockheed followed up the success of the Sirius with the Altair. Both the U.S. Army Air Corps and the U.S. Navy acquired Altairs, which were the first aircraft with fully retractable landing gear to be purchased by either service. Sir Charles Kingsford-Smith also used an Altair to fly from Australia to San Francisco in 1934, becoming the first person to cross the Pacific in that direction. Lockheed continued its success by constructing an airliner. The Orion made its first flight in April, 1931, and soon became a fixture in airports around the world. American, TWA, Northwest, and Swissair all made Orions part of their fleets. The Orion was particularly suited for high-speed routes, with one plane making the trip between San Francisco and Los Angeles in just 65 minutes.

Wartime Production

In 1931, the Detroit Aircraft Corporation went bankrupt, another victim of the Great Depression. A group of investors, including several employees, managed to get Lockheed out of receivership and founded the Lockheed Aircraft Corporation on June 6, 1932. The company began work on a new aircraft, the Electra. Amelia Earhart flew an Electra on her ill-fated attempt to become the first woman to fly around the world in 1937. Subsequent variations of the Electra would see service in airlines around the world. Also in 1932, Clarence "Kelly" Johnson became an engineer with the company. The Model 14 Super Electra, designed by Johnson, became the basis for the Hudson bomber, which ushered in a new era in Lockheed's history.

From the company's beginning, Lockheed had sought military contracts, but had enjoyed only marginal success. The war clouds looming over Europe in the late 1930's gave the company a fresh opportunity. Britain agreed to purchase more than two hundred Hudson bombers in 1938. Lockheed's factory in Burbank, California, produced 2,941 Hudsons during the war for a number of armed forces, including the U.S. Army and Navy.

Lockheed made a valuable contribution to the U.S. fighter arsenal during World War II with the creation of the P-38 Lightning. Designed by Kelly Johnson and Hall Hibbard, the plane featured an unusual twin-fuselage design to accommodate its engines. Lockheed secretly constructed the first Lightning in 1938 and the plane made its first flight on January 27, 1939. The Army Air Force bought more than 9,000 P-38 Lightnings during World War II. The Lightning served in all theaters, accounting for the destruction of 1,771 enemy planes in Europe. In the Pacific, the highest-scoring U.S. World War II ace, Dick Bong, flew the P-38, as did two other top-ten U.S. aces. The P-38 also accounted for perhaps the most famous mission of the war when eighteen Lightnings shot down the plane carrying Japan's famed naval strategist Isoroku Yamamoto on April 18, 1943.

Important Postwar Military Aircraft

Lockheed began work on a jet fighter in 1943. The company gave its top designer, Kelly Johnson, a team of workers and a crude building to start the project. Johnson's secret area in the Lockheed complex became known as the Skunk Works. The Skunk Works eventually designed all the company's high-performance fighters and reconnaissance planes. Ironically, this top-secret part of the company ultimately became famous for its research and development. Besides Lockheed's well-known fighter aircraft, the Skunk Works also produced such famous planes as the U-2 spy plane in 1954 and the SR-71 Blackbird in 1964.

The P-80 Shooting Star, the first plane designed in the Skunk Works, made its first flight in January, 1944. The Army Air Force soon ordered 5,000 Shooting Stars, but only a handful made appearances during the war. Lockheed continued production with successive upgrades of the Shooting Star and the aircraft represented half of the U.S. Air Force's jet fighter strength at the outbreak of the Korean War in 1950. Lieutenant Russell Brown used a P-80 to shoot down a Chinese MiG-15 on November 8, 1950, in the world's first dogfight between jet fighters. However, the Air Force relegated the P-80 to second-line status during the Korean War, as greater numbers of the more advanced North American F-86 Sabre jet became available.

Responding to the input of pilots during the Korean War, Kelly Johnson designed a new fighter that would outperform any aircraft in service. Lockheed started testing F-104 Starfighter in 1954, though early crashes marred the test flight program. Following corrections, the air force adopted the Starfighter in 1958. Despite having wings under 8 feet long, the F-104 flew at more than 1,400 miles per hour and higher than 100,000 feet. The Starfighter saw limited action in Vietnam before the air force phased out the aircraft in 1967.

In addition to building fighters, Lockheed produced a mainstay of the U.S. Navy's air arm, the P-3 Orion. After a three-year test program, the first Orions entered service in 1962. The plane was designed for antisubmarine duty and its four turboprop engines gave it a range of 5,200 miles. The Orion remained in service through the end of the twentieth century.

Lockheed's greatest postwar military planes were the company's transports. The first, the C-130 Hercules, flew in 1954 and the air force adopted the plane two years later. The C-130 family proved its versatility in places as diverse as Vietnam and the Arctic. The company followed up the success of the Hercules with the C-141 Starlifter. The C-141 used jet engines to extend its range and lifting capacity beyond the turboprop C-130. The first model flew in 1963 and entered service two years later. The C-141 played an important role in the Vietnam War because it could fly nonstop from California to Saigon, freeing up the shorter-range C-130's for tactical missions. In 1965, Lockheed won a contract to produce the largest transport plane in history, the C-5 Galaxy. The C-5 flew in 1968 and entered service in 1970. The Galaxy allowed cargo loading through both aft doors and the nose and could take off and land in the same distance as a jetliner. The plane became a foundation of the Air Force's transport system due to its ability to carry more than 100 tons of payload.

Lockheed also developed one of the most successful trainer aircraft in history, the T-33 T-Bird. The first T-Bird flew in 1948 and became Lockheed's biggest-selling jet. Air forces around the world adopted the T-33, and it remained in service in the U.S. Air Force for more than forty years.

Events in the History of Lockheed Martin

1926: Allan Loughead (name later changed to Lockheed) establishes Lockheed Aircraft Company in Hollywood, California, where he and Jack Northrup design the popular and record-setting Vega monoplane.

1929: The Lockheed Aircraft Company is purchased by the Detroit Aircraft Corporation, which declares bankruptcy three years later.

1932: The Lockheed Corporation is reorganized by a group of investors who improve the company's fortunes throughout the Great Depression with the production of the dual-engine Electra airliner.

1940's: Lockheed begins a long-term association with the U.S. military, providing P-38 Lightning bombers during World War II and establishing the Advanced Development Projects division, or Skunk Works, a top-secret facility for military aircraft development.

1980's: Lockheed develops the F-117A stealth fighter.

1995: Lockheed merges with the Martin Marietta Corporation.

1996: Lockheed absorbs the defense electronics and systems integration divisions of Loral.

Postwar Commercial Aircraft

Before World War II interrupted commercial air service, Lockheed and other American manufacturers developed four-engine airliners. In Lockheed's case, TWA and its majority stockholder, Howard Hughes, pushed the company to design the Constellation. In 1939, TWA ordered forty of the new airliners, but the war preparations halted production in May, 1941. TWA finally received its first commercial Constellation on October 1, 1945. Despite two early crashes, the Constellation and its successors, the Super Constellation and the Starliner, became great successes. Airlines from South Africa, India, West Germany, and many other countries made the Constellation part of their fleets. In the United States, the final plane in the series, the Starliner, remained in regular service with TWA until 1967 and made the airline's final piston-engine flight.

The success of the Constellation line ended with the advent of jetliners. In 1966, Lockheed began work on its first jetliner, the L-1011 Tristar. The L-1011 and McDonnell Douglas's competing DC-10 both began sales to airlines in 1968. Unfortunately for both companies, the planes were nearly identical and competed for the same marketplace. This competition, combined with the expense of developing the C-5 and L-1011 at the same time, drove Lockheed to the brink of bankruptcy. The company was saved only when the federal government guaranteed Lockheed's credit to lenders in 1971. Between 1970 and 1985, Lockheed built 250 L-1011's, but the program was not as successful as the company had hoped.

Missiles and Space

To take advantage of the demand for missiles in the Cold War, the company founded the Lockheed Missile Systems Division in 1954. This division developed the weapons for the U.S. Navy's ballistic missile submarines. The first missile, the Polaris, had a range of 1,200 nautical miles and became operational in 1960. Lockheed followed with two more variations of the Polaris, eventually increasing the range to 2,500 nautical miles. The missile remained in service until 1982, when the Navy replaced it with another Lockheed product, the Poseidon, first introduced in 1970. The Poseidon was similar to the Polaris, but had a wider diameter. Lockheed followed the Poseidon with the Trident, which came into service in 1981 and extended the Navy's ballistic missile range to more than 4,000 nautical miles. Lockheed's missile and space division also developed ceramic heat-resistant tiles for the space shuttles and built the Hubble Space Telescope.

Corporate Changes

Following the difficulties of the L-1011 program, Lockheed's directors rededicated the company to military and space products. Lockheed purchased General Dynamics F-16 Fighting Falcon division in 1992. In 1996, the company merged with Martin Marietta to form Lockheed Martin. Martin Marietta had designed the B-24 bomber during World War II and the Titan missile and rocket system. The new company entered the twenty-first century building the Air Force's new F-22 Raptor fighter, as well as working on a replacement for the space shuttle, the X-33 VentureStar.

Matthew G. McCoy

Bibliography

Boyne, Walter J. *Beyond the Horizons: The Lockheed Story*. New York: Thomas Dunne Books, 1998. An up-to-date examination of Lockheed from one of America's foremost aviation historians.

Rich, Ben R., and Leo Janos. *Skunk Works: A Personal Memoir of My Years at Lockheed*. Boston: Little, Brown, 1994. A insider's view of Lockheed's famed advanced design division.

Yenne, Bill. *Lockheed*. New York: Crescent Books, 1987. A photographic history of Lockheed's aircraft, suitable for readers of all ages.

See also: Aerospace industry, U.S.; Fighting Falcon; Manufacturers; Mergers; Missiles; Raptor; X planes

Lufthansa

Also known as: Deutsche Lufthansa AG
Date: Founded on January 6, 1953, as a successor to Deutsche Luft Hansa, founded on January 6, 1927
Definition: Flagship air carrier of Germany, and one of the largest airlines in Europe and the world.
Significance: With a careful growth strategy, Lufthansa has been successful in measuring up to the challenges of globalization and liberalization that have been prominent in the airline business. Following its full privatization in 1997, Lufthansa has emerged as one of the largest public companies in both Germany and Europe.

Corporate Structure

Lufthansa is a major German airline headquartered in Frankfurt. It was organized in Cologne on January 6, 1953, as a joint venture of the federal government of Germany,

Events in Lufthansa History

1926: Deutsche Luft Hansa Aktiengesellschaft is formed by the merger of Deutsche Aero Lloyd (DAL) and Junkers Luftverkehr and begins scheduled flights.
1933: The airline is renamed Lufthansa.
1934: Lufthansa makes the first regularly scheduled transoceanic airmail deliveries across the South Atlantic.
1939: The airline initially expands its route network, but it is suspended from operations with the outbreak of World War II.
1945: All Lufthansa flights are canceled, and the airline goes into receivership.
1953: After postwar German air traffic is reestablished, a new company is formed, which renames itself Lufthansa the following year.
1955: Lufthansa resumes scheduled flights.
1960: The airline takes delivery of its first jet aircraft, a Boeing 707.
1970: The airline takes delivery of its first wide-body jumbojet aircraft, a Boeing 747.
1971: Lufthansa retires from its fleet the last of its propeller-driven aircraft.
1990: After Germany's reunification, Lufthansa resumes flights to Berlin, its first in forty-five years.
1997: Lufthansa joins the Star Alliance, a global network of airlines including Air Canada, SAS, Thai Airways, and United Air Lines.

the German National Railway, and the state of Nordrhein-Westfalen. Later, the airline accepted private investors. It was successor to Deutsche Luft Hansa, or DLH, founded on January 6, 1926, which suspended service at war's end in 1945 and was formally liquidated in 1951. The new airline, initially called Aktiengesellschaft für Luftverkehrsbedarf or Luftag, adopted the old name, slightly respelled, in 1954; but whereas the old company had been familiarly called DLH, the new one was popularly called Lufthansa. Lufthansa was fully privatized in 1997. It has emerged, after its privatization, as one of Germany's biggest public companies, with 400,000 shareholders. In addition to flying, Lufthansa is active in several other areas, including ground services, IT services, catering, leisure travel, maintenance repair overhaul, logistics, and passenger services. Lufthansa operates in these areas through several subsidiary companies.

Route Structure

DLH, as the greatest and most comprehensive airline in prewar Europe, had resulted from the merger of Deutscher Aero Lloyd (formed in 1924) and Junkers Luftverkehr (formed in 1921), which together controlled a large network of lines throughout Germany and central Europe, with extensions to London, Moscow, Stockholm, Helsinki, Budapest, and the Persian Gulf. By 1931, DLH was serving Paris, Barcelona, Rome, and Oslo and accounted for one third of all passenger travel and air transport in Europe. The German-built Junkers Ju-52/3m, used by other airlines as well as by DLH, became the most familiar aircraft in European airports, until American-made airliners gradually surpassed it in the late 1930's. In 1934, DLH began the world's first scheduled transoceanic flights—between Germany and South America—but its other experiments in transatlantic and trans-Asian routes were cut short by the outbreak of World War II. Between 1936 and 1938, Lufthansa experimented with scheduled air services across the North Atlantic. After substantial expansion of the route network in 1939, which included flights to Bangkok, Thailand, and Santiago, Chile, the airline suspended air services, with the exception of flights to a handful of European countries.

Only two months after inaugurating scheduled services within Germany on April 1, 1955, Lufthansa began transatlantic flights to New York. In the same year, scheduled service began to Paris, London, Madrid, and Lisbon in Europe, and special flights began to Moscow. In 1956, the first flights were made to Chicago; Montreal, Canada; Rio de Janeiro and São Paulo, Brazil; Buenos Aires, Argentina; Baghdad, Iraq; and Tehran, Iran, followed by initial flights to India in 1958 and resumption of the flights to Bangkok in 1959.

Lufthansa's vast network radiates from Frankfurt am Main and Munich, its two hubs, to such distant cities as Santiago, Chile; Mexico City, Mexico; Los Angeles, California and Anchorage, Alaska in the United States; Tokyo, Japan; Hong Kong, China; Sydney, Australia; and Johannesburg, South Africa, as well as to several airports throughout Europe and the Middle East.

Lufthansa entered the jet age in 1960 with the arrival in the fleet of the Boeing 707, used initially on long-haul routes. Conversion to jet aircraft continued gradually until 1971, when Lufthansa's last propeller-driven aircraft, the Vickers Viscount, was retired. Lufthansa acquired the Boeing 727 and 737 starting in 1964. It took its first delivery of the Boeing 747 in 1970, which was later joined by the McDonnell Douglas DC-10 and the Airbus A300. As of 2001, Lufthansa's fleet included the following aircraft: Boeing 747-400 and 747-200 series, Airbus A340, Airbus

A300-600, Airbus A310, Airbus A321, Airbus A320, Airbus A319, Boeing B-737, Canadair CR1, and AVRO RJ85.

Alliances and Partnerships

Lufthansa, along with Air Canada, SAS, Thai Airways International, and United Air Lines, founded the Star Alliance in 1997. In subsequent years, membership grew to include Air New Zealand, ANA, Ansett Australia, Austrian Airlines, British Midland, Lauda Air, Mexicana Airlines, Singapore Airlines, Tyrolean Airways, and Varig. In 2001, the Star Alliance encompassed fifteen airlines and a network of 130 countries and 815 destinations, making it the world's largest alliance. In addition to its Star Alliance partners, Lufthansa cooperates with several other airlines on such matters as code-share flights and participation in one another's frequent flier programs. Lufthansa's partner airlines as of June, 2001, were South African Airways, Adria Airways, Air Baltic, Air Dolomiti, Croatia Airlines, Czech Airlines, Luxair, Qatar Airways, and Spanair. Additionally, for the regional market, Lufthansa cooperates with several regional carriers: Augsburg Airways, Cirrus Airlines, Contact Air, Rheintalflug, Air Littoral, and Cimber Air. These regional carriers bear the name Team Lufthansa.

Triantafyllos G. Flouris

Bibliography

Groenewege, Adrianus D. *The Compendium of International Civil Aviation*. 2d ed. Geneva, Switzerland: International Air Transport Association, 1999. A comprehensive directory of the major players in international civil aviation, with insightful and detailed articles.

Weimer, Kent J., ed. *Aviation Week and Space Technology: World Aviation Directory*. New York: McGraw-Hill, 2000. An excellent introductory guide on all global companies involved in the aviation business. The information is very basic but very essential as a first introduction to each company.

See also: Air Canada; Air carriers; SAS; Singapore Airlines; United Air Lines

Luftwaffe

Definition: Germany's air force from the early 1930's to the end of World War II.

Significance: The Luftwaffe used fast-moving offensives to destroy enemy aircraft. Although it was effective in the early years of World War II, it became less so as the war progressed, losing its air superiority due to aircraft obsolescence, economic inferiority, poor organization, and poor leadership.

History

After World War I, in which Germany had been roundly defeated by the war's length as much as by the economic superiority of its opponents, General Hans von Seeckt, the commander of the German Army, realized that fast, mobile offensives would be necessary to avoid prolonged future wars that Germany could not win. He therefore devised the military strategy of the Blitzkrieg, or lightning war, fast-moving surprise attacks.

The Luftwaffe, designed around the Blitzkrieg concept, was initially very effective during World War II in gaining air superiority via short, independent operations all over the European continent. As the European air war drew on, however, the Luftwaffe was engaged in a contest that it could not win.

From the beginning, the Luftwaffe's leaders saw the necessity of air superiority. Its chiefs of staff noted that air support of ground forces at the start of a war did not mitigate the damage inflicted by functional enemy air forces. From the start of any campaign, the Luftwaffe's primary efforts were focused on the destruction of all enemy aircraft. Its bombers crushed enemy bombers on the ground, disrupting potential sorties, and its fighters hunted down any enemy aircraft able to become airborne.

The Luftwaffe carried out its activities via autonomous air fleets, known as the Luftflotten. Each Luftflotte comprised both aircraft and support units. Technologically, the aircraft were suited for offensive counterair missions (OCAMs) that destroyed enemy aircraft on the ground. German Stuka bombers had the range and payload to reach and damage the air bases that held the most enemy aircraft. Twin-engine fighters escorted bombers, warding off enemy fighters until the OCAM was completed. Single-engine Messerschmitt fighters fought enemy aircraft.

Luftwaffe aircraft enabled short-offensive campaigns but had little use in other types of air warfare, such as attacks on training bases in the rear and other distant sources of enemy air power. German bombers had low ranges, meager payloads, and very little defensive armament. Later failure of newer escort fighters and the short ranges of all existing escorts exacerbated the problem, restricting German air power to use in the battlefield. Germany successfully applied its OCAM doctrine during the first two years of the war. These attacks destroyed numerous aircraft and caused the remainder to operate inefficiently. However, these victories cost the Luftwaffe huge aircraft losses. For example, in the two-month battle for France, 36 percent of all German aircraft were either damaged or lost. Such losses were initially acceptable, because they were suffered in the defeat of several Allied air forces. However, over the course of prolonged warfare, this high loss rate was damaging to the German cause, especially after German offensive campaigns failed against both England and the Soviet Union.

In 1940, the Luftwaffe was unable to defeat the Royal Air Force (RAF) in the Battle of Britain. After unsuccessful battles over the English Channel, a three-week German campaign against RAF bases made some progress but was changed to unsuccessful day attacks and then to nocturnal terror attacks. German inability to win was due to RAF defense strategy and absence of a ground war to distract the RAF.

Similarly, the Germans had initial success in their air war against Russia by employing the OCAM doctrine, but the German ground forces ultimately proved unsuccessful. The unanticipated Siberian air power, the untenable Russian winter weather, and the vastness of the eastern front all led to the campaign's failure and the Luftwaffe's weakening. As General von Seeckt had noted, opponents pushed to defense are broken by destruction of aircraft. German failures in Britain and Russia forced the Luftwaffe into defensive counterair battle (DCAB), as the need to win air battles over its homeland exhausted Germany's hope of air superiority.

The prolonged defensive air war forced the Luftwaffe to adopt a defensive strategy in its organization, equipment, and deployment. Overwhelmed by Allied aircraft production, German strategy consisted largely of annihilating Allied bombers. This strategy was impractical, given the Allied air superiority. Luftwaffe generals, however, clung to false hope that if they could decimate enough Allied bombers, they could cause the cessation of Allied air offensives. By 1944, two whole Luftflotten were used in this way. As the Allied threat grew, the German expansion and refinement of its air defense included the development of radar and automated fighter control systems, an increase in armor and armament, the use of aerial bombs and cannon on board fighter planes.

German aircraft manufacters shifted from the production of bombers to production of fighters, giving the Germans success throughout 1943. Although Allied bomber raids were not stopped entirely, they evolved into less effective, nighttime operations with huge bomber losses. However, these German victories were only temporary, because at the same time, hundreds of German planes and pilots were lost in the battles. The air war became a lost cause.

Although the Germans made other technological advances, including the use of jets and surface-to-air missiles, these came too late to be useful. Huge numbers of Allied air forces drove the Luftwaffe from the sky. Amid failing defenses, the German air force stubbornly held to its offensive practice. Its forces kept declining, however, and the last major OCAM achievements occurred as follows. In June, 1944, a night raid on Poltava, a Ukrainian city on the eastern front, destroyed many U.S. bombers caught on the ground. Operation Bodenplatte, the last major German fighter operation, was waged in Belgium, Holland, and France, in January, 1945. It used the entire German fighter force to raid Allied airfields. There, single-engine fighters and green German pilots carried out a mission in which 30 percent losses occurred. Both operations were destructive, but barely altered the numbers of Allied aircraft available in Europe.

Leadership

Possibly, the Luftwaffe had always been in an untenable position, because Nazi Germany was a dictatorship ruled by its inflexible chancellor, Adolf Hitler. The German General Staff was faced with this problem as well as with the politicking, drug addiction, and incompetentcy of high-ranking government officials.

An example is that of Hermann Göring. A former World War I fighter ace and the head of the Luftwaffe, he was unable to function adequately or consistently due to his drug abuse and his inability to counter Hitler's preference for the production of bombers instead of fighters. These weaknesses in the Luftwaffe's command led to the decrease and eventual collapse of the force's fighting ability.

A contrasting example is that of the able Adolf Galland, a fighter ace of the Condor Legion who also participated in the German invasions of Poland and France and the Battle of Britain. In 1941, he became the commander of the Luftwaffe's fighter arm and by 1943, had been promoted to the rank of major general. In 1943 and 1944, he ably commanded Germany's already-failing fighter squadrons against Allied bombers. Despite Galland's resourceful leadership of a crumbling air operation, Hitler and Göring blamed him for weakened Luftwaffe air defenses in 1944 and, soon thereafter, relieved him of his command.

Many critics blame the Luftwaffe's failure on its leaders, based on three flaws. First is the fact that the Luftwaffe high command used training units in battles such as

The Luftwaffe's field marshall Hermann Göring (left) discusses plans with chief of staff Major General Hans Jechonnek in 1940. (Hulton Archive)

Poltava. This decision was seen as damaging, because continued training operations were essential to winning the war. Second is the perception that the Luftwaffe was too slow in recognizing the war's attritional nature and implementing the defense measures needed for any chance of eventual success. Göring has been accused of overconfidence in the offensive air-war strategy and failure to see the need to prepare for failure. The third major Luftwaffe shortcoming was in its inferior equipment and inability to modernize or build heavy bombers that could compete with those of the Allies.

Aircraft

Much of the basis for eventual Luftwaffe failure may lie in Hitler's long-standing preference for bombers over fighters. Under Hitler's dictatorship, it was difficult for military leaders to work around such a prejudice. This theory may partly explain the relative obsolescence of the Luftwaffe aircraft toward the end of the war.

Although efforts were made to produce new aircraft, promising new designs apparently did not work out well. For example, the Junkers Ju-88, a twin-engine bomber planned as the successor to the Ju-87 Stuka, was not airworthy. In its production, designers increased the Ju-88's weight to enable dive-bombing, thereby reducing its effective range and speed and rendering it ineffective against the increasingly faster aircraft being produced by the Allies.

Furthermore, the Heinkel He-117 aircraft, an attempt to produce long-range bombers, was a disaster. Its planned weight was doubled in order to make it suitable for dive-bombing. More devastating was the aircraft's tendency to fall apart during dives and to explode in flight. Moreover, the Messerschmitt Me-210 fighter, planned to replace the Luftwaffe's fighter workhorse, the Me-109, was a dismal failure. This aircraft and others were canceled early in production, and the Germans were never able to build a successful four-engine bomber. These failures occurred at times when Germany could not afford to squander its slim resources.

Consequently, the Luftwaffe relied on a few tried-and-true aircraft, such as the Junkers Stuka bombers and the Messerschmitt Me-109 fighters. These aircraft were, by the early 1940's, relatively obsolete.

The Stuka dive-bomber, a low-winged, single-engine aircraft, was a very successful weapon during the first half of the war. Stukas employed dive-bombing techniques developed by the U.S. Navy, dropping bombs while diving and then moving into getaway flight mode. Special brakes slowed Stuka dives and gave pilots time to aim bombs. The bombers were armed with four 8-millimeter machine guns, two of which were operated by a rear-gunner. Late in the war, the rear-mounted guns were replaced with a heavier gun. The Stuka carried 1,100- or 550-pound bombs and had two 110-pound bombs under each wing. Although the plane was periodically modified throughout the war, its maximum speed remained 210 miles per hour. Eventually, it proved no match for faster Allied fighters.

The Me-109 fighter was used to great effect in World War II. Powered by a fuel-injected, Daimler-Benz engine, this low-winged, single-seater, monoplane had a top speed of 350 miles per hour and a ceiling of around 40,000 feet. It held two 20-millimeter cannons and two machine guns. Me-109's were the pride and joy of the Luftwaffe, faster and much more maneuverable than most Allied fighters. However, the Me-109's range was limited by a small fuel capacity, and by 1944, Allied fighters had outstripped it in every way.

Sanford S. Singer

Bibliography

Cooper, Matthew. *The German Air Force, 1933-1945: An Anatomy of Failure*. London: Jane's, 1981. A book discussing the Luftwaffe's operation and basis of failure.

Corum, James S. *The Luftwaffe: Creating the Operational Air War, 1918-1940*. Lawrence: University of Kansas Press, 1997. A fine text describing the Luftwaffe and the motivation of its creators.

Killen, John. *A History of the Luftwaffe*. Garden City, N.Y.: Doubleday, 1968. A solid description of the Luftwaffe written while its immediate memory lingered.

Pimlott, John. *Luftwaffe: The Illustrated History of the German Air Force in World War II*. Osceola, Wis.: Motorbooks International, 1998. An informative account of the history, armament, and operations of the Luftwaffe.

See also: Bombers; Fighter pilots; Messerschmitt aircraft; Royal Air Force; World War II

M

McDonnell Douglas

Date: Formed in April, 1967; combined with the Boeing Corporation in August, 1997

Definition: In combining the McDonnell Aircraft Company and the Douglas Aircraft Company, McDonnell Douglas became one of the largest airplane manufacturers in the world.

Significance: The corporation produced some of the best-known passenger airplane series, including the DC series and the MD series, such well-known military aircraft as the F-15 Eagle, the F-18 Hornet, the C-17 transport, and the Apache attack helicopter, while providing technical aid in developing the Tomahawk Cruise Missile and Skylab.

The Douglas Company

The McDonnell Douglas Aircraft Corporation was the creation of two pioneers in the commercial and military aircraft industry. Donald Douglas (1892-1981) began the Davis-Douglas Company in 1921. The aircraft company built both commercial and military planes, including the DT-1 and the DT-2 torpedo bombers for the U.S. Navy. The Douglas World Cruisers were the first passenger planes to complete an around-the-world flight. Douglas's partner soon sold his interest in the company, and Douglas incorporated the Douglas Company in July, 1921. Douglas used some of the great airplane engineering minds of his time, including Jack Northrop, to develop commercial airplanes for the burgeoning airline industry. Northrop left the company, but Douglas continued, spreading his military aircraft development to include the C-1 transport and the Devastator torpedo bomber for the United States in World War II.

Upon buying the Northrop Company, Douglas became even further involved in the production of military aircraft. Douglas produced some of the best-known and most reliable fighters and bombers for the Allied air forces. The A-20 Havoc was one of the war's most dependable bombers, able to withstand considerable punishment and fly after heavy damage from ground fire, flying many a crew member back safely. Some seven thousand of the planes were produced during the war. The Dauntless was a carrier bomber used in the Pacific theater and was effective and less likely to be shot down than many other bombers used in the theater. The A-26 bomber was used in three wars, including those in Korea and Vietnam, proving its effectiveness and durability.

The military projects were overshadowed, however, when compared to the company's success in the commercial plane business. In 1933, the Douglas Company began the DC series of passenger planes. It was those planes, particularly the DC-3, built in the 1930's, and the DC-9, built in the 1960's, that revolutionized air travel for ordinary people. It was those planes that also made the Douglas Company an attractive takeover target for one of its competitors.

The McDonnell Company

James McDonnell (1899-1980) started his first aircraft company, J. S. McDonnell & Associates, in 1928 but saw it dissolve under the strain of the Great Depression. After working as the chief engineer for another company from 1933 to 1938, McDonnell started a new company, McDonnell Aircraft Corporation, in 1939 and took advantage of the need for military planes to meet the crises of the time. With the United States rearming and then fighting a war, McDonnell's company, located in St. Louis, Missouri, began to provide parts for the American war effort. After the war, McDonnell became a major supplier for the military and the developing U.S. space program. The company built the F-4 Phantom, one of the fastest fighter jets of its generation. Its greatest contribution during the 1950's and 1960's was the development of rockets capable of lifting large payloads into orbit. In addition, McDonnell was a major player in developing the capsules for early crewed spaceflight. The company constructed the first Mercury spacecraft used for the United States' first crewed orbit of Earth. Through the early 1960's, McDonnell was one of the primary suppliers of spacecraft for the Gemini Program of the National Aeronautics and Space Administration (NASA). Missile technology created more growth for the company. McDonnell was responsible for building the Nike missile system, then the British Skybolt system. It also developed one of the first ballistic missiles, the Thor, capable of short launches, beginning in 1956.

The McDonnell and Douglas Merger

With financial difficulties looming as development costs for the DC-8 and DC-9 ballooned, the Douglas Aircraft

Company sought financial backing by means of a merger. Losses had totaled hundreds of millions of dollars, with many DC-8's completed but lacking engines to fly them. McDonnell proved to be the best fit for Douglas, as it wanted to expand its operations to include transport planes such as those built by Douglas. On April 28, 1967, the two companies formally merged to become McDonnell Douglas. The founders of the two partners continued to serve on the board of directors of the new company and added their input to major decisions. The main production facilities for the company included McDonnell's base of operations in St. Louis, Missouri, and Douglas's in Long Beach, California. While these would remain the major production headquarters, during difficult financial times in the 1970's some of the California subsidiaries were closed.

The first commercial transport developed by the company was the DC-10, the last plane to carry the designation of the DC series; the new company changed future planes to the MD series. First flown in the early 1970's, the DC-10 proved to be a popular aircraft, although it suffered through difficulties at the end of that decade. With the companies' merger, the new MD series was launched, with the first plane coming off the assembly line being the MD-80 or the Super Eighty. The MD-80 represented a different approach to passenger aircraft in the size of the fuselage, the wings, and the engines. During the 1980's and 1990's, the company built on the Douglas Aircraft Company's success with the DC-10 series and modified those planes to include the MD-90, the MD-95, and the MD-11, which was to replace the DC-10. While the MD-80 and MD-95 were partially successful airplanes, the MD-90 was less successful and was discontinued upon McDonnell Douglas's merger with Boeing in 1997.

While the construction of civilian passenger aircraft continued based on the Douglas designs, McDonnell Aircraft's emphasis on military flight gave the combined company another market to meet. One of the company's biggest sellers in the 1970's and the 1980's was the F-15 Eagle. The fighter plane became known as one of the most technologically advanced fighters of its time and one of the most maneuverable planes to fly. The F-15 not only served as the frontline aircraft for the United States Air Force during that time but also was coveted by other nations familiar with its capabilities. As the Air Force began looking for a new, more technologically advanced fighter, McDonnell Douglas began selling F-15's, with government approval, to such American allies as Japan and Israel. The company also built the F/A-18 Hornet for the Navy. The attack plane was based on aircraft carriers, providing the Navy with quick strike capabilities all over the world. Twelve hundred Hornets were built and used both in various combat situations and by the Blue Angels aerobatics team in their demonstration flights. The Hornet continued to be produced even as McDonnell Douglas was merging with Boeing. The next generation of the fighter, the F/A-18E/F Super Hornet began flying in 1995.

The company was also instrumental in developing vertical takeoff and landing aircraft. With experience in building helicopters, McDonnell Douglas began the difficult task of designing an airplane that could land and take off from a sitting stop, much like a helicopter. At the same time, once the plane reached the air, it could fly at speeds approaching many other fighter aircraft, making it less vulnerable in the air than were helicopters. During the 1960's, several prototypes proved to be too expensive to build. Only when McDonnell Douglas joined with British Aerospace was an affordable model built, the AV-8B Harrier jump jet. The planes could take off from a sitting position and land in most small clearings. The Harrier II Plus was a modified and updated version of the original aircraft and began flying in 1992.

The company's military aircraft wing was strengthened in 1984 with its purchase of Hughes Aircraft from General Electric. This combined two of the main competitors in the building of attack helicopters for the U.S. Army. With the addition of Hughes, McDonnell Douglas was responsible for the new generation of Apache attack helicopters used so effectively by American troops during the Persian Gulf War. McDonnell Douglas also continued its tradition of building dependable military transports. The C-17 or Globemaster III was the largest American military plane ever built. It flew for the first time in September, 1991, and allowed the military to move large amounts of matériel and troops across continents and oceans.

Missiles and Outer Space

With its passenger aircraft and military planes competing well with other companies, McDonnell Douglas continued to branch out and remain involved in developing missile technology for NASA and the U.S. military. For the U.S. space program, the company modified one of its Saturn rockets to create a permanent space station that became known as Skylab. Launched in May, 1973, Skylab allowed three people to live in what had once been the hydrogen holding tank for the Saturn rocket. This makeshift orbiting lab was used for little over a year, floating empty for five years before burning up in the atmosphere in July, 1979. It was the first U.S. space station and the only one until the International Space Station began operations in 2000. Closer to Earth, the company worked on some of the most advanced missile technology of the era. With the success of its Talon antiaircraft missile, McDonnell Douglas also developed its Harpoon antiship missile.

Its most important and most difficult task was development of the BGM 109 Tomahawk cruise missile. Cruise missiles are built to deliver ordnance, whether conventional explosives or nuclear weapons, beneath enemy radar. This requires the missile to fly only hundreds of feet above the ground and to have the capability of identifying a single target among all the surrounding ground clutter. The technological achievement in building a guidance system for the cruise missiles earned McDonnell Douglas the contract to build much of the military's missile supply.

The Boeing Merger
With military contracts on the decline and the severe losses suffered by major airlines during the energy crunch of the early 1990's, the orders for military and commercial passenger planes slipped. Failure to win contracts from the U.S. military placed McDonnell Douglas in financial difficulties. It was not alone, as during the 1990's several airplane manufacturers including Lockheed, Martin Marietta, Northrup, and Grumman began merging in order to survive the turbulent market. In August, 1997, McDonnell Douglas was formally merged with the Boeing Corporation. This move gave Boeing two of the largest-selling passenger jet series, the 700 series, including the 740 and 770, and the DC/MD series. Suddenly Boeing became the dominant player in the U.S. market and the main competitor with the European Airbus Companie for overseas contracts. During its thirty-year history, from 1967 to 1997, McDonnell Douglas proved to be an innovator in the development and modification of passenger airplanes. Its work in the military field included such far-reaching weapons as the Tomahawk cruise missile, the Apache attack helicopter, the F-15 Eagle, and the F-18 Hornet. By combining the two companies, each with its own expertise, McDonnell Douglas became a powerhouse in the aircraft production industry during the 1970's and 1980's. While the name itself has disappeared, many of the products created by both the individual and the combined companies continue to fly passengers all over the world.

Douglas Clouatre

Bibliography
Badrocke, Mike, and Bill Sunston. *The Illustrated History of McDonnell Douglas Aircraft: From Cloudster to Boeing.* Oxford, England: Osprey, 1999. A colorful, well-illustrated book describing the history of the McDonnell and Douglas airplane companies, their merger, and how their planes revolutionized air travel.

Francillon, Rene. *McDonnell Douglas Aircraft Since 1920.* Annapolis Md.: Naval Institute Press, 1990. Discusses the civilian and military aircraft developed by both companies prior to their merger and after their combination.

Jenkins, Dennis. *McDonnell Douglas F-15 Eagle.* Leicester, England: Midland, 1998. Examines in depth the capabilities and uses of one of the best fighter planes produced in the world. It includes pictures of the plane in the air and on the ground.

Norris, Guy, and Mark Wagner. *Douglas Jetliners.* Osceola, Wis.: Motorbooks International, 1999. Focuses on the Douglas passenger planes, with special emphasis on the DC family and its development and capabilities.

Singfield, Tom. *Classic Airliners.* Leicester, England: Midland, 2000. An introduction to many of the original planes used during the early years of the airline industry, including the DC-3 and other Douglas planes.

Waddington, Terry. *McDonnell Douglas DC-9.* Osceola, Wis.: Motorbooks International, 1998. Focuses on one of the best known of the Douglas planes, with pictures of the exterior and interior and an in-depth discussion of its capabilities.

_____. *McDonnell Douglas DC-10* Osceola, Wis.: World Transport Press, 2000. Examines the last of the DC models, providing details on its upgrades over its predecessors and its continued use.

See also: Aerospace industry, U.S.; Air Force, U.S.; Airbus; Airline industry, U.S.; Airplanes; Apache helicopter; Blue Angels; Boeing; Cargo aircraft; Commercial flight; DC plane family; Eagle; Harrier jets; Hornet; Lockheed Martin; Manufacturers; MD plane family; Mergers; Military flight; Missiles; Navy pilots, U.S.; Rockets; Saturn rockets; 707 plane family; Spaceflight; Transport aircraft

Mach number

Definition: The ratio between the speed of an object in a medium to the speed of sound in the same medium.
Significance: The speed of sound is the speed at which the weakest disturbances in pressure propagate through a medium. In a gas, the speed of sound is close to the average speed of random thermal motion of molecules, because disturbances propagate by the

Mach number

collisions between molecules. Thus, the Mach number is also viewed as the ratio between the speed of organized motion of the gas, or a body relative to the gas, and the average speed of random thermal motion in the gas.

Calculation

The Mach number is named in honor of Ernst Mach, a nineteenth century Austrian scientist who conducted experimental research on the aerodynamics of artillery shells. Speed ranges in the field of aerodynamics are classified according to Mach number. A Mach number of 1 corresponds to motion at the speed of sound. The speed of sound thus depends on the temperature of the gas. The speed of sound in air at a temperature of 0 degrees Celsius (273.15 Kelvins) is 331 meters per second. To find the speed of sound in meters per second at other air temperatures in the range 200 to 700 Kelvins (from minus 73.15 to 426.85 degress Celsius), divide 5,471 (obtained as product of 331 and the square root of 273.15) by the square root of the air temperature in Kelvins. The Mach number is then the ratio of an object's speed to this speed of sound.

Mach Ranges

The low-speed regime is generally identified with Mach numbers of less than 0.3. In this range, the maximum change in density that can occur when the flow is stopped is less than about 5 percent of the actual density. Hence, such flows are also described as being incompressible. Small propeller-driven airplanes and helicopters fly in this speed range, though their propeller or rotor tips move quickly enough relative to the air to encounter Mach numbers close to 1.

The subsonic range is generally the range from Mach 0.3 to 1.0. In this range, the changes in density associated with changes in Mach number become significant. The lift coefficient and drag coefficient rise more steeply with increased angle of attack as Mach number increases. According to the Prandtl-Glauert rule, the lift coefficient associated with a given angle of attack scales with the number resulting from 1 divided by the square root of 1 minus the square of the Mach number. The drag coefficient also increases with Mach number and with thickness. Thus, aircraft flying in this range use thinner airfoils and smaller angles of attack. Turboprop aircraft reach speeds well into the subsonic regime. Much of the close air combat between fighter planes that involves sharp maneuvers occurs in this speed range.

The range that includes Mach 1 and values slightly greater and less than Mach 1 is called the transonic regime, roughly taken as Mach 0.8 to 1.2. Transonic flows include both supersonic and subsonic regions. Most modern airliners cruise in the transonic regime. Although the actual flight Mach number is below 1.0, there is some supersonic flow over the wings. The critical Mach number is the lowest flight Mach number where sonic conditions, in which the Mach number equals 1, are first encountered on the airfoil.

When the flow speed, or the speed of an object relative to the medium, is clearly greater than the speed of sound, the speed is said to be supersonic. Bullets, artillery shells, surface-to-air missiles, and air-to-air missiles all typically operate in the supersonic regime, with Mach numbers up to about 3.5. Most modern fighter aircraft can fly at supersonic speeds for short durations, with their engines operating on afterburners. The Lockheed Martin F-22 is capable of cruising at supersonic speeds without afterburners. Large aircraft capable of cruising at supersonic speeds are the North American B-70 Valkyrie bomber, the British

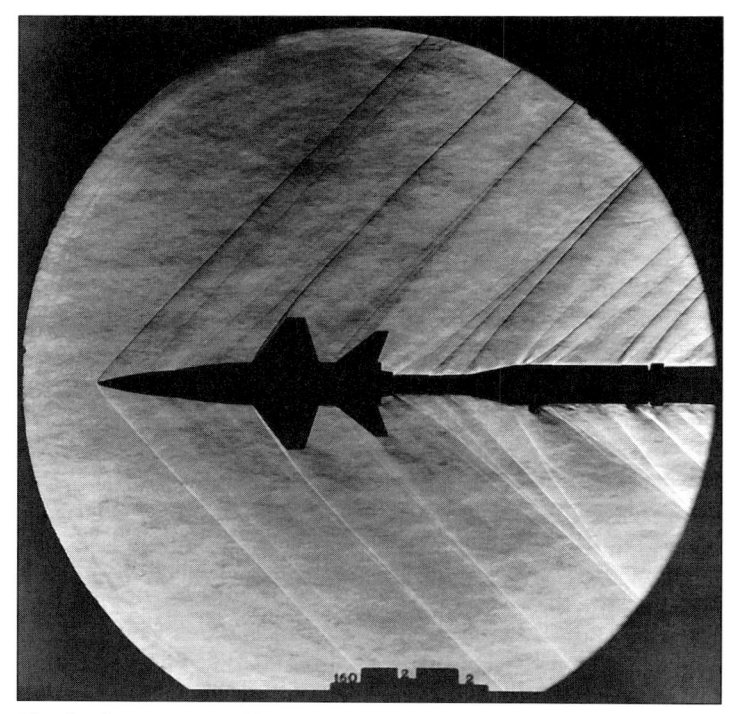

The shock waves caused by supersonic flight can be seen emanating from a model of the X-15 as it flies through a supersonic pressure tunnel. (NASA)

Aerospace/Aerospatiale Concorde, the Tupolev Tu-144, and the Tupolev Tu-44 Backfire Bomber.

Speeds greater than five times the speed of sound are described as hypersonic speeds. Spacecraft and missile warheads reentering Earth's atmosphere fly at hypersonic speeds, with Mach numbers as high as 36 for the Apollo capsule and about 25 for the space shuttle.

The importance of Mach number to flight can be seen from the Mach cone. An object moving at a Mach number of 2 through air generates pressure disturbances that propagate in all directions at the speed of sound in the medium of air. If the speed of sound were 300 meters per second, when the object reached a given point, the disturbances it had generated a second before would have spread within a sphere whose radius was only 300 meters, yet the object itself would have traveled 600 meters in the same second. Disturbances generated 0.1 seconds before would have reached a radius of only 30 meters, yet the object would have traveled 60 meters. The disturbances generated at each intermediate point propagate out to smaller and smaller distances, all lying within the Mach cone.

The Mach cone has its apex at the location of the object, and its axis is the path taken by the object to reach that point. The angle made by the axis of the Mach cone surface is called the Mach angle. This is the inclination of the weakest wave front generated by an object moving at supersonic speeds through a medium. Such a weak wave is called a Mach wave.

The region ahead of the Mach cone is called the zone of silence. In this region, the sound from the approaching object cannot have reached at the instant in question. The Mach angle is thus given by the inverse sine of the reciprocal of Mach number. For example, if the Mach number is 2, the Mach angle is 30 degrees, whereas for a Mach number of 3, the Mach angle is 19.47 degrees.

Most disturbances created by moving objects involve large pressure differences. These disturbances raise the temperature of the air, and hence move faster, accumulating along a shock front. Shocks formed by blunt objects can reach a shock angle of 90 degrees: Such shocks are called normal shocks, and they result in subsonic flow on the downwind side of the shock. As the flight Mach number of a wing exceeds the critical Mach number, the drag caused by the occurrence of shocks rises sharply. Early theoretical analyses predicted that the drag would rise to extremely high values, preventing an aircraft from accelerating through the speed of sound. This was called the sound barrier, the existence of which was conclusively disproved when Air Force Captain Charles E. "Chuck" Yeager flew the Bell X-1 rocket plane faster than the speed of sound in 1947 and became the first person to fly faster than Mach 1.

Narayanan M. Komerath

Bibliography

Anderson, J. D. *Hypersonic and High-Temperature Gas Dynamics*. Washington, D.C.: American Institute of Aeronautics and Astronautics, 2000. An authoritative text on flight at high Mach numbers, with historical discussions based on the author's research at the Smithsonian Air and Space Museum.

Bertin, J. J., and M. L. Smith. *Aerodynamics for Engineers*. 2d ed. Englewood Cliffs, N.J.: Prentice Hall, 1989. An undergraduate-level engineering text and an excellent source for methods and data on various aspects of flight.

See also: Aerodynamics; Forces of flight; High-speed flight; Hypersonic flight; Sound barrier; Supersonic flight; X planes; Chuck Yeager

Maintenance

Definition: Regularly scheduled inspections and periodic adjustment and repair of aircraft.

Significance: Ongoing maintenance operations enhance the safety of aircraft and the well-being of the flying public. They also ensure that aircraft operators comply with insurance companies' mandates to reduce risk and liability.

Inspections and Repairs

Every aircraft registered in the United States must be maintained in accordance with Federal Aviation Regulations (FARs) to ensure continued airworthiness. This is accomplished through regularly scheduled inspections and periodic maintenance. The largest segment of American aviation is commonly called general aviation and includes thousands of privately owned aircraft as well as those operated for business purposes. General aviation aircraft range from two-seater trainers to fully equipped corporate jets and also include experimental, or homebuilt, aircraft.

All small aircraft of up to 12,500 pounds gross weight must undergo an annual inspection of the entire airframe structure, the power plant, and propeller, if so equipped, and all accessories and systems. FAR 43 lists the required scope and detail of the annual inspection and includes an approval statement to be written in the aircraft maintenance record, or logbook, which allows that aircraft to be operated for another year. Any necessary repairs must be completed before the inspector signs the approval.

In addition to the annual inspection, there is a required inspection for every one hundred hours of operation, if the aircraft is being used for hire. Rental aircraft, flight training, and all passenger-carrying revenue flights fall in this category. The one-hundred-hour inspection is performed to the same scope and detail as the annual inspection.

In Appendix A of FAR 43, maintenance is divided into three categories: major, minor, and preventive. Major repairs and alterations pertain to the integrity of the aircraft type design, or, the original configuration chosen by the manufacturer and approved by the Federal Aviation Administration (FAA). An authorized inspector must approve such repairs and alterations before returning the aircraft to service. Minor repairs and alterations may be performed and approved by a certificated airframe or power plant mechanic. A licensed pilot may perform preventive maintenance. All these maintenance actions must be entered in the appropriate aircraft and engine logbooks.

Large aircraft of more than 12,500 pounds gross weight are usually maintained under a program designed by the aircraft manufacturer and custom-tailored to suit the particular owner or operator's needs. Each program is unique and must be reviewed and approved by the FAA.

The amount of time an aircraft is not available for use due to inspection and maintenance is known as downtime. To minimize downtime and maximize utility, an operator may place the aircraft in a progressive inspection program. Under the progressive inspection program, the entire aircraft is inspected during the course of a year, but the inspection itself is broken into several smaller segments at specified intervals. A typical progressive inspection program calls for inspection of the wings after one hundred hours of operation, the engine or engines at two hundred hours, the fuselage and tail section at three hundred hours, and the landing gear at four hundred hours, The cycle begins again with the wings at five hundred hours. Each progressive inspection program is designed for a specific operator using a specific aircraft and must be reviewed and approved by the FAA.

Maintenance Facilities

General aviation maintenance is usually performed by a fixed-base operator (FBO) at the local airport. The FBO may be a large, full-service complex offering fuel sales, aircraft rentals, flight instruction, engine overhauls, aircraft refurbishing, and charter flights. Some FBOs are one-person maintenance shops on private airstrips. An FBO may hold a Repair Station Certificate, issued by the FAA, that describes the types of specialized maintenance the FBO is equipped and qualified to perform. Repair stations are regulated under FARs 43 and 145 and may be certified to perform inspections, repairs, and maintenance on instruments, propellers, navigation and communication equipment, and accessory components, as well as on complete aircraft.

Many corporations have full-time flight and maintenance personnel to ensure aircraft availability and readiness. This advantage enhances the convenience of executive travel and provides additional support for corporate growth and development.

Airline Maintenance

Major air carriers are regulated under FAR 121 and usually operate large, transport-category jet aircraft. Their complex and detailed maintenance programs are designed by the aircraft manufacturer. They are tailored to each airline's operational needs and must be separately approved by the FAA.

A typical airline maintenance program may include daily preflight inspections, weekly service checks, and periodic inspections, known as phase checks. Phase checks are usually lettered alphabetically, with each inspection being more detailed and occurring at longer intervals. An A-check may be scheduled every ninety days to check tires, fluid quantities, systems operation, and general aircraft conidition. A D-check, however, is a comprehensive inspection and overhaul of the complete airframe, engines, and accessories, along with electronics upgrades, corrosion control and subsequent repainting. This type of inspection and repair usually occurs about every five to six years and may take several months to complete.

Commuter airlines operate smaller aircraft to serve the outlying areas away from the major hubs of large cities and large airline activity. Commuter airlines are regulated under FAR 135 to operate and maintain less complicated aircraft without compromising safety. A commuter airline maintenance program is generally a progressive inspection and repair schedule designed to interface with that airline's flight profile. It is usually based on the aircraft manufacturer's maintenance manuals and must be approved by the FAA.

Military Maintenance

Military aviation is mission specific. Each type of military aircraft is designed for a particular task. Bombers, fighters, tankers, and trainers play exclusive roles in the overall military aviation effort. Such type division is reflected in military maintenance. Technicians are trained on a specific type of aircraft, on which they may continue to work for several years.

In addition, each aircraft is subdivided by system, such as engines, hydraulics, electrical, and fuel. A different team of trained specialists maintains each system. A crew chief, trained and experienced in several systems, is assigned to each aircraft, and serves as the maintenance coordinator for the specialist teams.

Maintenance Training

The privileges and limitations of aircraft mechanic ratings are listed in FAR 65. Each mechanic must perform maintenance operations in compliance with the regulation.

Maintenance Ratings. Airframe mechanics may inspect, repair, and maintain airframe structures, systems, and components according to the applicable manufacturers' maintenance manuals. They may not repair instruments, navigation equipment, or communication equipment, and they may not approve major repairs and alterations as defined in FAR 43. They may, however, perform one-hundred-hour inspections on airframes and approve them for return to service after repairs.

Power plant mechanics may inspect, repair, and maintain engines, accessories, and propellers according to applicable manufacturers' maintenance manuals. They may not approve major repairs and alterations, and they may not perform major repairs on propellers. They may, however, perform 100-hour inspections on power plants and approve them for return to service after repairs.

Most aircraft mechanics working in the general aviation maintenance industry hold both the airframe and power plant (A&P) ratings. Both ratings are granted indefinitely and are valid until surrendered, suspended, or revoked. Although not required by regulation in the aircraft manufacturing and major airline industries, the A&P ratings usually bring higher salaries and better job positions.

An employee of a FAR-145-certified repair station may qualify for a Repairman Certificate. This certificate is issued after the employee has been sufficiently trained and experienced in the particular maintenance tasks performed. Unlike Airframe and Power Plant Certificates, the Repairman Certificate is valid for the specified tasks only while the holder is in the employ of that particular repair station.

A Repairman Certificate may also be issued to the primary builder of an experimental, or homebuilt, aircraft. The repairman may then perform condition inspections on that aircraft. A condition inspection is similar to the annual inspection required on standard-category aircraft.

Aircraft mechanics holding both airframe and power plant ratings may also hold an inspection authorization. They may perform annual inspections of the entire aircraft and approve or disapprove it for return to service. They may also inspect any major repairs or alterations to the aircraft and approve it for return to service. Unlike Airframe and Power Plant Certificates, the Inspection Authorization must be renewed every year.

License Requirements. The requirements for the Airframe, Power Plant, and Repairman Certificates and for the Inspection Authorization are given in FAR 65. The regulation includes training and experience requirements, as well as written tests for subject knowledge and practical tests for demonstration of acquired skills.

There are two ways to obtain an A&P license: one must either graduate from an approved school or qualify through documented relevant experience. There are approximately 150 certificated aviation maintenance technician schools in the United States. Under FAR 147, these schools must provide a minimum of 1,900 hours of classroom instruction and shop experience. The FAA inspects these schools periodically to ensure regulatory compliance and to assist graduates in the certification process.

Aircraft maintenance personnel wishing to obtain A&P licenses may also present documented evidence of their work experience for FAA review and evaluation. The minimum requirements are eighteen months of full-time appropriate maintenance experience for either the airframe or the power plant rating or thirty months for both ratings together. Applicants may obtain their experience while serving in the military in selected job classifications or while being employed by a certified repair station, airline maintenance base, or aircraft modification facility. After reviewing and verifying the applicants's documents and experience, the FAA issues permission for the applicant to take the written examination for the rating sought.

Testing Procedures. The written examination for the A&P license comprises three parts. The general test covers information that could apply to either airframe or power plant maintenance, such as regulations, publications, proper use of tools and equipment, aircraft hardware, and other related subjects. The airframe and power plant tests are subject-specific, as their names imply. The general test must be taken in conjunction with either of the other tests but is not repeated for the second rating.

After successful completion of the written examinations, the applicant schedules an appointment with the local designated mechanic examiner (DME). The DME is an experienced mechanic who has been appointed by the FAA to administer oral and practical examinations. The oral examination consists of a dialog between the examiner and the applicant to ascertain the applicant's knowledge of aircraft maintenance theory and application. The practical examination is a series of maintenance tasks assigned to the applicant. The DME observes the applicant to evaluate the applicant's use of technical data, mechanical skill, and proper procedures in performing the assigned tasks. Upon successful completion of the practical examination, the examiner issues a temporary mechanic certificate, that is immediately valid. The permanent certificate is mailed from the FAA registry within a few weeks.

The Airframe and Power Plant Certificates are issued for life and continue to be valid unless voluntarily surrendered by the mechanic or suspended or revoked by the FAA. The certificates, however, must be kept current by recent experience. FAR 65 requires that, in order to exercise the privileges of a mechanic certificate, the mechanic must have been actively engaged in aircraft maintenance for six of the preceding twenty-four months.

David E. Fogleman

Bibliography

Kovach, Kenneth J. *Corporate Aviation Management*. 2d ed. Dubuque, Iowa: Kendall/Hunt, 1998. An overview of the corporate and business aviation industry, including history, management, flight and maintenance operations, and safety and security issues.

United States Department of Transportation. *FAR/AMT 2000*. Newcastle, Wash.: Aviation Supplies & Academics, 1999. Federal aviation regulations for the aviation maintenance technician.

Wanttaja, Ronald J. *Airplane Ownership*. New York: Tab Books, 1995. A digest of valuable information on all aspects of aircraft ownership, including annual inspections and owner maintenance procedures.

Welch, John F., ed. *Van Sickle's Modern Airmanship*. 8th ed. Blue Ridge Summit, Pa.: Tab Books, 1998. A comprehensive reference book on current aviation technology, including flying techniques, performance standards, airframe structures, engine operation, and maintenance procedures.

See also: Airplanes; Federal Aviation Administration; Safety issues; Training and education

Manufacturers

Definition: Companies that produce vehicles for travel in air or space, or components of those vehicles.

Significance: By the end of the twentieth century, aerospace manufacturers had grown to become one of the most important employers in the industrialized world.

Beginnings

The Wright brothers made the first powered flight in 1903, but the early years of aviation did not prove very lucrative for aircraft manufacturers. Most designers were sons of wealthy families with the time and money to pursue their interest in flying. Experienced engine designers migrated from the automotive industry, but even relatively successful manufacturers such as the Wright Company and the Curtiss Aeroplane Company had difficulty finding a consistent market for their planes. Most companies hoped for military contracts, but armed forces around the world were reluctant to adopt an unfamiliar weapon, and military purchases remained minuscule.

World War I

The demands of modern war soon demonstrated the usefulness of aviation. Aircraft had been used in reconnaissance roles in minor conflicts before the war began, and both sides soon recognized the potential of aviation. At first, aircraft served as spotters for the artillery, but fighters soon developed, followed later in the war by bombers. In Germany, Dutch designer Anthony Fokker created a device that allowed a machine gun to fire through a spinning propeller. Fokker's E-I fighter entered service in 1915 and soon dominated the skies over the western front. Subsequent Fokker models demonstrated continuous improvement, culminating in the highly advanced D-VII, which so frightened the Allies that they demanded the surrender of all D-VII's as a condition of the armistice. Other German manufacturers followed Fokker's lead. Albatros and Rumpler produced excellent aircraft, particularly in the reconnaissance sector. Late in the war, Gotha developed a heavy bomber that Germany used to bomb targets in Great Britain. Despite Germany's defeat, the nation's aviation industry produced more than 44,000 aircraft during the war and utilized twenty-six engine and thirty-five airframe manufacturers.

To meet the German threat, Britain's manufacturers expanded their operations. Sopwith proved one of the most effective, and the company's Pup and Camel models pushed the existing limitations of performance. Other British companies, including Handley-Page and Vickers, competed strongly with Sopwith's aircraft. Perhaps the most important manufacturing outgrowth of World War I on Britain's industry was the development of two important engine manufacturers, Napiers and Rolls-Royce. Rolls-Royce would use its wartime experience to become one of the world's foremost engine designers over the next eighty years.

Interwar Developments

After World War I, manufacturers to turned increasingly to the civilian market. The notoriety of aircraft during the war had done a great deal to increase public interest in aviation. In the United States, the federal government established air mail service and supported research into increased performance. Charles A. Lindbergh's solo transatlantic flight in 1927 also caused a sensation. Responding to these developments, U.S. manufacturers found an increasing market for their products. Lockheed developed its Vega monoplane, which set a number of speed and altitude records. Other manufacturers, notably Douglas and Boeing, recognized the developing airliner market. By the end of the 1930's, both companies had developed planes that incorporated such modern features as a comfortable cabin, retractable landing gear, and all-metal construction. U.S. manufacturers even designed airliners for transatlantic service, but World War II interrupted plans to produce these aircraft.

Despite the newfound commercial market, many aircraft makers still looked to the military as their primary customer. Despite Douglas's success in the airliner sector, more than half of the company's sales went to the military. Military designs took on a greater importance as war seemed more likely in the 1930's. Many theorists, anxious to avoid the stalemate of World War I, saw air power as the deciding factor in future conflicts.

Germany's rearmament program took place in direct contradiction of the Treaty of Versailles, which expressly forbade Germany to have an air force. Despite some resistance from leaders in the industry, most notably Hugo Junkers, Germany's new military expansion began in earnest in 1933. Leaders such as Junkers who opposed the idea were swept aside and their companies became integral parts in the development of a new air force. Junkers, Domier, Messerschmitt, Focke-Wulf, and Heinkel emerged as the leading aircraft manufacturers in Hitler's Third Reich. Throughout the 1930's, these companies perfected designs such as Messerschmitt's Bf-109 fighter, Junkers's Ju-87 dive-bomber, and Heinkel's He-111 bomber. These planes formed the backbone of Germany's Luftwaffe at the outset of World War II and represented a serious challenge to the Western Allies. Germany's aviation industry did not simply rearm the nation, however. Manufacturers provided employment for Germany's depression-ravaged population and helped reinvigorate the economy. In 1934, Britain determined that it had to maintain parity in aviation with Germany and began its own rearmament program. The new surge in defense spending more than tripled employment in the aviation industry between 1930 and 1936. British companies lagged behind their German and American counterparts in terms of modern production facilities, and the sudden demands created by the decision to rearm revealed serious shortages in machine tools and trained personnel. Some companies, including Rolls-Royce, undertook training programs, but manufacturers often resorted to luring trained workers away from competitors. British companies also had difficulty adjusting their designs and manufacturing techniques to the requirements of mass production, something designers in the United States and Germany had already embraced. Nonetheless, British firms turned out such outstanding designs as the Hawker Hurricane and Supermarine Spitfire fighters and the Avro Lancaster heavy bomber.

World War II

World War II meant enormous changes in the technology of aviation. Wartime demands put a great deal of money at the availability of manufacturers. Companies used these funds to design advanced aircraft and to convert their manufacturing processes to mass-production techniques. Most of the companies that came to dominate world aviation in the latter half of the twentieth century gained notoriety during World War II.

In the United States, giants such as Boeing, Douglas, and Lockheed continued work on large bombers and transports, which would give these companies a significant advantage in the postwar airliner market. Other companies, such as Grumman and North American, concentrated primarily on fighters and established themselves as leaders in the sector. Across the United States, thousands of people moved to take jobs in the aircraft industry, located primarily in Southern California, creating a significant demographic shift. The trend toward mass production in the prewar era became an absolute requirement with the demands of war. U.S. companies streamlined designs and production techniques to allow fast manufacturing with unskilled labor.

Britain's wartime experiments with such ideas as jet propulsion and radar made that country's manufacturers leaders in those important fields. The success of the Hurricane and the Spitfire in combat proved that Britain could produce aircraft of the highest quality. Unfortunately, the British aviation industry still had difficulty matching its competitors in the area of production. The creative designs of De Havilland helped make that company a fixture in Britain's aviation industry, but its famed wooden Mosquito fighter-bomber required too much time and skill to produce on the scale demanded by total war. Even more conventional aircraft such as the Spitfire required three times as many man-hours to produce as the German Bf-109. Britain's aircraft industry emerged from World War II with creative designs and world leaders in engine technology at Rolls-Royce and Bristol Siddley Engines, but the United States' greater emphasis on mass production would relegate Britain's manufacturers to a peripheral role in coming years.

Postwar Commercial Manufacturers
Britain emerged from World War II with a great advantage because of the country's research into jets. U.S. companies continued to build planes such as Lockheed's luxurious, piston-powered Constellation, but these models did not represent the future of air travel. The De Havilland Comet became the world's first jet-powered airliner when it began service to the Middle East in 1952. The Comet's smooth, fast performance made it a favorite of air travelers and presented a formidable challenge to U.S. manufacturers. Unfortunately for De Havilland, the Comet suffered a series of in-flight explosions due to metal fatigue that grounded the plane for two years while investigators tracked down the problem. During the interim, U.S. manufacturers caught up to De Havilland's lead. Boeing's 707 and Douglas's DC-8 established American supremacy in the airliner sector. In the equally important engine manufacturing sector, U.S. companies Pratt & Whitney and General Electric overtook Rolls-Royce and Bristol Siddley as the world's foremost manufacturers, adding to the United States's competitive advantage. France's Sud Aviation managed to sell a handful of its Caravelle medium-range jets to U.S. air carriers, but could not hope to compete with the highly efficient U.S. companies. By 1970, U.S. manufacturers produced 80 percent of the world's commercial airliners.

European manufacturers realized by the mid-1960's that they could not hope to compete with the powerful American companies and turned to international cooperation in order to maintain the continent's struggling aerospace industry. Britain and France agreed in 1962 to undertake a supersonic transport program. The resulting Concorde proved to be a commercial disappointment, with only sixteen of the supersonic airliners being produced due to high manufacturing costs. Air France and British Airways began flying the Concorde in the mid-1970's, but operated the transatlantic flights at a loss. Despite the difficulties, Concorde did give British and French manufacturers increased prestige and income at a time when American airliners had almost eliminated European companies from the sector. In an effort to reestablish a European presence in airliner manufacturing, corporate and government officials in Britain, France, and West Germany established a consortium called Airbus Industrie in 1967. After a great deal of political negotiating, Airbus produced the A300B, which entered service with Air France in 1974. Airbus continued to expand its product line in an effort to match Boeing's offerings, and the European conglomerate found customers around the world but fared poorly in the United States. Airbus's success through the end of the twentieth century assured European manufacturers of a promising future, though the consortium could not match the overwhelming success of Boeing.

Boeing's dominance in the airliner industry was a result of the company's diverse aircraft designs. The Seattle-based giant produced planes that offered air carriers a number of options in terms of range, passenger capacity, and engine configuration. Boeing's U.S. competitors, Lockheed and McDonnell Douglas, did not provide the same diversity and assured Boeing's position in the United States market. Airbus provided stiffer competition throughout the rest of the world, but Airbus could not offer anything that matched Boeing's enormous 747 jumbojet, which became a fixture on long-distance routes.

Postwar Military Manufacturers
The prominence of air power during World War II grew during the Cold War, requiring nations to spend a significant portion of their defense budgets on aviation. This dependence proved to be very lucrative for manufacturers. In the United States, the demand for varying kinds of fighters, bombers, and transports offered an opportunity for most of the nation's aircraft companies to find a segment of the market for their products. This new affluence did not come without challenges, the most significant being cost. The United States hoped to offset the Soviet Union's numerical superiority with technology, and the resulting aircraft proved increasingly expensive. Companies sought to combine designs in the hope of saving money. Boeing used the same basic design for both its KC-135 tanker and its 707 airliner. In doing so, the company reduced its expenses by saving time in the design phase and by using many of the same tools, jigs, and other equipment on both aircraft.

European companies found the cost of the new high-tech military aircraft prohibitive, and so these manufacturers looked to combine operations with American or other European firms. When several European nations decided to adopt General Dynamic's single-engine F-16 fighter in the early 1970's, European manufacturers won the right to fill 40 percent of the European orders and 10 percent of American orders. This agreement helped solidify Europe's aerospace industry while drastically cutting costs by eliminating the need for research and development.

In other cases, European nations combined their resources to produce original designs. When North Atlantic Treaty Organization (NATO) countries decided to replace their American-designed F-104 attack fighters in the late 1960's, the various governments decided to create a new European aircraft. The resulting effort, the Tornado, utilized components from Britain, West Germany, and Italy. The Tornado provided European nations with an aircraft that compared favorably with its American counterparts, and though rather expensive, the Tornado program gave European aerospace manufacturers valuable experience. Manufacturers learned the intricacies of managing such an effort in three different countries, each with its own currency, bureaucracy, and interests. The Tornado program also gave European manufacturers much-needed practice in designing high-performance fighters. European nations hoped to repeat the success of the Tornado with the European Fighter Aircraft, or Eurofighter. Work on the Eurofighter began in the 1980's, but the enormously complex program ran into technical and political difficulties and remained in the developmental phase at the end of the twentieth century.

Behind the Iron Curtain, the Soviet Union established its reputation as an aerospace power. The Soviets enjoyed a closed market within their sphere of influence, but they also represented a threat to Western companies by competing in the developing world. The Soviet design bureaus of Antonov, Ilyushin, Mikoyan-Guryevich, Tupolev, and Yakovlev sold military and civilian aircraft to nonaligned nations in an effort to strengthen ties between the Soviet Union and the rest of the world. While less capable than Western aircraft, Soviet models were cheaper and generally adequate for most customers.

Corporate Changes

The escalating costs of manufacturing aircraft forced an ongoing series of mergers around the world beginning in the 1960's. In Britain, consolidation throughout the 1960's and 1970's ultimately led to the creation of a single nationalized British company, British Aerospace (BAe) in 1977. The development of BAe followed a government takeover of bankrupt engine-designer Rolls-Royce in 1971, which had already merged with Bristol Siddley Engines in 1966. The Conservative government of Margaret Thatcher privatized both BAe and Rolls-Royce during the 1980's, but the costs of manufacturing modern aircraft had forced British manufacturers to combine under one single parent company. France's aerospace industry underwent a similar consolidation in 1970 when the government merged the nation's already nationalized manufacturers into one state-owned consortium, Aerospatiale, to handle France's commercial aviation production. Military production in France remained the province of Dassault, a privately held but strictly controlled firm.

American manufacturers fared better but still went through difficult times. Manufacturing giant Douglas merged with the smaller McDonnell Corporation in 1965, starting a series of mergers that continued throughout the remainder of the century. A downturn in orders in the late 1960's and early 1970's damaged the industry severely. Boeing laid off two-thirds of its workforce, and Lockheed was saved from bankruptcy only when the U.S. Congress guaranteed the company's credit. Despite these setbacks, U.S. manufacturers maintained their dominant position in the world market. Boeing's airliners proved enormously popular, while competing models from McDonnell Douglas and Lockheed found niches in the market. Increased military spending during the 1980's also offered greater opportunity for U.S. manufacturers, but the new generation of U.S. military aircraft were extraordinarily expensive, and the government's spending reductions following the end of the Cold War meant that only a handful of the new planes actually entered service.

Increased competition from Airbus irritated American manufacturers, but the U.S. government did not take direct action against European imports. Throughout the 1980's, U.S. companies pressed for protection, but the government settled for a 1992 agreement in which European governments agreed to limit the direct subsidies they gave to Airbus in return for the U.S. government cutting back on indirect subsidies it offered to its own manufacturers. This agreement did little to limit Airbus's continued pressure on the U.S. market, but Boeing remained the world's leading commercial aircraft manufacturer through the remainder of the twentieth century.

Foreign firms also made headway in the small aircraft market, with models from Brazil, France, and Sweden challenging established U.S. companies such as Cessna and Beech.

Matthew G. McCoy

Bibliography

Bilstein, Roger. *The American Aerospace Industry: From Workshop to Global Enterprise.* New York: Twayne, 1996. A solid historical examination of corporate development in American aviation. The book also examines the role of general aviation manufacturers such as Cessna and Piper.

Hayward, Keith. *The World Aerospace Industry: Collaboration and Competition.* London: Duckworth, 1994. A recent study that addresses trends in globalization, as well as political conflict over trade issues.

McGuire, Steven. *Airbus Industrie: Conflict and Cooperation in U.S.-E.C. Trade Relations.* New York: St. Martin's Press, 1997. A thorough investigation of the history of Airbus and its attempts to enter the U.S. market. The book also looks at the individual aerospace industries in Britain, France, and Germany.

Pisano, Dominick, and Cathleen Lewis, eds. *Air and Space History: An Annotated Bibliography.* New York: Garland, 1988. An extraordinarily thorough bibliographical guide. This book covers a wide range of topics in flight, including economic, political, technical, and corporate subjects.

See also: Aerospace industry, U.S.; Airbus; Airline industry, U.S.; Beechcraft; Bell Aircraft; Boeing; Cessna Aircraft Company; Fokker aircraft; Learjets; Lockheed Martin; McDonnell Douglas; Messerschmitt aircraft; Military flight; Piper aircraft

Marine pilots, U.S.

Definition: Aviators among the officer ranks of the United States Marine Corps.

Significance: The U.S. Marine Corps is unique among the armed forces in having an aviation component capable of operating independently of the other services. To perform their various tasks, Marine pilots fly a variety of aircraft.

Naval Aviators

U.S. Marine Corps pilots constitute one of three groups of military pilots designated as naval aviators, the other two of which are the pilots of the U.S. Navy and the U.S. Coast Guard. All three groups of pilots undergo their initial aviation training under the auspices of the U.S. Navy, beginning their schooling at the Naval Aviation Schools Command in Pensacola, Florida.

U.S. Marine Corps pilots train to fly transports, fighters, attack aircraft, observation aircraft, and helicopters. Their principal mission is to support U.S. Marine Corps infantry, artillery, and other components in combat operations. Marine amphibious forces include all the equipment necessary to exercise command and control of such operations independently of the other military forces, if necessary. Marine pilots are trained to conduct operations from aircraft carriers and from special naval amphibious ships designed to accommodate helicopters during ship-to-shore landing operations.

Career Marine Corps pilots also serve with ground units one or more times in their careers, typically for periods of about two years. When serving with ground units, Marine pilots often fill the role of forward air controllers (FACs), taking responsibility for guiding Marine and Navy attack aircraft during combat operations. Pilots also serve as advisors to commanders of Marine battalions and regiments and to the commanding generals of Marine divisions and amphibious task forces.

The Making of a Marine Aviator

The close link between Marine pilots and their colleagues on the ground forms early in their careers. Although there are many ways to become a Marine officer, all Marines begin in the same officer procurement programs. Some come from the U.S. Naval Academy; others take what is called the "Marine option" in the Naval Reserve Officer Training Program (NROTC) conducted at many universities. The U.S. Marine Corps also operates several officer procurement programs of its own, including a ten-week, post-baccalaureate Officer Candidate School (OCS) and another program called the Platoon Leaders Class (PLC) that requires two six-week training periods during college summers. Both programs are conducted by the Officer Candidate School at the Marine Corps Development and Education Command near Quantico, Virginia. However future Marine pilots obtain their commission, they must also complete the Officer's Basic Course at Quantico. All officers must complete this rigorous six-month program before reporting for flight training in Pensacola.

During World War II (1939-1945) and the Korean War (1950-1953), the Marine Corps took pilots from the enlisted ranks. They were known unofficially as "flying master sergeants." Most of those who stayed on active duty eventually received commissions. During the early 1960's, when the airlines exchanged propeller-driven aircraft for the first passenger jets, many civilian pilots lost their jobs. Some of these pilots who belonged to the U.S. Marine

Corps Reserve returned to active duty but gave up their lieutenant and captain ranks to become flying warrant officers.

The Organization of Marine Aviation

The U.S. Marine Corps is the only military service with a completely integrated aviation component capable of deploying with its ground combat units. The aircraft flown by Marine Corps pilots include a fixed-wing fighter-attack aircraft, the F/A-18 Hornet, and the multiengine transport and in-flight-refueling aircraft, the KC-130 Hercules. Marine pilots also fly the vertical-takeoff attack aircraft the AV-8B Harrier. In addition, Marine Corps pilots fly several types of helicopters, including the AH-1W Super Cobra, the UH-1N Huey, the CH-46E Sea Knight, and the CH-53E Super Stallion.

Marine Corps aviation is organized into three active-duty aircraft wings and one reserve wing. Each wing is subdivided into air groups, which are, in turn, the parent units of the various squadrons. Each wing is organized to support a corresponding division. The active-duty wings are the First, Second, and Third Marine Aircraft Wings; the reserve wing is the Fourth Marine Aircraft Wing.

When Marine ground units are deployed, they normally travel aboard and are landed from naval amphibious ships. An infantry battalion deploys along with an aircraft squadron as a Marine Expeditionary Unit (MEU). Larger forces include a Marine Expeditionary Brigade (MEB), organized around an infantry regiment and an air group, and a Marine Expeditionary Force (MEF), organized around a division and an aircraft wing. These combination air-and-ground-operational units are collectively referred to as Marine Air-Ground Task Forces (MAGTFs).

Early History of Marine Corps Aviation

May 22, 1912, is considered the birthday of U.S. Marine Corps aviation. It was on that date that a young Marine Corps first lieutenant, Alfred A. Cunningham, reported to the superintendent of the United States Naval Academy in Annapolis, Maryland, for "duty in connection with aviation." It was the custom of the day for aircraft manufacturers to provide flight instruction, so shortly after arriving in Annapolis, Lieutenant Cunningham was sent to the Burgess Corporation for flight instruction. He was designated Naval Aviator Number 5 on March 4, 1913.

On becoming the Corps' first aviator, Cunningham joined several other Marine officers to campaign for continued development of Marine Corps aviation. Finally, in February of 1913, he received orders to organize the Corps' first aviation unit, which was called the Marine Corps Aeronautical Company. This unit, organized at the Philadelphia Naval Yard, had seven officers and forty-three ground personnel.

After World War I broke out in Europe in 1914, Cunningham visited France, where he met the American pilots in the famous squadron known as the Lafayette Escadrille. He also participated in combat flights with French pilots.

After returning from France, Cunningham presented a report of his findings to the commandant of the Marine Corps, helping to further expand Marine aviation. When the United States entered World War I in 1917, Cunningham was directed to organize the First Marine Aviation Force for duty in France. This force was the first Marine aviation unit to ever fly in combat.

Development of Close Air Support

Another date of great historical importance to Marine Corps pilots is July 15, 1927. In what is known as the Second Nicaraguan Campaign, Marines were deployed in Nicaragua to protect American interests during civil strife in that country. On July 15, some Marines came under fire, and, in response, Marine pilots conducted the first of a type of air attack that would come to be called close air support (CAS). From that day forward, the close support of ground combatants would become a governing philosophy of Marine aviation. In the years following the Second Nicaraguan Campaign, Marine pilots worked to perfect the delivery of ordnance close to their counterparts on the ground.

Later Developments in Close Air Support

Precision bombing by aircraft underwent refinement during World War II and the Korean War, and it saw service in the war in Vietnam (1961-1975) and in Operation Desert Storm (1991). During the Korean War, another major philosophical principle emerged in Marine Corps aviation, as the helicopter assumed a large role in medical evacuation, aerial observation, and the delivery of matériel to front-line troops.

From that experience, the Marine Corps, together with the Navy, developed the concept of "vertical envelopment." They converted some World War II-vintage aircraft carriers to helicopter carriers called LPHs, a term often mistaken to mean "Landing Platform, Helicopter." The Navy designates amphibious ships with the letter "L" and ships that carry personnel with the letter "P." Thus, the term "LPH" really means "Amphibious Ship, Personnel, Helicopter." Today, larger and more efficient naval helicopter carriers support the Marine Corps amphibious forces.

Part of the impetus for developing the concept of vertical envelopment was based on the looming of the atomic age. The naval services, both the Navy and Marine Corps, sought strategies to avoid concentrating in a small beach area troops that could be annihilated with just one nuclear weapon. In the exercise of vertical envelopment, Marine pilots flying helicopters deliver troops from amphibious ships deep into enemy territory, while other Marines land over beaches in more traditional landing craft.

Moreover, Marine pilots in such attack aircraft and helicopters as the AV-8B Harrier and the AH-1W Super Cobra provide troops on the ground with close air support. This mission is additionally important in the landing of Marine forces when the threat of mechanized counterattack exists. Marine mechanized and antimechanized units may not land early in an amphibious operation, and Marine infantry depend on aircraft to play this role in the opening phase of an assault.

Finally, Marine pilots in fighter aircraft can conduct operations to protect the beachhead and landing zones from attack by enemy aircraft. In fact, the main mission of the KC-130 aircraft that some Marine pilots fly is to refuel such fighter aircraft for sustained operations or for moving long distances.

Famous Marine Corps Pilots

Several Marine Corps pilots have become famous for their exploits in the air. One of them, World War II fighter ace Joseph J. Foss, went on to become governor of South Dakota in 1954. After serving two terms in that office, he became the first commissioner of the American Football League in 1966.

During World War II, Foss shot down twenty-six enemy aircraft and was the number-two Marine Corps ace in that war. He was also one of five Marine pilots to receive the Medal of Honor for bravery during the campaign for the island of Guadalcanal. He was shot down once by enemy aircraft.

After the war, Foss took a commission in the South Dakota Air National Guard, which he helped organize, and served in the Korean War as a U.S. Air Force colonel. He retired from the Air National Guard as a brigadier general.

The top Marine Corps ace of World War II, Gregory "Pappy" Boyington, is credited with destroying forty enemy aircraft. Boyington was, for a time, commanding officer of Squadron 214, the famous Black Sheep Squadron.

Both Foss and Boyington served on Guadalcanal in what Marine pilots called the Cactus Air Force, a name derived from the fact that the call sign for the island was "cactus." The Cactus Air Force was commanded by another famous Marine Corps aviator, Brigadier General Roy Geiger, who had served in France in World War I.

Geiger's principal legacy, however, centers on the fact that just before his death, he urged the commandant of the Marine Corps to examine the concept of vertical envelopment in conjunction with the nuclear threat. Geiger, who had retired as a lieutenant general, thus hastened the now-standard tactics for modern Marine Corps amphibious operations, tactics in which all Marine pilots play an essential role.

Robert L. Ballantyne

Bibliography

Alexander, Joseph H. *A Fellowship of Valor: The Battle History of the United States Marines*. New York: HarperCollins, 1997. Excellently illustrated in color and arranged in chronological order, the book describes all the wars and battles in which the Marine Corps has participated and includes descriptions of the roles played by aircraft.

De St. Jorre, John. *The Marines*. New York: Doubleday, 1989. A book that focuses on how the contemporary Marine Corps trains individuals to perform their duties. Section 2 includes discussions on Marine pilots and aircraft.

Halberstadt, Hans. *U.S. Marine Corps*. Osceola, Wis.: Motor Books International, 1993. A beautifully illustrated 128-page paperback. Marine aviation is covered in Chapter 5.

See also: Black Sheep Squadron; Fighter pilots; Harrier jets; Helicopters; Korean War; Military flight; Navy pilots, U.S.; World War I; World War II

Beryl Markham

Date: Born on October 26, 1902, in Ashwell, Leicestershire, England; died on August 4, 1986, in Nairobi, Kenya

Definition: A bush pilot pioneer and famous adventurer.

Significance: Markham is most widely known for her record-breaking 1936 solo flight from east to west across the Atlantic Ocean and for her best-selling memoir *West with the Night* (1942).

Beryl Markham was born in England and, at age four, went with her father, Charles Baldwin Clutterbuck, to British East Africa, where she was raised on a ranch. She grew up hunting with local tribesmen and learned to speak Swahili and several African dialects. She was married three times, and her second marriage, to Mansfield Markham, produced her only child, Gervase. Markham was the first woman in Africa to receive a racehorse trainer's license, and in 1921, she began an illustrious career as a horse trainer. Her love of horses and her skills as a trainer were known throughout East and South Africa, but her ultimate fame was derived from her adventures and skills as a pilot. After learning to fly during her twenties, she flew between Kenya and Britain several times during the early 1930's. While in British East Africa (now Kenya), she flew for safari companies as an elephant spotter and also transported people and supplies. An active bush pilot, she was eventually considered the best and boldest pilot to fly out of Kenya.

In 1934, Markham was challenged to fly across the Atlantic, alone and against the wind, from east to west. On September 4, 1936, she took off alone, from Abingdon, England, heading west with the night. She made most of this famous twenty-two-hour flight in the dark, flying on instruments. She began having problems halfway across the Atlantic, battling headwinds and a fuel shortage. At one point, her plane dropped from a 2,000-foot cruising altitude, flying only 50 feet above the waves. In a desperate attempt to land near Sydney, Nova Scotia, Markham nose-dived into a bog, slightly injuring herself and totally disabling the plane. She switched planes and flew on to New York City, her intended destination. She became internationally famous and was received in New York with a ticker-tape parade and the cheers of thousands. The fame and attention brought her little financial reward, however. She traveled the world looking for another opportunity to break a flying record, but with no luck.

In 1938, Markham moved to California, where she began writing her memoir *West with the Night*. The book was published in 1942 to wide critical acclaim but little popular success. Disillusioned, depressed, and near penniless, she returned to British East Africa in 1949 to revive her career as a horse trainer. Her book was republished in 1983 to great acclaim and popularity, and the royalties finally allowed Markham freedom from poverty. She died on August 4, 1986, at the age of eighty-three. Through her book, stories, and accomplishments, Markham will be remembered as a pioneer of aviation.

Lori Kaye

In 1936, Beryl Markham became the first person to fly across the Atlantic Ocean from east to west, against the prevailing winds. Her memoir of her flight career, West with the Night, *became a best-seller.* (Hulton Archive)

Bibliography

Lovell, Mary S. *Straight on Till Morning: The Biography of Beryl Markham*. New York: St. Martin's Press, 1987. A well-researched portrait of Markham. Illustrated.

Markham, Beryl. *West with the Night*. San Francisco: North Point Press, 1983. A reprint of her 1942 memoir.

Trzebinski, Errol. *The Lives of Beryl Markham*. New York: W. W. Norton, 1993. A biography that emphasizes Markham's scandalous love life, such as her affair with Denys Finch-Hatton.

See also: Record flights; Transatlantic flight; Women and flight

MD plane family

Date: First built in 1979, with the first flight in September, 1980, and with modifications and upgrades through the 1990's

Definition: The next generation of passenger aircraft built upon the features of the successful DC series and was intended to replace that series.

Significance: The MD series brought new innovations to passenger airplanes with such features as an expanded fuselage to hold more passengers, large fuel tanks and larger engines to increase the thrust and range of the plane and an expanded flight deck with electronic instruments to allow for easier control of the plane.

With the 1967 merger of the McDonnell and the Douglas Aircraft companies, the popular DC series of passenger planes, originally built by Douglas, became part of the new company. Two of the most popular and widely flown airplane designs, the DC-9 and the DC-10, served as the starting point for the new generation of planes developed by McDonnell Douglas. The MD series maintained many of the features of their predecessors while adding ones for the new generation of planes. The MD class of passenger planes replaced the DCs starting in the 1980's. However, problems in development slowed their construction, while a merger of McDonnell Douglas with Boeing Corporation threatened to end the line before it could become a major contributor to the U.S. passenger air fleet.

From DC to MD

The DC-9's popularity and dominance in the airline industry could be attributed to the willingness of McDonnell Douglas to change the plane's design in response to the requirements of airlines. During the 1970's, McDonnell Douglas developed new planes that expanded on the size and capabilities of the DC-9 series. Some of those modifications were used to develop the MD-80 series. This airplane, the first in the MD class, was a lengthened version of the DC-9, allowing for more passengers and a better-equipped flight deck. It added to the already produced DC-9-50 and was also known as the DC-9 Super 80. It was given this name based on the expectation that the first planes would begin commercial airline flight starting in 1980. Exactly on schedule, the plane had its first commercial flight in September, 1980, and was soon flying in more than a dozen airlines worldwide.

The MD-80 Series

As with the DC-9's, McDonnell Douglas produced several versions of the plane, adding length and seats, improving fuel economy and range, and putting into place new electronic equipment for the flight deck. While the planes were being built and during their early years of flight, the DC name was attached, but as their popularity grew, in 1983 the company changed the name to the MD to represent the company's sixteen-year-old merged name. The DC-9 Super 80 became the MD-81. The next plane, the MD-82, was first flown commercially in January, 1981. Six years passed before the next addition, the MD-83, was used by airlines beginning in February, 1987. All three of the planes closely resembled each other in size, fuel capacity, and range.

The MD-82 was the first modification of the MD-81. It had improved maximum takeoff weight, allowing for more passengers and cargo. The thrust engines were also improved, allowing for easier takeoff. The MD-83 was intended for longer flights with larger fuel capacity on the plane, even greater takeoff weight, and improved thrust over the MD-82 model.

The next modification, the MD-87, eventually served as the main replacement plane for the DC-9. Smaller than the MD-82, the MD-87 included an advanced flight deck that allowed for a larger crew and easier-to-read instruments. The new turbofan engines also improved fuel efficiency. The interior of the plane was changed as to the arrangement of the seats and various classes of passenger. It was able to seat as many as 130 people in a single economy class. Because of that size, it was seen as the true successor to the DC-9. The MD-87 had its first commercial use in November, 1987.

The last of the MD-80 series was the MD-88. It was a combination of the MD-83 and the MD-87. It had the MD-83's engines and airframe while using the same type of electronic readouts in the flight deck and the same interior for the passengers. The plane began commercial flights in 1988. At the same time, a freight version of the MD-80 was introduced by the company but there were few takers.

The MD-80 broke further ground in its production as McDonnell Douglas licensed a Chinese firm, the Shanghai Aviation International Corporation, to build planes in that country. The arrangement lessened production backlogs and allowed the companies to build nearly 1,200 of the planes. The last of the planes, an MD-83, was delivered in December, 1999, and was dubbed the "Spirit of Long Beach" after the plant where many of the MD models were produced in the United States. The relative success of the MD-80 for American and foreign airlines spawned its successor, the MD-90.

The MD-90 Series

The MD-90 series had a similar history as its predecessor, the MD-80. Also built by McDonnell Douglas, the MD-90 began as a modified version of the DC-9 and was known as the DC-9 Super 90. Originally the MD-90 was built as one of the most fuel-efficient planes in the world, but by the mid-1980's the energy crisis of the mid-1970's had passed and that feature became less important. For this reason, the MD-90 became an updated version of the MD-80, with the fuselage, the exterior of the plane, and the flight deck resembling its predecessor. Most of the improvements added to the plane involved an electronic flight instrument system and a pair of new engines. The control system allowed for easier management of the plane by the pilots and for conserving fuel. The new engines lessened the level of noise and also conserved energy. Another change was a slightly longer fuselage—approximately 4.5 feet longer. With the added space, the MD-90 could carry 163 first- and economy-class passengers, 10 more than the MD-81. The MD-90 first carried those passengers in February, 1993, and was purchased by several American and foreign airlines.

Two more versions of the plane were built. The MD-90-30 began flying in April, 1995. It had larger fuel tanks and a stretched fuselage for more passengers. The MD-90-30ER began flying in April, 1997, and had room for 170 economy-class passengers, larger fuel tanks, and greater maximum takeoff weight. Two additional MD-90 versions, the 10 and the 50, were not produced before McDonnell Douglas merged with Boeing. For this reason the MD-90 became a casualty of the merger because it was the main competitor of the Boeing 737 and the company halted its production. Because of this decision, only 117 planes found their way to the airlines between 1995 and 2000.

The MD-95 was the last of this series and went into action only after McDonnell Douglas was purchased by the Boeing corporation. The MD-95 was another replacement for the DC-9 and included many of the features of one part of that series, the DC-9-30. The major improvement over the DC-9 was the flight deck, in which six LCD screens were installed to make it easier for the pilots to read flight information. The interior of the plane was also enlarged, with bigger seats and expanded room for carry-on luggage. The MD-95 began operation in September, 1998, and at that time became known as the Boeing 717-200. Its success spawned the smaller 717-100 and the larger 717-300.

The MD-11

The aging of the DC-10 fleet and the slowdown in production of the plane after a series of fatal crashes caused McDonnell Douglas to search for a plane design to replace it. Several such designs were developed, dramatically changing the exterior and interior of the DC-10 model. These planes, with names such as the MD-100, were ultimately rejected as too costly or not feasible for mass production. It was the MD-11 which became the accepted replacement of the DC-10, a plane built using the major features of its predecessor rather than creating an entirely new plane.

The MD-11 was specifically based on the DC-10-60. Some 18 feet longer than the DC-10, the interior of the plane was reconfigured to expand seating to a possible capacity of 405 economy-class passengers or 323 economy- and first-class passengers. In the MD-11, the pilot and copilot were both given the six-screen LCD layout for monitoring the plane. Winglets were added as one of the major new features to exterior of the plane. Winglets are small, upraised additions to the edge of each of the plane's wings. Pointing skyward, the winglets provided better aerodynamics and increased the plane's range and fuel efficiency. The redesigned tail of the plane also improved fuel efficiency. With added technology in the flight deck, the plane required only two crew members to fly it.

The MD-11 design proved versatile, and four different types of the plane were built. The MD-11P was the main passenger model. The MD-11F was the major freight carrier, favored by many package delivery companies. The MD-11 combi was, as the name suggests, a combination passenger and freight carrier. Finally, the MD-11CF was the convertible model, able to serve as a passenger jet or as a freight carrier depending upon the immediate need.

Despite all of these improvements, the MD-11 proved to be a troublesome aircraft in its production. The development of the MD-11 came at the same time as increased competition in the airline industry created by government deregulation. Then came the oil crunch of the early 1990's, followed by a wave of mergers and bankruptcies as weaker airlines began to collapse. This led to a decline in orders, as airlines no longer had the business that required an up-to-date fleet of planes. Initially, the MD-11 was dependent upon European air carriers, with Finnair being the first company to fly one commercially. In addition, company problems hurt the plane. The MD-11 was consistently behind in meeting its delivery deadlines, leading to many canceled orders from passenger airlines. However, the plane became more widely used by overnight freight companies. After fifteen years of development and ten years of production, fewer than two hundred of the planes were flying. Yet the MD-11 survived the Boeing-McDonnell Douglas merger, unlike some of the other planes in the MD series.

Never as popular as its predecessor, the DC series, the MD series of passenger aircraft represented the new generation that was to take over for the DC-9 and the DC-10. However, the McDonnell Douglas Corporation found that economic factors and production difficulties prevented the MD's from taking hold. Only the MD-80, with its multiple versions for different-range flights and different types of airfields, was able to make a considerable penetration of the airline market. The MD-90 barely got off the ground before production was halted by the Boeing takeover of the company, while the MD-95 became part of the 700 series for Boeing. The MD-11 also failed as a commercial airliner, unable to take the place of the more popular DC-10. Overall, the MD series added little to the DC legend and McDonnell Douglas's reputation as a great innovator in the field.

Douglas Clouatre

Bibliography

Badrocke, Mike, and Bill Sunston *The Illustrated History of McDonnell Douglas Aircraft: From Cloudster to Boeing.* Oxford, England: Osprey, 1999. A colorful, well-illustrated book describing the history of the McDonnell and Douglas airplane companies, their merger, and how their planes revolutionized air travel.

Francillon, Rene. *McDonnell Douglas Aircraft Since 1920* Annapolis Md.: Naval Institute Press, 1990. Discusses the civilian and military aircraft developed by both companies prior to their merger and after their combination.

Graves, Clinton H. *Jetliners.* Osceola Wis.: Motorbooks International 1993. A wide-ranging book, with illustrations of many of the major McDonnell and Douglas aircraft used for civilian and military purposes.

Pealing, Norman, and Mike Savage. *Jumbo Jetliners.* Oxford, England: Osprey, 1999. Discusses the newest generation of enlarged jetliners, including the MD model built during the 1980's and 1990's.

Pearcy, Arthur. *McDonnell Douglas MD-80 and MD-90.* Osceola, Wis.: Motorbooks International, 1999. An in-depth look at the last generation of McDonnell Douglas passenger airliners with illustrations and analyses of their capabilities.

Shaw, Robbie. *McDonnell Douglas Jetliners.* Osceola, Wis.: Motorbooks International, 1998. A wide-ranging look at the many passenger planes produced by the separate companies up to the last MD model.

See also: Airline industry, U.S.; Airplanes; Boeing; DC plane family; Manufacturers; 707 plane family

Mercury project

Date: From May 5, 1961, to May 16, 1963
Definition: The first phase of the U.S. crewed spacecraft program in which individual astronauts were launched to extremely high altitudes (over 100 miles) and, later, into Earth orbit.
Significance: Initiated by the National Aeronautics and Space Administration (NASA), Project Mercury opened the first phase of the U.S. crewed space exploration program by sending individual astronauts into space to study the engineering parameters and human factors of spaceflight. The two suborbital and four orbital flights that constituted Project Mercury served as instrumental preparation for the later two-person Gemini spacecraft flights (1965-1967) and the Apollo Program missions to the moon (1968-1972). The seven Mercury astronauts were the first U.S. pioneers in the long, costly, and sometimes tragic exploration of outer space.

Preliminary Developments

In the decade following World War II, high-altitude atmospheric research accomplished with crewed balloon flights, uncrewed sounding rockets, and later, experimental rocket planes such as the X-15, established the feasibility of sending crewed rocket-powered vehicles beyond the upper layers of Earth's atmosphere. These early experimental flights were followed by a number of small electronic satellites, or "artificial moons," launched successfully into orbit. The first of these was the 184-pound Russian Sputnik 1 (launched October 4, 1957). These orbital satellites were followed almost immediately by pressurized space capsules containing live research animals wired for telemetric data (such as the dog Laika, the first living creature in space, launched aboard Sputnik 2 on November 3, 1957). Within four years, Russian cosmonaut Yuri Gagarin became the first human in space when he completed a single orbit of the earth aboard Vostok 1 (launched April 12, 1961).

In these early years of space exploration, great political emphasis was placed upon the attainment of space firsts and, in this area, the United States space program was consistently outpaced by Russian accomplishments. In fact, the space race that eventually developed between the two countries became as much a test of patriotic pride as it was a competition of scientific and technical accomplishment. In October, 1958, at the recommendation of President Dwight D. Eisenhower, the National Advisory Committee for Aeronautics (NACA) was restructured into NASA and placed under the direction of James E. Webb. By utilizing the talents of rocketry experts such as Wernher von Braun, who had headed the German army's V-2 rocket development center at Peenemünde during World War II, the U.S. space program would eventually close the U.S.-Soviet missile gap and succeed in landing the first astronauts upon the Moon, but those successes were still years ahead.

Mercury Mission Highlights

Astronaut	Spacecraft	Date of Flight	Duration	Orbits
Shepard	Freedom 7	May 5, 1961	15 minutes	suborbital
Grissom	Liberty Bell 7	July 21, 1961	16 minutes	suborbital
Glenn	Friendship 7	February 20, 1962	4 hours, 56 minutes	3
Carpenter	Aurora 7	May 24, 1962	4 hours, 56 minutes	3
Schirra	Sigma 7	October 3, 1962	9 hours, 13 minutes	6
Cooper	Faith 7	May 15-16, 1963	34 hours, 20 minutes	22

At the Threshold of Space

NASA's launch complex at Cape Canaveral, Florida, in use since 1947 as the Atlantic/Eastern Test Range for military and scientific rockets and missiles, became the staging ground for Project Mercury. (After November 28, 1963, Cape Canaveral was temporarily renamed Cape Kennedy to honor the memory of President John F. Kennedy, who had been instrumental in fostering America's spaceflight ambitions.) Launch Complex 56, located near the southwestern end of "Rocket Row," served as the launch pad for the first two Mercury-Redstone flights. Launch Complex 14, further up the eastern shore, served as the launch pad for all later Mercury-Atlas orbital flights. The Cape Canaveral site had been established near to Earth's equator in order to save fuel by taking advantage of Earth's rotational velocity (amounting to a gain of approximately 1,500 feet per second at the equator), thus reducing the velocity needed for a rocket to attain orbit when launched in an eastward direction.

In 1960, after a regimen of rigorous physical, technical, and psychological testing, seven military test pilots were chosen as the first Mercury astronauts: Commander Alan Shepard, U.S.N.; Captain Virgil "Gus" Grissom, U.S.A.F.; Lieutenant Colonel John Glenn, U.S.M.C.; Lieutenant Commander M. Scott Carpenter, U.S.N.; Commander Walter M. Schirra, Jr., U.S.N.; and Major L. Gordon Cooper, U.S.A.F. The seventh member of the original Mercury 7, Donald "Deke" Slayton, was grounded due to an erratic heart rate and replaced in the Mercury flight lineup by M. Scott Carpenter.

Spacecraft and Booster Rockets

Project Mercury flights utilized existing liquid-fueled launch vehicles such as the 83-foot, 30-ton Redstone rocket, and the 93-foot Atlas missile, as booster rockets. Ironically, the hefty Atlas booster, pressed into service for all of the Project Mercury orbital launches, was actually an intercontinental ballistic missile (ICBM) originally designed to deliver a nuclear warhead payload. The Redstone and Atlas rockets' propellants consisted principally of mixtures of liquid oxygen, liquid hydrogen, and kerosene.

Mounted atop its booster rocket, the black bell-shaped Mercury spacecraft, measuring 9 feet, 6 inches long and approximately 7 feet in diameter, carried a single space-suited astronaut. Sandwiched between the shingled outer hull of the Mercury capsule and its corrugated titanium inner hull was a layer of insulation 1.5 inches thick. Every available niche inside the pressurized capsule's battleship-grey interior was crammed with research instruments, monitoring equipment, and control switches. (Shepard once joked that the tight fit of the capsule's interior made it seem as though the capsule was something he "put on," rather than climbed aboard.) The first Mercury space capsule, produced by McDonnell Aircraft for automatically controlled uncrewed flights and test animals, had only a small porthole and a hatch that had to be bolted into place by hand. For the crewed model, a pilot's viewing portal was added, along with a quick release escape hatch with explosive bolts, and a manual back-up control system for piloting the spacecraft. McDonnell also outfitted the nose of its Mercury spacecraft with a 16-foot cylindrical red abort/escape rocket capable of separating the crewed capsule from the booster and carrying it to safety in the event of a mishap; this eventuality, however, was never encountered on any of the crewed flights.

During liftoff, the Mercury astronaut was positioned flat upon his back in a seated posture, legs elevated, to better withstand the tremendous force produced by the rocket's initial acceleration as well as the stresses of reentry, estimated to reach a maximum gravitational force (g) equivalent of approximately 8 g's on liftoff and 11 g's on reentry. The astronaut remained strapped into his form-fitted couch throughout the flight, which typically lasted several hours. After completing the specified number of orbits, the spacecraft was maneuvered into an ideal reentry position angle of between 5 degrees and 7 degrees approximate negative inclination with respect to the horizon. This reentry angle proved critical; a steeper reentry would cause the spacecraft to fall too fast and burn up, while too shallow an angle would cause the spacecraft to skip off into space, unable to return. After positioning the spacecraft, aft end first, the astronaut fired the retro-rockets to slow the spacecraft sufficiently for it to safely reenter Earth's atmosphere. During reentry, the ionization effect caused by the tremendous friction heating of the capsule's reentry through the atmosphere resulted in a brief radio blackout during which contact with the spacecraft was lost for several minutes. During those most dramatic moments of the flight, the astronaut was protected by an ablative heatshield that absorbed the searing 3,000 degree Fahrenheit heat of reentry. Finally, the spacecraft descended by parachute to a splashdown at sea to be recovered by an aircraft carrier helicopter and a team of navy divers.

Mission Highlights

Each Mercury mission focused upon resolving a specific domain of engineering and design-related problems associated with future crewed spaceflights as well as answering questions of human endurance. The basic flight data of the individual Project Mercury missions are summarized in the accompanying table.

The first two Mercury flights, *Freedom 7*, crewed by Shepard, and *Liberty Bell 7*, crewed by Grissom, were suborbital missions during which, for the most part, the spacecrafts' systems functioned automatically, relegating the astronauts to little more than onboard observers. The spacecraft were launched along a ballistic trajectory to the fringe of outer space and returned by parachute to a recovery in the Atlantic Ocean. During the second Mercury mission, a mishap with the explosive bolts securing the capsule's hatch caused a premature opening after splashdown that foundered the capsule and nearly drowned astronaut Grissom. (The ill-fated *Liberty Bell 7* capsule, lost at sea for almost forty years, was eventually recovered from the bottom of the Atlantic virtually intact in 2000.)

On the third crewed Mercury mission, Lieutenant Colonel John Glenn became the first American to orbit Earth, completing three orbits in his 4-hour, 56-minute flight. A crisis occurred when, halfway through the mission, a sensor aboard the *Friendship 7* spacecraft indicated that the capsule's heatshield had been jarred loose. NASA Ground Control advised Glenn not to jettison his retro-rocket pack after firing, in the hope that the metal straps securing the retro-pack would help to hold the heatshield safely in place during reentry. Glenn later recounted seeing large white-hot fragments of the incinerated retro-pack hurtling past his viewing portal as he endured the awful stresses of reentry. Fortunately, *Friendship 7*'s heatshield held.

During the second Mercury orbital flight, the mission priority shifted from testing the spacecraft's systems in-

The final touches are added to the second Mercury capsule at the Lewis Hangar, now the Glenn Research Center, near Cleveland, Ohio. (NASA)

tegrity, now well established, to testing the handling and performance characteristics of *Aurora 7* under astronaut Carpenter's manual control. Near the end of the mission the spacecraft became endangered by excessive fuel usage, hit the atmosphere at a steeper angle than anticipated and, consequently, missed the target recovery zone by 250 miles. After a tense search, astronaut Carpenter was recovered from a life raft, unharmed, along with his space capsule.

Less than three months after Carpenter's flight, Russian cosmonauts Adrian G. Kikolayev (Vostok 3, launched August 11, 1962) and Pavel R. Popovich (Vostok 4, launched August 12, 1962) scored yet another space first when they maneuvered their two Vostok spacecraft to within sight of one another, completing the first crewed rendezvous in space.

The third orbital Mercury flight, *Sigma 7*, crewed by Schirra, logged six orbits in a superbly executed textbook flight, but during the fourth and final Mercury orbital mission a massive electrical systems failure occurred on board the *Faith 7* spacecraft as astronaut Gordon Cooper completed his twenty-second orbit. Having lost all of his spacecraft's automatic systems, Cooper flew the *Faith 7* spacecraft manually to a splashdown, landing east of Midway Island in the Pacific.

Project Mercury effectively concluded with Cooper's *Faith 7* orbital mission of May 15-16, 1963. Less than one month later (June, 1963), Russian Valentina Tereshkova became the first woman in space. The 26-year-old lieutenant completed forty-nine Earth orbits, more orbits than all the Project Mercury spaceflights combined.

The engineering- and human-factors data gleaned from the Mercury spaceflights proved instrumental in the development of the later two-man Gemini spacecraft, which served as the final engineering stopgap before the Apollo Program's lunar landings of 1969-1972.

Of the seven original Mercury astronauts, Cooper, Grissom, Schirra, and Shepard flew on later Gemini missions; Grissom was killed in a launchpad fire aboard the Apollo 1 spacecraft on January 27, 1967; Schirra flew on Apollo 7; Shepard flew on the Apollo 14 lunar landing mission; Slayton flew on the Apollo-Soyuz docking mission; and Glenn, who became a U.S. senator after ending his space career, flew as a mission specialist on the U.S. space shuttle *Discovery* in 2001, nearly forty years after his first orbital mission aboard *Friendship 7*.

Larry Smolucha

Bibliography

Harding, Richard. *Survival in Space: Medical Problems of Manned Spaceflight*. New York: Routledge, 1989. A detailed yet accessible survey of significant medical and human factors data derived from the crewed space program.

Wolfe, Tom. *The Right Stuff*. London: Jonathan Cape, 1980. An insightful and accurate sketch of the Mercury astronauts containing exceptional characterizations that contrast their private and public lives.

See also: Apollo Program; Wernher von Braun; Crewed spaceflight; Gemini Program; John Glenn; National Aeronautics and Space Administration; National Committee for Aeronautics; Orbiting; Alan Shepard; Spaceflight; Valentina Tereshkova; Uncrewed spaceflight

Mergers

Also known as: Consolidation

Definition: The process of consolidation among air carriers.

Significance: The deregulation of air carriers caused a number of airlines to merge, causing concerns about antitrust issues, customer service, and airfare costs.

Competition and Deregulation

A wave of mergers, or consolidations, hit the airline industry in the 1980's, caused in part by the end of government regulation. From 1938 until the passage of the Airline Deregulation Act of 1978, the Civil Aeronautics Board (CAB) had regulated the industry. The CAB oversaw airline fares, determined routes, and ensured that no major airline went out of business. Any mergers had to be approved by the CAB. During the era of regulation, a significant wave of consolidation eliminated some independent airlines. In 1952, Western Air Lines took over Inland Airways, and Braniff acquired Mid-Continent Airlines. Chicago & Southern merged with Delta in 1953. Continental bought Pioneer Airlines in 1955. Eastern obtained Colonial Airlines in 1956. In 1961, United Air Lines acquired Capital Airlines, thereby becoming the largest airline in the United States.

Congress passed the Airline Deregulation Act of 1978, disbanding the CAB and giving its authority to review airline industry practices to the Department of Transportation. The review process, including the ability to approve proposed mergers, passed to the Department of Justice's Antitrust Division on January 1, 1989.

Consolidation swept the airline industry after deregulation, with twenty major airline mergers occurring in the first eight years of deregulation. The high point of consolidation activity was in the mid 1980's. In 1985, Southwest Airlines bought Muse Air, taking over a Dallas rival. A number of large mergers took place in 1986: Delta bought Western Airlines; Northwest took over Republic Airlines; Frank Lorenzo's Texas Air Group bought Eastern Air Lines; TWA bought Ozark; United Air Lines took over Pan American's Pacific routes. The mergers continued into 1987, when American Airlines bought Air Cal and USAir took over Pacific Southwest Airlines (PSA). USAir also purchased Piedmont. By 1987, there were ten airline holding companies operating nationally: Texas Air, United, American, Delta, Northwest, TWA, Pan American, USAir, Piedmont, and Southwest Airlines. These airlines controlled about 95 percent of the market in the United States.

Several factors explain the wave of airline consolidations in the 1980's. One is the lack of antitrust enforcement by the Reagan administration. Critics of this perspective point out that consolidation swept through many other industries in the United States during the 1980's. Had the airline industry not been regulated until 1978, the consolidations would have taken place earlier. Airline holding companies were seeking critical mass in order to cope with increased costs and the decreased profits caused by fare wars. Economic pressures encouraged smaller regional airlines to merge into larger units.

Consolidation, Legislation, and Backlash

A further wave of mergers struck the airline industry in the late 1990's. By 2001, only five major airlines, American, United, Delta, Northwest, and Continental, plus the discount airline Southwest, remained. Since the end of regulation, more than fifty airlines were acquired or merged. American Airlines bought TWA in 2001, saving the troubled carrier from bankruptcy. Also in 2001, the proposed acquisition of US Airways by United was frustrated by concerns that the combined airline would control up to 95 percent of the departure gates at East Coast airports.

The fresh wave of mergers caused U.S. lawmakers to consider a moratorium on airline mergers. Representative Louis Slaughter, a Democrat from New York, and Representative Peter DeFazio, a Democrat from Oregon, introduced the Airline Merger Moratorium Act of 2001 in the 107th Congress (2001-2002). The bill would have made it unlawful, for a one-year period, for a major air carrier to acquire assets or voting securities of another major airline carrier. In a press release announcing the bill's introduction, Representative DeFazio identified the problem when he stated, "The airline industry should focus on improving customer service and increasing consumer choices, rather than rushing to gobble each other up."

Merger Effects

The intent of airline deregulation was to make the airline industry susceptible to the effects of a free-market economy. The intended goal was to increase competition among the airlines. This competition caused massive consolidation as some airlines failed under economic pressure and poor management and were acquired by stronger airlines. Consumer groups have noted that customer service has suffered because of the numerous mergers, as airlines try to remain profitable to protect themselves from acquisition. In some parts of the country, travelers are not able to choose among airlines, forcing them to pay higher airfares. Mergers also significantly affect airline employees' morale, as a newly merged airline lays off employees to recognize the cost savings of combining two corporations.

Airline consolidation has spread beyond the United States. Particularly in the newly united Europe, national airlines are seeking alliances with each other and with American carriers. Because federal law prevents a foreign carrier from having a controlling interest in a U.S. airline, most of the relationships are in the form of alliances. The oneworld Alliance is an effort by thirty-one airlines traveling to 550 destinations in 130 countries. American Airlines is the major U.S. carrier in the alliance. With the restrictions on foreign ownership of U.S. airlines, these alliances could be the future of airline consolidation.

John David Rausch, Jr.

Bibliography

Hawkins, Chuck. "You'll Buy Tickets, Airlines Will Buy Each Other." *Business Week* no. 2980 (January 12, 1987). Brief analysis of the wave of airline mergers in 1986. Offers predictions for the industry.

Mann, Paul. "Airline Daggers Drawn in Merger Convulsion." *Aviation Week & Space Technology* 154, no. 7 (February 12, 2001). This article discusses some of the challenges faced by the airline industry as a result of the decrease in airline competition.

Peterson, Barbara Sturken, and James Glab. *Rapid Descent: Deregulation and the Shakeout in the Airlines.* New York: Simon & Schuster, 1994. An excellent examination of the changes in the airline industry caused by deregulation. Includes illustrations and bibliography.

Petzinger, Thomas. *Hard Landing: The Epic Contest for Power and Profits That Plunged the Airlines into Chaos*. New York: Times Books, 1995. Critical analysis of the challenges facing airlines as the industry consolidates.

See also: Air carriers; Airline Deregulation Act; Airline industry, U.S.; American Airlines; Continental Airlines; Delta Air Lines; Northwest Airlines; Southwest Airlines; Trans World Airlines; United Air Lines; US Airways

Messerschmitt aircraft

Definition: A major make of German aircraft.
Significance: Tens of thousands of various Messerschmitt aircraft were produced and served as the foundation for the German Luftwaffe in World War II. These aircraft aided the early German victories and introduced numerous innovations into the aircraft industry.

Origins

In 1923, engineer Willy Messerschmitt established an aircraft company in Bamberg, Germany. In 1927, he moved his firm to Augsburg, Germany, where he merged with another company and created the corporation of Bayerisch Flugzeigwerke (BFW). BFW, with Willy Messerschmitt as chief designer, initially produced gliders and sport and transport aircraft, but in 1933 it secured a contract from Adolf Hitler's Reich air ministry and began to produce military aircraft (designated by the prefix Bf) for the Luftwaffe. In 1936, Willy Messerschmitt seized complete control of the company, renamed it Messerschmitt AG, and continued to focus production on military aircraft (now designated by the prefix Me). During World War II, Messerschmitt AG produced fifteen distinct series of aircraft, ranging from fighters and bombers, to the first jet-powered aircraft.

Bf-109 Series

The most famous of the Messerschmitt aircraft is the Bf-109; a single-seat fighter used by the Luftwaffe from 1935 to 1945 and produced in greater numbers (approximately 33,000) than any other World War II aircraft except the Russian Il-2. The Bf-109 was the first "modern" German fighter. It possessed such advancements as a light alloy stressed skin construction, low cantilever wings with trailing edge flaps, a retractable tail wheel landing gear, and an enclosed cockpit. The first version of this aircraft, the Bf-109A, was produced in 1935, but met with pilot resistance due to its limited agility compared with biplanes. Newer versions of the Bf-109, the Bf-109B, Bf-109C, and Bf-109D, added greater agility, horsepower, and armament and were delivered in modest numbers to the Luftwaffe in the late 1930's.

By February, 1939, however, such variants were removed from front-line duty and replaced by the Bf-109E, known as the Emil. The numerous versions of the Emil saw the plane used as a fighter, fighter-bomber, and reconnaissance fighter. The Bf-109E-4 was the most widely used of the Emil aircraft. A fighter, weighing 4,685 pounds empty, it had a wingspan of 32 feet, 4.5 inches, was 28 feet, 4.2 inches in length, and 8 feet, 2.42 inches in height. Powered by one Daimler-Benz DB-601 Aa inverted-V piston engine, the Bf-109E-4 had a maximum speed of 348 miles per hour, a cruising speed of 300 miles per hour, a ceiling of 34,450 feet, and a maximum range of 410 miles. It was armed with two 20-millimeter MGFF fixed, forward-firing cannons built into the leading edge of the wing and two 7.92-millimeter MG17 fixed, forward-firing machine guns in the upper part of the forward fuselage with synchronization to fire through the propeller.

The Emil, however, was difficult to maneuver at high speeds, and production ceased in 1942 as the Luftwaffe sought a more aerodynamic and better handling plane. Efforts to provide such a plane resulted in the production of the Bf-109F, known as the Friedrich. The Bf-109F-2 was the best of this series. A fighter and fighter-bomber weighing 5,188 pounds empty, it had a wingspan of 32 feet, 6.5 inches, was 29 feet 3.9 inches in length, and stood 8 feet, 6.33 inches in height. Powered by one Daimler-Benz DB 601N inverted-V piston engine, the Bf-109F had a maximum speed of 373 miles per hour, a cruising speed of 348.88 miles per hour, a ceiling of 36,090 feet, and a maximum range of 547 miles. It was armed with one 15-millimeter MG151/15 fixed, forward-firing cannon and two 7.92-millimeter MG17 fixed, forward-firing machine guns with synchronization to fire through the propellers.

The Bf-109F was used throughout 1942, but was replaced in 1943 with the Bf-109G. The Gustav, as it was known, added a more powerful engine, a pressurized cockpit, and was used solely as a fighter by the Luftwaffe throughout the remainder of the war. Later versions of the Bf-109, the Bf-109H and Bf-109K, were introduced in 1945, and although both versions added new improvements to the Bf-109 line, they were produced in significant numbers. The Bf-109 series served the Luftwaffe over

Spain during the Spanish Civil War and over Poland, France, England, and North Africa during World War II.

Bf-110 Series

The Bf-110 was produced by BFW on request from the Luftwaffe for a heavy fighter. As with the Bf-109, the Bf-110 was produced in several versions, with a total output of approximately six thousand aircraft. The most noteworthy version was the Bf-110C-4. This heavy fighter carried a pilot, navigator/observer, and radio operator/gunner in an enclosed cockpit. Weighing 11,354 pounds empty, it had a wingspan of 53 feet, 1.8 inches, was 39 feet, 8.33 inches in length, and stood 13 feet, 6.5 inches in height. Powered by two Daimler-Benz DB 601A-1 inverted-V piston engines, the Bf-110C-4 had a maximum speed of 348 miles per hour, a cruising speed of 304 miles per hour, a ceiling of 32,810 feet, and a maximum range of 680 miles. It was armed with two 20-millimeter MGFF fixed, forward-firing cannons, four 7.92-millimeter MG17 fixed, forward-firing machine guns, and one 7.92-millimeter MG15 trainable, rearward-firing machine gun.

A later version, the Bf-110G-4c/R3, was reconfigured to serve as a night fighter. Carrying the same three-man crew as the Bf-110C-4, it weighed 11,230 pounds empty, had a wingspan of 53 feet, 3.77 inches, was 42 feet, 9.78 inches in length, and stood 13 feet, 8.5 inches in height. Powered by two Daimler-Benz DB 605B-1 inverted-V piston engines, the Bf-110G-4c/R3 had a maximum speed of 342 miles per hour, a cruising speed of 317 miles per hour, a ceiling of 26,245 feet, and a maximum range of 808 miles. It was armed with two 30-millimeter MK108 fixed, forward-firing cannons, two 20-millimeter MG 151/20 fixed, forward-firing cannons, and one 7.92-millimeter MG81z trainable, rearward-firing two-barrel machine gun. This plane also carried several varieties of radar which, although increasing drag and hampering performance, enabled it to enter night service. The various versions of the Bf-110 served the Luftwaffe over Poland, Norway, England, North Africa, and Russia throughout World War II.

Me-163 Series

The Me-163 Komet was the first rocket-powered aircraft used in World War II. Although it did not come on line until 1944, the Me-163B-1a Komet was the best known of these rocket aircraft. It was a single seater that weighed 4,206 pounds empty, had a wingspan of 30 feet, 7.33 inches, was 19 feet, 2.33 inches in length, and stood 9 feet, 0.67 inches in height. Powered by one Walter HWK 109-509A-1/2 rocket motor, it had a maximum speed of 593 miles per hour, a climb rate of 15,951 feet per minute, and a ceiling of 39,370 feet. It was armed with two 30-millimeter MK108 fixed, forward-firing cannons or two 20mm MG151/20 fixed, forward-firing cannons. The Komet, however, had several problems. It functioned for only 7.5 minutes under power, and frequently suffered from premature engine shutdown at high altitude or immediately after takeoff. Such problems, combined with the late stage of the war when the Komet was introduced, resulted in only 279 of the aircraft actually reaching Luftwaffe service.

Me-262 Series

The world's first operational jet fighter was Messerschmitt's turbojet-powered interceptor fighter, the Me-262. The most popular of the Me-262 class was the Me-262A-1a. This was a single seater that weighed 9,742 pounds empty, had a wingspan of 41 feet, 0.5 inches, was 34 feet, 9.3 inches in length, and stood 12 feet, 6.8 inches in height. Powered by two Junkers Jumo 004B-1/2/3 Orkan turbojet engines, it had a maximum speed of 540 miles per hour, a climbing rate of 3,937 feet per minute, and a range of 652 miles. It was armed with four 30-millimeter MK-108 fixed, forward-firing cannons located in the nose cone. In 1944, Messerschmitt produced the Me-262a-2, a fighter-bomber, nicknamed Sturmvogel (storm bird). This aircraft was basically the same as the Me-262a-1a, with the notable exception that the Sturmvogel was equipped to carry one 1,102-pound (500 kilogram) bomb or two 551-pound (250 kilogram) bombs. Although unstable, difficult to fly, and used in limited numbers by the Luftwaffe, the Me-262 was a nearly unstoppable aircraft that changed the course of the aircraft industry by ushering in the jet age.

Me-323 Series

The most unique of the Messerschmitt aircraft was the Me-323 Gigant (giant). The Me-323E-2 Gigant was a heavy transport plane operated by a pilot, copilot, flight engineer, and radio operator on the flight deck, plus a load master and up to six gunners in its belly. Its empty weight was 65,256 pounds, but the Gigant had a maximum takeoff weight of 99,206 pounds. It could carry a payload of 120 troops or freight up to 34,000 pounds. The Gigant had a wingspan of 180 feet, 5.35 inches, was 93 feet, 6 inches in length, and stood 31 feet, 6 inches in height. It was powered by six Gnome-Rhone 14N-48/49 radial piston engines, which provided a maximum speed of 157 miles per hour, a cruising speed of 140 miles per hour, a ceiling of 14,760 feet, and a range of 808 miles. To protect this rather slow-moving aircraft, the Gigant was armed with one 20-

millimeter MG151/20 trainable cannon in each of two power-operated EDL 151 wing turrets, one 13-millimeter MG131 trainable, forward-firing machine gun in each of two nose positions, one 13-millimeter MG131 trainable, rearward-firing machine gun in the rear of the flight deck, and one 13-millimeter MG131 trainable, lateral-firing machine gun in each of the two forward and two beam positions. The Gigant was used to support the Afrika Corps in North Africa and the Wehrmacht in Russia.

Me-210/410 Series

The Me-210 was constructed by Messerschmitt to replace the Bf-110 and to act as a dive-bomber. The Me-210, however, suffered from serious technical and aerodynamic problems from the beginning. These problems plagued the Me-210 throughout its production and it never acted as a serviceable aircraft. Messerschmitt never gave up on the craft, and in 1943, the Me-410 Hornisse (hornet), a modified version of the Me-210, entered Luftwaffe service. The best known of the Hornisse was the Me-410A-1/U2. This heavy fighter and fighter-bomber carried a pilot and radio operator/gunner, and weighed 16,574 pounds empty. It had a wingspan of 53 feet, 7.7 inches, a length of 40 feet, 11.3 inches, and stood 14 feet, 0.5 inches in height. It was powered by two Daimler-Benz DB 603A inverted-V piston engines, which provided for a maximum speed of 388 miles per hour, a cruising speed of 365 miles per hour, a ceiling of 32,810 feet, and a maximum range of 1,050 miles. It was armed with two 20-millimeter MG151/20 fixed, forward-firing cannons in the nose, two 20-millimeter MG151/20 fixed, forward-firing cannons in a ventral tray, two 7.92-millimeter MG17 fixed, forward-firing machine guns in the nose, and one 13-millimeter MG131 trainable, lateral/rearward-firing machine gun. The Me-410 served the Luftwaffe over France, Russia, and Eastern Europe during the last two years of World War II.

Postwar Messerschmitt

After the war, Messerschmitt AG briefly left the aircraft industry to produce products as varied as sewing machines and motor scooters. By the mid-1950's, the company had returned to the aircraft industry to produce passenger, transport, and training aircraft. The company survived Willy Messerschmitt's death in 1978 and, as a result of mergers and reorganizations, in the 1990's Messerschmitt AG became Messerschmitt Bolkow-Blohm GmbH. The company continues to produce aircraft, but also produces missiles, parts for spacecraft, as well as railroad and highway vehicles.

Gregory S. Taylor

Bibliography

Boyne, Walter. *The Messerschmitt 262: Arrow to the Future*. Washington, D.C.: Smithsonian Institution Press, 1980. A brilliant study of the first operational jet-powered aircraft.

Chant, Chris. *German Warplanes of World War II*. London: Amber, 1999. A thorough study of all the major German aircraft of World War II, including numerous illustrations and technical notations.

Ebert, Hans. *The History of German Aviation*. Atglen, Pa.: Schiffer, 1999. An extensive study of the German aircraft industry, including pre- and post-World War II developments.

Ethell, Jeffery. *The German Jets in Combat*. London: Jane's, 1979. A thorough survey of the major advances in jet technology made by the German aircraft industry.

Kobel, Fritz, and Jakob Mathmann. *The Messerschmitt 109*. Translated by David Johnston. Atglen, Pa.: Schiffer, 1996. A detailed and well-illustrated study of the Messerschmitt Bf-109 series.

See also: Bombers; Fighter pilots; Jet engines; Luftwaffe; Mergers; Manufacturers; Military flight; Rocket propulsion; Turbojets and turbofans; World War II

Microgravity

Definition: A condition in which the apparent effects of gravity are very small.

Significance: Microgravity is useful for many scientific applications that cannot be performed in an environment where gravity is a dominating force. It is also a problem humans encounter when traveling in space.

Microgravity Environments

Microgravity is sometimes used interchangeably with terms such as weightlessness, free fall, or zero gravity. However, some of these terms can be misleading. For example, the term microgravity implies a condition in which very little gravity present. This condition would be possible to achieve at very large distances from any planet or star, but it is a condition that is currently not easily obtained.

From a practical standpoint, microgravity environments occur in relatively strong gravitational fields. To obtain the effects of microgravity, an object is dropped or put into a state of free fall. For example, astronauts orbiting the earth in the space shuttle can be described as being in a mi-

Parabolic Trajectory for Microgravity

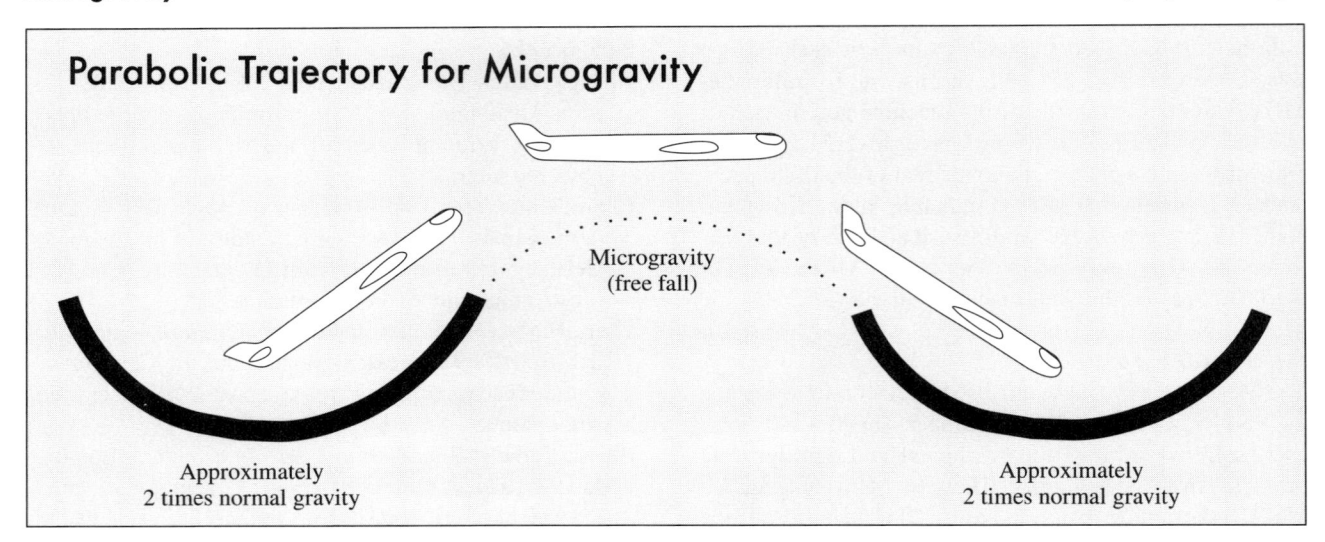

crogravity environment. However, in this orbit, gravity is still about 90 percent as strong as it is on the surface of the earth. The difference is that the astronauts and the shuttle are in free fall around the earth. They are all falling, but they have enough horizontal velocity so that the earth's surface curves away from them about as fast as they drop and therefore, they do not hit the ground.

Research Uses of Microgravity

Microgravity environments can be used for many different applications that are impossible to achieve in a normal-gravity environment. One such application involves the creation of certain alloys. On Earth, when two materials are mixed, the new compound contains elements that have different densities. In this new compound, the elements that are denser will settle to the bottom of the mixture in a process called sedimentation. In a microgravity environment, sedimentation does not occur, and the material can be cured in a state where the elements with different densities are equally distributed. Many high-quality materials can be manufactured this way.

Microgravity is also used to develop and study many topics associated with biology and life sciences. By studying things such as crystals, plants, animals, and medicines in a microgravity environment, scientists can learn more about how each of these works, both in microgravity and in normal gravity. The result is a better scientific understanding and the potential to create new and better medicines.

Along with the benefits of microgravity also come problems. One of the big problems of microgravity relates to human space travel. Although the human body functions well in a one-gravity environment, when it is subject to a microgravity environment, as in orbit, the body experiences a decreased hydrostatic gradient, a shift of fluid from the lower body to the upper body. The body eventually rids itself of this extra fluid in the upper body, but upon return to Earth, the problem is reversed. When it leaves the free fall environment, the fluid pools in the lower body and can causes light-headedness or blackouts. Vestibular functions that sense a body's orientation are confused by microgravity and can cause space sickness. Fortunately, the body usually adapts within the first few days of orbit. While in microgravity, the muscles in the body begin to atrophy due to the lack of use and bones lose calcium, which causes them to weaken. Vigorous exercise in orbit can help alleviate the muscle atrophy and some of the calcium loss, but no good long-term solution to these problems has yet been developed.

Obtaining Microgravity Conditions

There are several methods that have been used to simulate microgravity via free fall. For centuries drop facilities have been used to create microgravity conditions. In the mid-sixteenth century, artillerists discovered that lead shot for muskets could be made almost spherical by dropping molten lead from a tall tower. During free fall, the lead would cool into a spherical shape and then land in a container of water. There are several different drop facilities around the world and in order to get relatively long periods of free fall, these facilities must be very tall. For example, one of the longest drop times comes from a facility in Japan that has been built in a vertical mine shaft that is 490 meters deep. This drop facility can provide free fall for up to 10 seconds.

Aircraft such as the National Aeronautics and Space Administration (NASA) KC-135 are used for free-fall environments by flying parabolic curves. During these parabolic trajectories, the occupants feel alternating 15- to 30-second forces of near-free fall and twice normal gravity.

Sounding rockets launched to high altitudes are yet another way to simulate microgravity. When their engines shut off, the coasting rockets can experience several minutes of free fall. To obtain longer periods of free fall, orbiting spacecraft can be used. These orbiting spacecraft, such as shuttles and space stations, are in constant states of free fall, achieving very long periods of microgravity. One problem that may develop in these situations is that as astronauts move around, they must push off the walls of the vehicle. The pushing causes small accelerations in the vehicle and this can disturb experiments that require an almost perfect free fall environment.

Scott R. Dahlke

Bibliography

Logsdon, Tom. *Orbital Mechanics: Theory and Applications.* New York: John Wiley & Sons, 1998. A generally readable introduction to the theory of satellite motion, with technically challenging mathematical points.

Rogers, Melissa J. B., Gregory Vogt, and Michael Wargo. *Microgravity.* Washington, D.C.: National Aeronautics and Space Administration, 1997. A publication dedicated to the topic of microgravity, with many diagrams and examples that help explain the concept of microgravity and how it is used.

Sellers, Jerry Jon. *Understanding Space: An Introduction to Astronautics.* 2d ed. New York: McGraw-Hill, 2000. A great book about many different aspects of space with technical details in the appendices for those wanting more information.

See also: Astronauts and cosmonauts; Crewed spaceflight; Forces of flight; Gravity; Orbiting; Rockets; Spaceflight; "Vomit Comet"

Military flight

- **Definition:** The use of aircraft for the purposes of warfare and national defense.
- **Significance:** The development of military flight allowed warfare to be waged more rapidly and more powerfully than ever before.

Background

At the beginning of the twentieth century, despite vastly increased firepower and mobility, armies were still tied to the ground, and strategists thought in terms of smashing enemy defenses through sending literally millions of soldiers against them. The development of military aircraft in the twentieth century changed the nature of warfare, which could now be waged more rapidly and more destructively than ever before. Beginning in World War I and continuing at an ever-increasing pace, military aircraft have performed many functions, including reconnaissance and spotting; the bombing of military and civilian targets; aerial combat and protection for bombers; providing support for ground troops; causing disruption of enemy logistical movement; and, perhaps most important, threatening to deliver weapons of mass destruction in the nuclear age. The twentieth century has been marked by the extremely rapid evolution of more efficient and effective aircraft designs and types, ranging from the slow and awkward biplanes of World War I to the highly sophisticated spy satellites of the late twentieth and early twenty-first centuries.

Pioneering Efforts: 1861-1918

The age of military aircraft began with the use of balloons to gather information on enemy positions. Although military strategists experimented with balloons during the wars of the French Revolution (1792-1802), the first systematic attempt to use balloons in warfare was made during the American Civil War (1861-1865). A new era in warfare dawned on July 31, 1861, in Virginia, when Union general Benjamin Butler sent John LaMountain above the nearby Confederate lines in a balloon. LaMountain, who before the war had achieved fame by sailing more than 1,000 miles in a balloon, reported that the rebel defenses were less strong as Union commanders believed. Although both armies during the Civil War periodically, but often ineffectively, used balloons for reconnaissance and to direct artillery fire, air power did not seriously challenge the use of cavalry for effective scouting and reconnaissance. Balloons, most of which were filled with hydrogen gas, were expensive and cumbersome to maintain and move and were highly vulnerable to enemy fire—few stayed aloft very long. The possibility of aerial photography was discussed during the war but never attempted.

New possibilities were developed for military aircraft in 1903, when Orville and Wilbur Wright performed the first successful series of heaver-than-air, machine-powered flights. By the beginning of World War I in 1914, two-wing, wooden aircraft were able to carry a pilot and observer over enemy lines and back on valuable reconnaissance missions. By 1915, British, French, and German airplanes were equipped with cameras for fixing enemy positions in photographs and with radios for relaying data back from the air. By the following year, armies on both sides considered air reconnaissance vital to the planning of any offensive.

However, as soon as the combatants realized the effectiveness of air power, they set out to stop it by developing single-pilot planes armed with machine guns that were synchronized to fire through the aircrafts' propellers. The first flying aces and dogfights emerged during World War I. Perhaps most famous flying ace was the German fighter pilot Manfred von Richthofen, who was credited with destroying eighty enemy aircraft before he himself was shot from the skies and killed in April, 1918.

World War I also marked the beginning of strategic bombing from the skies. In 1915, bombs rained down on London from a German zeppelin—air power now meant that not even civilians back home, far from the fighting, were truly safe. By 1918, German and British airplanes were regularly bombing enemy cities and civilians. The United States entered the war in 1917, and in 1918, during the first major American offensive against the Germans, ground troops were supported by more than one thousand aircraft. Although air power had not proved decisive in the outcome of World War I, it had proved highly effective as a reconnaissance tool, and its uses had multiplied rapidly. Furthermore, by 1918, engine and structural design was improving. Air power would become even more crucial to the outcome of future wars.

Air Power and Total War: 1918-1945

Between World War I and the outbreak of World War II in 1939, military aircraft were improved through a number of technical developments. First, new and more powerful engines were devised, greatly improving both speed and carrying capacity. Second, aircraft design shifted from that of biplanes, with wings that were supported by external structures, to monoplanes with internally supported single wings. The amount of dead or empty weight dropped dramatically, as the space given to pilots, fuel, and cargo expanded. Third, retractable landing gear appeared. Fourth, aircraft became much more destructive, with additional bombing ordnance and defensive armament. Speed, maneuverability, and firepower all increased as a result. Fifth, aircraft carriers were developed, which greatly widened the range of aircraft in a number of military roles. Sixth, and most significant, the major powers in the world developed aircraft industries that could produce aircraft tailored to specific uses while constantly updating and improving models. Finally, military strategists developed complex theories of air warfare, most of which continued to see air power as playing a supporting role for ground operations.

However, a few analysts devised more ambitious theories of air power. The Italian general Giulio Douhet emphasized the use of aircraft to bomb enemy cities, including not only the military targets in those cities but the people themselves. Such strategic bombing would demoralize the enemy's population while destroying its production capabilities. This theory was put into effect during the Spanish Civil War (1936-1939) by the German Luftwaffe, which bombed undefended civilians in cities with little or no military value. During the Spanish conflict, the Germans also placed voice-operated radios in their bombers and fighters, enabling true coordination between ground and air forces for the first time. Meanwhile, the British had installed the first radar system to provide early warning of enemy attack.

By September 1, 1939, when the Germans invaded Poland, all the major nations who would eventually be involved in World War II had for several years been producing fighters, bombers, and other specialized aircraft. At the beginning of the war, Germany was ahead of the field both in numbers of aircraft and in performance.

One example of the German air arsenal was the Messerschmitt Me-109 fighter plane. More Messerschmitts were produced during World War II than any other fighter by any combatant. The Me-109 saw action in all theaters of the war, and although it was out-performed by the American P-51 Mustang and the British Spitfire, it remained a formidable weapon. Another of Germany's most effective aircraft was the Stuka bomber, a light and small plane designed to prepare the way for the advance of ground troops disrupting and destroying communication and supply routes.

Although German air power dominated the skies of Europe during 1939 and 1940, the Luftwaffe failed in its attempt to reduce England to submission through air power alone in the summer and fall of 1940. British radar stations and the information they provided about the direction and strength of German attacks gave the Royal Air Force (RAF) a great advantage. Equally important, however, was the skill with which British pilots intercepted and destroyed German aircraft during the campaign. Of great importance was the Spitfire fighter plane, which was superior to German fighter planes in both speed and maneuverability.

From 1939 to 1941, air power in the form of bombers and fighters ranged over Europe and the Pacific, wreaking havoc and supporting ground and naval operations, mainly

The increasing use of airplanes in military capacities also required the development of aircraft carriers to provide mobile bases for refueling and maintenance. (Digital Stock)

for the Axis Powers of Japan and Germany. However, the use of aircraft launched from carriers was also introduced. The most dramatic example of the use of aircraft carriers was the Japanese attack on the U.S. naval fleet at Pearl Harbor, Hawaii, on December 7, 1941. The Japanese bombers were protected by the very effective Japanese Zero fighter planes. The Zero had a maximum speed of 330 miles per hour, two cannons mounted on its wings, and two machine guns that fired through its propeller. Despite inflicting considerable damage on American cruisers and destroyers at Pearl Harbor, the Japanese missed the U.S. aircraft carriers, which were not in Hawaii. Only five months after the Pearl Harbor attack, the Americans' carrier-based air fleet inflicted a crushing defeat upon the Japanese at the Battle of Midway, which shifted the momentum of the war in the Pacific.

By the beginning of 1943, the balance of power in both the European and Pacific theaters had shifted to the Allies, who had matched and were rapidly surpassing German and Japanese air power. Moreover, Allied air superiority was crucial to the success of Allied ground troops in 1944 and 1945. For example, for weeks before the D-day invasion of June, 1944, Allied bombers and fighters prowled behind German lines in France, hitting supplies and reinforcements moving by rail and road and thereby helping to ensure a successful landing at Normandy. The dropping of one thousand airborne troops behind German lines was another important part of D day's success.

In 1943 and 1944, a new type of aircraft took center stage in the Allied air campaign—the long-range heavy bomber. Both British and American bombers began raids over German cities in 1943, and despite heavy losses from enemy antiaircraft fire and enemy fighters, these bombing runs did tremendous damage to German war production. By 1944, air fields recaptured in Western Europe were being used as bases from which to reach cities throughout Germany.

The American B-17 Flying Fortress, with a range of 3,750 miles, could carry up to 17,600 pounds of bombs. The B-17 carried a crew of ten. Its ceiling was 35,000 feet, and its cruising speed was 170 miles per hour. The more than 12,000 B-17's built during the war dropped about

640,000 tons of bombs; about 4,750 B-17's were lost in combat. The British Lancaster bomber could hold more bombs than could any other Allied aircraft except the B-29 Superfortress. The destruction produced by such heavy bombers, flying with fighter escorts, was tremendous. In February, 1945, the German city of Dresden was flattened, and more than 100,000 people, many of whom were civilians, were killed. By the war's end, almost 600,000 German civilians had been killed in air raids, while the death toll for British victims of German bombing totaled about 60,000.

By 1945, air power had helped to create what military historians call total war—an expansion of the battlefield to encompass all enemy cities and their civilian occupants, along with a total dedication of a nation's economy to the production of war matériel. A new stage in warfare and military flight was also dawning, with the use of atomic power and the development of jet and missile technology. By 1943, Germany was working toward the creation of a massive bomb that could be delivered not by an airplane, but by a rocket. The V-1 and V-2 flying bombs, as they were called, were the world's first intercontinental ballistic weapons. Although these weapons killed more than two thousand London citizens during 1944 and 1945, they could not change the war's outcome. About 35,000 V-1 rockets were produced, of which about 5,000 actually hit the British. These bombs, with enough power to destroy a city block, indicated the future direction of air power, as did the jet-powered fighter planes that were being produced by Germany by the end of the war.

Of even greater importance for the future of military flight was the use of air power to deliver the first atomic weapons in warfare. The American bombing of the Japanese cities of Hiroshima and Nagasaki in August, 1945, heralded the Cold War, in which enemies could destroy not only each other but the earth itself. In this new era, when the doctrine of mutual assured destruction (MAD) would paradoxically help to maintain peace, aircraft would be an essential part of nuclear arsenals and military strategy.

Military Flight During the Cold War: 1945-1990

After the Soviet Union attained atomic power in 1949, the ensuing arms race included aircraft of many types. The first important innovation in military flight after World War II was the replacement of propeller-driven aircraft with jet aircraft, which were first produced in World War II as fighter planes. The Germans produced the first operational model, the Messerschmitt Me-262E. The Me-262E was clearly superior to its rivals, but it had arrived too late in the war to make much of an impact. In 1943, a British twin-engine jet plane named the Gloster Meteor flew in combat formation. The first U.S. jet aircraft was the Lockheed P-80 Shooting Star, which first flew in 1944 but never saw combat in World War II. The first Soviet jet fighter plane appeared in 1946.

In addition to jet fighter planes, jet-powered bombers also became a part of the Cold War arms race. One such aircraft was the U.S. B-52 Stratofortress, which appeared in 1955 and became an important part of the U.S. nuclear arsenal. A nuclear bomb was first dropped successfully from an airplane in 1956. By 1960, each B-52 could drop up to four nuclear bombs and more than forty 750-pound bombs. By 1955, the Soviet Union had produced its own long-range bombers, including the Tu-95 Bear, capable of reaching U.S. cities from Northern Siberia. By 1960, U.S. bombers substantially outnumbered those of

---

Events in the History of Military Flight

1861: Balloons are used for reconnaissance during the American Civil War, one of the first effective uses of military air power.

1903: The Wright brothers achieve the first heavier-than-air sustained flight, laying the foundation for future development of military aircraft.

1914: Airplanes provide vital reconnaissance for the first time in a major conflict during the Battle of the Marne in World War I.

1915: German zeppelin raids on London are the first example of strategic bombing by military aircraft.

1944: V-1 and V-2 rockets launched by Germany during World War II are the first intercontinental ballistic missiles; German Me-262 and British Meteor are the first military jet aircraft.

1945: U.S. bombings of the Japanese cities of Hiroshima and Nagasaki mark the first time nuclear weapons are delivered by air.

1947: U.S. test pilot Chuck Yeager breaks the sound barrier, paving the way for modern supersonic military aircraft.

1956: The United States first employs the U-2 spy plane for high-level reconnaissance.

1957: The Soviet Union launches Sputnik satellite, setting the stage for future deployment of satellites for military use.

1964: The United States employs missiles with multiple warheads.

1968: In relief of Khe Sanh during the Vietnam War, U.S. B-52's carry out the most concentrated bombing raid in military history.

1991: A U.N. coalition exhibits a full range of modern military aircraft to defeat Iraq during the Persian Gulf War.

the Soviets, although there was a perception of a so-called bomber gap, in which the Soviets had the advantage.

Air reconnaissance was also revolutionized during the Cold War by jet power and new designs. Planes with extremely high ceilings and long ranges gathered information on the enemy—one example was the U.S. U-2, which flew its first mission in 1956 and was able to fly above 70,000 feet. In 1960, a Soviet fighter plane shot down a U-2 piloted by Gary Powers over Soviet airspace, and a tense series of allegations between the United States and the Soviet Union followed. It was also a U-2 that photographed clear evidence of offensive Soviet missiles being built in Cuba in 1962. Later, satellites would replace such aircraft as the principal means of gathering intelligence.

Another innovation in military flight after World War II was the development of ballistic missiles capable of carrying nuclear warheads thousands of miles. By 1960, the debate over the bomber gap between the two superpowers had turned into a discussion over the missile gap. During the 1950's, America produced two classes of intercontinental ballistic missiles (ICBMs): the Titan and the Atlas. Both were designed to deliver a 1-megaton warhead over a distance of 5,000 miles. By 1960, such ICBMs could be launched from U.S. submarines.

Although the Soviet Union initially lagged behind the United States in missile production during the 1950's, it launched its first successful ICBM in Siberia in 1957. Soon afterward, the Soviets sent by rocket into Earth orbit two satellites, Sputnik 1 and Sputnik 2, the latter of which carried a live dog. During this period, the Soviets also began to fit their submarines with nuclear warheads with short initial ranges. By the early 1960's, a second generation of U.S. ICBMs, the Minuteman I and Titan II, were in production. The numbers of Soviet ICBMs soared during the 1960's, with series such as the SS-11, the SS-9, and the SS-13. By 1970, the Soviet Union's 1,299 ICBMs surpassed the U.S. total of 1,054. However, the United States retained superiority in numbers of bombers and submarine-launched ballistic missiles (SBLMs). The range of the U.S. Polaris missile, carried by nuclear submarines, increased from 1,375 to 2,850 miles during this period.

Cold warfare also promoted the development of the helicopter. Although helicopters appeared in World War II, they came into their own in the 1950's and 1960's, during the Korean War and Vietnam War. Used for a variety of needs, the helicopter was suited to the rugged terrain of many battle zones during this period. An example was the American UH-1 Huey, which served many functions: troop transport, evacuation of wounded, and attack on enemy ground troops. The Huey was part of the air cavalry created by the U.S. Army in Vietnam. The First Airmobile Cavalry Division, created by the United States in 1965, was capable of moving ten thousand troops into battle within a few hours. The Soviet Union began regular production of military helicopters in 1948, with many models of various sizes to follow.

Still another and more advanced form of Cold War military flight was the use of surveillance satellites. In 1957, after the Soviet Union launched Sputnik 1, the world's first satellite, into space, the United States began work on the Corona satellite, designed to snap photographs of selected territory at regular intervals from space. Although often unsuccessful, by 1972, the Corona series of satellites had provided more information about the Soviet Union than all previous surveillance flights by U-2 planes. By 1962, the Soviets had launched its first Cosmos satellite, larger than the Corona and with more cameras. During the 1970's and 1980's, satellite surveillance was improved as it was employed by more nations. Satellites helped to detect telemetry signals and to wage electronic warfare by jamming transmission signals. The administration of U.S. president Ronald Reagan called for the development of the Strategic Defense Initiative (SDI), a satellite missile defense system that could block incoming ICBMs.

Beyond the Cold War: 1990-Present

In 1990, at the beginning of Operation Desert Shield, the first major conflict since the decline of the Soviet Union, it appeared that U.S. military air power might be able to achieve victory substantially on its own. With cruise missiles launched from ships and submarines combined with a massive bombing campaign, tremendous damage was done to the Iraqi army of Saddam Hussein. Once again, new technology, such as the U.S. Air Force's stealth bomber, which could not be detected by Iraqi defenses, surfaced. Military aircraft could now be used effectively at night because of infrared viewing devices. In fact, the transportation of about 35,000 U.S. military personnel by air, most by commercial aircraft, was a massive undertaking necessary before the war could begin. Bombers hit Iraqi targets with smart bombs, which provided new and astounding levels of accuracy—the F-117A stealth fighter was one such aircraft. However, despite a massive air campaign by the United States and its allies, ground troops still proved necessary to dislodge the Iraqi army from Kuwait. For all of its advances since the Wright brothers' achievement in 1903, military flight still required careful integratation with other forms of military power to achieve its desired results.

Robert Harrison

Missiles

Bibliography

Doughty, Robert, et al. *Warfare in the Western World*. Vol. 2. Lexington, Mass.: D. C. Heath, 1996. An excellent history of modern war, including a clear description of the rise and development of military flight.

Hastings, Max. *Bomber Command*. London: Pan, 1999. An informative and interesting study of the effectiveness of the Allied strategic bombing campaign in World War II, including its effects on German civilians.

Morrow, J. H., Jr. *The Great War in the Air: Military Aviation from 1909 to 1921*. Washington, D.C.: Smithsonian Institution Press, 1993. An excellent introduction to the rapid development of military flight during World War I.

See also: Aerospace industry, U.S.; Air force, U.S.; Air force bases; Aircraft carriers; Airplanes; Antiaircraft fire; Apache helicopter; Battle of Britain; Black Sheep Squadron; Bombers; Glenn H. Curtiss; Dogfights; Jimmy Doolittle; Dresden, Germany, bombing; Eagle; *Enola Gay*; Fighter pilots; Fighting Falcon; Flying Fortress; Flying Tigers; Franco-Prussian War; Guernica, Spain, bombing; Gulf War; Harrier jets; Helicopters; Hornet; Jennys; Kamikaze missions; Korean War; Charles A. Lindbergh; Luftwaffe; Marine pilots, U.S.; Missiles; Billy Mitchell; Navy pilots, U.S.; Osprey helicopter; Pearl Harbor, Hawaii, bombing; Raptor; Hanna Reitsch; Manfred von Richthofen; Eddie Rickenbacker; Rotorcraft; Royal Air Force; Sopwith Camels; Spanish Civil War; Stealth bomber; Stealth fighter; Strategic Air Command; Stratofortress; Superfortress; Tactical Air Command; Tomcat; Transport aircraft; Tuskegee Airmen; Vietnam War; Women's Airforce Service Pilots; World War I; World War II

Missiles

Also known as: Arrows, bullets, rockets, ICBMs

Definition: Any type of aerial projectile delivered against a target, normally with a high trajectory and over greater distances than personal weapons. In modern times, the term "missile" usually refers exclusively to pilotless air vehicles carrying a warhead and powered by a rocket or jet engine.

Significance: Missiles provided two-thirds of the Triad, the combination of bombers, sea-launched missiles, and land-based missiles that the United States maintained to deliver a nuclear strike against the Soviet Union during the Cold War. In the late twentieth and early twenty-first centuries, the development of small yet sophisticated computers coupled with the desire within the United States to avoid risking the lives of air crew members led to an increased dependence on smaller tactical missiles to carry out military objectives.

Premodern Missiles

Air-delivered projectiles have been used since before the dawn of civilization. Although for thousand of years, armies depended primarily on hand-held weapons, such as swords and spears, kinetic-energy missiles in the form of arrows fired from bows and, later, bolts fired from crossbows had an auxiliary role on battlefields. Heavier projectiles were developed for use against fortifications and city walls. Roman armies employed artillery in the form of large engines that could hurl boulders at enemy fortifications. However, the birth of the modern missile came when gunpowder, a Chinese invention, was made to burn inside a tube that was closed at one end, causing the thrust to push out the other end and force the tube to lift. This use of missiles with their own propulsion, called rockets, slowly began to change warfare.

Pre-World War II Missiles

Early rocket-type missiles caused little physical destruction on the battlefield, but European armies began employing them in the late eighteenth century for illumination and psychological purposes. Military missiles remained mostly a curiosity until World War II. Missile development got its greatest boost in the early twentieth century from Dr. Robert H. Goddard, a physicist from Massachusetts, who began to experiment with liquid-fueled rockets. Although his experiments were largely ignored in the United States, his work became highly influential in Germany and became the basis for later German missile development.

World War II Missiles

Germany led the world in missile development during World War II. To make an effective weapon, missiles were fitted with warheads, which were bombs designed to explode either on impact or at a certain altitude. By 1943, Germany began to place more emphasis on so-called wonder weapons, high-tech weapons which would compensate for Germany's deficiencies in manpower and resources. Among these were missiles. Nazi leaders believed that missiles might be able to inflict enough physical and psychological damage on the British that they might sue for a separate peace.

The German V-1 rocket was essentially a pilotless jet aircraft that would be pointed in the general direction of London, and would fly until it ran out of fuel. It would then crash and explode. The V-1 was followed by the V-2, a much more sophisticated device. The V-2 rocket was a true liquid-fueled guided missile. London received strikes from these weapons in 1944 and 1945. Of more than 8,000 V-1's launched against London, fewer than 2,500 found their target. Only eleven V-2's exploded in England. Fortunately for the British, the Germans were never able to produce them in large enough numbers to make a real impact on the British war effort. Even more importantly, the Germans neglected research into nuclear weapons, which, if fitted to even a small number of V-2's, would have given Germany a means to inflict catastrophic damage on its enemies.

Post-World War II Missiles

After the war, both the United States and the Soviet Union became interested in German research into the field of missiles. Both nations began to expedite the movement of top German scientists to their own nations. The United States began its ballistic missile program under Wernher von Braun at Redstone Arsenal, outside of Huntsville, Alabama. Von Braun, a former Third Reich scientist who had developed the German V-1 and V-2, directed American missile research through the development of the intercontinental ballistic missile (ICBM) into the space program, including the Apollo missions. The United States became more focused on missile development when the Soviets launched the Sputnik 1 satellite in October, 1957, from a Soviet rocket. Sputnik showed the Americans that the Soviets had the technology to shoot a nuclear-tipped missile to the United States.

The Air Force's Strategic Air Command (SAC), which originally focused on using crewed bombers to deliver nuclear and conventional weapons to targets around the world, primarily in the Soviet Union, began in the 1950's to develop ICBMs to counter the Soviet threat in this area. The Air Force had to struggle against both the Army and the Navy to acquire the missile missions. The Army argued that missiles were essentially very long-range artillery, whereas the Navy thought missiles would best be launched from ships and naval aircraft. In the end, the Air Force got the mission to develop and field the largest missiles, the ICBMs, which would carry nuclear warheads from inside the United States to strike cities and military targets in the Soviet Union. The Navy received authority to develop and field sea-launched ballistic missiles (SLBMs) and other missile systems that would operate with the fleet. Eventually the Navy would build large submarines that functioned as platforms for launching ballistic missiles from the safety of the floor of the continental shelf. The Army received authority to develop and deploy intermediate-range ballistic missiles (IRBMs) and other missile systems that could be used on the battlefield.

U.S. ICBMs

The first major American ICBM was the Atlas, which the U.S. Air Force first fielded in 1958. An offshoot of the Atlas was the development of the Thor, an IRBM. Although the Atlas had the ability to strike targets in the Soviet Union, it needed several hours prior notice for launch and was vulnerable to a first strike. In the event the Soviet Union attacked the United States first, the Atlas site would be a priority target. In the event of a Soviet nuclear strike within a mile or more or of an Atlas launch site, the United States would be unable to launch its Atlas missiles.

As a response to this vulnerability, the U.S. Air Force developed and fielded in April, 1962, the first of the Titan series of ICBMs, which had a faster launch time, carried a larger payload, and were housed in protected underground silos. Throughout the life of the Titan system, including after the Titan missiles were removed from the strategic force in the 1980's, the missile had a secondary role in launching crewed spacecraft, such as the Gemini Program, and satellites into orbit. The Titans were soon joined by the Minuteman series, which first became operational in November, 1962. Unlike earlier missiles, the Minuteman missiles had a solid propellant and could be launched within a few minutes of receiving an emergency war launch order. The Minuteman III would carry up to three warheads per missile. After heated debate over basing systems, fifty Peacekeeper missiles, each of which had the capacity to carry up to ten warheads, were based in hardened Minutemen silos by 1988. The Minuteman IIIs and Peacekeepers would be the mainstay of the U.S. ICBM force through the end of the Cold War.

Missiles in the Soviet Union

After World War II, the Soviet Union placed great emphasis on missiles in their military establishment. Unlike the United States, the Soviets created a new branch of their armed forces, the Strategic Rocket Forces, for missiles, although early Soviet rockets had impressive payloads and intercontinental ability, their accuracy was poor. By the early 1960's, the Soviets placed more emphasis on IRBMs and medium-range ballistic missiles (MRBMs) to counter the American threat. The placing of 1,000-mile-range MRBMs and 2,000-mile-range IRBMs in 1961 in Cuba, from where they could strike most parts of the continental United States, led to the Cuban Missile Crisis in 1962.

In the 1980's, the Soviet decision to field their SS-20 missiles in Eastern Europe led the North Atlantic Treaty Organization (NATO) to allow American IRBMs into Western Europe. The U.S. Army fielded the Pershing missile while the U.S. Air Force fielded the ground-launched cruise missile (GLCM). These were tactical weapons and had for their targets areas of troop concentration and supply depots. The Intermediate Nuclear Force Treaty, signed in December, 1987, by U.S. president Ronald Reagan and Soviet premier Mikhail Gorbachev, required both nations to withdraw and destroy those missiles, the first such reduction in nuclear weapons.

Strategic Air Command

Throughout its existence, the SAC focused on its ability to deliver a devastating counterstrike against the Soviet Union after the Soviet Union had attacked the United States. This formed part of the strategy known as mutually assured destruction (MAD), whereby the United States and the Soviet Union were each discouraged from launching a first-strike nuclear attack against the other because of the ability of the other nation to inflict a major counterstrike that would cause an unacceptable level of damage to the nation that struck first. This ability to withstand a nuclear attack and maintain enough assets to strike back, thereby discouraging the Soviet Union from attempting a first strike, became known as deterrence. In order to provide a credible deterrent, the SAC physically and operationally adopted measures to allow it to function after receiving such an attack. This included burying Titan and Minuteman missile silos and surrounding them with steel-reinforced hardened concrete. Although the SAC maintained a large missile force, it never contemplated discontinuing the use of the crewed bomber because, while a bomber once launched could be recalled, a missile once launched could not be stopped.

Post-Cold War Developments

During the Gulf War, U.S. missiles played a prominent role. Although the Patriot missiles, which became an important defense against Iraqi Scud missiles, received most of the press, much of the strategic air campaign of January and February, 1991, depended on missiles. The Air Force's air-launched cruise missiles (ALCMs) and short-range attack missiles (SRAMs), combined with the Navy's Tomahawk land-attack missiles (ThANs), destroyed the Iraqi command and control networks before the United Nations ground offensive began.

After the collapse of the Warsaw Pact and of the Soviet Union, the U.S. Air Force began to implement a major reorganization. In 1992, most of the SAC was incorporated with most of Tactical Air Command to create the Air Combat Command. This arrangement lasted about one year, when the Air Force's ICBM units were again transferred to Space Command. The end of the Cold War led the United States to scale back its numbers of and reliance on ICBMs, and instead ALCMs became an increasingly important weapon, as shown by their widespread use during the NATO air war with Yugoslavia in 1999. With their increasingly sophisticated guidance systems, which allow targets as small as a square meter to be regularly hit without exposing air crews to danger, guided missiles have become increasingly vital to the United States to carry out military objectives.

Barry M. Stentiford

Bibliography

Boyne, Walter J. *Beyond the Wild Blue: A History of the U.S. Air Force, 1947-1997*. New York: St. Martin's Press, 1997. A solid overview of the first fifty years of the Air Force as a separate branch of the U.S. military establishment. Emphasizes the people, equipment, and missions that shaped the development of the U.S. Air Force.

Neufeld, Jacob. *The Development of Ballistic Missiles in the United States Air Force, 1945-1960*. Washington, D.C.: Office of the Air Force History, 1990. An institutional history of the Air Force's development and fielding of several missile systems, with the Air Force fielding the Atlas ICBM after a long period of technical and political development.

Stumpf, David K., and Jay W. Kelley. *Titan II: A History of a Cold War Missile Program*. Fayetteville: University of Arkansas Press, 2000. Follows the development, testing, and fielding of a single ICBM system. Provides a useful overview of how technical developments, politics, financial restraints, and national strategy all influenced the eventual form the Titan II would take.

See also: Air Combat Command; Air force, U.S.; Wernher von Braun; Robert H. Goddard; Gulf War; Korean War; Rockets; Strategic Air Command; Tactical Air Command; World War I; World War II; Vietnam War

Billy Mitchell

Date: Born on December 29, 1879, in Nice, France; died on February 19, 1936, in New York, New York

Definition: Commanded the U.S. air effort in World War I and thereafter was an outspoken advocate of air power and of an independent U.S. air force.

Significance: Mitchell lobbied, cajoled, and bullied the U.S. governmental and military power structure to gain recognition of the role of air power in warfare.

William "Billy" Mitchell grew up in Milwaukee, Wisconsin, and in Washington, D.C. The son of a U.S. senator, he was deeply steeped in patriotism and military history. In 1898, at the outbreak of the Spanish-American War, he dropped out of George Washington University to join the U.S. Army and served in the aviation section of the Signal Corps. The armed forces were Mitchell's home and his love for the remainder of his life. Mitchell was an Army representative to a flight demonstration by Orville and Wilbur Wright, and he himself learned to fly in 1915. From 1917 to 1918, he commanded the Army Air Service of the U.S. Expeditionary Forces in Europe and was promoted to brigadier general in 1920.

Mitchell traveled widely, observed other countries' increasing interest in air power, and became a strong proponent for air power and for an independent Air Force. He worked hard to develop strategic doctrines that would utilize air power in the conduct of modern warfare and gathered many supporters. In 1921, the Army and the Navy held a demonstration of air power with a captured German battleship as the target. Mitchell's pilots sank the ship with heavy bombs, disregarding the rules set for the demonstration. Mitchell gained support in Congress but alienated his military colleagues by regularly and publicly criticizing the military's mismanagement of air power. At his 1925 court-martial, personally ordered by President Calvin Coolidge, he was found guilty of insubordination, reduced in rank to colonel, and suspended from active service for five years. Mitchell resigned a few months later and continued speaking out against the military command and for air power. His rank was posthumously restored, and he was decorated for his service.

Kenneth H. Brown

Bibliography

Burlingame, Roger. *General Billy Mitchell: Champion of Air Defense.* Reprint. Westport, Conn.: Greenwood Press, 1978. Chronicles the life of Mitchell and his campaign to establish a strong air defense for the country.

Hurley, Alfred F. *Billy Mitchell: Crusader for Air Power.* Reprint. Bloomington: Indiana University Press, 1975. A factual and objective biography that balances Mitchell's often overstated claims about his role in the development of air power.

Mitchell, William. *Memoirs of World War I: "From Start to Finish of Our Greatest War."* New York: Random House, 1969. Published years after Mitchell's death, these reminiscences show the origin of Mitchell's thoughts about the role of air power.

_____. *Winged Defense: The Development and Possibilities of Modern Air Power, Economic and Military.* New York: Putnam, 1925. A definitive statement of Mitchell's thought and strategic air-power doctrines.

See also: Air Force, U.S.; Bombers; Fighter pilots; Military flight; World War I; World War II

Brigadier General Billy Mitchell was one of the earliest advocates of the use of aircraft by the U.S. military. (Library of Congress)

Model airplanes

Definition: Facsimiles ranging in size from a few inches to many feet in length intended to represent actual or imagined airplanes in reduced scale, for display or flying purposes.

Significance: Model airplanes were used, before full-scale airplanes had flown, to investigate the science of flight. Models are also used for aeronautical research and aerial reconnaissance. They provide youth with an aeronautical education, and many pilots have become interested in flying through modeling. Modeling is a passionately followed hobby worldwide, providing pleasure of both building and flying. For those who compete in regional, national, and world contests, flying model airplanes is a highly demanding sport.

Flying models take many forms. They can be unguided after launch and known as free-flight, or FF, models; constrained and controlled by wires and known as control-line, or C/L, models; or controlled remotely by radio signals and known as radio-control, or R/C, models. From an aerodynamics standpoint, models will always suffer from what is known as scale effect, obtaining smaller maximum lift coefficients and greater drag coefficients. However, wing loadings, or weight divided by wing area, are much lower, so landing speeds are much lower than for full-scale aircraft. Modern model engines are sufficiently light and powerful that it is possible to build a model that has more thrust than its weight and can climb straight up or even hover. Structurally, models profit from a different scale effect and are less likely to suffer in-flight or landing damage.

Free-Flight Models

Free-flight, or FF, models can be the least expensive flying models, the easiest to build from raw materials, and the easiest and safest to fly by oneself. However, they are the most demanding of trim and stability because of their "launch-and-pray" nature. The smallest and lightest models can be flown indoors or on very calm mornings or evenings.

Powered models are normally flown outside. They usually utilize a timer-controlled dethermalizer that tips up the leading edge of the horizontal stabilizer to prevent them from being lost if rising air and wind would otherwise take them out of sight. Contests with free-flight models usually involve trying to keep them aloft for the maximum amount of time for each of the different classes of models.

Control-Line Models

Control-line, or C/L, models are the next least expensive flying models and have the additional advantage that they cannot fly out of sight and be lost. They also provide tactile feedback to the flier, because they are flown on steel lines, mostly stranded stainless-steel cables, that range from about 30 feet to about 70 feet in length. The lines are attached to a control handle in the flier's hand that operates the elevator through a bellcrank. Manipulation of this handle grants the flier the option of using a full hemisphere of space, inverted or upright. Control-line flying has a unique dependence on surface winds, because the planes are connected to the ground through the flier. Inverted flight requires extra learning, because response to control handle movements is reversed.

Control-line models include sport/trainers, scale, stunt, carrier, speed, and race types. Scale control-liners feature engine power, retractable gear, "bombs," and other realistic details. Stunt models are optimized for aerobatics and use a symmetrical wing section that enables them to make inverted and upright maneuvers. They often use a flap on the trailing edge of the wing that is mechanically linked to the bellcrank, so that it deflects oppositely to the elevator and enhances the maximum lift available for abrupt maneuvering. Carrier models are judged on the difference between their maximum and minimum speeds and for their ability to grab a wire with their tail hook for landing. Speed models are used in contests, which are won by the fastest speeds, with either piston or jet power, for a specified number of laps. Racer-type models are flown with two or more fliers in the circle, to a specified number of laps and with mandatory pit stops. Combat contests require two fliers in the circle, each trying to cut the opponent's trailing streamer, often flying at speeds of more than 100 miles per hour.

Radio-Control Models

Radio-control, or R/C, models require a battery-powered miniature receiver with a separate channel for each servo. A servo is an electric motor that rotates a shaft one way or the other from the neutral position, based on the movement of a lever in the transmitter held by the flier. The number of channels utilized varies from two or three for trainers to six or more for sophisticated models that are determined to fully emulate their full-scale counterparts.

Radio-control models are the most popular form of model airplane flying, no doubt because of the challenge involved with flying them well and because of their good simulation of full-scale flight. They also require the most time to learn how to fly without crashing. They are the most expensive type of flying model and require the most sophisticated models. However, the best R/C models, both airplanes and helicopters, can perform all the same aerobatic maneuvers, and more, as can their full-scale counterparts.

The most difficult problem to overcome in first learning to fly R/C airplanes is that the airplane apparently responds differently whether it is going away or coming toward the flier. It is also difficult for the beginner to judge the landing approach and landing. In this, computer-based simulators can be of considerable assistance. Competitive R/C events include combat, precision aerobatics, and pylon races.

Power Plants

Gravity was the original power plant for both FF and R/C gliders. Twisted rubber strands were the next power plant, used until the 1930's, when the first miniature spark-ignition engines were commercially produced. In the 1940's, the much simpler and lighter glow-plug engine, which required a battery only for starting, appeared. Diesel and compressed-air engines are used in small models. Jet engines have been available since the 1940's. Electric motor engines are the newest type of power plant, providing quiet and clean power.

W. N. Hubin

Bibliography

Lennon, Andy. *R/C Model Aircraft Design*. Wilton, Conn.: Air Age, 1996. A comprehensive text with minimal mathematics that includes coverage of canard and tailless designs.

Mackey, Charles. *Pioneers of Control-Line Flying*. Anniston, Ala.: Precision Aerobatic Model Pilots' Association, 1995. An account of how C/L flying dominated powered model flying from the early 1940's to 1960's, when R/C models became more available and more reliable.

Simons, Martin. *Model Aircraft Aerodynamics*. 4th ed. Herts, England: Model & Allied Publications, 1999. A good general reference for the aerodynamics and performance of model aircraft, including many suitable airfoils.

Thornburg, Dave. *Do You Speak "Model Airplane?": The Story of Aeromodeling in America*. Albuquerque, N.Mex.: Pony X Press, 1992. A history of the national championships, the people, the models, the FF beginnings, and the C/L and R/C revolutions, written in an engaging, easy-to-read, and amusing style.

Winter, William J. *The World of Model Airplanes: Building and Flying Free-Flight, Control-Line, and Radio-Controlled Models*. New York: Charles Scribner's Sons, 1983. An excellent overview of the building and flying aspects of all three types of model airplanes.

See also: Aerodynamics; Experimental aircraft; Forces of flight; Tail designs; Testing; Wing designs

Monoplanes

Definition: Airplanes possessing only one primary lifting surface.

Significance: Monoplanes are less expensive to build, more efficient in flight, and are capable of higher speeds than two-winged biplanes. After their early structural problems were solved, monoplanes quickly became the favored configuration for transports (in the 1920's) and for light airplanes and fighter aircraft (in the 1930's).

Development

The earliest practical airplanes were biplanes, with low-powered engines and very large wing areas. The braced-wing biplane design was considered the lightest and strongest aircraft configuration, especially for the thin wing sections then thought to be necessary.

The first airplane to cross the English Channel, however, was Louis Blériot's wire-braced monoplane, the Blériot XI, on July 25, 1909, six years after the Wright brothers flew their first biplane at Kitty Hawk, North Carolina. In 1912, the streamlined Deperdussin monoplane established a world speed record of more than 100 miles per hour.

Biplanes continued to predominate during World War I, because their rapid climb to a fighting altitude and their maneuverability for fighting were favored over high speeds. However, a few monoplanes, such as the Fokker Eindecker, the first to have a machine gun synchronized to fire between propeller blades, were used. Early monoplane designers did not appreciate the twisting to which a wing is subjected in flight, and there were a number of structural failures due to the elimination of external bracing to reduce drag.

In 1927, the greater efficiency of the monoplane was decisively demonstrated by Charles A. Lindbergh's New

York-to-Paris flight in his Ryan monoplane, the *Spirit of St. Louis*. In the 1930's, the development of the Douglas DC-1 and DC-2 models, using the modern configuration of a single low wing, a retractable landing gear, streamlined engine cowlings, and flaps for good low-speed performance, instantly made all biplane transports obsolete. A DC-2 carrying passengers nearly won the 1934 London-to-Australia race against specialized racing machines. The military, requiring extra strength and maneuverability from its aircraft, took longer to be convinced of the monoplane's advantages and still maintained a few biplanes at the beginning of World War II in 1939.

The 1937 Piper J-3 Cub, a strut-braced, high-wing monoplane with an inexpensive four-cylinder opposed engine, was far less expensive to produce and fly than were biplanes with much more powerful radial engines. This configuration has dominated the lower end of light-plane flight ever since.

Design

In the traditional monoplane design, a single large wing is followed by a much smaller horizontal surface containing both a stabilizing surface and a pitch-control surface, or elevator. For pitch stability with this configuration, the airplane's center of gravity must be sufficiently forward that the horizontal tail generates a downward force, or negative lift. Pitch stability means that the aircraft will tend to maintain a constant nose attitude relative to the horizon, even when disturbed by atmospheric turbulence. However, a monoplane's wing can be made into a very efficient lifting surface, because it does not compete with another nearby lifting surface, as does a biplane's wing.

Different monoplane designs differ in their relative vertical locations of the wings on the fuselage. If the wing is mounted on top of the fuselage, as in high-wing aircraft, the critical upper surface of the wing is minimally disturbed by airflow around the fuselage. The placement of the primary lifting surface above the center of gravity also enhances lateral stability because of the pendulum effect, in which the airplane tends to return to wings-level flight if it is banked. High-wing aircraft give pilots and passengers a particularly good view of the ground but the upward and sideways views are typically restricted when the aircraft is banked.

The most efficient location for a monoplane's wing, from an aerodynamic standpoint, is considered to be in the middle of the fuselage. In this mid-wing configuration, the interference drag between the wing and the fuselage can be minimized. Therefore, many racing airplanes use this efficient design. The pilot typically must sit close to the center of gravity, about one-quarter or one-third of the way back from the leading edge of the wing to the trailing edge. The pilot's field of view is thus severely restricted, and the pilot's location obstructs any carry-through structure for the wing spar.

The low-wing airplane is favored for most high-speed airplanes, because the wing provides a good place to house retracted gear. To minimize interference drag, both the leading and trailing edges of the wing normally require rather elaborate fairings. To obtain lateral stability, the wing of a low-wing airplane must incorporate more of a dihedral angle, the upward tilt of the wingtips, than that of a high-wing airplane.

In the 1980's, a number of canard-type airplanes, efficient aircraft with a horizontal lifting surface in front of the main wing, were designed for both low- and high-speed flight. The low-speed canard-type aircraft are mainly those linked to Burt Rutan's very successful VariEze and later designs. Canard aircraft with two nearly equal wings, the dragonfly configuration, may be thought of as either two-surface monoplanes or biplanes with a great deal of stagger. High-speed military aircraft often use a canard for extra pitch control at high angles of attack. Propeller-powered canard aircraft normally use pusher propellers, which tend to be less efficient because they operate in the wake of the wing. A few three-surface aircraft, with both a canard surface and a conventional tail surface, have also been designed and flown; they have the advantage of placing the pilot and passengers ahead of the wing.

W. N. Hubin

Bibliography

Jarrett, Philip, ed. *Biplane to Monoplane: Aircraft Development, 1919-1939*. London: Putnam Aeronautical, 1997. The authors document the historical developments in aerodynamics, structures, and power plants that led from a predominance of biplanes to almost entirely monoplanes, first for transport aircraft and then for fighter aircraft.

Lennon, Andy. *Canard: A Revolution in Flight*. Hummelstown, Pa.: Aviation, 1984. A useful discussion of the history and aerodynamics of canard-type aircraft, from ultralights and homebuilts to high-speed aircraft.

Spenser, Jay P. *Bellanca C. F.: The Emergence of the Cabin Monoplane in the United States*. Washington, D.C.: Smithsonian Institution Press, 1982. The C. F.'s first flight was on June 8, 1922, at a time when most aircraft in the United States were open-cockpit biplanes. It was entered in three flying meets that year and won first place in every event it entered, including speed, climb rate, and glide rate contests. It also won the speed and efficiency contests at the 1923 National Air Races.

See also: Airplanes; Biplanes; Experimental aircraft; Charles A. Lindbergh; Burt Rutan; *Spirit of St. Louis*; Triplanes; Wing designs; World War I; Wright brothers

Montgolfier brothers

Joseph-Michel Montgolfier
Date: Born on August 26, 1740, in Vidalon-les-Annonay, Ardeche, France; died on June 26, 1810, in Balaruc-les-Bains, France

Jacques-Étienne Montgolfier
Date: Born on January 6, 1745, in Vidalon-les-Annonay, France; died on August 2, 1799, in Serrières, France
Definition: Aviation pioneers who first accomplished successful human flight.

Joseph-Michel Montgolfier, pictured here, and his brother Jacques-Étienne pioneered human balloon flight in the 1780's. (Hulton Archive)

Significance: The Montgolfier brothers were pioneer developers of the hot-air balloon. Their work opened the way for exploration of the earth's upper atmosphere.

Joseph-Michel and Jacques-Étienne Montgolfier were two of sixteen children born to Pierre Montgolfier and his wife. Pierre's success in the paper industry provided the necessary finances for Joseph-Michel and Jacques-Étienne to obtain good educations and to conduct a variety of scientific experiments. Inspired by wood chips floating over a fire in the family fireplace, the two brothers theorized that when heated air was collected inside of a paper bag, the bag would rise. This discovery led to their invention of the first hot-air balloon in 1782.

On June 5, 1783, the Montgolfier brothers made the first public demonstration of their hot-air balloon at the marketplace in their hometown. The balloon was constructed from multiple sections of cloth and lined with paper that was coated with alum to provide a form of fireproofing. The sections were held together with approximately two thousand buttons. The fuel to heat the air inside the balloon was a mixture of straw and carded wool. Once released, the balloon stayed in the air for ten minutes, reached an altitude of about 6,560 feet, and traveled a distance of more than 1 mile.

On September 19, 1783, the Montgolfier brothers sent the first living creatures, a duck, a sheep, and a rooster, on a balloon flight in Versailles. Watched by King Louis XVI; his wife, Marie Antoinette; and some 130,000 spectators, the balloon stayed aloft for about 8 minutes, reached a height of 1,640 feet, and safely landed 2 miles from the point of departure. This successful exhibition made the Montgolfier brothers national figures, and a gold medal was issued in their honor.

In Paris, on November 21, 1783, the Montgolfier brothers conducted the first untethered human flight. It was manned by Jean-François Pilâtre de Rozier, a science teacher, and Marquis François-Laurent D'Arlandes. The balloon sailed over Paris for about 25 minutes and traveled approximately 7 miles from the launch site.

In later life, Joseph-Michel invented a type of parachute, a calorimeter, and a hydraulic ram and press. In 1807, he was made a knight of the Legion of Honor. Jacques-Étienne developed a process for producing a new type of paper called vellum. Both brothers were honored by the French Academy of Sciences.

Alvin K. Benson

Bibliography

Gillispie, Charles Coulston. *The Montgolfier Brothers and the Invention of Aviation*. Princeton, N.J.: Princeton University Press, 1983. Excellent account of the lives and accomplishments of the Montgolfier brothers.

Heppenheimer, T. A. *A Brief History of Flight: From Balloons to Mach 3 and Beyond*. New York: Wiley, 2001. Overview of all the important developments in aeronautical history, including the contributions of the Montgolfier brothers.

Scott, Phil. *The Shoulders of Giants: A History of Human Flight to 1919*. Reading, Mass.: Addison-Wesley, 1995. In-depth account of the balloon flights of the Montgolfier brothers.

See also: Balloons; Buoyant aircraft; History of human flight; Hot-air balloons; Lighter-than-air craft

N

National Advisory Committee for Aeronautics

Date: From 1915 to 1958

Definition: A U.S. government organization formed to promote the scientific development of aircraft and flight.

Significance: The premier American research facility on aeronautics and rocketry, the National Advisory Committee for Aeronautics maintained U.S. leadership in aircraft development through the mid-twentieth century.

Established in 1915, the National Advisory Committee for Aeronautics (NACA) promoted the scientific advancement of aircraft at a time when U.S. technological prowess in the field was declining. Although the Wright brothers had pioneered powered flight in 1903, both private and government research in aircraft technology declined in the United States over the following decade. Although flight was considered by many Americans to be an impressive technical achievement, many others considered flight an often-dangerous passing fad. Unreliable engines and haphazard construction led to many deaths, and many people believed powered flight to be a science that was ahead of its time. During this period, various European designers emerged as the leaders in aerospace research, and the United States' early lead in aircraft development disappeared.

World War I

With the outbreak of World War I in 1914, the U.S. government, pondering the possibility of U.S. involvement in the war, came to the realization that the United States could not produce the advanced aircraft needed to wage modern warfare. Although prewar European and U.S. military planners had considered the use of aircraft merely as observation platforms, as the war progressed, airplanes were used for increasingly important tasks, such as air defense and bombing.

Under pressure to prepare the United States for a possible war, Congress established NACA as a branch of the Smithsonian Institute on March 3, 1915. The administration of President Woodrow Wilson, afraid that American citizens would consider NACA a purely military facility at a time of neutrality, added the proposal for NACA funds as a rider on the annual naval appropriations bill. NACA was originally limited to a $5,000 annual budget and twelve unpaid staffers who directed research projects at the Smithsonian and various university facilities. However, NACA's contributions to wartime research, most notably the development of the ubiquitous JN-4 Jenny aircraft, earned the institution a long-term future as an institution separate from the Smithsonian and the creation of a permanent research facility of its own. Constructed in the middle of swampy ground owned by the U.S. Army north of Norfolk, Virginia, NACA's first facility, the Samuel Langley Memorial Aeronautical Laboratory, known simply as "Langley," opened in 1920. The new laboratory boasted four buildings and a full-time staff of eleven.

The Interwar Years

In the post-World War I era, NACA grew at an extremely slow pace. Postwar disillusionment and pro-neutrality sentiments reduced the amount of military-related research that was conducted at Langley. Also, the low pay associated with government employment relative to that of the private sector, coupled with Langley's remote location, led many engineers to accept jobs elsewhere. Despite its limitations, however, NACA continued to make significant scientific breakthroughs. Although military research lagged, the number of civilian aircraft boomed in the 1920's, due to the large number of surplus military aircraft, interest generated by traveling air shows and wing-walkers, and the exploits of civilian pilots, such as Howard Hughes and Charles A. Lindbergh. Driven by the growth of the civilian aircraft market, NACA made several contributions to aircraft development and technology. For instance, NACA pioneered the use of specially trained test pilots. Although other institutions had used full-time pilots, NACA was the first to employ pilots with backgrounds in engineering to identify problems in the air as well as on the ground. Langley's labs also developed advanced wind tunnels that measured precise aircraft takeoff and landing speeds. By 1931, Langley boasted the largest wind tunnel in the United States, capable of conducting tests on full-sized aircraft instead of scale models. NACA's

The first meeting of the National Advisory Committee for Aeronautics on April 23, 1915. The committee promoted scientific advancement in aircraft from World War I until the onset of the space age in 1958. (NASA)

wind tunnels proved particularly valuable in the development of early airliners, planes too large for their manufacturers to test themselves. These aircraft, the Boeing 247 and Douglas DC-1, pioneered civilian air travel before World War II, and the development of these two planes formed the backbone of commercial air travel after the war.

NACA also developed an innovative aerodynamic engine cowl that greatly reduced drag on the early piston-powered aircraft. In the 1920's and 1930's, the biggest goal of aircraft designers was speed, and European aircraft designers opted for complex liquid-cooled engines to boost top speed. The NACA cowl, however, boosted speed by reducing drag, permitting U.S. manufacturers to use less complex and less expensive air-cooled engines. Although NACA grew slowly during the 1920's and 1930's, the organization's contributions during this period ensured its long-term future and greatly aided the U.S. war effort in World War II.

World War II

If World War I had provided the motivation for the creation of NACA, World War II proved the value of its research facilities. As it had in World War I, the United States began World War II with aircraft that were less capable than those of its enemies. NACA faced the task of improving the United States' air arm as quickly as possible. Toward this end, NACA expanded its presence and roles to aid the war effort. In addition to new facilities at Langley, NACA constructed new specialized laboratories in other parts of the country. In 1939, NACA opened a laboratory at the U.S. Army Air Corps base at Moffett Field, south of San Francisco, California. NACA's Moffett Field facility tapped into the pool of skilled engineers on the West Coast and was situated close to the region's developing aircraft industry. In 1940, the West Coast lab was renamed the Ames Aeronautical Research Laboratory in honor of NACA's long-time director. In the same year, NACA opened a propulsion research lab in Cleveland, Ohio, to support research in engine development in conjunction with the major engine manufacturers in the Midwest. In 1948, the Cleveland facility became the Lewis Flight Propulsion Laboratory.

The new laboratory and propulsion laboratories proved their worth by improving upon the new aircraft types introduced during the war. NACA wind tunnels allowed for improvements to new fighters, such as the P-38 Lightning, by solving serious dive-instability problems and boosted the speed of the P-51 Mustang by introducing a laminar flow airfoil that moved air over the wing at peak efficiency. NACA's participation in the development of Boeing's B-29 bomber, particularly in aerodynamic and wing-loading issues, helped to expedite an advanced aircraft design into an effective weapon in only three years. During the war, NACA laboratories improved the performance of eighteen different warplanes, stretching speed, bomb load, and endurance beyond the capability of their original designs.

NACA also branched into the field of rocketry during World War II. Although earlier rocket pioneers such as Robert H. Goddard conducted research on their own, the widespread use of rockets during the war attracted NACA attention, both in the development of its own rocket designs and in the improvement of Army and Navy projects. Although NACA concentrated on the military applications of rockets, as bombardment weapons or air-to-air ordnance, late in the war, the agency began research in ballistic missiles that paved the way for future work.

Postwar Contributions

Deserving of praise for its wartime contributions, NACA received some undeserved criticism when the United States turned to jet propulsion in the mid-1940's. NACA conducted initial research on jet engines in the mid-1930's, but found that contemporary manufacturing methods made the technology unfeasible. By World War II, however, British breakthroughs had made the jet a viable means of propulsion, and the British shared their innovation with their American allies. Instead of allowing NACA to develop the new engines, however, the U.S. Army gave General Electric, a private corporation, the development rights. Bell Aircraft received a contract to develop an airframe for the new jet engine, an airplane that eventually emerged as the XP-59. Bell, however, lacked NACA's research capability, and the XP-59 could not match the performance of its European rivals, the British Gloster Meteor and German Me-262 aircraft. Because NACA had had a hand in the development of so many of U.S. wartime aircraft, many Army and aviation observers incorrectly believed that NACA had developed the XP-59 and had failed in the task. However, NACA knew nothing about the XP-59 until 1943, a full year after the aircraft's first test flight.

Once involved in jet aircraft development, NACA's facilities proved invaluable in integrating captured German data into the U.S. Air Force's growing arsenal of jet warplanes. NACA wind tunnels provided aerodynamic data on swept-wing configurations that resulted in the advanced F-86 Sabre, the premier U.S. fighter of the Korean War. NACA's wind tunnels also suggested solutions to the problem of shock waves that formed on wingtips near speeds of Mach 1, the mythical sound barrier. Using the ballistic data of a .50-caliber machine gun bullet, NACA collaborated with Bell Aircraft to build the X-1, the first in a series of legendary experimental aircraft. On October 14, 1947, test pilot Charles E. "Chuck" Yeager took the X-1 beyond Mach 1 and became the first pilot to break the sound barrier.

As aircraft broke the sound barrier with increasing frequency throughout the 1950's, another problem, known as transonic drag, surfaced. Because subsonic aircraft shapes were inappropriate for supersonic flight, jet aircraft of the 1950's continually failed to meet speed and altitude expectations in supersonic flight. NACA's solution to transonic drag was to create a design element known as area ruling. Transonic drag occurred at the wings, where the mass of the airplane, the fuselage plus the wings, suddenly increased, and the air simply could not move out of the way quickly enough. Because airplane designers could not dispense with the craft's wings, they had to make the fuselage thinner. On aircraft designed with area ruling, the fuselage narrowed as the wings spread, resulting in an airplane with an hourglass or Coca-Cola-bottle shape. With this innovation, aircraft speeds continued to rise, and engineers could predict aircraft performance beyond the sound barrier.

NACA's early forays into rocketry beginning in World War II increased throughout the late 1940's and early 1950's. The United States acquired advanced rocket technology, along with jet propulsion, from the defeated Nazis, and began a series of rocket testing by several different agencies. The U.S. Army, having secured the services of the top German rocket scientist, Wernher von Braun, began rocket testing at the Redstone Arsenal in Alabama. At the same time, the U.S. Navy and the U.S. Air Force began their own rocket programs with the intent of developing nuclear delivery systems. In addition, the Smithsonian and the National Academy of Sciences developed rockets for scientific research.

NACA contributed to these military projects primarily by testing internal systems and lightweight materials. NACA's role in the U.S. rocket program became preeminent, however, after October 4, 1957, when the Soviet Union launched Sputnik 1, the first human-made Earth-orbiting satellite. Although Sputnik was a minor technical achievement, its launch created widespread public fears of Soviet atomic bombs raining down upon American cities from orbit, and the U.S. government demanded a response from its own rocket programs. The U.S. response to Sputnik, the first launch of the Navy's Vanguard rocket, embarrassingly exploded on the launch pad on December 6, 1957. One month later, a smaller Army rocket known as Explorer 1 finally put a small satellite into orbit.

The public demand for a response to Sputnik, coupled with the inefficient system of multiple rocket programs, generated the idea of a single space agency, which NACA, as a civilian agency with advanced research labs, was in the best position to lead. Many Americans, particularly in Congress, worried that a military-led project would create only rockets for military use. Congress also blamed the various military rocket projects for allowing the Soviets to take the lead in rocket technology. Therefore, on July 29, 1958, President Dwight D. Eisenhower signed the National Aeronautics and Space Act into law. The law merged NACA with the various military rocket programs, scientific rocket projects, and several other government laboratories into a new entity to run the U.S. space program. On October 1, 1958, the newly amalgamated institutions became the National Aeronautics and Space Administration (NASA).

Steven J. Ramold

Bibliography

Bilstein, Roger. *Orders of Magnitude: A History of the NACA and NASA, 1915-1990*. 3d ed. Washington, D.C.: National Aeronautics and Space Administration, 1989. A thorough history that emphasizes crewed flight.

Hansen, James R. *Engineer in Charge: A History of the Langley Aeronautical Laboratory, 1917-1958*. Washington, D.C.: National Aeronautics and Space Administration, 1987. A thorough history, at more than six hundred pages.

Hartman, Edwin P. *Adventures in Research: A History of the Ames Research Center, 1940-1965*. Washington, D.C.: National Aeronautics and Space Administration, 1970. A book by an authority on the agency.

Murray, Charles, and Catherine Bly Cox. *Apollo: The Race to the Moon*. New York: Simon & Schuster, 1989. A definitive account of the Apollo Program from a behind-the-scenes perspective.

See also: Air shows; Crewed spaceflight; Experimental aircraft; Howard Hughes; Jet engines; Samuel Pierpont Langley; Charles A. Lindbergh; Military flight; National Aeronautics and Space Administration; Rockets; Sound barrier; Spaceflight; Sputnik; Supersonic aircraft; Test pilots; Uncrewed spaceflight; Wind tunnels; Wing-walking; World War I; World War II; X planes; Chuck Yeager

National Aeronautics and Space Administration

Date: Established on October 1, 1958
Definition: The civilian space agency and aeronautical research agency for the United States of America.
Significance: The National Aeronautics and Space Administration oversees all U.S. civilian space exploration activities and coordinates the U.S. involvement in international space coventures. It also is the primary U.S. agency for civilian government research in aeronautics.

Origins

The idea of a central agency for aeronautical research in the United States dates back to 1915, when an amendment to another bill created the National Advisory Committee for Aeronautics (NACA) to help the United States catch up with European countries in aeronautical research. NACA was primarily involved in aircraft design and testing. An aeronautical research center, later to be named the Langley Aeronautical Laboratory, was founded with NACA. In the years leading to World War II, additional aeronautical facilities were constructed at Moffett Field in California (later named the Ames Research Center) and at Lewis Field in Cleveland, Ohio. Rockets and space travel were of little interest to NACA until the 1950's. During the 1930's, however, rocketry experiments were being conducted at the Guggenheim Aeronautical Laboratory at the California Institute of Technology (GALCIT). During World War II, GALCIT became the Jet Propulsion Laboratory (JPL) and was under Army control. Besides developing missiles for the Army, such as the WAC Corporal, JPL also developed the Aerobee, a version of the WAC Corporal designed for civilian high-altitude research activities. After the war, the U.S. Army also created a separate missile unit, which eventually became the U.S. Army Ballistic Missile Agency (ABMA), near Huntsville, Alabama. During the early 1950's, the Navy and the Air Force began their own missile programs.

Each of the separate missile and rocket programs eventually began to develop rocket boosters with a goal of launching satellites into orbit around the earth. By the mid-1950's, the Air Force and the Army were both looking at possible lunar space probes, and JPL was considering the possibility of interplanetary space probes. The Air Force was also investigating rocket-propelled aircraft, an area of research that overlapped with NACA's mission. At this time, there was no central unified agency overseeing rocket development or space exploration. Multiple agencies, and even separate departments within each agency were working independently of one another, often duplicating efforts and competing with one another for resources. Possibly as a result of the fragmented approach to space exploration and rocket development, the United States appeared to lag slightly behind the Soviet Union in these areas during the 1950's. The Soviet Union's rocket development and space exploration activities were coordinated under one authority, largely working under the leadership of Sergei Korolev. A working group, called the Upper Atmospheric Rocket Research Panel (UARRP), consisting of representatives from the different U.S. agencies involved in space exploration, including NACA, was formed in the mid-1950's to address some of these concerns. In January, 1956, UARRP issued a report suggesting that all U.S. space-related activities be centralized in one agency. A later report suggested that civilian space exploration be formed into an agency separate from Department of Defense space activities.

Little real progress had been made in consolidating U.S. space efforts until the Soviet Union launched Sputnik 1 on October 4, 1957, and Sputnik 2 on November 3, 1957, with Sputnik 2 carrying a dog into space. The United States tried to respond with the Navy's Vanguard rockets, but the early Vanguards failed to launch a satellite. Finally, on January 31, 1958, the Army succeeded in launching Explorer 1, built by JPL, atop a modified intercontinental ballistic missile (ICBM) built by ABMA. The U.S. government finally began to take seriously the need for a unified effort at space exploration. On July 29, 1958, President Dwight D. Eisenhower signed into law the National Aeronautics and Space Act of 1958. This act dissolved NACA and created the National Aeronautics and Space Administration (NASA), effective October 1, 1958. NASA was responsible not only for aeronautical research, as NACA had been, but would also be the U.S. civilian space agency. NASA acquired all NACA facilities, including the Langley Research Center, the Lewis Research Center, and the Ames Research Center, along with two flight stations. On December 3, 1958, JPL was transferred to NASA. Much of ABMA was also transferred to NASA, becoming the Marshall Space Flight Center on July 1, 1960. Since that time, NASA has built numerous research centers and other stations throughout the country. Though space exploration gets most of the public attention, NASA has always remained active in aeronautical research, with several research centers devoted primarily to non-space-related activities.

Early Crewed Spaceflight

One of NASA's early goals was to launch a person into space. This goal was formally stated on October 7, 1958, shortly after NASA's formation. The first U.S. crewed spacecraft project was named Mercury. Prior to the Mercury project, two competing ideas for crewed spaceflight had existed. Wernher von Braun and many others believed that a crewed spacecraft should take off like an aircraft, fly into space, and land again like an aircraft. Such a spacecraft would be fully reusable, and would be an extension of well-proven flight technology. Preliminary work toward such a space plane had already begun. Like the Soviet Union's Korolev, many of the engineers in NASA were not willing to wait for the development of a safe and reliable space plane. Rather, they wanted to use modified ICBMs to launch a crewed capsule into space. Such an approach would yield results much faster. NASA engineers realized that the Soviet Union would likely beat the United States in sending a human into space if the United States were to wait to develop a method of flying a space plane into orbit. Thus the Mercury project aimed to launch a small capsule containing a human being atop a modified ICBM. Researchers at Ames showed that a nuclear warhead could safely survive reentry into the atmosphere with a blunted body. The Mercury capsule, therefore, would be shaped with a blunted bottom and use an ablative heat shield to prevent the capsule from burning up due to friction as it reentered Earth's atmosphere at the high speeds required for Earth orbit. Such a craft could not land as an aircraft, so it deployed a parachute and floated down to a landing in the ocean, called a splashdown. The first launch of a Mercury capsule was an uncrewed test flight on September 9, 1959. The first crewed launch was May 5, 1961, when Alan B. Shepard was launched into space atop a modified Redstone rocket. The Redstone, however, was not powerful enough to put the Mercury capsule into orbit. Rather, Shepard's flight, lasting only about fifteen minutes, was merely a suborbital ballistic trajectory. The first U.S. crewed spaceflight took place on February 20, 1962, when a modified Atlas missile carried a Mercury capsule containing John H. Glenn into orbit. The United States, however, did not beat the Soviet Union into space, for a modified ICBM had carried Yuri Gagarin into orbit around the Earth in a Vostok capsule on April 12, 1961.

With the Soviet Union beating the United States in sending a human into space, President John F. Kennedy consulted his science advisors for a goal that the United States might hope to accomplish ahead of the Soviet Union. That goal was for a U.S. crewed mission to the Moon within a decade. President Kennedy made this goal public in a speech on May 25, 1961, even before the United States had put a human into orbit. NASA had to scramble to accomplish this goal. The crewed lunar mission, called the Apollo Program, was born in November 1961. In order to launch a spacecraft to the Moon, NASA had to create the largest rocket ever known, eventually dubbed the Saturn V. Realizing that it would take a rocket bigger than they could build to launch a spacecraft to the Moon's surface and back, they opted to launch a spacecraft into orbit around the Moon. Astronauts would then descend to the lunar surface in a small landing craft, and then ascend to rendezvous with the orbiting spacecraft, which would carry them back to Earth. Such a mission would involve extended missions in space, and spacecraft rendezvous. None of this was at that time possible. Thus, as work progressed on the Apollo missions, NASA created the Gemini Program to develop the skills and test the procedures needed in the upcoming Apollo missions. The Gemini Program ran from December 7, 1961, until December 23, 1966, with the first crewed flight on March 23, 1965. While the Mercury capsules held just one astronaut, the Gemini capsules each had a crew of two astronauts. The first crewed Apollo spaceflight was Apollo 7, launched October 11, 1968. Apollo 7 was an Earth orbital test flight. The first lunar landing mission was Apollo 11, launched July 16, 1969, crewed by Edwin "Buzz" Aldrin and Neil Armstrong, both of whom walked on the surface of the Moon, and by Michael Collins, who piloted the command module that orbited the Moon during the landing mission. The last lunar mission was Apollo 17, launched December 7, 1972.

Crewed Spaceflight After the Moon

The last three scheduled Apollo missions to the Moon were cancelled. The hardware for these missions, however, was not wasted. The third stage of a Saturn V rocket was adapted to be used as a crewed space station called Skylab, launched May 14, 1973. Three Apollo capsules were used to ferry astronauts to and from Skylab from May 25, 1973, to February 8, 1974. Left in low-Earth orbit, Skylab eventually reentered the Earth's atmosphere and burned up on July 11, 1979, with some solid pieces striking the Indian Ocean and Australia.

The final Apollo mission was the Apollo-Soyuz Test Project. This program was a rendezvous mission between the U.S. Apollo spacecraft and a Soyuz spacecraft from the Soviet Union during July, 1975. This rendezvous mission was primarily a political mission, designed to show good will between the two superpowers. It was, however, one of the first space missions involving more than one nation. This project eventually became a model for later international space coventures.

One of the major drawbacks of the spacecraft used in the early days of the U.S. space program was that they could only be used one time. By the 1970's, the United States was no longer in a space race with the Soviet Union, so NASA took the time to investigate a reusable spacecraft, much as had been envisioned in the earliest days of space exploration. A compromise vehicle was eventually developed that would take off as a rocket, with strap-on solid rocket boosters and a discardable external fuel tank. The spacecraft would land, however, as a glider. Designed to transport satellites and equipment into orbit and to carry astronauts and equipment to a permanent space station, this partially reusable spacecraft was called the space shuttle. The first operational flight of a space shuttle was on April 12, 1981. The worst accident in NASA's history involved the explosion that destroyed the space shuttle *Challenger* on January 28, 1986, seventy-three seconds after launching, when the shuttle's external fuel tank ruptured after being penetrated by a plume of gas escaping from a failed solid-rocket joint seal. On July 27, 1995, the space shuttle *Atlantis* launched to rendezvous with the Russian space station Mir to exchange crew. Over the next three years, there were several more missions to Mir, fulfilling some of the hopes of the Apollo-Soyuz Test Project.

Beginning in 1998, the first elements of the International Space Station (ISS) were launched. This space station was a scaled-down version of the proposed space station Freedom authorized by President Ronald Reagan in 1985. The space shuttle is scheduled to have many dozens of flights through the 2000's, constructing the ISS and transporting crew and equipment to the station. The space shuttle missions to Mir and the ISS finally fulfill some of the original design plans of the space shuttle project.

Uncrewed Space Exploration

In addition to crewed spaceflight, NASA is responsible for most U.S. uncrewed space flights. Some of these missions, such as the Ranger Moon probes (1961-1965) and the Surveyor Moon landers (1966-1968) were precursors to crewed missions. Others, such as the Explorer series, which began as an Army project but was transferred to NASA after its formation, were scientific missions designed to study the Sun, Earth, and space environments. NASA has been a leader in interplanetary explorations, with spacecraft in the Mariner series that visited Mercury, Venus, and Mars. The Pioneer series of spacecraft were designed as small interplanetary spacecraft. Some were lunar flyby missions, others were placed into solar orbit to study the solar wind, several of which remained in operation for over thirty years. Pioneer 10 and Pioneer 11, launched in the early 1970's, were the first spacecraft to fly past Jupiter and achieve escape velocity to leave the solar system. They were joined by the two Voyager spacecraft as the only four spacecraft ever launched from Earth to leave the solar system. Voyager 1, launched September 5, 1977, flew past Jupiter and Saturn. Voyager 2, though launched on August 20, 1977, before Voyager 1, arrived at Jupiter and Saturn after Voyager 1 and continued on to pass Uranus in January, 1986, and Neptune in August, 1989. NASA launched the Galileo spacecraft to Jupiter on October 18, 1989, and the Cassini spacecraft to Saturn on October 15, 1997. On August 20 and September 9, 1975, NASA launched two Viking spacecraft to the planet Mars, both of which achieved the first successful surface landing missions on Mars. Starting on December 4, 1996, with the launch of the Pathfinder mission, NASA began a decade-long series of missions to study Mars. In addition to interplanetary missions, NASA has launched many astronomical satellites into orbit around Earth to study the universe. These satellites contained telescopes of various types to study the entire range of the electromagnetic spectrum. The most famous of these orbiting observatories is the Hubble Space Telescope, deployed from the space shuttle in April, 1990.

Aeronautical Research

When NASA was formed in 1958, it absorbed NACA, and was charged with not only space exploration but also aeronautics. Though most public attention, and much of NASA's budget, is directed toward space exploration activities, a major portion of NASA's activity has involved aeronautical research. Upon its formation, NASA inherited the Air Force X-15 project. The first X-15 rocket plane flew in 1959 as a NASA aircraft. X-15 flights continued until 1968. Other aeronautical research involved lifting-body aircraft designs, such as the X-24, the HL-10, and the M-2 aircraft of the 1950's. Such aircraft use the shape of the aircraft rather than wings to provide lift.

In 1975, NASA began the Aircraft Energy Efficiency Program, designed to increase flight efficiency and develop less-polluting aircraft engines. The new engine designs from this program were incorporated in Boeing's 767 and McDonnell Douglas's MD-80 commercial aircraft. Additional designs showed that wingtip winglets also increase efficiency, and many aircraft designed from the 1980's and later have included these winglets.

In addition to efficiency, NASA has also promoted aircraft safety. NASA conducts crash tests to design safety systems that maximize the likelihood of survival during an aircraft crash. NASA also works to develop improved guidance systems for both commercial and private aircraft. During the 1990's, NASA undertook a study at major commercial airports to determine the optimal spacing between arriving and departing aircraft. The Lewis Research Center has had a long history of studying icing on aircraft and ways of dealing with this problem, dating back to NACA days. During the 1970's, NASA developed fly-by-wire technology, whereby aircraft control could be done electronically rather than using mechanical means.

NASA has not limited itself to fixed-wing aircraft. The Ames facility oversees NASA's helicopter research. Ames was also the lead site for the XV-15, an experimental aircraft with tilting rotors designed as a hybrid between helicopters and traditional fixed-wing aircraft.

NASA also operates research aircraft designed to carry infrared and radar instruments to study the ground under the aircraft's flight path. Additional science aircraft include the Kuiper Airborne Observatory that flew from 1977 to 1995. The Kuiper was a modified C-141 aircraft carrying a 36-inch-diameter infrared telescope high above much of Earth's atmosphere anywhere it was needed in the world. The Kuiper is to be replaced with another airborne observatory called the Stratospheric Observatory for Infrared Astronomy (SOFIA), expected to begin operations in 2002. The SOFIA is a modified Boeing 747SP designed to carry a 2.5-meter reflecting telescope into the lower stratosphere. Unlike the Kuiper, which was entirely a NASA project, the SOFIA is to be jointly operated with the Deutschen Zentrum für Luft- und Raumfahrt (DLR), the German equivalent to NASA. SOFIA, like Kuiper before it, is operated out of NASA's Ames facility.

NASA Centers

Due to the complex and varied nature of NASA's mission, the agency has many research and operations centers, each with its own specialty. NASA headquarters in Washington, D.C., handles administrative duties. The Kennedy Space Center on Cape Canaveral, Florida, is NASA's primary launch facility, supported by the White Sands Test Facility at Las Cruces, New Mexico, and the Wallops Flight Facility on Wallops Island, Virginia. The Jet Propulsion Laboratory in Pasadena, California, is NASA's primary center for interplanetary spacecraft development and operations. The Johnson Space Center in Houston, Texas, coordinates all crewed spaceflight activities. The Goddard Space Flight Center in Greenbelt, Maryland, handles most Earth-orbiting satellites and oversees much of NASA's astronomical studies. Aeronautical research is performed at the NASA Ames Research Center (at Moffett Field, California), the Dryden Flight Research Center (at Edwards Air Force Base, California), Langley Research Center (at Hampton, Virginia), and the Glenn Research Center (at Lewis Field, Cleveland, Ohio). Ames is also the headquarters for NASA's astrobiology program, and Dryden supports space shuttle landings if the shuttle cannot land at Kennedy due to weather. The Marshall Space Flight Center (at Huntsville, Alabama) and the Stennis Space Center (in southern Mississippi) are the primary centers for rocket research and development.

Raymond D. Benge, Jr.

Bibliography

Bilstein, Roger E. *Orders of Magnitude: A History of the NACA and NASA, 1915-1990*. 3d ed. Washington, D.C.: Government Printing Office, 1989. A very thorough history of NASA and NACA, with a major emphasis on crewed flight research, both spaceflight and aeronautics.

Dewaard, E. John, and Nancy Dewaard. *History of NASA, America's Voyage to the Stars*. Rev. ed. New York: Exeter Books, 1988. A good description of NASA's space exploration activities.

Koppes, Clayton R. *JPL and the American Space Program*. New Haven, Conn.: Yale University Press, 1982. A very thorough history of the Jet Propulsion Laboratory from its beginnings in rocket studies through its interplanetary exploration activities in the early 1980's.

Launius, Roger D., and Bertram Ulrich. *NASA and the Exploration of Space*. New York: Stewart, Tabori & Chang, 1998. An excellent chronicle of NASA activities, with explanations for the layman, with the added benefit of a great deal of artwork related to the space program.

Shepard, Alan, and Deke Slayton. *Moon Shot: The Inside Story of America's Race to the Moon*. Atlanta, Ga.: Turner Publishing, 1994. A narrative from an astronaut's perspective of the crewed space program from its beginnings to the Apollo-Soyuz Test Project.

See also: Air Force, U.S.; Apollo Program; Neil Armstrong; Astronauts and cosmonauts; Crewed spaceflight; Gemini Program; John Glenn; Jet Propulsion Laboratory; Johnson Space Center; Mercury project; Military flight; Missiles; National Committee for Aeronautics; Orbiting; Rockets; Rocket propulsion; Satellites; Alan Shephard; Spaceflight; Uncrewed spaceflight; Uninhabited aerial vehicles; X planes

National Transportation Safety Board

Date: Created April 1, 1967
Definition: Independent U.S. agency responsible for the investigation of civil aviation, railroad, highway, marine, and pipeline accidents within the United States and for the issuing of safety recommendations designed to prevent future accidents.
Significance: The National Transportation Safety Board provides independent crash-site analysis and offers recommendations for improving the safety of all forms of transportation.

History

The National Transportation Safety Board (NTSB) was established by Congress in 1967 to investigate the causes of all transportation-related accidents involving aviation, railroads, highways, marine craft, or pipelines. Although the NTSB's funding appropriations came from the Department of Transportation (DOT), the NTSB functioned independently of the DOT. In 1975, Congress passed the Independent Safety Board Act, which formally severed all ties between the NTSB and DOT.

NTSB investigators operate twenty-four hours a day, seven days a week, investigating accidents within the United States as well as accidents involving U.S. crafts overseas. Once NTSB teams reach the crash site, they evaluate the evidence to determine the probable cause of the accident and issue safety recommendations to prevent a recurrence.

Since opening its doors in 1967, the NTSB has investigated more than 110,000 aviation accidents. Although the NTSB does not have the regulatory power to enforce its recommendations, approximately 82 percent of its 11,000 safety recommendations have been implemented by the Federal Aviation Adminstration (FAA).

Recommendations

The NTSB is responsible for investigating all civil aviation accidents in the United States. The number of civilian takeoffs and landings exceeded 63 million in 1997, and the number of passengers flying rose from 580 million in 1995 to 630 million in 1997. The safety of these commercial flights rests with the NTSB, which focuses on specific problems, such as operations, cabin safety, weather, and aircraft design, when issuing its recommendations for improved safety.

One of the principal recommendations in the area of operations involves the addition of ground proximity warning systems (GPWS) for aircraft equipped with ten or more seats. The recommendation was issued after an Eastern Air Lines Lockheed L-1011 crashed into the Florida Everglades on December 29, 1972 and a TWA Boeing 727 crashed into a mountain on its approach to Washington Dulles International Airport in Virginia on December 1, 1974. One hundred ninety-one people died in these two crashes, and, after thorough investigations of each, the NTSB determined that the cause of both accidents was "controlled flight into terrain," which could have been prevented if the aircraft had been equipped with warning systems. In 1975, the FAA implemented the NTSB recommendation that all large passenger aircraft be equipped with ground proximity warning systems that alert the crew if terrain is approaching, if the plane is descending too quickly, and if the landing gear is not functioning properly. In 1994, the original recommendation was expanded to include smaller aircraft capable of carrying as few as ten passengers.

A second area of concern for the NTSB involves fire safety. On several occasions, fires that started in aircraft lavatories or cargo areas have resulted in fatalities. In July, 1973, the NTSB recommended that airplanes be equipped with smoke detectors after a Boeing 707 crashed near Paris, France, after a fire started on board. After several more incidents, the NTSB recommended, and the FAA mandated, that automatic-discharge fire extinguishers be installed in all aircraft trash receptacles. Airline attendants are also required to routinely check the containers. After a fatal fire occurred on board an Air Canada flight that was forced to land at Cincinnati, the NTSB recommended that all lavatories be equipped with smoke alarms, that floor-level lighting be installed for passenger safety during an emergency evacuation, and that fire-blocking materials be used in all cabin and seat material. In addition, the NTSB recommended that all emergency slides be equipped with a heat-resistant coating to prevent injury to passengers during a postcrash evacuation. In 1981, after a fatal fire on board a Lockheed L-1011 out of Riyadh, Saudi Arabia, the NTSB issued a recommendation for aircraft modifications aimed at preventing the spread of fires from cargo areas to the cabin. Additional restrictions on the containment of cargo fires followed the crash of a South African Airways Boeing 747 that crashed into the Indian Ocean with the loss of all 160 people on board.

The most serious weather-related problem addressed by the NTSB involves wind shear. The first instance of NTSB involvement with the weather phenomena occurred in 1968, and since that time, the NTSB has issued more than sixty safety recommendations. The most serious crash involving wind shear occurred at Dallas-Fort Worth International Airport on August 2, 1986, when a Delta Air Lines Lockheed L-1011 crashed, killing 135 people on board. Investigators examined the data and suggested the need for additional pilot training specifically geared toward this type of weather condition and for the installation of low-level wind shear alert systems at all major airports. As a result, the terminal Doppler weather radar (TDWR) warns pilots and air traffic controllers allowing them to prevent possible disasters. Since 1985, only one wind shear-related accident has occurred, at Charlotte, North Carolina, where the TDWR system was not yet operational.

Another potential weather-related issue that the NTSB has investigated deals with icing. The accumulation of ice on airplanes has been a problem since the early days of aviation, but it was not until the crash of a USAir Fokker F-28 at New York's LaGuardia International Airport in 1976 that the NTSB issued specific recommendations concerning the measurement and forecasting of icing on airplanes and protection against it. The FAA implemented these recommendations. In 1994, the NTSB issued additional warnings about icing problems on the ATR-72 passenger planes, and the FAA ordered the modification of deicing systems the following year.

As the number of aircraft operating in limited airspace multiplied, midair collisions began to increase. As early as 1967, the NTSB advocated the development of a system designed to prevent such accidents. The proposed technology would be separate from the air traffic control system and would offer the earliest possible warning of a potential crash. In 1993, the FAA ordered that all aircraft used for transport be equipped with traffic alert and collision avoidance systems (TCAS). Mode C transponders, located near major airports, analyze the altitude of airplanes equipped with the device and alert air traffic controllers, who then warn the airplanes before a disaster occurs. Since the implementation of this recommendation, the number of near-midair collisions has dramatically decreased.

When evaluating the causes of crashes, the NTSB examines aircraft design and has revealed several areas where modifications were necessary. While investigating a crash that occurred when an American Airlines DC-10 attempted to take off from Dallas-Fort Worth International Airport on May 21, 1988, the NTSB discovered that the minimum specifications for the brake friction material were inadequate for a rejected takeoff that required more than twice the minimum amount of material to stop safely. As a result, the FAA increased the safety standard and ordered additional training for pilots to improve passenger safety during aborted takeoffs.

Another area of concern involves the length of airport runways. The FAA requires a 1,000-foot safety area at the end of runways for emergencies. Newer airports have allowed for plenty of room, but older airports frequently have sharp drops in terrain at the ends of runways. A 1994 crash at LaGuardia International Airport prompted investigators to recommend the use of soft-ground arresting systems to slow airplanes down in the event of an emergency. Arrestor-beds have prevented accidents at many airports, including John F. Kennedy International Airport in New York.

Always cognizant of the possibility of human error, the NTSB has advocated several changes that would improve the safety of passengers. One recommendation included cross-referencing pilots' licenses with the National Driver Register (NDR) to check for alcohol-related violations that could indicate a potential problem that would adversely affect a pilot's performance during flights. Since the late 1980's, the NTSB has also recommended random drug screening. Another area of particular concern involves the interaction of crew members. The NTSB found that on numerous occasions, because the pilot remains the final authority in the cockpit, other crew members were hesitant to warn the pilot of potential problems for fear of reprimand. On December 28, 1978, a United Air Lines DC-8 ran out of fuel and crashed on approach to Portland, Oregon, killing ten people, because the first officer had failed to communicate the problem to the pilot. The NTSB found that improved crew management would reduce potential fatalities, and the FAA ordered a crew management training program for all major airlines.

Aircraft design flaws account for many fatalities, and the NTSB has issued numerous recommendations based on their investigations of accidents caused by such flaws. In 1991, the NTSB examined the wreckage of an Atlantic Southeast Airlines EMB-120 that crashed in Georgia and found that excessive wear on the propeller-control unit had rendered the aircraft uncontrollable. After the NTSB issued its report, the FAA required the installation of a fail-safe device that prevents propellers from rotating too far. In its investigation of another crash in Georgia in 1995, the NTSB found that a small crack had developed in the aircraft's propeller, resulting from the improper installation of a propeller blade. As a result of this investigation, the NTSB advocated the use of ultrasonic inspection techniques to detect future problems. After the crash of a Turkish Airlines DC-10 near Paris, France, in 1974, the NTSB suggested the use of blowout pressure-relief doors to prevent a recurrence of an explosion that would buckle the cabin floor and damage flight controls. In 1989, the NTSB investigated a similar incident. On February 24 of that year, a United Air Lines Boeing 747 took off from Honolulu, Hawaii, bound for New Zealand. During the airplane's ascent, the lower cargo door flew off, but the modifications implemented as the result of the Turkish Airlines crash saved the 355 lives on board.

In addition to accidents caused by faulty airline design, the NTSB also investigates accidents involving structural fatigue and corrosion. On April 28, 1988, the NTSB investigated the structural failure of an Aloha Airlines Boeing 737-200 that lost a portion of its fuselage during takeoff from Hilo, Hawaii. The force of decompression during the accident resulted in one flight attendant being sucked out of the plane. After examining the aircraft, the NTSB recommended numerous changes in the structure and design of similar aircraft.

The NTSB offers additional recommendations in numerous areas, including the improved quality of off-wing escape slides, fuel-tank protection, and safety belts. In addition to airplane safety, the board is also interested in the safety of helicopters and investigates problems involving the in-flight loss of the main rotor control and the need for flight restrictions during adverse weather conditions. More recently, the NTSB has worked with the National Aeronautics and Space Administration (NASA) to determine the survivability of space orbiters. The NTSB was involved in the investigation of the 1986 space shuttle *Challenger* explosion. NTSB investigators also located a flaw in a crashed Titan 34D military launch vehicle, enabling the problem to be addressed before another accident occurred.

Over the past four decades, the National Transportation Safety Board has gained a reputation for its fair and impartial analysis of crash sites. The recommendations made by the board have been implemented with a high degree of success. Many lives have been saved, and the board continues to improve the safety conditions on commercial aircraft, earning the confidence of the traveling public. With only four hundred employees, the agency provides an invaluable service.

Cynthia Clark Northrup

Bibliography

Collar, Charles S. *Barnstorming to Air Safety.* Miami, Fla.: Lysmata, 1997. Addresses the issues of safety and the recommendations and changes necessary to ensure the safety of persons who fly.

Watson, Thomas W. *Uphappy Landings: Why Airplanes Crash.* Melbourne, Fla.: Harbor City Press, 1992. Deals with the causes of airplane accidents resulting from design and structural problems and weather-related issues.

Wolfe, Louis. *Disaster Detectives*. New York: Julian Missner, 1981. An excellent look at NTSB investigators and the techniques they employ while analyzing transportation disasters.

See also: Accident investigation; Airline industry, U.S.; Emergency procedures; Federal Aviation Administration; Midair collisions; National Aeronautics and Space Administration; Runway collisions; Safety issues; Space shuttle

Navy pilots, U.S.

Date: Beginning in 1910
Definition: Aviators who are part of the United States Navy, who fly combat as well as search and rescue missions around the world.
Significance: The addition of aviation into the United States Navy provides greater flexibility and an extension of air power globally.

U.S. Naval Test Pilot School

At the end of World War II, aviation entered a period of rapid change. The development of new technology required extensive evaluation of experimental aircraft involving test flights. Although Navy pilots participated in the testing process, the military offered no formal training program. In 1945, Commander Thomas F. Connolly, assistant flight test officer at the Naval Air Station at Patuxent River, Maryland, and Commander Sydney Sherby, his chief project engineer, recognized the need for additional pilot training and recommended a curriculum. Navy pilots would receive instruction in aerodynamics, procedures for aircraft performance testing, evaluation of aircraft stability and control characteristics, miscellaneous tests and trials, actual in-flight performance testing, and standardized flight test reporting during thirty-seven hours of classroom instruction. Commander C. E. Giese, the flight test officer, approved the proposed training and appointed Sherby as the officer-in-charge of the U.S. Naval Test Pilot School. Sherby conducted several classes during the next two years, and by 1947 the Chief of Naval Operations approved a request to establish a nine-month school. Funding appropriations allowed for the purchase of seven aircraft used for training purposes including a PB4Y-2 Privateer, an F6F-5 Hellcat, an XNQ-1, an F7F-3 Tigercat, an F8F-1 Bearcat, a PBY-6A, and an SNB-1. In 1948, Sherby and Connolly compiled the lecture material into a textbook, *Airplane Aerodynamics*, which the U.S. Navy continues to use in its training program. Since 1950, advances in technology have resulted in the addition of curriculum in three separate areas: Fixed Wing, Rotary Wing, and Airborne Systems. Due to increased course content, the length of the school has been increased from nine to eleven months. Alan Shepard and John Glenn are two of the most famous graduates of the U.S. Naval Test Pilot School.

Civilians seeking a career as a Navy pilot must have a B.A. or B.S. degree, pass the Aviation Selection Test Battery exam, and have twenty-twenty vision and normal depth and color perception. Only U.S. citizens between the ages of 19 and 26 qualify for a commission. Once candidates are accepted, they attend a thirteen-week course at Officer Candidate School (OCS) at the Naval Air Station in Pensacola, Florida. An additional six-week indoctrination program completes the training program. Pilots are then promoted to the rank of ensign and receive basic and advanced pilot training. The service obligation for Navy pilots is eight years of active duty if designated for Naval Aviation (Jets) and seven years if designated Naval Aviation (Props/Helos). All pilots must then remain on Ready Reserve status.

Blue Angels

At the end of World War II, interest in all military activity declined dramatically. In an effort to garner public support for the continuation of naval aviation, Admiral Chester W. Nimitz, the chief of naval operations, formed a flight demonstration team that became known as the Blue Angels. The first flight demonstration, lead by Commander Tony Less, occurred in 1946 at the Naval Air Station in Jacksonville, Florida, with the pilots flying Grumman F-6F Hellcats. The following year the Blue Angels flew the Grumman F-8F Bearcat and adopted the famous diamond formation that became the trademark of the precision flying team. When war broke out again in 1950, the Blue Angels, flying Grumman F-9F Panther jets, joined United Nations forces in Korea. In 1951, the squadron returned to the United States and reported to the naval air station at Corpus Christi, Texas, where new Panther F-9F5's awaited them. After spending three years in Texas, the Blue Angels made one final move to their new headquarters at the Naval Air Station at Pensacola, Florida. Since 1954, the Blue Angels have flown in the swept-wing Grumman F-9F9 Cougar, the F-11F Tiger, the McDonnell Douglas F-4 Phantom II, and the McDonnell Douglas A-4F Skyhawk II. After 1986, the Navy Flight Demonstration Squadron has flown

McDonnell Douglas F/A-18 Hornets, a plane that functions as both a fighter and an attack aircraft. Each year, the Blue Angels perform at air shows around the country and since 1946, over 260 million Americans have witnessed the precision flying of these naval aviators.

World War II Navy Aces

The era of flight for the U.S. Navy began in 1910, but combat missions remained under the direction of the United States Air Service during World War I. Navy pilots did not fly combat missions during this war so none of them qualified as an ace. During World War II, the importance of naval aviation increased dramatically. As the United States recovered from the loss at Pearl Harbor, naval ships sailed toward the South Pacific equipped with F-4F Wildcats. In 1942, the Navy pilots experienced difficulty against the Japanese Zeros, but even though they remained outnumbered, several Navy pilots scored an impressive number of kills. Edward "Butch" O'Hare received a Medal of Honor after shooting down seven Japanese aircraft in his F-4F. Stanley W. "Swede" Vejtasa, during the Battle of Santa Cruz, destroyed two Japanese Vals headed for the USS *Enterprise*. He also downed five more low-flying torpedo planes before running out of ammunition. Although the *Enterprise* sustained two hits by Japanese bombs, the ship remained afloat. Navy pilots destroyed over 150 Japanese planes in this one battle. Some Navy pilots flew both F-4F Wildcats and F-6F Hellcats after the new planes arrived in the Pacific during the last part of 1943. Lieutenant Elbert McCuskey, a Navy Cross recipient, scored thirteen confirmed kills flying the Hellcat and the Wildcat planes. Once the Hellcats arrived, Navy pilots gained a technological advantage over the Japanese fliers and the number of kills increased as the United States military fought battles for the Marshall and Marianas Islands.

Alexander Vraciu, a remarkable Navy pilot who ended World War II as the fourth highest ace, received his wings in August, 1942. Assigned to the USS *Wolverine*, Vraciu shot down his first plane over Wake Island in October, 1943. By January, he had shot down a total of five enemy aircraft. During the next six months, he destroyed seven additional Japanese planes and sank a Japanese merchant ship with a direct hit to the stern. On June 19, 1944, Vraciu joined other Navy pilots in a battle over the Marianas Islands. Twenty-five miles west of his home ship, the USS *Lexington*, Vraciu spotted twenty-five bombers. Although he managed to shoot down six planes within eight minutes, the remaining Japanese planes continued directly toward the ship. Vraciu destroyed another bomber, this time at a range of two hundred feet. While dodging the debris, he realized that to continue pursuing the Japanese required chasing them into the antiaircraft fire from his own ship. He downed several more bombers before chasing a bomber headed directly for the *Lexington*. Vraciu put his plane in a steep dive to catch the enemy and destroyed the plane just in time. Almost shot down by his own ship, Vraciu returned with six confirmed kills for that one mission, and by the following day, the number of enemy aircraft that he had destroyed totaled nineteen. After the Battle of the Philippine Sea, Vraciu transferred to the Patuxent River facility, where he spent the remainder of the war as a test pilot. After the war, Vraciu commanded the VF-51 squadron.

The list of Navy aces during World War II is lengthy. Commander David McCampbell, a native of Alabama, remained the Navy's top ace, with thirty-four confirmed kills during one tour of duty, nine of them in one battle. He commanded a squadron off the USS *Essex* and participated in the Battle of the Philippine Sea as well as Leyte Gulf. During his career, which lasted until 1964, McCampbell received the Congressional Medal of Honor, the Navy Cross, the Silver Star medal, the Legion of Merit, and the Distinguished Flying Cross.

Cecil E. Harris maintains the position of the second highest-ranking Navy ace, with twenty-four confirmed kills. He served on the USS *Intrepid* in the South Pacific and fought against the dreaded Japanese kamikazes. A teacher from South Dakota, Harris returned to his former occupation after the war with the Navy Cross, the Distinguished Flying Cross, a Silver Star, and two Gold Stars.

Eugene Valencia earned the position of third highest-ranking Navy ace during World War II with twenty-three confirmed kills. Flying a Hellcat F-6F, Valencia and his squadron, commonly referred to as the Flying Circus, mowed down Japanese kamikaze pilots in record numbers. During one mission over the island of Okinawa, Valencia downed six Japanese planes, while his division returned to their ship that day with a total of fourteen kills. Other notable Navy aces are Comelius N. Nooy, Patrick D. Fleming, Douglas Baker, Ira Cassius Kepford, Charles R. Stimpson, Arthur R. Hawkins, John L. Wirth, George Duncan, Roy Rushing, John Strane, Wendell V. Twelves, James Shirley, Daniel A. Carmichael Jr., Roger Hedrick, William J. Masoner, Jr., Hamilton McWhorter III, and P. L. Kirkwood, who all had twelve or more kills. Navy aces with fewer kills, ranging from seven to eleven, include Frederick E. Bakutis, John T. Blackburn, James B. French, William A. Dean, Jr., Donald E. Runyon, Stanley W. "Swede" Vejtasa, Harris A. Mitchell, Whitney Feightner, Ralph E. Elliott, and Edward "Butch" O'Hare.

Navy Aces of Korea and Vietnam

Since the majority of battles in the South Pacific during World War II involved Navy aircraft, the number of Navy aces is the highest during this period. During the Korean War, most of the flying missions remained under the control of the U.S. Air Force. On occasion Navy pilots flew into combat situations but only one achieved the distinction of being called an ace. Lieutenant Guy Bordelon of the V-3 Squadron flew F4U's over Korea and managed to down five planes, the minimum number of kills to qualify as an ace. Bordelon flew night missions over North Korea to destroy depots of aviation fuel and other supplies. Air Force jets flew too fast to harass the prop-driven North Korean planes, so Bordelon was assigned to a Marine base for that purpose. He managed to score five kills in three weeks and then rejoined his squadron on the USS *Princeton* as the Navy's first prop ace in Korea.

As in Korea, Navy pilots saw limited combat action during the Vietnam conflict. Only two Navy pilots during this period achieved the status of ace. On May 10, 1972, Lieutenant Randy "Duke" Cunningham and Lieutenant Junior Grade Willy Driscoll engaged enemy MiGs, including one flown by Colonel Toon, North Vietnam's deadliest pilot with thirteen confirmed kills. Cunningham and Driscoll managed to achieve a triple kill before returning, with heavy damage, to their base. The previous day, the two pilots had destroyed two MiGs.

As technology has advanced the number of Navy Aces has declined. Computer-guided missiles and armed, unmanned aerial vehicles account for many of the kills previously made by pilots. World War II will always remain the era of the Navy ace.

Cynthia Clark Northrup

Bibliography

Morrison, Wilbur H. *Pilots, Man Your Planes! The History of Naval Aviation*. Central Point, Oreg.: Hellgate Press, 1999. The author outlines the history of naval aviation from 1910 to the present and offers insight into the resistance to the inclusion of aircraft in this branch of service by politicians, the Air Force, and elements within the Navy. Detailed accounts of naval air battles are also provided.

Veronico, Nicholas A., and Marga R. Fritze. *Blue Angels: Fifty Years of Precision Flight*. Osceola, Wis.: Motorbooks, International, 1996. This book describes the people, aircraft, and maneuvers of this elite U.S. Navy precision flying team from its inception.

Waller, Douglas C. *Air Warriors: The Inside Story of the Making of a Navy Pilot*. New York: Simon & Schuster, 1998. Excellent source of information detailing the training of U.S. Navy pilots including split-second decisions, dogfights, landing procedures, and other exciting aspects of naval aviation.

See also: Blue Angels; Hornet; Kamikaze missions; Korean War; Military flight; Rescue aircraft; Test pilots; Vietnam War; World War II

Ninety-nines

Also known as: International Organization of Women Pilots
Date: Founded on November 2, 1929, at Curtiss Field, Valley Stream, Long Island, New York
Definition: An international club of more than 6,000 licensed women pilots from about thirty-five countries, with its headquarters in Oklahoma City
Significance: In 1929, ninety-nine female aviation pioneers banded together to provide one another with moral support and to promote aviation. Since that time, the mission of the Ninety-nines has evolved "to promote world fellowship through flight, to provide networking and scholarship opportunities for women and aviation education in the community and to preserve the unique history of women in aviation."

History

The Ninety-nines owe their beginnings to an air race, and they have been involved in air racing ever since. At the start of the 1929 Women's Air Derby, from Santa Monica, California, to Cleveland, Ohio, the first airplane race in which women were permitted to compete, humorist Will Rogers remarked that it looked like a "powder puff derby." Twenty licensed women pilots competed in the grueling nine-day race, flying fragile, unstable aircraft with unreliable engines.

After the race, Amelia Earhart, Gladys O'Donnell, Ruth Nichols, Blanche Noyes, Phoebe Omlie, and Louise Thaden gathered under the grandstand to plan the formation of an association of women pilots. Louise Thaden, winner of the race and holder of numerous flying records, served as secretary, and Blanche Noyes was treasurer. Opal Kunz served as acting president until Amelia Earhart was elected in 1931. The organization's name, the Ninety-nines, was taken from its ninety-nine charter members.

In addition to the U.S. pilots, the original ninety-nine included Thea Rasche from Germany; Jessie Keith-Miller, from Australia; and Lady Mary Heath, from Ireland. Members came from all walks of life and included socialites, test pilots, nurses, housewives, and barnstormers.

Powder Puff Derby

The Ninety-nines are often identified with the Powder Puff Derby, officially known as the All-Woman Transcontinental Air Race. The first race, in the summer of 1947, was flown from Palm Springs, California, to Tampa, Florida, where the Florida chapter of the Ninety-nines was staging the Florida All-Woman Air Show.

Although only one of the two planes entered in the race actually finished, the 1947 Powder Puff Derby was the first of more than thirty annual derbies, which became so popular that the number of entrants had to be limited and qualifications raised. Government officials, celebrities, costumed comic strip characters, and aviation leaders participated in the Powder Puff Derbies as racers, workers, and contributors.

The Powder Puff Derby became an aviation icon, but the All-Woman Transcontinental Air Race Board decided that the 1976 race would be the last. Fuel shortages loomed, airspace was becoming more restricted, and costs were escalating. The 2,926-mile-long 1976 race stretched from Sacramento, California, to Wilmington, Delaware, with two hundred aircraft from all over the world competing. Encouraged by the Smithsonian Institution, a final commemorative race was flown in 1977, retracing the original route.

The members of the Ninety-nines continue to represent diverse occupations and interests, with a love of flying as their bond. For many members, flying is a hobby, but because of their mutual support and encouragement, an increasing number are enjoying productive aviation careers.

Organization

The headquarters of the International Organization of Women Pilots, located located at Will Rogers Airport in Oklahoma City, Oklahoma, is run by an executive director and staff. Officers and the board of directors, who are elected every two years, volunteer their services. The president appoints committee chairs, who coordinate the group's many activities. The local chapters and sections throughout the world are the soul and strength of the Ninety-nines. Their members work together to fulfill the organization's mission.

Membership in the Ninety-nines is open to any female pilot who is licensed by the laws of her country. There is a special membership category for female student pilots. Husbands and significant others of Ninety-nines are affectionately known as Forty-nine-and-one-halfs. Members keep informed and in touch with an international bimonthly magazine, an annual directory, chapter and section newsletters, and an e-mail service.

Scholarships

The Amelia Earhart Memorial Scholarship fund is a living tribute to the Ninety-nines' first elected president and inspirational leader. Established in 1940 by Betty Gillies and Alma Harwood, it has helped many hundreds of women reach their career goals by helping to pay for new flight ratings.

Contributions to the scholarship fund are invested and managed by a board of trustees, and awards are made from the earnings. Individual chapters and sections award their own scholarships and also contribute to the Amelia Earhart Memorial Scholarship fund. The first award of $150 was given to Patricia Gladney in 1941. As the fund has prospered into the twenty-first century, ten to twenty scholarships of many thousands of dollars each are presented at the international convention each July. From time to time, special research scholar grants are also awarded.

United Parcel Service was the first air carrier to participate in the awards in 1992. Since then, companies have awarded training that leads to employment in the airline cockpit for the young women.

Activities

One of the Ninety-nines' highest priorities has always been the promotion of aviation safety. The Ninety-nines host most of the Federal Aviation Administration (FAA) safety seminars that are held throughout the country and conduct survival and flying companion courses, fear-of-flying clinics, and aerospace workshops for teachers. Ninety-nines volunteer their skills and airplanes for rescue missions, transporting patients, blood, organs, animals, and supplies.

Ninety-nines introduce young people to aviation by visiting schools, taking youngsters on flights and airport tours. They serve as judges and coaches for the National Intercollegiate Flying Association meets and for international proficiency competitions. They sponsor, direct, and compete in air races and rallies throughout the world.

Since 1935, Ninety-nines have, with the blessings of federal and local governments, volunteered their time and energy to paint airport names and other helpful information on rooftops and airport taxiways. In the days before pilots were able to make use of the electronic navigation aids that currently exist, airmarking was an important source of directional information. Ninety-nines continue to provide the vital service of painting markers and compass roses on airport surfaces so that pilots and mechanics can check the accuracy of aircraft compasses.

Historical Preservation

The Amelia Earhart Birthplace Museum, a cottage overlooking the Missouri River in Atchison, Kansas, has been restored and preserved by the Ninety-nines and the city of Atchison. A National Historic Site, the home was built in 1861 and is open to the public. Led by charter member Fay Gillis Wells, the Ninety-nines and the city of Atchison also cooperated to create the International Forest of Friendship in Atchison.

In July, 1999, the 99's Museum of Women Pilots was dedicated on the second floor of the International Headquarters Building in Oklahoma City. It secures and displays papers, personal items, and artifacts that highlight the accomplishments of women in aviation from 1910 to the present.

Ursula Malluvius Davidson

Bibliography

Holden, Henry M. *Ladybirds: The Untold Story of Women Pilots in America.* Mt. Freeman, N.J.: Black Hawk, 1991. A collective biography of female aviators from pioneers to the space age that includes formation of the Ninety-nines.

_____. *Ladybirds II: The Continuing Story of American Women in Aviation.* Mt. Freeman, N.J.: Black Hawk, 1993. A second volume of stories and photos of women succeeding in all facets of aviation.

Thomas, Julie Agnew. *The Ninety-nines: Yesterday, Today, Tomorrow.* Paducah, Ky.: Turner, 1996. A detailed history with photographs of the organization, its members, and their achievements.

See also: Air shows; Amelia Earhart; Federal Aviation Administration; Safety issues; Training and education; Women and flight

Northwest Airlines

Date: Founded on September 1, 1926
Definition: A worldwide commercial airline with one of the largest route structures of any U.S. airline.
Significance: Northwest Airlines, founded in 1926, was a pioneer of the North America-Asia air route. Through the acquisition of the domestic carrier, Republic Airlines, in 1986 and a long-term alliance with KLM Royal Dutch Airlines signed in 1997, Northwest entered the twenty-first century offering truly global service.

As was true for many U.S. airlines, Northwest Airways began as a mail carrier. In 1926, it inaugurated mail service between Minneapolis, Minnesota, and Chicago, Illinois. It began passenger service in the following year, carrying a total of 106 passengers in 1927, mostly on a route between Chicago and Minneapolis with intermediate stops. It even became an international carrier when, in 1928, it instituted service to Winnipeg, Manitoba. The service was stopped after three months due to opposition from the Canadian government, but in 1931 it was resumed in a fashion, with flights that actually landed just south of the Canadian border, connecting with a Canadian plane for the last few miles. In 1935, this restriction was lifted and Northwest flew regularly into Canada.

By 1934, the airline had changed its name to Northwest Airlines and passenger service had become a major source of revenue. It expanded its service to the West Coast, serving Seattle, Washington, and cities along a northern route to the west of Minneapolis. In 1939, Northwest Airlines introduced the remarkably able DC-3 aircraft. The Northwest DC-3 carried twenty-one passengers and attained a speed of 140 miles per hour. In the same year, Northwest employed its first stewardess to serve passengers on the DC-3. An interesting record was celebrated in 1999, when a Northwest stewardess, Connie Walker, hired only eighteen years after the introduction of stewardess passenger service, retired at age seventy after forty-two years of service.

Northwest Airlines became a publicly traded company in 1941, when common stock was first made available to the public. It remained on the open stock market until 1989, when it was purchased by Wings Holdings for $3.5 billion.

During World War II, the airline became engaged in defense work for the U.S. government. In the postwar years, the airline began using four-engine planes, beginning with the unpressurized DC-4. At this time, the airline expanded its service to become a transcontinental carrier, initiating flights from the Midwest to New York and to Anchorage. Soon after, it began service to Asia, serving Tokyo, Seoul, Shanghai, Manila, and Okinawa. Starting in 1948, Northwest painted the tails of its aircraft red, the distinctive insignia of the airline that endures into the twenty-first century.

In 1949, Northwest scheduled the giant, two-deck, four-engine Boeing Stratocruiser on its long-distance flights across the United States and to Asia. Ten years later, it introduced jet service to Asia, flying long-range DC-8's to Tokyo and beyond. Flights to Asia were somewhat dependent on the political situation in each country. Flights to Shanghai had to stop in 1949 when China experienced its communist revolution, and Seoul had to be dropped a year later due to hostilities in Korea. Flights to Seoul were reinstituted after the Korean War, but it was not until 1984 that flights to Shanghai were reintroduced. In 1996, an alliance was announced with Air China, the national airline, greatly facilitating travel to and within China.

Travel to Asia, including extensive flights devoted all or mostly to freight, became a major part of Northwest Airlines' business. The company even went so far as to purchase an entire island, Shemya Island in the Aleutian chain, in order to have a useful stop on the route to Asia. Another important development was the introduction of polar flights, which originally followed a New York-Anchorage-Tokyo route, considerably reducing the travel time between the U.S. East Coast and Asia.

In the 1960's, the airline introduced pressurized aircraft, including the DC-6 workhorse and the unusual and elegantly designed Lockheed Constellation, allowing for more comfortable flights over the Rockies and other mountain chains. These craft were soon replaced with jets such as the 707 and the DC-8. Greatly increased capacity came in the 1970's with the introduction of wide-body jets, including both 747's and DC-10's. During this period, Northwest remained unique among U.S. airlines in attempting to be both a local carrier and an international one, concentrating its foreign ports in Asia. Only TWA made a similar attempt, concentrating on European destinations.

The 1980's saw several mergers and consolidations among U.S. airlines. Hughes Airwest, Southern Airlines, and North Central Airlines combined to form a new company called Republic Airlines. Northwest acquired Republic Airlines in 1986, adding its many short-hop routes to Northwest's domestic network and making it one of the largest U.S. airlines.

The next development of this kind occurred in 1991, when Northwest reached an agreement to become partnered with KLM Royal Dutch Airlines. Together, the two airlines offered service to virtually the entire world, with Northwest adding the extensive KLM network of European ports, as well as cities in Eastern Europe, the Caribbean, South America, Africa, and Southeast Asia. This arrangement having been found to be mutually beneficial, the two airlines signed a long-term agreement of partnership in 1997.

The early 1990's saw some troubled periods involving restructuring of the airline's route systems and changes in its hub design, as well as financial restructuring. Later problems included a pilots' strike in 1998, which caused the entire airline to cease operations for three weeks.

By the end of the twentieth century, Northwest Airlines was involved with a complex combination of favorable alliances with other airlines, including Continental, Alaska, Mesaba, Hawaiian, American Eagle, America West, Big Sky, and Horizon in the United States. It was also teamed with several foreign carriers in addition to KLM, such as Malaysian, Japan Air System, Alitalia, Jet Airways of India, Pacific Island Aviation, Braathens, CebuPacific, Cyprus, Garuda Indonesian, and Kenya Airways. With these in place, Northwest serves a total of about 750 cities in 120 different countries on seven continents.

Paul Hodge

Bibliography

Jones, G. *Northwest Airways*. Plymouth, England: Plymouth Press, 1999. A short but informative coverage of statistics and other quantitative details regarding the airline. For some reason, the title uses the original name of the company, which was changed in 1934.

Mills, S. E. *A Pictorial History of Northwest Airlines*. New York: Bonanza Books, 1980. A well-illustrated review of the airline, though all illustrations are in black and white. It is very much out of date, but interesting as a history of the airline's equipment in the 1970's and earlier.

See also: Air carriers; Airline industry, U.S.; Airmail delivery; Alitalia; Continental Airlines; Flight attendants; Food service; Jumbojets; KLM

Hermann Oberth

Date: Born on June 25, 1894, in Hermannstadt, Siebenbergen, Transylvania; died on December 28, 1989; in Nürnberg, Germany

Definition: An early pioneer of the physical principles of spaceflight and designer of some of the first liquid fuel rockets.

Significance: Oberth's calculations proved that spaceflight was possible with multistage liquid-fueled rockets. Many of his visions, such as the space telescope, space suits, and reuseable space vehicles, have been realized.

As a youth, Hermann Julius Oberth became interested in rockets after reading Jules Verne's novel *Autour de la lune* (1870; *From the Earth to the Moon . . . and a Trip Around It*, 1873). His later thesis *Die Rackete zu den Planetenräumen* (1923; the rocket into interplanetary space) was rejected at Heidelberg University, but when it was published as a book in 1923, it sold out two editions and attracted interest all over Germany.

To support his growing family, Oberth taught mathematics, physics, and chemistry at a grade school in Mediasch, Siebenburgen. In 1927, he helped found the Verein für Raumschiffahrt (VfR), Germany's first society for space travel, becoming its president in 1929. He went on lecture tours defending the scientific possibility of spaceflight. In collaboration with Rudolf Nebel and Wernher von Braun, who was then a student, he built and tested liquid fuel propulsion systems for rockets, using liquid oxygen and gasoline.

In 1936, the German army opened the famous installation at Peenemünde to develop ballistic missiles. At Peenemünde, Oberth and von Braun helped develop the so-called Vergeltungswaffen, or "revenge weapons," the V-1 and V-2 rockets. In 1941, Oberth took up residence at Peenemünde under the alias Felix Hann. He patented the fuel pump used in liquid fuel rockets and also helped develop an ammonium nitrate-propelled antiaircraft rocket.

After a period of incarceration at the end of World War II,

Hermann Oberth first proved that multistage rockets could make spaceflight possible. (Library of Congress)

Oberth returned to rocket research in Germany and Italy, and published the book *Menschen im Weltraum* (1954; *Man into Space*, 1957), which contained novel ideas for propulsion systems. In 1955, he went to Huntsville, Alabama, where he joined von Braun, who now headed the U.S. rocket program. In 1958, Oberth returned to the town of Feucht, Germany, where he wrote prolifically on technical and philosophical subjects and moved into retirement. He died in 1989 at the age of ninety-five at a hospital in Nürnberg, Germany.

John R. Phillips

Bibliography

Freeman, Marsha. *How We Got to the Moon: The Story of the German Space Pioneers*. Washington, D.C.:

Twenty-first Century Science Associates, 1993. The first part of this history treats Oberth's early work, with photographs and an extensive bibliography.

Ley, Willy. *Rockets, Missiles, and Men in Space.* New York: Viking, 1968. An authoritative history by a participant in some of the events.

Oberth, Hermann. *Man into Space.* New York: Harper, 1957. Translation of the eight essays and technical appendix first published in Düsseldorf.

Ordway, F. I., and M. R. Sharpe. *The Rocket Team.* New York: Crowell, 1979. A history of rocketry and astronautics in the twentieth century, with photos of Oberth and others.

Walters, Helen B. *Hermann Oberth: Father of Space Travel.* New York: Macmillan, 1962. Details of Oberth's student days, his family, and his struggle for the acceptance of his ideas.

See also: Wernher von Braun; Missiles; Rocket propulsion; Rockets; Spaceflight

Orbiting

Definition: Sustained repetitive motion about a gravitating body, generally consisting of closed circles or ellipses.

Significance: Orbiting is the type of motion exhibited by both natural and artificial satellites.

The Laws of Motion

Isaac Newton in 1684 published three laws of motion that put its study on a firm scientific basis for the first time.

The first law states that a body at rest will remain at rest, and a body in motion will remain in motion in a straight line at constant speed, unless acted on by an outside force. Sometimes referred to as the law of inertia, this law first articulated the principle that motion, not rest, is the natural state of objects. Contrary to commonsense observation, and to the beliefs of many philosophers prior to 1684, a force is not necessary to keep objects moving; rather, a force is necessary to bring them to a halt once they are moving.

The second law states that the application of a force to an object will cause it to accelerate in the direction of the force, with the magnitude of the acceleration equal to the strength of the force divided by the mass of the object. Acceleration is defined as a change in velocity; velocity covers both speed and direction of motion. An acceleration can be a change in speed in a constant direction, or it can be a change in direction of motion at constant speed, or it can be a simultaneous change in both speed and direction. An airplane increasing its speed from 100 to 200 miles per hour is accelerating. So is an airplane banking in a tight circle to the left at a constant 100 miles per hour.

The third law states that for every action, that is, a force exerted by one body on a second, there will be an equal and opposite reaction, that is, a diametrically opposite force exerted on the first body by the second.

In addition to the three laws of motion, Newton also discovered the law of gravitation, which states that any two objects will attract each other with a force which is proportional to the product of their masses divided by the square of the distance between their centers. The gravitational attraction of Earth and an object is the force of weight.

Free Fall

Objects solely under the influence of gravity are said to be in free fall. In such a situation, weight is the only force acting on the object and the law of gravitation states that the direction of this force is toward the center of Earth. From the second law, it follows that the object will accelerate toward the center of Earth. If the object is initially at rest or in pure vertical motion, then the resultant acceleration will be a change in speed only: an object traveling vertically upward will slow to a halt and then begin to travel downward at an ever-increasing rate, or if initially traveling vertically downward, will simply increase its downward speed.

An object traveling horizontally will also accelerate downward, but in this case the acceleration will include a change in direction. The initial horizontal velocity will accumulate a downward component in addition to the initial horizontal component, and the combination of the two will result in a curved path. The object will travel on a parabola. In both of these two cases, the force is the same—the object's weight does not change—and the acceleration is the same. The effect of the acceleration is different because of the different initial velocities of the two situations.

Orbiting

The force of gravity extends to infinity and cannot be canceled or screened. At altitudes where Earth's atmosphere is too thin to exert the aerodynamic forces of lift and drag, the motion of an object is governed solely by the force of gravity: it is in free fall. Such is the case for the Moon. It accelerates toward the center of Earth, but because its initial velocity is horizontal, the acceleration results in a curved trajectory. Because the gravitational force decreases with distance, the curvature of the trajectory is shallow and the path of the Moon does not bend enough to intersect the surface of Earth. Instead of falling toward Earth, the Moon falls around Earth and circles it repeatedly. The horizontal velocity and downward acceleration are delicately matched to give the Moon a trajectory which is almost a perfect circle.

Three laws of planetary motion were discovered by Johannes Kepler in the years between 1601 and 1618. The first law expresses the discovery that contrary to all previous expectation, the orbits of the planets are ellipses instead of circles. The Sun occupies a special position at one focus of the ellipse, placing it offset from the geometric center. As a result, the distance from planet to Sun changes from a minimum (perihelion) to a maximum (aphelion) and back to a minimum as the planet completes an orbit. The orbit lies entirely in one plane that contains the center of the Sun.

The second law expresses Kepler's discovery that the speed of a planet varies along its orbit, being greatest at perihelion and smallest at aphelion. The variation of the speed is such that a line drawn from the Sun to the planet will sweep out equal areas in equal times.

The third law expresses Kepler's discovery that the size of an orbit is related to the time a planet takes to complete one orbit, called the period. The size of an orbit is indicated by the average distance (mean radius) of the planet from the Sun. The cube of the mean radius divided by the square of the period is the same for all planets.

Newton's demonstration that all three laws follow mathematically from the three laws of motion and law of gravitation was a magnificent scientific triumph and marks the beginning of the modern scientific age.

Earth Orbit

Kepler's three laws apply to satellites in Earth orbit with minor changes. The closest approach of a satellite to Earth is called perigee. The most distant point is called apogee. The orbits are still ellipses with Earth at one focus, and they lie in a plane that contains the center of Earth. The cube of the mean radius of the orbit divided by the square of the period is a constant for all satellites, but is not the same constant that is associated with orbit around the Sun.

Ellipses vary from near-circular to very long and narrow. The degree of narrowing is referred to as the eccentricity. A circle is considered to be an ellipse of zero eccentricity. As ellipses get longer and narrower, the eccentricity approaches one.

The plane of the ellipse may be tilted with respect to the equator. The angle between the plane of the orbit and the plane of the equator is the inclination zero. Inclinations from 0 to 90 degrees are associated with satellites orbiting Earth counterclockwise as seen from a vantage point over the North Pole. Inclinations from 90 to 180 degrees are associated with satellites orbiting clockwise as seen from above the North Pole.

Positive inclination orbits are called prograde. Negative inclination orbits are called retrograde. Prograde orbits are easier to attain because the counterclockwise rotation of Earth adds a free contribution to the velocity of the satellite. Satellites destined for retrograde orbit must launch to the west against the rotation of Earth, making orbit harder to achieve.

Inclinations near 90 degrees are referred to as polar orbits. Satellites in polar orbit will eventually pass over every spot on Earth, making them extremely useful for scientific, remote sensing, and photographic missions.

A satellite in low-Earth orbit has an orbital period of just over ninety minutes. As altitude decreases, orbital period increases. At an altitude of 35,780 kilometers (22,360 miles) the orbital period is exactly twenty-four hours. A satellite in circular equatorial orbit (zero eccentricity, zero inclination) at this altitude will travel along its orbit at exactly the same rate as Earth turns beneath it. The satellite appears to have a fixed position in the sky as seen from Earth. These geostationary orbits are particularly advantageous for communications satellites. Since satellites in these orbits never change their apparent position, no antenna tracking is necessary and the satellites are always available since they never go below the horizon.

Earth Orbit Decay

Ideally, orbits are perfect ellipses which never change. In reality, complications due to the irregular shape of Earth, aerodynamic drag from the thin residual air at orbital altitudes, and the extra gravitational tug of the Sun and Moon continually change the shape and size of satellite orbits.

For low-Earth orbits, the predominant effect is aerodynamic drag. Drag is a dissipative force which converts an object's energy of motion into heat. Ordinarily, it slows things down, but as a satellite loses kinetic energy, it drops closer to Earth. When this happens, gravitational potential energy is converted into kinetic energy and a satellite gains more kinetic energy this way than it loses due to drag. The paradoxical result is that a satellite actually ends up going faster (albeit at a lower altitude) due to the drag. Since drag increases with speed, so does the loss of altitude, and eventually the satellite reenters the atmosphere. The resulting high speeds through dense air create a powerful shock wave in front of the satellite, which compresses and heats the air to the point of incandescence. The satellite burns up like a meteor.

At higher altitudes, aerodynamic drag is negligible and the change in size, shape, and orientation of the orbit due to the irregular shape of Earth and the extra gravitational tug of the Sun and Moon predominate. These orbital changes can be measured with such accuracy that they can be used to refine knowledge of the shape of Earth and the distribution of mass within its interior. Geology now looks to the motion of objects in the sky to find out what is buried in the ground beneath.

Escape Orbits

The apogee height of a satellite increases as the total energy of the satellite increases. If the total energy is great enough, apogee height becomes infinite and the satellite is on an escape orbit. The eccentricity of an escape orbit is greater than 1 and the orbit is an open curve called a hyperbola rather than a closed ellipse. The minimum velocity required to put a satellite on an escape trajectory is called the local escape velocity. For low-Earth orbit, local escape velocity is about 11 kilometers per second (7 miles per second). Satellites with this velocity or greater will leave Earth forever and become artificial planets, satellites of the Sun.

The Solar System and Beyond

Kepler's third law may be rephrased as the principle that the cube of the mean orbital radius divided by the square of the orbital period equals a constant value multiplied by the mass of the gravitating object at the focus of the orbit. For Earth orbits, this formula gives the mass of Earth. For the solar system, it gives the mass of the Sun. The principle can be used to determine the mass of any object in the universe which has detectable satellites whose orbital radius and period can be measured. It is thus that astronomers know the mass of distant objects ranging from tiny asteroids to immense galaxies.

Billy R. Smith, Jr.

Bibliography

Layzer, D. *Constructing the Universe.* New York: Scientific American Library, 1984. A history of astronomy's changing view of the structure of the universe. Includes an in-depth discussion of Kepler's and Newton's discoveries.

Montenbruck, Oliver, and Eberhard Gill. *Satellite Orbits: Models, Methods, Applications.* New York: Springer Verlag, 2000. A textbook on orbital mechanics covering all aspects of satellite orbit prediction and determination.

Sellers, J. *Understanding Space: An Introduction to Astronautics.* New York: McGraw-Hill, 1994. Orbital mechanics is unavoidably a deeply mathematical subject. Little true understanding is possible without some mastery of algebra, geometry, trigonometry, and elementary physics. This text is designed for and highly recommended for anyone who has successfully mastered these subjects at the general college level.

See also: Apollo Program; Crewed spaceflight; Forces of flight; Gemini Program; Gravity; Mercury project; Microgravity; National Aeronautics and Space Administration; Satellites; Spaceflight; Uncrewed spaceflight

Osprey helicopter

Also known as: Bell-Boeing V-22, MV-22, CV-22, HV-22

Definition: A tilt-rotor aircraft designed for military applications.

Significance: The Osprey was the first tilt-rotor aircraft ever to be designed, built, and put into production.

Tilt-Rotor Aircraft

The Osprey is a tilt-rotor aircraft, a hybrid of a helicopter and fixed-wing aircraft. Its unique design allows it to take off and land vertically and hover, like a helicopter, and to fly at high forward speeds, like a turboprop airplane. The Osprey weighs 33,140 pounds and can carry almost 20,000 pounds of cargo. Its top speed is 340 knots and its maximum range is 700 miles. From nose to tail, the Osprey measures more than 57 feet. With its 38-foot-diameter rotors, it is almost 84 feet wide.

The Osprey, built under a team agreement between Bell Helicopter Textron and the Boeing Company, is the first tilt-rotor aircraft ever to be approved for production. There are three variants on the basic V-22 design: the MV-22, the CV-22, and the HV-22. The MV-22 was built for the U.S. Marine Corps as a replacement for its aging CH-46 Sea Knight helicopters, which performed combat-assault and assault-support missions. The CV-22 is built for U.S. Air Force long-range, special-operations missions. The U.S. Navy's version, the HV-22, is intended for combat search and rescue, special operations, and logistics support.

The MV-22 was temporarily grounded in 2000 following a crash that killed nineteen Marines; flights were resumed after an investigation found that the helicopter had descended too quickly. Its future with the Marine Corps was placed in doubt.

In forward flight, the Osprey looks like a fixed-wing aircraft with very large propellers attached to the nacelles located at the wingtips. The nacelles contain the turboshaft engines and transmissions that provide power to the rotors. In the event of an engine failure, an interconnect shaft between the two nacelles allows one engine to power both rotors. The Osprey is unique compared to propeller-driven aircraft or helicopters because its nacelles are designed to pivot. When the nacelles are pivoted such that the rotors are pointed up like those of a helicopter, the Osprey can take off and land vertically or hover. In cruise flight, when the rotors are in their horizontal position, they provide propulsive force like propellers, while the wings provide the lift necessary to keep the aircraft aloft.

Evolution of the Osprey

Although helicopters have superior performance for vertical takeoff and landing (VTOL) and hovering flight, they are limited in forward speed. A typical helicopter has a cruise speed of less than 150 knots, which is far more slow than that of many propeller-driven, fixed-wing aircraft. In order to achieve speeds approaching those of fixed-wing aircraft, aircraft designers since the 1950's have investigated concepts for aircraft that can hover, take off, and land vertically and achieve high forward speeds.

In December, 1954, the Model 1-G, built by the Transcendental Aircraft Company, became the first tilt-rotor aircraft ever successfully to perform a transition from hover to forward flight. Before being lost in an accident, the Model 1-G flew more than twenty hours in more than one hundred flights. The Model 1-G was followed by the Model 2, which was tested in 1956 and 1957. Despite these accomplishments, the Air Force, which was supporting tilt-rotor development, chose to shift its support to the Bell Helicopter Company, which completed the first of two XV-3 prototypes in 1955.

In 1973, under contract to the National Aeronautics and Space Administration (NASA) and the Army, Bell Helicopter, by now a subsidiary of Textron, began the development of the XV-15 as a tilt-rotor technology demonstrator aircraft. The XV-15 made its first flight in May, 1977, and performed its first conversion in July, 1979. The two XV-15 aircraft built under this program have flown hundreds of research and demonstration flights and continue to be flown. The unprecedented success of the XV-15 contributed directly to the development of the V-22 Osprey.

Osprey Flight Regimes

Unlike helicopters and fixed-wing aircraft, the Osprey must operate in three flight regimes, cruise, hover, and transition. In cruising flight, it is flown in a manner similar to that of fixed-wing aircraft. Fixed control surfaces on the aircraft allow the pilot to change the aircraft's attitude. A large elevator on the horizontal tail controls pitch; flaperons, which operate both as flaps and ailerons, on the wings control roll; and rudders on the twin vertical tails control yaw. In order to increase the forward speed of the aircraft, the pilot increases the pitch angle of the rotor blades, thereby increasing the thrust.

The Osprey helicopter is designed to fly either vertically, like a helicopter, or horizontally, like an airplane. Unfortunately, the aircraft has been plagued by fatal crashes. (AP/Wide World Photos)

> **V-22A Osprey Characteristics**
>
> Primary Function: Vertical takeoff and landing (VTOL) aircraft
> Builder: Bell-Boeing
> Propulsion: Two pivoting Rolls Royce/Allison AE1107C engines
> Main Rotor Diameter: 38 feet
> Blades per Rotor: 3
> Maximum Gross Weight: 60,500 pounds
> Service Ceiling: 25,000 feet
> Cruise Speed: 272 knots
> Armament: Provisions for two .50-caliber cabin guns

Source: Data taken from (www.chinfo.navy.mil/navpalib/factfile/aircraft/air-v22a.html), June 6, 2001.

In hovering flight, the Osprey's fixed control surfaces are not effective, because the aircraft has no forward velocity. Therefore, all of the control must come from the rotors. Collective pitch changes are obtained by changing the pitch angle of all rotor blades on one rotor by the same amount. To increase the altitude of the aircraft, the pilot increases the collective pitch on both rotors by the same amount. Roll is obtained with differential collective pitch, which involves increasing the collective pitch on one rotor while decreasing the collective pitch on the other. Changing pitch angle of each rotor blade in a sinusoidal pattern during each revolution effects cyclic pitch changes on a rotor. Unlike collective pitch, cyclic pitch does not change the total thrust produced by the rotor but does produce a movement about an axis perpendicular to a line between the points where the largest and smallest pitch angles are obtained. Control of the aircraft pitch in hover is obtained by changing the cyclic pitch of both rotors by the same amount. Yaw control is obtained by using differential cyclic pitch.

During the transition flight regime, the Osprey changes from being an aircraft that is controlled like a helicopter to one that is controlled like a propeller-driven, fixed-wing aircraft. Through control system software, which relies primarily on measurement of forward speed, the pilot's control of the aircraft is gradually transitioned between the helicopter flight regime and the cruise flight regime. Once the cruise flight regime has been attained, with the rotors in their horizontal position, the rotation speed of the rotors is changed from its helicopter mode value of 397 revolutions per minute to a cruise value of 332 revolutions per minute.

Donald L. Kunz

Bibliography

Emert, P. R. *Special Task Aircraft*. Englewood Cliffs, N.J.: Silver Burdett, 1990. Specifications and uses of various aircraft designed for special tasks.

Jackson, Paul. *Jane's All the World's Aircraft: 2000-2001*, Alexandria, Va.: Jane's Information Group, 2000. The definitive source for aircraft photographs and specifications.

Thornborough, Anthony. *V-22 Osprey Bell-Boeing Tilt Rotor*. Essex, England: Linewrights, 1990. Part of the publisher's Aeroguides series, this volume is an in-depth study of the Osprey tilt-rotor aircraft.

See also: Helicopters; Military flight; Rescue aircraft; Rotorcraft; Vertical takeoff and landing

Overbooking

Definition: The degree to which an airline will allow more reservations for a flight to be made than there are seats on an airplane.

Significance: Because airlines sell a perishable product, and an empty seat at departure time is gone forever, overbooking is the airlines' attempt to balance the number of passengers with the reservations of those who do not fly, no-shows, so that every possible seat is filled.

Reasons for Overbooking

Airlines face the dilemma of providing scheduled transportation services to the traveling public, whose demand for transportation is variable. During vacation periods, more passengers will fly to vacation destinations. During the beginning or end of any weekday, business passengers can be expected between business destinations. During a convention, air traffic to the convention's location is predictable. The challenge that all airlines face is to maximize the sale of seats during those times when demand for transportation is high.

To determine the number of reservations that an airline will authorize to sell above the actual number of existing airplane seats, historical data of past departures are considered. These data include the number of passengers on similar flights during past time periods. Elaborate mathematical and statistical computer programs calculate these variables to predict as closely as possible the demand for seats.

The number of reservations that are then allowed to be sold is called the authorization level. On the average, the authorization level is set ninety days before departure, which is approximately how far in advance passengers typically begin to make reservations. Prior to the day of departure, authorization levels may be changed from their original estimates to take into account cancellations or changes that passengers have made to travel on other flights. On the day of departure, airline personnel initiate overbooking procedures for those flights that have more reservations than seats.

Overbooking planning assumes that all passengers holding reservations will show up for the flight. The first step is to determine by how many reservations a flight is overbooked. The second step is to arrange alternate flights for the extra passengers, preferably on the same airline. Other airline departures that are reasonably close to the flight's departure may also be considered. The third step is to establish what the airline will offer to motivate passengers to volunteer to give up their seats. Most airlines offer two kinds of voluntary compensation, as it is called. Voluntary compensation can be a voucher, in the form of either a dollar amount that can be applied to another trip or an outright free trip at a later date.

Every passenger who checks in for the flight is told that the flight is oversold and informed of the voluntary compensation and alternate flights. If passengers are interested in volunteering to give up their seats, the airline personnel enters these data into the computer, so that the gate agents know who and how many volunteers have been generated. If all the seats are taken prior to departure, passengers to whom seats cannot be assigned are considered potentially to be involuntarily denied boarding. Other computer entries are made so that the gate agents know to whom they owe a seat. If passengers to whom seats cannot be assigned wish to volunteer, they may do so.

As the departure time approaches, it is the objective of overbooking planning that the number of volunteers will exceed the number of involuntary passengers. At thirty minutes prior to departure, those passengers with reservations who have not as yet purchased tickets may be cancelled from the flight. At twenty minutes prior to departure, the seats of those passengers who have not checked in for their reserved seat assignments are released. These entries establish the actual situation of the overbooking. Often the cancelled reservations and the released reserved seats free enough seats to accommodate the passengers who require seats. If they do not, other

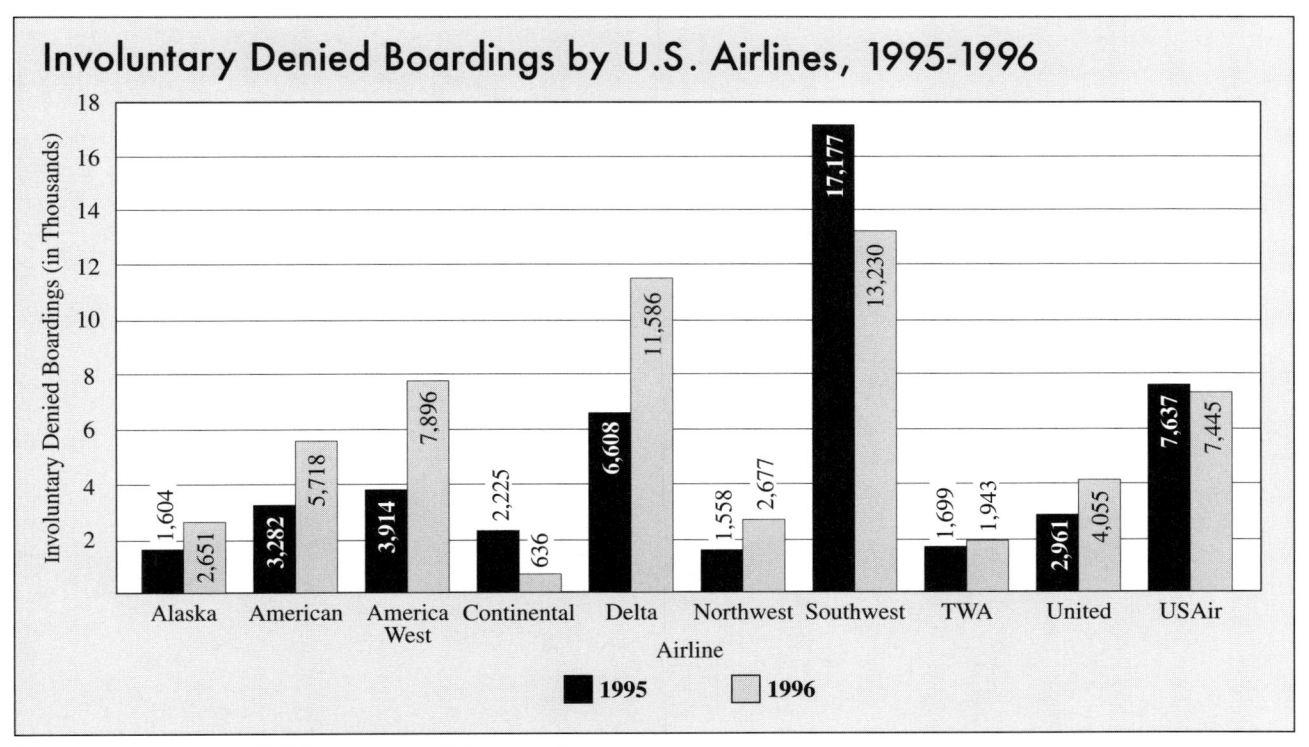

Involuntary Denied Boardings by U.S. Airlines, 1995-1996

Airline	1995	1996
Alaska	1,604	2,651
American	3,282	5,718
America West	3,914	7,896
Continental	2,225	636
Delta	6,608	11,586
Northwest	1,558	2,677
Southwest	17,177	13,230
TWA	1,699	1,943
United	2,961	4,055
USAir	7,637	7,445

Source: Data taken from U.S. Department of Transportation.

computer entries are made to give the seats of volunteers to those who still require them. If, after that step, all passengers have been accommodated, the volunteers are notified that their seats were taken. Either the gate agents or other designated agents then arrange the alternate flights and issue the voluntary compensation.

If, however, there still remain passengers who will be left behind, these passengers are due what is called involuntary denied boarding compensation. This type of compensation may be the same as the voluntary compensation that had been previously offered or some other form of compensation, depending on how soon the airline can get the passengers to their destination. If the airline can get the passengers to their destination within one hour, no compensation is due. However, the voluntary compensation is usually offered. If the airline can get the passengers to their destination within two hours, they are due 100 percent of the value of their one-way ticket or $200, whichever is less. If the two-hour time frame is not possible, they are due 200 percent of the value of their one-way ticket or $400, whichever is less. Airlines are obliged to provide payment on the day or within twenty-four hours of the denied boarding.

After the aircraft departs, the numbers of volunteer and involuntarily denied passengers are communicated to the departments that set authorization levels for their consideration and analysis.

Overbooking is both an emotional and a financial issue. No passenger wants to be left behind, and every airline wants to fill every seat. Although every attempt is made on the part of the airlines to accurately predict and analyze actual passenger numbers, the fact that customers make reservations and do not show up for their flights remains a sensitive issue.

Jim Oppermann

Bibliography
Butler, G. F., and M. R. Keller. *Handbook of Airline Marketing*. Washington, D.C.: Aviation Week Group, 1998.
Wells, Alexander. "Economic Characteristic of Airlines." In *Air Transportation: A Management Perspective*. Belmont, Calif.: Wadsworth, 1999. An explanation of the issue of managing and matching changing passenger demands and patterns of booking transportation with unchanging aircraft capacities.

See also: Air carriers; Airline industry, U.S.; Boarding procedures; Ticketing

P

Pan Am World Airways

Date: First regularly scheduled service on October 28, 1927; ceased operations on December 11, 1991

Definition: One of the largest and most successful airlines in history until 1991.

Significance: Pan Am was, for a time, the largest, most successful airline in the world and the chosen instrument of the U.S. State Department in international air transportation, establishing routes throughout Central and South America and across the Atlantic and Pacific Oceans.

Early History

Pan American World Airways began as the vision of one man, Juan Terry Trippe, a Yale University graduate who had learned to fly during World War I. Trippe was convinced that the future of commercial aviation lay in international air transportation with operational guarantees furnished by governments in the form of airmail contracts. He founded what was to become Pan American Airways by outmaneuvering other companies in acquiring a mail contract and exclusive landing rights in Cuba. To accomplish this feat, he used political and financial connections cultivated in his undergraduate days at Yale.

Thus, what would become one of the largest and most successful airlines in history began operations with a 90-mile route from Key West, Florida, to Havana, Cuba. Throughout the airline's history, Trippe repeatedly applied the lessons he learned in obtaining this route. He ruthlessly used political, family, and financial ties to expand Pan Am. With the assistance of the U.S. State Department and the U.S. Post Office, he negotiated landing rights throughout the Caribbean, Central America, and South America. Whenever possible, these landing rights were exclusive, in effect prohibiting other airlines from operating in these countries.

Pan Am, under Trippe's leadership, expanded by winning every airmail contract offered through the U.S. Post Office in Central and South America. By November, 1930, the airline was operating to Buenos Aires, Argentina. In fewer than four years, the original 90-mile route had been expanded to one of more than 13,000 miles.

Acquisitions and Mergers

When Pan Am found it impossible to operate within a foreign country or found an established airline already operating, it simply bought controlling interest in the operating airline and continued to operate it as a subsidiary. Thus, airlines such as Compania Mexicana de Aviacion became part of the Pan Am empire in 1929. Pan Am also joined with the W. R. Grace steamship line to form PANAGRA to operate along the west coast of South America. In a 1930 hostile takeover allegedly sanctioned by the U.S. postmaster general, Pan Am acquired the New York, Rio, Buenos Aires Line (NYRBA), which had established a route along the east coast of South America. At the same time, Pan Am established a Brazilian subsidiary, Panair do Brazil, in order to comply with prior agreements between Brazil and NYRBA. Pan Am gained controlling interest in the Colombian airline SCADTA in a secret agreement of which even the governments of Columbia and the United States were unaware. Pan Am did not limit its grasp to Central and South America, however, purchasing two small airlines in Alaska and an interest in China National Airways. Trippe's dream for Pan Am had expanded across both the Atlantic and Pacific Oceans.

Two major obstacles stood in the way of this expansion. The first was the technology of existing aircraft, which were, in their range and payload, inadequate for long, transoceanic flights. The second impediment was international relations. European countries, particularly Great Britain, were unwilling to grant Pan Am landing rights in their territory until their national airlines were capable of competing. Trippe, in typical fashion, placed Pan Am in the position to overcome both of these difficulties.

Aircraft Technology

Pan Am worked closely with manufacturers to develop aircraft capable of servicing the developing transoceanic routes. Although Pan Am's first aircraft had been the Fokker Trimotor, it was soon apparent that more advanced designs were required. Pan Am began to rely heavily on the designs of Russian American aeronautical engineer Igor Sikorsky, who produced large flying boats. Pan Am decided that the flying boat was the most appropriate design for their operation, because many of the countries to which they were operating had no major airports. Virtually all, however, had adequate areas for waterborne operations. Sikorsky designed multiengined flying boats that could carry up to forty-two passengers at 140 miles per hour. These aircraft serviced the routes throughout Central and South America and conducted proving runs across the Atlantic and Pacific Oceans.

Pan Am also hired aviation pioneer Charles A. Lindbergh as a technical consultant. Much of Lindbergh's expertise went into the development of the advanced designs that soon appeared, such as the famous Pan Am Clippers built by Sikorsky, Martin, and Boeing. The range and payload of these aircraft were in direct response to Pan Am's operational needs. These designs culminated in the Boeing 314, considered the ultimate development of the flying boat. With suitable aircraft, Pan Am began to pursue expansion across both the Atlantic and Pacific. The major problem remaining was the resistance of foreign governments to Pan Am's encroachment. Lindbergh, who played the role of goodwill ambassador, made a number of transatlantic and transpacific proving flights for the airline.

International Relations

Although Pan Am's immediate goal was transatlantic service, major difficulties remained in negotiating agreements with European governments. Great Britain was especially reluctant to allow Pan Am access until British Imperial Airways was capable of flying comparable routes. On February 22, 1937, a reciprocal agreement was reached, and Pan Am's transatlantic service finally began on July 8, 1939. Unfortunately, Britain was soon at war. The difficulties in negotiating reciprocal agreements with European nations had caused Pan Am to pursue expansion across the Pacific. Taking maximum advantage of U.S. State Department concerns about Japanese expansion and fortification of its possessions in the Pacific, Pan Am worked closely with the U.S. Navy to establish a series of bases from Hawaii to Midway, Guam, and the Philippine Islands. Pan Am's service to Hong Kong began on November 22, 1935. As the United States became inevitably drawn into World War II, the State Department began to utilize the services of Pan Am more openly. On November 2, 1940, a subsidiary of Pan Am, the Pan American Airport Corporation, contracted to construct bases across Central America. These bases were designed to allow the ferrying of aircraft to North Africa to supply the Allied forces there. Pan Am also contracted to fly a regular service across the Atlantic to Cairo, Egypt, in support of British troops. Another subsidiary, Pan Am-Africa, constructed a series of bases across Africa. Pan Am began scheduled service to Khartoum in July, 1941. Pan Am continued to increase operations throughout the war years, emerging from the war as the world's dominant international airline. However, the war also introduced an element of competition into Pan Am's monopoly, and a shift in the political winds spelled trouble for the airline.

Postwar Difficulties

Pan Am enjoyed unparalleled success during the 1930's. International passenger traffic increased from approximately 44,000 in 1930 to more than 246,000 by 1939. Mail rates in the Pacific were increased significantly beginning in 1939, primarily due to the recommendation of the Navy. By 1942, Pan Am had a gross income of $109,000,000 and a staff of 88,000.

World War II introduced competition for Pan Am in the form of Trans World Airlines (TWA) and American Airlines. These hitherto domestic operators were awarded international routes in support of the war effort. These awards were particularly troubling to Pan Am, because they included the lucrative transatlantic route on which Pan Am had expended so much effort and expense. By war's end, although Pan Am remained the major transatlantic carrier with more than 15,000 flights, American and TWA had also become major international carriers. Both airlines had garnered significant international experience: TWA had made 10,000 transatlantic crossings, and American had made 5,000.

In addition to international competition, Pan Am had other problems. With only four domestic terminals and no domestic routes, the company was not positioned to benefit from the dramatic increase in domestic air traffic caused by the war. Although Pan Am had lost its exclusivity in international operations, it was unable to expand domestically to contend with its new international competitors. Additional concerns arose as early as 1943, with the Roosevelt administration's call for an international open-skies policy to be enacted after the war. This would open international operations to a number of airlines and further threaten Pan Am's position of primacy. Roosevelt chose not to recognize any one airline as the chosen instrument of the United States and invited bids from airlines interested in establishing international routes. Two Atlantic and three Pacific routes were opened for competitive bidding.

Pan Am attempted unsuccessfully to use political pressure to forestall Roosevelt's efforts, and was confirmed on its routes to London, continuing to Calcutta, India. Although this confirmation in effect allowed Pan Am to fly around the world, with its Atlantic and Pacific routes meeting at Calcutta, both TWA and American were confirmed in their transatlantic routes. Roosevelt's death did not improve Pan Am's government relations; his successor, President Harry S. Truman awarded routes to Central and South America to Braniff and Eastern. In 1945, National, American, and Chicago and Southern were awarded routes that ventured into Pan Am's prewar empire. Northwest Airlines was allowed to compete with Pan Am in the Pacific, connecting with TWA to form an around-the-world service. Finally, United Air Lines was granted a San Francisco-to-Hawaii route that actually duplicated the route pioneered by Pan Am in the 1930's.

The Jet Age
Despite the changes that eroded Pan Am's position of dominance, Pan Am remained a very successful airline. Under Trippe's guidance, it was poised to enter the jet age. Trippe negotiated with a number of manufacturers to develop a jet transport that would adequately service long-haul routes, and Pan Am placed the largest aircraft order ever made, totaling $265,000,000 and including twenty Boeing 707's and twenty-five Douglas DC-8's. On October 19, 1958, Pan Am officially launched the jet age of transatlantic travel, with its first jet flight carrying 111 passengers at a speed of 475 miles per hour. This tremendous gamble paid off, and the aircraft dominated the transatlantic route. However, Pan Am's lack of domestic routes would cause the airline increasing difficulties.

Trippe's final major decision was to purchase the widebody Boeing 747. In April, 1966, Pan Am announced the purchase of twenty-five Boeing 747's at a cost exceeding one-half billion dollars. Pan Am made its first 747 flight in January, 1970. By this time, Trippe had retired as Pan Am president and had been replaced by a succession of leaders who were unable to continue the pattern of innovation and success Trippe had carried out for forty-three years. Economic factors, a slowdown in passenger growth, and politically motivated decisions by the Johnson administration to increase competition in the Pacific had a dire effect on Pan Am. In addition, the airline experienced a series of crashes that destroyed eleven aircraft and resulted in numerous fatalities.

The seemingly invincible airline's hard times grew worse. Attempts to merge with other major airlines were unsuccessful. In just three years, Pan Am lost more than $120 million, and its debt exceeded $1 billion. In 1974, Pan Am was denied a government subsidy. As the airline struggled to survive, employment was reduced to 27,000, and a number of international routes were relinquished to TWA. In an attempt to establish a domestic route structure, Pan Am acquired National Airlines at a cost of $374 million; however, the purchase only intensified the airline's problems. By 1980, Pan Am was losing more than one million dollars a day, and the first quarter of 1981 saw a record loss of $118.8 million. The company's New York headquarters were sold, as were other resources, and orders for new aircraft were cancelled. In 1985, the employees went on strike, and Pan Am sold its Pacific routes to United.

On December 21, 1988, the final catastrophe occurred. A terrorist bomb destroyed Pan Am Flight 103 over Lockerbie, Scotland. This tragedy, coupled with the Iraqi invasion of Kuwait in 1990, sealed Pan Am's fate. Most remaining assets and aircraft were sold to Delta Air Lines. Pan American World Airways ceased to exist on December 11, 1991.

Ronald J. Ferrara

Bibliography
Christy, Joe. *American Aviation: An Illustrated History*. 2d ed. Blue Ridge Summit, Pa.: Tab Books, 1994. A good presentation of the history of the major airlines in the United States, including Pan Am.
Davies, R. E. G. *Airlines of the United States Since 1914*. Washington, D.C.: Smithsonian Institution Press, 1998. An extremely well-researched, well-written, and well-illustrated work on the history of U.S. airlines.
Gandt, Robert. *Skygods: The Fall of Pan Am*. New York: William Morrow, 1999. A well-written analysis of Pan Am's final days.

See also: Air carriers; Airline industry, U.S.; Airmail delivery; Commercial flight; Jumbojets; Mergers; Igor Sikorsky; Terrorism; Trans World Airlines; United Air Lines

Paper airplanes

Definition: Paper folded and creased into the shapes of airplanes.
Significance: Learning to fold and fly a paper airplane is a basic study of aerodynamics.

History of Paper Airplanes
Human experimentation with flying did not begin with the Wright brothers. People have been fascinated by flight since ancient times. The first flying devices made from paper were kites, constructed by the Chinese around 1 C.E. Even Leonardo da Vinci tried to devise a way for humans to fly. It is said he used parchment folded into winged fly-

ers during his experiments. At the beginning of the twenty-first century, paper airplanes were used as a common technique to study aerodynamics. During World War I, flying paper airplanes became a popular activity with children. In the 1940's, the General Mills Company offered a series of fourteen paper model warplanes.

How Airplanes Fly

The wings of an airplane share a shape with those of insects, bats, and birds, called an airfoil. An airfoil is curved on top and flat on the bottom. Air rushing over the wing travels faster than the current going under the flat bottom of the plane. The eighteenth century Swiss scientist Daniel Bernoulli discovered that when air speeds up, its pressure is reduced. When air slows down, its pressure is increased. Therefore, the slower air going over the wing pushes down, which is known as weight, or gravity. The faster air under the wing pushes upward. This tug-of-war between opposing forces is what causes lift. During level flight, lift and weight pull equally. If lift pulls harder, the plane will rise. If weight pulls more, the plane will fall.

The center of lift on a paper airplane is the point at which lift seems to be working. The center of gravity is the balance point of the plane, the point at which gravity seems to be working. On paper airplanes, the center of gravity needs to coincide with the center of lift. If the center of lift is in front of or behind the center of gravity, the nose of the plane will pitch up or down accordingly.

Another set of opposing forces present during flight are drag and thrust. These two forces are what pull the plane forward or back. Real planes get their thrust from a propeller or engine. Paper airplanes get their thrust from being launched or thrown by a person. A throw gives a plane its initial speed, and gravity pulls it along.

When a plane flies level, drag is what pulls it back. Most of drag comes from air resistance. As a plane flies, air sticks to it, creating turbulence, or resistance to motion. If the nose of a plane points down, gravity will add thrust and the plane will crash. Any surface not parallel to the flow of air adds drag. Sharp creases and accurate folding will reduce drag and increase time aloft. Lift also contributes to drag by pulling up and a little back. A typical paper airplane's drag is one fifth of its weight.

This paper airplane, constructed in 1992, broke the world record for size. (NASA)

Differences in wing loading, the specific amount of weight a standard size area of the wing lifts in flight, will create difference in speeds. Wing loading is how many pounds per square foot the wing is lifting. The larger the wing area, the less wing loading and more slowly the plane will glide.

Building a Stable Craft

Another factor that affects flight is stability, which helps an airplane return to steady flight after a bad throw or a strong gust of wind. There are three basic types of stability: pitch, directional, and spiral.

Pitch stability keeps the airplane flying at a constant speed. If the nose of a plane pitches up, the plane will slow down. If it pitches down, the speed will increase. There is a small distance along the length of a plane where it must balance to provide optimum pitch stability. On a paper airplane, this distance is less than one inch long. If the balance point is too far forward, the plane will dive; too far back, and it will spin out of control.

Directional stability can be maintained by creating a fin on the back of the plane to counteract the tendency to spin. On most paper airplanes, the body acts as the fin. If most of the plane's body is behind the balance point, it will be directionally stable. Bending the wing tips up will add to its stability.

Spiral stability is when the plane flies straight and smooth. A spirally unstable plane will circle, turning tighter and tighter, until it spins into a dive. To correct a spirally unstable plane, the wings, as viewed from the nose, should be bent up slightly so that they make a Y shape with the body.

Flying Techniques

Getting a good flight out of a paper airplane requires a good throw. To get the most out of a throw, the plane should be held on the bottom near the front, using the forefinger and thumb. How a plane is thrown depends on the type of flying intended. The types of flying include slow flight, fast flight, and high (world record) flight.

Slow flight is achieved by holding the plane in front of the shoulder and pushing the plane forward and slightly downward. For fast flying, the plane should be held in front of the shoulder for short flights and above the shoulder for long flights. The high throw is mainly used for competition and is achieved by throwing the plane straight up as hard as possible. If done properly, the plane will spiral up, level off, and glide slowly forward.

Maryanne Barsotti

Bibliography

Blackburn, Ken, and Jeff Lammers. *The World Record Paper Airplane Book*. New York: Workman, 1994. Informative source of theory of flight. Contains black-and-white sketches as well as color models of paper airplanes. Also discusses flight contests. One of the authors is a Guinness World Record holder for paper airplane time aloft.

Botermans, Jack. *Paper Flight*. New York: Henry Holt, 1983. Contains folding and flying instructions for paper airplanes. Discusses the origins of paper airplanes.

Collins, John M. *The Gliding Flight*. Berkley, Calif.: Ten Speed Press, 1989. Provides tips and techniques on folding and flying paper airplanes. Discusses the theory of paper airplane flight.

Kenneway, Eric. *Complete Origami*. New York: St. Martin's Press, 1987. Provides probable history of paper airplanes. Offers tips and techniques on folding paper airplanes and other origami.

See also: Aerodynamics; Airfoils; Airplanes; Flying Wing; Forces of flight; Model airplanes; Tail designs; Wing designs

Parachutes

Definition: Large, umbrella-like devices attached to people or other objects by ropes called shrouds and used to slow down falls to the ground from aircraft or any other great height.

Significance: Parachutes are the best known devices for emergency escape and descent from endangered aircraft. Their other uses include deploying paratroops; distributing airborne food, supplies, weapons, and assault or other vehicles; decelerating aircraft for landing; recovering space vehicles; and skydiving, or sport parachuting.

Development

A parachute is a very light, flexible device which is intended to retard the passage of an object through Earth's atmosphere to the ground. Parachutes resemble huge umbrellas. They are most frequently used to slow the fall of a human or of other valuable objects from high-flying aircraft or from any other great height, most often ensuring a safe landing. The term "parachute" derives from a French term which means to protect one from a fall or a bad tumble.

The theory of the parachute is credited to the fifteenth century Italian genius Leonardo da Vinci. However, the first practical application of a parachute occurred in the late eighteenth century. At that time, parachutes were used for exhibition purposes in France to allow aeronauts quick descent from gas-filled balloons. By the beginning of World War I, this use had evolved into the application of parachutes as life-saving devices for emergency jumps from damaged aircraft. By the 1920's, parachutes had become familiar devices with widespread military uses, including the dropping of airborne troops (paratroopers), weapons, vehicles, and supplies. Parachutes have developed many additional uses related to peacetime aircraft recovery and to spaceflight.

Operation

Parachute operation is based upon several simple principles of physics. Two forces act on falling objects. These are gravity (or Earth's gravitational force) and air resistance. Gravity pulls any object initially suspended in the atmosphere downward, toward Earth's surface. Air resistance, due to particles of matter in the air, slows a falling object's movement. The pull of gravity is so much stronger than air resistance that the downward speed of a falling object, whether a rock or a human, is only slowed very slightly.

With two objects of the same weight, air resistance is much greater for the one which has the larger surface area. This is because objects of the same weight with large, flat surfaces, such as clay saucers, offer greater areas of resistance to the air than those with small surfaces, such as a clay brick of the same weight as the saucer. Therefore, when an object is shaped like a saucer, it falls more slowly than a sphere of the same weight.

Design and Construction

Parachutes designed for human use are all oblate hemispheres 2 to 3 feet across when open, and of weights ranging between 22 and 30 pounds. Parachutes used to drop cargo are often 100 feet across or larger, and heavier. Parachutes used to decelerate aircraft or spacecraft for landing and recovery are even larger than this. They are also most often used in assembled groups of three or more parachutes. The most common parachute used by humans is the seat pack model associated with a seat in an aircraft. The other kinds of parachutes attach directly to the chest or the back of a wearer.

All parachutes are worn on harnesses. Each parachute harness is made up of a group of straps fitting around the shoulders and the legs of a parachutist. The parachute harness straps connect parachute and parachutist, also supporting the parachutist during descent to the ground. Straps called risers are attached to the shoulder portions of the parachute harnesses to hold the lines, called shrouds, that attach to the parachute canopy. The canopy is the umbrella-like part of the parachute. A rip cord is also attached to a harness strap, usually on the parachutist's left side. It terminates in a ring that the parachutist pulls soon after jumping. Pulling a rip cord causes the parachute canopy and its shrouds to leave their enclosing pack. This process is accomplished by the ejection of a small parachute from the pack. The small chute opens and pulls the larger one out after it. As each canopy leaves the pack, air enters it and causes it to open. All parachutes are carefully folded before insertion into their carry packs. This careful treatment makes sure that the parachute will open properly when the rip cord is pulled by a parachutist.

The initial opening of the canopy can slow down the descent through the air so quickly that the parachutist is jerked sharply upward in "opening shock." To reduce the extent of this opening shock and to stabilize the parachutist's descent, manufacturers use several canopy modifications that lead to a planned canopy air porosity. Often, ribbon canopy material, having planned holes (slots), is used. These slots allow enough airflow through the canopy to reduce air resistance and minimize opening shock. They also help to minimize parachutist sway and maximize comfort during the descent. Another type, the vortex-ring parachute, is composed of four sections that rotate during the descent, functioning like a helicopter rotor to produce maximum parachute stability.

A parachute is most often made of one type of material, usually nylon, silk, cotton, rayon, or a plastic film, although mixed materials are used in some cases. The fiber is turned into cloth for canopies, cord for shrouds, and webbing for harnesses. The most important parachute construction factors include proper air porosity, adequate material strength, good aerodynamic behavior, the lightest weight possible, and easy operation. The materials experimented with and used increase as new fabrication techniques, new artificial polymers, and new fabrics develop.

Parachute Jumping and Parachute Uses

Parachutes are decelerators (or air brakes) that allow parachutists to descend toward Earth at rates of 9 to 11 miles per hour, depending on the parachutist's weight and the canopy's diameter. All parachute jumps made from under 500 feet above ground level are very dangerous because this height does not allow enough distance and time for complete parachute opening. Even safe jumps can lead to parachutists landing with great force, due to the excessive rate of

Nylon in Parachute Construction

Nylon is a synthetic polymer widely used for brush bristles, molded items, and textiles such as those from which parachutes are made. Characterized by great strength, toughness, and elasticity, nylon 66 was developed in the 1930's by scientists working for E.I. du Pont de Nemours & Company. It is made by polymerizing two chemicals called adipic acid and hexamethylenediamine. Another good nylon, nylon-3, is a similar polymer made from an amino acid called 3-aminopropanoate. Nylons are insoluble in water and most other solvents, and nylon 66 melts at 263 degrees Celsius.

To make nylon textile fibers, chips of the nylon polymer, a tough, whitish solid, are melted and pushed through holes in devices called spinnerets. The filaments are then partly solidified by air blown over them. The diameter of the solid filament is controlled by changing the rates at which molten nylon is pumped into a spinneret and at which filaments are pulled away from them. Strong filaments much thinner than those of natural textile fibers can be made from nylon. Nylon can be made to look like silk or can resemble fibers such as cotton. It can be dyed in liquid or filament forms, and its tensile strength is higher than that of wool, silk, rayon, or cotton. A nylon rope or thread can hold up three times as much weight as a steel cable of the same weight.

---

their decelerated fall, and spraining their ankles or breaking bones. This is most often true of jumps over rough terrain. Winds also add to landing dangers, because they engender sideways parachute motion through the air. The addition of this motion to air-braked fall speed causes some landings to seem like jumps from fast-moving automobiles and can cause similar injuries. It is therefore crucial that the parachutist be well trained in how to control a parachute. The other skills needed include a well-honed ability to judge the current wind speed, the altitude, the direction of sideways motion, and potential ground speed. Parachute jumping, or skydiving, nonetheless has become a popular sport that has a great many enthusiasts in Europe and America.

In skydiving, a slow-moving aircraft, cruising at a 2-mile altitude, is used as a jumping platform and skydivers often perform stunts while falling. Sport parachutes are unlike those used for simple descent. Many safety features are removed for ease in maneuvering. Also, the sport parachutes are often designed to be rotated by a control that regulates the direction of air passing through the canopy. In addition, skydivers do not pull their rip cords quickly after leaving the plane. Rather, they use an altimeter, which notes the rate of descent and indicates the last instant when the parachute can be opened safely.

In addition to the classical application of parachutes as devices to carry humans, parachutes are used to deploy paratroops in military assaults; to distribute supplies from aircraft; to slow, as needed, the rates of descent of bombs or flares; to decelerate jet airplanes during their landing; and to recover space vehicles and weather or flight recorders.

Sanford S. Singer

Bibliography

Fechet, James E., Joe Crane, and Glenn H. Smith. *Parachutes*. New York: National Aeronautics Council, 1942. A solid exposition of parachutes, their composition, and their uses.

Hearn, Peter. *The Sky People: A History of Parachuting*. Shrewsbury, England: Airlife, 1990. Contains a great deal of information on parachutes, their uses, and their evolution from the early days.

Lanza, Joseph. *Gravity*. London: Quartet, 1997. An excellent work on gravity and gravitation that also covers topics relating to parachuting.

Lucas, John. *The Big Umbrella*. New York: Drake, 1975. A fine, brief book holding much information on parachutes, their uses, and parachuting.

Poynter, Dan. *The Parachute Manual: A Technical Treatise on Aerodynamic Decelerators*. 4th ed. Santa Barbara, Calif.: Parachuting Publications, 1992. A useful parachuter's manual, discussing parachutes and their aerodynamic properties.

_____. *Parachuting: The Skydivers's Handbook*. 8th ed. Santa Barbara, Calif.: Parachuting Publications, 2000. An interesting book on parachutes, parachuting, and sport parachuting or skydiving.

U.S. Department of the Army. *Organizational and DS Manual for General Maintenance of Parachutes and Other Airdrop Equipment*. Washington, D.C.: Headquarters, Department of the Army, 1996. Part of an ongoing series of manuals, with clear information on parachute and other airdrop maintenance and repair.

See also: Forces of flight; Gravity; Military flight; Skydiving; Spaceflight

Parasailing

Definition: A recreational activity that allows a participant wearing a harness attached to a round parachute to be towed into the air behind an automobile or boat.

Significance: Parasailing is a popular form of recreational flight.

The inventor of parasailing was Pierre Lemoigne of France. In 1961, Lemoigne altered the design of a round parachute to ascend when towed behind an automobile. Parachutists referred to this method of lift as parascending. The development of parascending was triggered from a need of parachute instructors to lower the cost of training a new parachute trainee. Also, parascending allowed the instructor to tow the trainee to a specific altitude, one that would be a suitable dropping height from which the trainee would be released to make a landing on the ground. As this training method became popular, advancements in parascending led Lemoigne to the water. A boat was introduced as the towing vehicle in late 1961 and that introduction led to the renaming of parascending to parasailing.

Beach Method

With increased awareness of parasailing, more individuals were willing to participate not as parachute trainees but as ticket holders for a ride. Parasail concessions began offering rides at beachfront resorts. The parasailing rides offered to vacationers also created safety issues.

Injuries and deaths were connected to parasailing rides in the 1960's as a result of the combination of inexperienced parasail participants and inexperienced concessionaires' flight crews. A participant would be given instructions about the parasail and information on how a person would lift off the ground. The execution of the launch had two elements. First, the participant ran down the beach behind the boat. Second, the boat accelerated as the participant ran until lift was created. After the person was in the air and ready to end the ride, the descent began. The participant was visually instructed to pull certain lines on the parasail to land on the beach.

The beach method of launching and recovering a parasailer may look simplistic on paper, but it is simple only in theory. Injuries, including abrasions, cuts, and broken bones, occurred on launch and recovery. Some parasailers even died. These types of injuries occurred when participants were dragged through the sand during the launch or recovery procedure.

Platform Method

Although accidents occurred using the beach method of parasailing, the recreational sport increased in popularity as the activity evolved the platform method of launch and recovery. In 1971, Mark McCulloch designed a stationary parasail platform. The platform was positioned in a body of water to allow for the launch and recovery of the parasailer. Although platform parasailing was safer for participants, it was more costly to operate than the beach parasailing method because a five-member crew was needed to operate the ride. The beach method needed only a two-member crew for the launch and recovery operation.

Winchboat Method

Two years following the development of the platform method, the winchboat method evolved from it. The platform would no longer be stationary in the water, but was attached to the back of a boat so that it would move. This method allowed the concessionaire to have fewer crew members to operate the ride. By the 1990's, improvements in equipment, crew-member training, and participant awareness had made winchboat parasailing a safe aeronautical activity.

Parasailing has grown to capture the hearts of vacationers everywhere, which has led to an increased demand for the sport. This would not have happened if the beach resorts had not embraced it. Since the 1960's, concessionaires who offer parasail rides to their customers have forced the parasail manufacturers to improve the equipment and the training given to the buyers of the equipment. This has provided a safer environment for both parasailers and ride operators.

Willie Jane Cave-Dunkel

Bibliography

Carminito, David. "The History of Parasailing, the Winchboat, and the Evolution of Skyrider." (www.skyrider.net/history.htm) An excellent article about the history of the recreational sport of parasailing, with technical information about advanced equipment that is being developed for the year 2001 and beyond.

Parasail Safety Council. (www.parasail.org) A World Wide Web site listing methods of launch and recovery and rules and regulations that apply to parasailing.

Will-Harris, Tony. *Hang Gliding and Parasailing*. Minnetonka, Minn.: Capstone Press, 1992. A forty-eight-page, elementary-level illustrated book that includes basic information about parasailing.

See also: Hang gliding and paragliding; Heavier-than-air craft; Parachutes; Safety issues; Skydiving

Passenger regulations

Definition: Government-imposed rules to govern passenger behavior, consumer financial transactions, access to transportation by persons with disabilities, and treatment of victims and relatives after accidents.

Significance: Passenger regulations assist in the safe, secure, and efficient operation of air transportation and generally address three areas: safety and passenger behavior, such as compliance with crew commands, noninterference with performance of flight and cabin operations, and abiding by regulations of smoking and electronic and communications equipment use; consumer financial issues such as fares, fair advertising, refunds, and overbooking; and access to transportation by persons with disabilities.

Underlying Reasons for Passenger Regulations

Passenger regulations have been promulgated over the years to address different problems and the changing needs of both planes and people. Thus, passenger regulations have many origins and are under the jurisdiction of several different government offices. Generally, however, these regulations serve three purposes.

First and foremost is the need for passenger regulations to help ensure the safe operation of aircraft and to aid the crew in the event of an emergency. These passenger regulations generally restrict rights and freedoms that citizens might otherwise have if they were not in an airplane or airport. Such regulations aid in the safe operation of the aircraft and airlines and are found in the Federal Aviation Regulations (FARs), which are part of the U.S. Code of Federal Regulations (CFR). Implementation of these regulations and enforcement are the jobs of the Federal Aviation Administration (FAA). Regulations have the effect of law, and if passengers fail to comply and thereby endanger the safe operation of the aircraft or airport, they can be subject to legal enforcement action, including fines and imprisonment.

Examples of passenger regulations and restrictions of passenger behavior include compliance with orders of the crew regarding seat belt and tray table usage, baggage stowage, no smoking, emergency exit seating restrictions, and other emergency preparations. Passenger interference with air crew duties and engaging in behavior which endangers or harms the plane crew or other passengers, now commonly referred to as air rage, are also prohibited and punishable by fine or imprisonment. Regulations imposing age and physical capability restrictions on who can sit in an emergency exit row were added in response to disasters in which evacuation was hampered by persons unable or unwilling to open emergency exits. The requirements imposed by the Aviation Disaster Family Assistance Act of 1996 sought to remedy abuses and provide more information and assistance to families of crash victims. The act sets forth the obligations of airlines and others in the event of a plane crash, and gives passengers and victims' families rights to information and property after an accident.

The second major body of passenger regulations concerns economic issues. Somewhat like a codification of fair business practices, these passenger regulations are also in the Code of Federal Regulations but are under the jurisdiction of the Department of Transportation Consumer Protection Division. These passenger regulations give passengers some rights to prompt refunds, access to lower fares if available, compensation and substitute transportation arrangements or prompt refund if involuntarily bumped because of overbooking, and the right to have the class and type of service purchased, such as first or business class, and jet aircraft if the ticket was purchased on a jet service flight.

The third major area of passenger regulations guarantees access to and reasonable accommodation in air transportation to persons with disabilities. These regulations forbid airlines to have a policy of denying handicapped persons access to planes and require the airlines to make reasonable accommodations for aids such as wheelchairs, guide dogs and assistance animals, and certain medical equipment. Codified in federal law, the Department of Transportation Consumer Protection Division has oversight, but other federal laws also protect discrimination against persons with disabilities and give other legal remedies to persons with disabilities wrongly denied access to air, as well as any other, public transportation service.

Areas Not Covered by Passenger Regulations

Perhaps the biggest problems that frustrate and confuse passengers and airlines, and cause a great amount of air rage, are issues which are not covered by passenger regulations. In purchases of comparably priced or even less expensive consumer goods or services, consumer protection laws provide customers with warranties and product and service protection guarantees. However, even though airline tickets are more expensive than most other consumer goods and services, the U.S. Congress and the airlines have resisted comparable consumer protection regulations for airline passengers. Airline passengers may be left without remedies for poor service and other complaints, such as failure of airlines to provide passengers timely and truthful information about their flights. The issues typically involve canceled or delayed flights and the provision of hotel rooms, food, and other amenities when a flight is delayed or canceled. Other airline rules address rebooking on the same or another carrier after a flight cancellation or delay, the numbers and size of carry-on and checked luggage, and recovery and temporary assistance in the event of lost or delayed bags. Even though these issues are covered in each airline's rules, these rules are not government regulations and do not have the same force and effect. Furthermore, airline rules are not typically enforced by the federal government, although the Department of Transportation Aviation Consumer Protection Division does accept complaints and publishes a report about the number and nature of complaints against airlines.

The airlines' rules are, however, legally part of the airline's contract of carriage, or the tariff, which governs the terms of a ticket purchase. Failure of a carrier to abide by its own rules is a tariff violation, but passengers rarely bring such a legal action because the costs of doing so usually far outweigh the possible award for a violation of the contract of carriage. Airlines must make their contract of carriage available to any passenger who requests it. An airline's rules are to be available at the airline's airport facility and by mail upon request, and they can be accessed on the World Wide Web.

Mary Fackler Schiavo

Bibliography

Federal Aviation Administration, Aviation Consumer Protection Division. (www.faa.gov/airconsumer) Summarizes regulations, rules and guidelines, accepts complaints and reports of problems, provides an air travel consumer report, and offers advice to passengers. Publications available on line include *Fly Rights*, *New Horizons: Information for the Air Traveler with a Disability*, *Industry Letters—Guidance Regarding Aviation Rules and Statutes*, and a list of other government publications.

Schiavo, Mary. *Flying Blind, Flying Safe*. New York: Avon, 1998. An overview of the U.S. aviation industry and the national aerospace system; several chapters are devoted to passenger regulations and aviation consumer issues.

U.S. Code of Federal Regulations. Washington, D.C.: U.S. Government Printing Office, published annually. Also available on the World Wide Web (www.faa.gov) and at other Web sites. See especially 14 C.F.R. and the sections thereunder.

See also: Air rage; Airline industry, U.S.; Federal Aviation Administration; Safety issues

Pearl Harbor, Hawaii, bombing

Date: December 7, 1941
Definition: Aerial attacks conducted by Japanese aircraft above on the U.S. fleet at Pearl Harbor, Oahu, Hawaii.
Significance: The Japanese attack on Pearl Harbor left two-thirds of the U.S. military aircraft stationed there destroyed or disabled and killed more than 2,400 servicemen. The Pearl Harbor bombing immediately drew the United States into World War II and opened up the Pacific theater of war.

Background

The Pearl Harbor attack represented the culmination of a decade of deteriorating relations between the United States and Japan over the status of China and the security of Southeast Asia. Since the early 1900's, Japanese military leaders had been gradually expanding their territory within the Asian mainland, as military extremists had overrun the northernmost Chinese province of Manchuria in 1931 without consent of the Japanese civil government. Upheavals within the infrastructure of the Japanese government became an ongoing and constant occurrence, most notably evidenced by repeated attempts by the civil government to exert more control over the previously independent Japanese military. Japanese generals began to resent receiving armed forces orders from bureaucrats rather than directly from the emperor, as had been the tradition.

Many Japanese military leaders felt that Nazi Germany's 1940 defeat of France, Britain, and the Netherlands had left Japanese territories in Southeast Asia exposed to invasion. As Japan joined Germany in the Axis alliance, many Japanese military leaders focused on the ambitious goal of establishing an empire that would be immune to economic sanctions, such as the oil embargo by which the United States was attempting to curtail Japan's expansion into China. As both the United States and Japan publicly established positions from which they could not retreat without loss of international prestige, Japanese generals plotted to attack Pearl Harbor as a preemptive strike to gain command of the western Pacific.

Although the Japanese had formally declared war on China in 1937 and the nations of Europe had launched

The Japanese bombing of the U.S. Naval Base at Pearl Harbor, on the island of Oahu, Hawaii, on December 7, 1941, brought the United States into World War II. (Digital Stock)

World War II in September of 1939, the United States had remained uninvolved in both conflicts. The American public, previously divided over U.S. entry into World War II, rallied together after the bombing of Pearl Harbor in commitment toward victory over Japan and its Axis partners. The aviation industry then received considerable focus as it became obvious that victory would come to whichever side controlled the skies.

U.S. Entry into World War II

On Sunday, December 7, 1941, 7:50 A.M., Japanese carrier-borne aircraft attacked Pearl Harbor, prompting the entry of the United States into World War II. In fewer than two hours, 365 Japanese aircraft flying from 33 warships and auxiliary craft temporarily crippled the U.S. Pacific fleet. After the smoke cleared, fewer than 80 of the 231 operational aircraft assigned to the Hawaiian Air Force were flyable.

In two successive waves, Japanese bombers, torpedo planes, and fighters either sunk or disabled eighteen U.S. ships. Commander Mitsuo Fuchida sent the coded messages "To, To, To" and "Tora, Tora, Tora," telling the Japanese fleet that a complete surprise attack had been accomplished.

More than 200 U.S. aircraft, most of them still grounded, were either destroyed or heavily damaged, along with six land air bases. Seven of the Pacific fleet's nine battleships were lined up unsuspectingly in the harbor along "Battleship Row," on the Northeast shore of Ford Island. The battleships USS *West Virginia*, USS *California*, and USS *Nevada* were sunk in shallow water, the USS *Oklahoma* was capsized, and the USS *Arizona* became a nonfunctional wreck, with 1,177 crew members killed. U.S. losses included 2,117 Navy and Marine Corps dead, 218 Army dead, and 68 civilians dead, in addition to 1,300 wounded and 1,000 temporarily missing in the resulting chaos. Five minutes after the first Japanese bomb landed, U.S. antiaircraft fire began to register hits, although many American shells actually fell on Honolulu, where civilians initially assumed them to be Japanese bombs. U.S. Army Air Corps pilots managed to get a few fighters into the air and shoot down twelve enemy planes before the second wave of Japanese warcraft entered the area at 8:40 A.M. Japanese losses included only 55 casualties, 5 midget submarines that had attempted simultaneously to enter Pearl Harbor and launch torpedoes, and 29 of the 365 planes that made the attack.

Pearl Harbor, Hawaii, bombing

Japanese Air Strategy

Immediately after General Hideki Tojo took on the premiership of the Japanese empire in October, 1941, other military leaders warned him that only the U.S. Navy had the power to block Japanese expansion into Asia. The plan to cripple the U.S. Pacific fleet in one massive blow was deliberately masked behind false statements by Japanese representatives that implied their hope for continued peace with America. Japan was aware at the time of the bombing that Pearl Harbor functioned as a base to more than 75 U.S. warships, including battleships, cruisers, destroyers, submarines, and auxiliaries. What Japan did not know at the time, however, was that all U.S. aircraft carriers, essentially floating platforms from which air operations at sea were launched, were not then stationed in Hawaii, and that these carriers would later prove crucial to U.S. success in the Pacific.

The Japanese attack was devised and commanded by Admiral Isoroku Yamamoto, commander in chief of the Japanese combined fleet and one of Japan's stronger air power advocates. Although personally opposed to war with the United States at the time, Yamamoto knew that the success of the Pearl Harbor bombing was dependent upon a quick and silent attack. The U.S. military was not totally surprised by the possibility of a Japanese attack in the Pacific, although the bombing was essentially a complete shock to American civilians. However, U.S. leaders were embarrassingly caught off guard by Japan's unexpected ability to quickly achieve such a long-range air strike.

On November 26, six Japanese aircraft carriers, two battleships, three cruisers, eleven destroyers, and several tankers, carrying a total of 365 combat aircraft, had departed in secret from the Kuril Islands under the command of Vice Admiral Chuichi Nagumo. Their launching position 275 miles north of Hawaii was reached at 6:00 A.M. on December 7. By 7:55 A.M., the first of two waves of Japanese planes struck Pearl Harbor, bom-

Japanese Attacks on Pearl Harbor and the Central Pacific, December, 1941

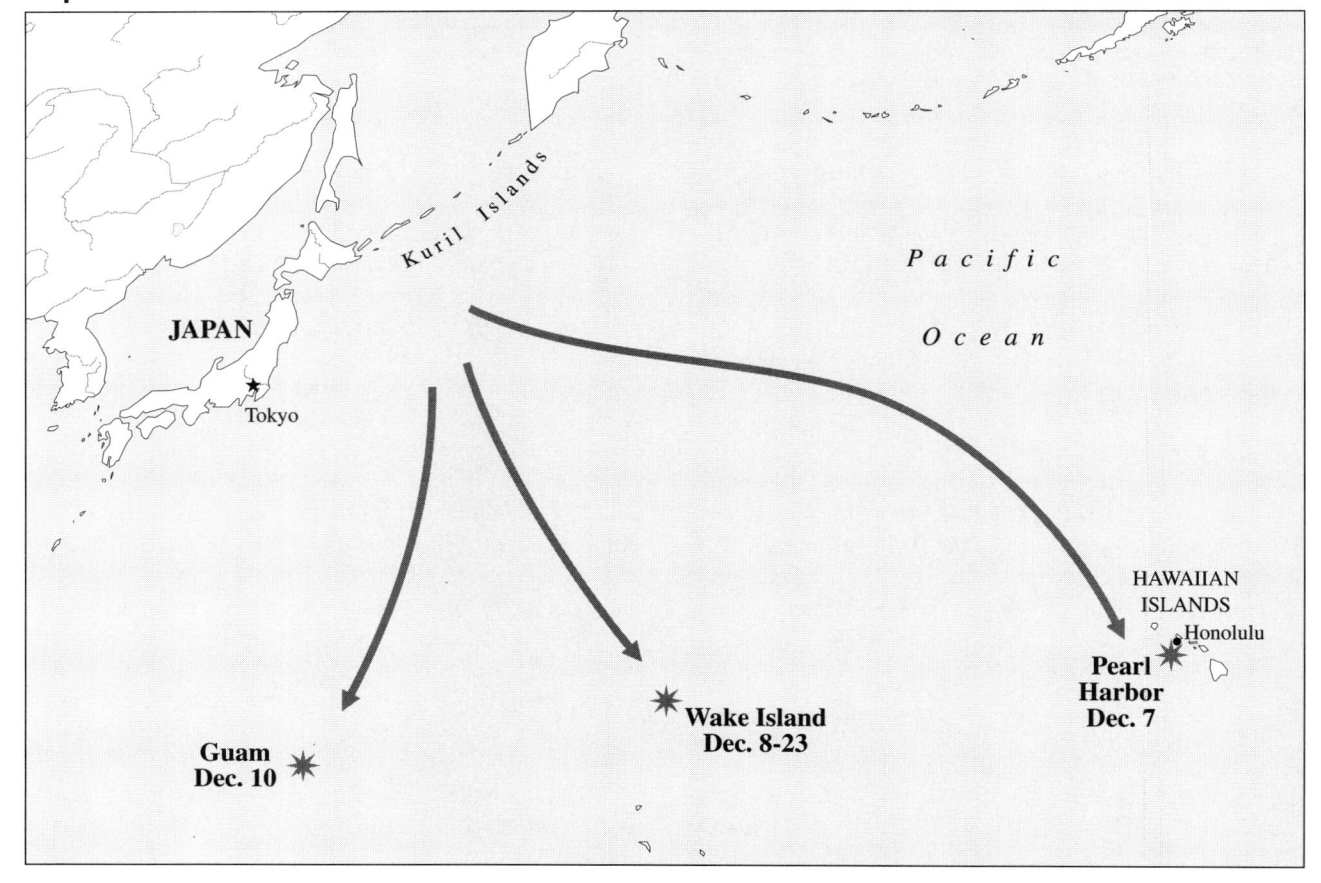

barding airfields and battleships moored at the concrete quays.

The Pearl Harbor bombing was just one of a series of Japanese strikes throughout the Far East. Almost simultaneously, Japanese naval and air forces attacked Wake Island, Guam, British Malaya, Singapore, the Dutch East Indies, Burma, Thailand, and the Philippine Islands, destroying many U.S. land-based combat aircraft in the Pacific. Japanese troops later occupied Siam with the consent of that government.

Japan's clear intention in attacking Pearl Harbor was to disable the U.S. fleet and reduce opposition against their war of conquest across the eastern Pacific. After Pearl Harbor, Japanese ambassadors publicly accused the United States of standing in the way of their "new order in East Asia." The destruction of Allied sea power in the Pacific would win Japan access to Malaya, the East Indies, and other Southeast Asian areas, which all had supplies of raw materials the Japanese felt would ensure their success in future World War II battles.

U.S. Retaliatory Strategy

The Pearl Harbor bombing was described the following day by President Franklin D. Roosevelt as "a date which will live in infamy." Two and one-half hours after the surprise attack, Japan declared war on the United States and Great Britain. The following morning, Roosevelt called on the U.S. Congress formally to declare war on Japan. On the afternoon of December 8, 1941, the United States, Canada, and Great Britain declared war on Japan, and on the next day, China declared war on the Axis powers. On December 11, Germany and Italy, bound by treaty to Japan, declared war on the United States. World War II had become a global conflict. Although Honolulu was the only U.S. city to be attacked, the U.S. Army proclaimed martial law in fear of an invasion attempt, the act of which was later found to be unconstitutional by the Supreme Court. Not until October, 1944, was the civil government of the United States officially restored.

Because the United States had expected any potential Japanese aggression first to take place in the Philippines or Southeast Asia, no U.S. aircraft carriers were in port in Pearl Harbor on December 7, 1941. These carriers would later prove crucial to U.S. military success in the Pacific. Although the Pearl Harbor bombing was initially a tremendous success for the Japanese, it enraged a vast majority of Americans enough to show immediate public support for entry into World War II. Also significant was the fact that the Japanese had failed to destroy the vast oil supply adjacent to Pearl Harbor, thus leaving a significant fuel supply for American ships and planes.

Although many Japanese-Americans and persons of Japanese birth were interned, a vast majority of Asian-Americans worked peaceably on the plantations and on construction projects. Many Hawaiian-born Japanese-American troops achieved a notable combat record in Italy during the war.

Aircraft Development

Historians often note that nothing speeds up the development of machinery and technology in the aviation industry faster than war or even the threat of war. At the time of the bombing, the U.S. Army Air Force had only 1,100 combat-ready aircraft. By 1944, the Army Air Force had nearly 80,000 combat aircraft in sixteen separate air forces stationed around the world. U.S. airplane technology went through more changes immediately following the initial events of World War II than during the previous two decades of peace. The best piston-engine fighters developed during World War II were able to reach speeds of 460 miles per hour, nearly twice the speed of previous biplanes. The B-29 was America's most effective combat aircraft against both land- and sea-based antiaircraft guns and enemy fighters in the sky. As piston-engine planes reached their full potential, jet-propelled aircraft began to be developed. The economy of the aviation industry turned into a war machine, utilizing manpower and materials at record levels, as the Allied and Axis powers raced against time and each other.

Daniel G. Graetzer

Bibliography

Christy, Joe. *American Aviation: An Illustrated History*. Blue Ridge Summit, Pa.: Tab Books, 1987. An excellent review text on U.S. aviation history, with interesting insights into the past and potential future of air warfare.

Condon, John Pomeroy. *Corsairs and Flattops: Marine Carrier Air Warfare, 1944-1945*. Annapolis, Md.: Naval Institute Press, 1997. An account of the pilots and crews who pioneered air support in the World War II-ending defeat of Japan, with emphasis on warcraft technology stimulated by the Pearl Harbor attack and in battles such as Iwo Jima, Okinawa, Indochina, the Philippines, and Tokyo.

Cooksley, Peter G., and Bruce Robertson. *Air Warfare: The Encyclopedia of Twentieth Century Conflict*. London: Arms and Armour Press, 1998. A chronology of significant events, inventions, and aeronautic milestones in armed flight.

Donald, David, ed. *The Complete Encyclopedia of World Aircraft*. New York: Barnes and Noble Books, 1997. A superb text with essays that examine the critical role of air power in international security by looking systematically at strategy and targeting, with photos, drawings, and statistics on essentially every airplane ever constructed.

Matricardi, Paolo. *The Concise History of Aviation, 1903 to Present*. New York: Crescent Books, 1984. A nontraditional view of the history and evolution of aviation, with an excellent chapter on aircraft utilized throughout World War II.

Price, Alfred. *Sky Battles: Dramatic Air Warfare Battles*. Dulles, Va.: Continuum International, 1999. A fascinating text for the lay reader that sensationally and accurately lives up to its title.

See also: Air force, U.S.; Aircraft carriers; Antiaircraft fire; Navy pilots, U.S.; Kamikaze missions; Military flight; Superfortress; World War II

Auguste Piccard

Date: Born on January 28, 1884, in Basel, Switzerland; died on March 24, 1962, in Lausanne, Switzerland

Definition: Physicist noted for explorations in both the upper atmosphere and in the ocean.

Significance: Piccard pioneered the development of pressurized airtight compartments. His design became the basis for such structures in modern airplanes.

Auguste Piccard was among the most prominent members of a family devoted to scholarship. His father, Jules Piccard, was a professor of chemistry at the University of Basel. Auguste's twin, Jean, earned a degree in chemistry and eventually held positions at several universities.

Piccard early developed a fascination for science. As a child, he was interested in the biology of the oceans; eventually this led him to design a ship to study ocean depths. Piccard enrolled in the Swiss Federal Institute of Technology in Zurich, studying physics. In 1904, he published his first scientific paper.

In 1910, Piccard was awarded a degree in mechanics from the institute, becoming a member of its faculty. He soon developed a gauge for measuring air pressure, and participated in his first balloon ride into the lower atmosphere. In 1914, he was awarded a doctorate by the institute.

Piccard's research during this period dealt with the study of cosmic rays. His appointment as a professor of applied physics at the University of Brussels in 1922 provided him with the opportunity to combine his expertise in mechanics and engineering with such study. A major difficulty in the observation of cosmic rays was caused by their absorption by the atmosphere. Piccard reasoned that if one could travel into the upper reaches of the atmosphere, interference could be negated. The low atmospheric pressure at such heights, however, had proven fatal to those who had made such attempts. With funding provided by the Belgian government, Piccard designed a pressurized, airtight cabin in a balloon, which would allow penetration into the stratosphere.

On May 27, 1931, Piccard and his assistant Paul Kipfer reached an altitude of 51,762 feet. Unable to release enough hydrogen to land, Piccard and Kipfer waited until sundown, when the cooler temperature allowed the balloon to land on an Austrian glacier; altogether, they were in the air approximately seventeen hours. On August 18, 1932, Piccard and Max Cosyns made a second ascent into the stratosphere in a redesigned cabin, reaching a height of 61,221 feet.

In the late 1930's, Piccard began the design of a bathyscaphe (a navigable submersible) that could be used to study the ocean depths. Interrupted by World War II, Piccard did not complete his design until 1948. In 1953, Piccard, accompanied by his son Jacques, made a dive to a depth of over 10,000 feet. Piccard retired from the University of Brussels in 1954, returning to Switzerland, where he died in 1962.

Richard Adler

Bibliography

Field, Adelaide. *Auguste Piccard: Captain of Space, Admiral of the Abyss*. Boston: Houghton Mifflin, 1969. A juvenile biography of Piccard.

Honour, Alan. *Ten Miles High, Two Miles Deep: The Adventures of the Piccards*. New York: Whitlsey House, 1957. A biography relating the exploits of both Auguste and his brother Jean.

Piccard, Auguste. *Between Earth and Sky*. Translated by Claude Apcher. London: Falcon Press, 1950. Firsthand account of Piccard's work and record-setting ascents. Written as a popular account for the layperson.

_____. *In Balloon and Bathyscaphe*. London: Cassell, 1956. A more detailed account of Piccard's work and career.

See also: Aerodynamics; Balloons; Buoyant aircraft; Heavier-than-air craft; High-altitude flight; History of human flight; Lighter-than-air craft

Pilots and copilots

Definition: Pilots are the men and women in command of flying aircraft. Helping pilots are their assistants, copilots, also known as first officers.

Significance: Pilots and copilots are the people who take an aircraft where it needs to go. Whether amateur or professional, they must demonstrate their mastery of the skills needed to fly an aircraft and obtain licensing before they are allowed to fly solo. The pilot and copilot are responsible not only for their own safety but also the safety of their passengers, of others flying near them, and those on the ground beneath them.

The majority of pilots are hard-working men and women who work in an office in the sky. It is a mobile, dynamic working environment. Although the skills necessary to pilot a plane are many and the responsibilities great, with proper training almost anyone can learn to fly.

Requirements

For those aspiring to the professional track, there are many different jobs in the aviation industry, such as military pilots, charter pilots, and flight instructors. There are also jobs flying the bush in Alaska and Canada; fish spotting off the coast all around North America; towing gliders and aerial signs; or flying sightseers and photographers.

Pilots do not have to be perfect specimens of health. Some pilots fly challenged by shortcomings such as impaired hearing, paralysis, and even the loss of a limb. However, those who fly must meet certain minimum health standards. For example, they must be able to see and they must have normal cardiovascular function. Although some medical situations will prevent people from working as professional pilots, many can still fly their own aircraft.

As a private pilot, there is some relief from the pressure of medical examinations. A working airline transport pilot, for instance, must undergo a complete flight physical every six months. Professional pilots under a Commercial Pilot Certificate have a physical examination by an authorized medical examiner once each year. Private pilots are required to undergo a physical once every three years before their fortieth birthday and once every two years after they turn forty.

Pilots are not required to have college degrees. However, professional piloting positions on the high end of the scale require individuals to have completed their baccalaureate degree or, in some cases, a graduate degree. For a Private Pilot Certificate, the only educational requirement is that one be able to read, speak, and understand the English language. An applicant for the private pilot license must be seventeen years of age for certification by the Federal Aviation Administration (FAA).

The equivalent of a high school education will provide the required background to develop the skills and knowledge required in becoming a private pilot. After private pilot certification, if a pilot decides to pursue advanced ratings and a commercial pilot's license, formal study in the fields of aviation, math, and physics will be helpful, but not required. The military services require a college degree of pilot candidates. In the airline industry, baccalaureate degrees are preferred but may not be required, depending on the pilot situation. Fluctuations in the pool of available pilots may also affect the minimum education requirements for professional pilots; in times of pilot shortage, college degree requirements may be waived, while in times of pilot abundance, requirements become more stringent.

Becoming a Private Pilot

The first step in becoming a pilot is taking flying lessons. These rather simple lessons culminate in a written test, an oral test, and a flight check that allows the student to fly as a private pilot. The Private Pilot Certificate allows one to fly throughout U.S. airspace, with a few exceptions.

The first step in the process is to find a good flight instructor at a smaller airport. It is far preferable to fly at a smaller airport than at one used by the airlines and other larger aircraft. With less traffic, the student pilot and the flight instructor can devote more time to teaching and learning than waiting for a takeoff clearance.

After meeting a flight instructor for the first time, the new student will be able to go flying on an introductory ride. This is an important flight, in that it allows the potential student to taste the flavor of flight without becoming too financially committed. Upon completion of the first flight, the student can then start thinking about consigning more time and funds to the process of obtaining a pilot certificate.

The investment of time and money required for a pilot certificate will vary. The requirement in terms of flight experience is only forty hours, according to the FAA. Typically, an average student is going to spend about fifty

Pilots and copilots

Estimated Number of Active Pilot Certificates Held, 1987-1996

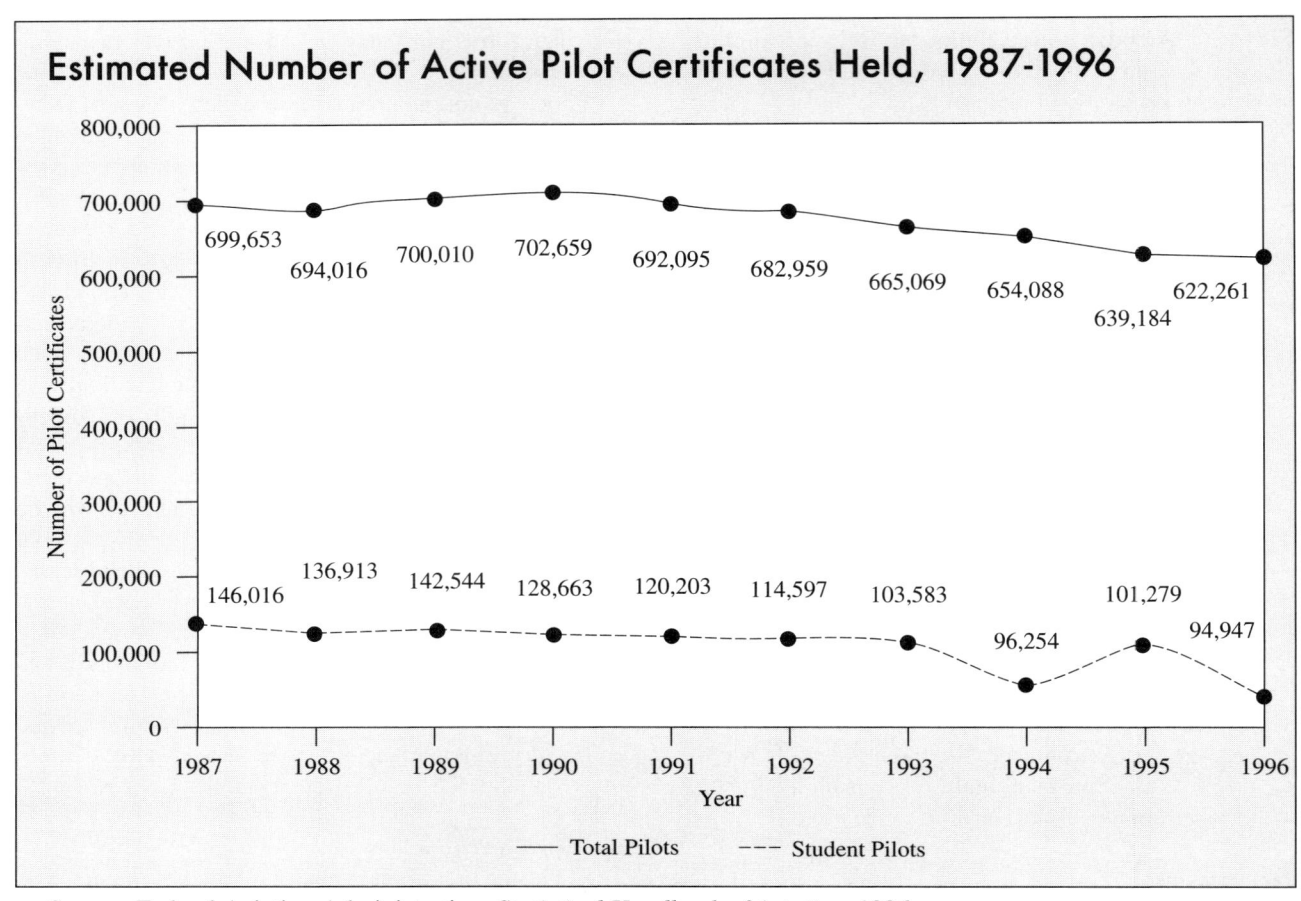

Year	Total Pilots	Student Pilots
1987	699,653	146,016
1988	694,016	136,913
1989	700,010	142,544
1990	702,659	128,663
1991	692,095	120,203
1992	682,959	114,597
1993	665,069	103,583
1994	654,088	96,254
1995	639,184	101,279
1996	622,261	94,947

Source: Federal Aviation Administration, *Statistical Handbook of Aviation*, 1996.

hours flying for a private license. Of this, approximately half will be with a flight instructor while the other half will be alone, or solo.

Regarding the costs, as of 2001 in the United States, typical two-seat training aircraft rented in the range of $50 to $65 an hour. Therefore, fifty hours of private pilot training curriculum would entail rental costs ranging from $2,500 to $3,250. Flight instructor fees also vary. A young flight instructor, just starting out in the industry, may charge a fee of $15 per hour. A more established flight instructor may charge a fee approaching $50 per hour. The combined rental and instructional fees, therefore, can run from approximately $2,900 to $4,500. To this must be added flight check fees, incidentals, and supplies.

During the course of training, the student will fly the first ten to twenty hours with the flight instructor. During this time, the student learns the rudiments of flying and the flight instructor makes certain the neophyte has learned enough to stay out of trouble while flying alone.

Solo is the pivotal point in a new pilot's life. The first solo occurs at some time in the first twenty hours of flight training. After soloing, the student will fly in the local area for practice, becoming more comfortable with the airplane and flying.

After this solo practice, the instructor will again join the student for cross-country (X-C) training. In other words, the student will learn how to fly from one airport to another. The instructor will teach the student how to read charts, use navigational tools, and find the way from one place on the earth to the next. After proving proficient in these tasks, the student will fly ten hours of solo cross-country flights.

After completing the solo X-C requirements, the student is back with the flight instructor for the final preparations for the private pilot check ride. During this final phase of training, the student will learn rudimentary instrument flying skills, advanced stalls, and other maneuvers.

The test has written, oral, and flight elements. The written test is taken first. When this portion is passed, the student meets the designated examiner for a two-hour talk about flying. After passing the oral portion of the flight check, the student and examiner will climb into the airplane and fly. At the completion of the flight, the paperwork is completed and a license issued. Now comes the next monumental flight in the career of a pilot: flying with passengers.

After obtaining a Private Pilot Certificate, the new pilot may stop there or continue training. One step would be to work on obtaining Instrument Rating, certification that allows the pilot to fly without reference to the outside world. This is the most practical rating in that when the weather is not perfect, the instrument-rated pilot can take off and fly through the clouds. Another rating is the Commercial Pilot Certificate, which allows the pilot to work as a professional pilot. A Multiengine Rating allows operation of an airplane with more than one engine.

The highest pilot certificate, which comes after attaining a total of 1,500 hours of experience, is the Airline Transport Pilot Certificate, or ATP. Pilots who hold the ATP are usually working pilots who will eventually go on to become professional airline pilots.

Airline Pilots

Aviators include everyone on the aircraft who has a job to do. Members of the crew perform their duties in one of two areas, the cockpit or the cabin. Personnel in the cabin include the flight or cabin attendants. Members of the cockpit crew include the pilot, the first officer or copilot, and if the aircraft requires a flight engineer, the second officer.

Flight engineers and copilots usually are younger aviators building time and experience on the way to the captain's seat. The usual career path for an airline pilot begins with flying smaller aircraft in the charter business or as a flight instructor. After gaining experience and logging flight time to increase competitiveness, the next step is application to a commuter airline. Commuter airlines fly smaller aircraft that carry between twenty and fifty passengers. The young pilot begins as a first officer under the eye of an experienced captain. The new pilot will serve in this capacity for two or three years.

Advancement to captain requires additional training and examinations, and certification to act as the pilot-in-command. Service as a commuter captain continues for another period of time in which skills and knowledge are further developed. This makes the pilot more marketable to the large air carriers.

Airline pilots often say that they have the best job in the world. Those who achieve a position with a major airline work approximately twelve to fifteen days a month. For the few days they work, they enjoy good pay and benefits. In 2001, salaries for jumbojet captains were in the $150,000 to $300,000 range. Of course, pilots do not begin at that pay scale. The beginning flight instructor, working toward the goal of becoming an airline captain, may realize an annual salary of $12,000 to $25,000. Charter and corporate pilots fare better than flight instructors. A few charter jobs command higher pay than does flight instructing, whereas some corporate pilot salaries rival that of the airline captain.

Corporate Pilots

Pilots wanting greater security than that provided by flying charter flights, but who desire to avoid the rigidity of an airline position, often opt for employment with a corporate flight department. In this industry, pilots can find a company of the proper size to fit their requirements, such as a specific location or type of aircraft. The company may own only one aircraft, or it could operate a fleet of executive jets.

Like other positions in aviation, corporate aviation has advantages and disadvantages. On the plus side, pilots may fly into more varied destinations, avoiding the boredom of flying the same route over and over, as in airline flying. Corporate pilots tend to fly one or two aircraft of the same make, enabling them to become intimately familiar with their aircraft. An advantage or disadvantage, depending on the individual, is the ability to return home at night, or stay out on the road. Single pilots tend to request overnight trips while older, more established pilots may seek the short, out-and-in hops.

Military Pilots

Flying tactical jets is probably one of the most exciting jobs in the world for an aviation enthusiast. Military pilots may eventually become airline pilots, but for the time being, these young men and women are flying the most advanced fighters in the inventory.

All military pilots are college graduates, although they need not have studied aeronautical engineering or acquired degrees in aviation. After graduation, the prospective military pilot attends Officer Candidate School, a course of study lasting approximately twelve weeks. Upon graduation and commissioning in their respective branch of service, they receive orders to flight training.

Flight training takes one to two years, depending on the branch of service. New flight students go through primary flight training, where they gain their first introduction to airplanes. Unlike their civilian counterparts in the airlines, military pilots can start out in training knowing absolutely nothing about aviation. After primary training, students step up to more complex aircraft in intermediate training. Finally, in advanced training, they fly highly sophisticated jet trainers. When the training is complete, newly winged aviators go on to train in the tactical aircraft to which they have orders. At completion of training in a particular aircraft and weapons systems, they are posted to stations in defense of the country.

Flight Instructors

Flight instruction, or teaching others to fly, is the most important job in aviation. As with the teaching profession in general, the financial rewards may be less than deserved, yet many instructors realize rewards that go far beyond the financial. A flight instructor has some of the greatest responsibilities in the aviation industry.

Flight instructors are often young fliers just starting their aviation careers. They use flight instructing positions to develop themselves as aviators while building experience and logging flight time. This group of pilots is an enthusiastic lot, eager to learn, eager to teach, impatient to get on with their flying careers. That creates the possible drawback of younger flight instructors. Sometimes they are too eager to begin careers with airlines and will leave students in the middle of their training to take a more prestigious flying job elsewhere. Older flight instructors, on the other hand, may be content to stay where they are, enjoying the experience of passing their knowledge on by training new pilots.

Joseph F. Clark III

Bibliography

Anderson, David F., and Scott Eberhardt. *Understanding Flight*. New York: McGraw-Hill, 2000. Written by authors who are both scientists and pilots, this book explains the theories behind flight that are relevant to flying a plane.

Bergman, Jules. *Anyone Can Fly*. 3d ed. Garden City, N.Y.: Doubleday, 1986. This text is an outstanding explanation of aviation and learning how to fly. Written for the beginner, it is very easy to understand and explains flight in simple terms.

Langewiesche, Wolfgang. *Stick and Rudder: An Explanation of the Art of Flying*. 7th ed. New York: Tab Books, 1990. Hailed as the most important book on aviation, this text explains basic principles of flight in a simple manner.

Maher, Gay D. *The Joy of Learning to Fly*. New York: Delacorte Press/Eleanor Friede, 1978. Well-written text regarding what one has to do in learning how to fly. Examines everything from flight instructor personalities to airwork to ground reference maneuvers.

See also: Airline industry, U.S.; Airplanes; Commercial flight; Federal Aviation Administration; Marine pilots, U.S.; Military flight; Navy pilots, U.S.; Test pilots; Training and education

Piper aircraft

Definition: Piper aircraft are small airplanes intended for the general aviation market. Many are owned by amateur pilots who fly as a hobby.

Significance: The term Piper has become synonymous with small personal aircraft. Thousands of pilots, both amateur and professional, enjoyed their first flying experience in a Piper Cub, a small single-engine fixed-wing aircraft.

Beginning in the early 1930's, the Piper Aircraft Corporation aggressively promoted low-cost amateur aviation as a way to increase aircraft sales. As a result, thousands of people obtained pilots' licenses. Many of those people eventually bought airplanes. Between 1935 and 1984, Piper Aircraft built and sold over 77,000 airplanes.

In addition, Piper aircraft have proven to be well designed and highly useful in a variety of settings. Pipers were used extensively as trainers during World War II, with approximately 80 percent of all U.S. military pilots beginning their flight training in Piper L-4's. Pipers were also used in both the European and Pacific combat theaters as reconnaissance aircraft, where their small size and agility made them almost impossible to shoot down. The Pipers were able to fly so low and slow that fighter aircraft could not pursue them safely.

Early History

The Piper Aircraft company took its name from a most unlikely founder. William T. Piper has gone down in history as "the Henry Ford of aviation," but acquired the title almost by accident. Piper, born January 18, 1881, in Knapps Creek, New York, apparently had little interest in aviation prior to purchasing $400 worth of stock in the Taylor Brothers aircraft company in the 1920's. Piper, a Harvard graduate, had worked in the construction industry in Texas and as an oil company executive in Pennsylvania prior to becoming active in Taylor Brothers. Historians of the Piper company describe Piper as being pushed by civic leaders in Bradford, Pennsylvania, in 1929 to serve on the board of Taylor Brothers to help protect the city's investment. Bradford city officials had invested $50,000 in Taylor Brothers as an inducement to the firm to set up its aircraft manufacturing facility in their town. The local oil industry was in decline, and city officials were trying to attract new businesses to town to provide jobs for area workers.

At the time, Taylor manufactured a two-seater airplane known as the Chummy. The Chummy sold for $4,000, a price that William Piper considered too high. Taylor was aiming for the luxury market; Piper believed the path to financial success lay in designing and building a plane that anyone could buy. Taylor wanted to develop planes that would sell for $10,000 or more, while Piper wanted to go in the other direction. Piper was quoted as saying he wanted the airplane to become as accessible to the average person as the automobile.

Piper was convinced that an economical personal aircraft could be built using the assembly line techniques pioneered in the auto industry. He used salvaged materials from Ferris wheels and other scrap to create the jigs and fixtures necessary for mass production and pushed to develop a plane that could sell for under $1,000. A myth persists that the original Piper Cubs sold for $999. This is not quite true, but it is close: in 1931, the company began marketing the E-2 Cub, an inexpensive, small, easy-to-fly aircraft that sold for many years for only $1,350.

Piper's salesmen promoted flying by inviting would-be pilots first to Bradford and later to Lock Haven to take flying lessons for only $1 an hour. Every potential licensed pilot was seen as a potential customer. Piper employees were also encouraged to take advantage of the inexpensive lessons, with the result that at one time one out of every ninety people in town was a licensed pilot. A novice to aviation himself prior to becoming involved with Taylor Brothers, William Piper earned his private pilot's license several years after taking control of the company. Although some accounts describe him as learning to fly at the age of 60, he was actually slightly younger, in his early fifties.

Piper in the 1930's

In 1932, Piper hired a young aeronautical engineer, Walter Jamouneau. Jamouneau produced a fictitious resume claiming a degree from Rutgers University, but Piper hired him anyway. Jamouneau's credentials may have been dubious, but his engineering talents were not. He eliminated the E-2's boxy silhouette, giving it a more rounded profile and streamlined appearance. These design changes became a source of friction between Piper and Gilbert Taylor. In the end, Piper modified the E-2 Cub to the point where it became known as the J-2, after Jamouneau. In 1937, the J-3 Cub appeared. This was the plane that changed the face of general aviation.

At the same time that Piper and Taylor clashed over aircraft designs and the company's direction, the effects of the economic depression beginning in 1929 were being felt. The initial capital raised through the sale of stock was exhausted, Taylor was in debt to the bank for $15,000, and no new investors could be found. Taylor Brothers was forced into bankruptcy. No one bid on the company's assets. Piper acquired them for $761 and gave a half interest to Taylor.

As the company struggled to survive the Great Depression of the 1930's and to market the Cub, the friction between Piper and Taylor increased. Piper eventually bought out Taylor's interest in exchange for payments of $250 per month for three years and the promise to maintain the payments on Taylor's life insurance.

In 1937, the company suffered a disastrous fire at the Bradford plant. Debris soaked with highly flammable aircraft dope in the paint room ignited. The source of the fire was later traced to sparks from an electric drill. The plant was a total loss. The building had been uninsured. Money was tight, so Piper decided to do a public stock offering to raise the money necessary to rebuild. At the same time, due to a lackluster response from the city of Bradford toward helping with rebuilding, Piper decided to move the assembly plant. A company salesman told Piper about a former textile mill located next to an airstrip that was available in Lock Haven, so that was where Piper moved. It would remain the main Piper manufacturing facility for almost fifty years. The company name was changed to Piper Aircraft at the time of the move.

World War II

As the political situation in Europe worsened in the late 1930's, U.S. president Franklin D. Roosevelt pushed for the creation of the Civilian Pilot Training program. He and his advisors feared that in the event of war, the United States would not have enough trained pilots ready. Piper Cubs became the most common airplane used for flying lessons, with four out of five new pilots being trained in them. Thousands of American military pilots first learned to fly in a Piper, including future astronaut and senator John Glenn.

When the United States entered World War II in 1941, many military men were at first skeptical of the value of small aircraft outside of pilot training facilities. As the war progressed, however, doubters were won over. The Piper L-4, the military version of the J-4 Coupe, was used for reconnaissance in Europe and Asia. In addition to serving as scouts, Pipers were used to drop supplies such as food, ammunition, and blood plasma to ground troops. William Piper, Jr., later noted that turning Piper Cubs into military aircraft was easy—all that was required was a drab coat of camouflage paint and a J-4 became an L-4.

Postwar Years

Following the war, a boom in personal aviation occurred. Piper produced 8,000 Piper Cubs and Super Cruisers to meet pent-up demand. Competing companies, such as Beech and Cessna, also increased production. For a few years it seemed as though companies could not manufacture small airplanes fast enough to satisfy the market in general aviation. It has been estimated that over three dozen new aircraft manufacturing companies entered the market between 1945 and 1947. Piper established an assembly plant in Ponca City, Oklahoma. Then, just as quickly as the boom had appeared, it vanished. By 1948, sales numbers were dropping and the companies that had emerged to compete with Piper only two or three years earlier began vanishing as quickly as they had been formed.

William T. Piper, Jr., recognized the flying public wanted a different type of airplane than the original Piper Cub. The Cub was ideal for sport flying, that is, for short excursions leaving and returning to the same airport, and for training student pilots. As a two-seater, however, the Cub was simply too small for any distance flying. Piper Aircraft Corporation had acquired Consolidated Vultee's Stinson Aircraft division in 1948. The Stinson assets included a design study for a twin-engine, four-passenger airplane. Piper waited four years, and in 1952 came out with the prototype for the Apache. The prototype had a twin-fintail design which performed poorly in flight testing. It was replaced with a more conventional tail, and went into full production shortly thereafter. Piper began delivering Apaches, which handled well even in stormy weather, in March, 1954.

Beginning in 1960, the Apache was replaced by the Aztec, an aircraft with more powerful engines than its predecessor. The Aztec B had seating for six, and subsequent models introduced improvements such as fuel injection and turbocharging. Piper stopped production of the Aztec in 1984. By the 1960's, the corporate executive market was supplanting personal aviation. Piper responded with the Navajo, Mohave, and Cheyenne aircraft. Fully pressurized, the Cheyenne IV was capable of cruising at 400 miles per hour at an altitude of 40,000 feet. Although Piper is best known for its passenger aircraft, the company also developed the Pawnee PA-25, an airplane designed for use in crop dusting.

William T. Piper, Sr., died in 1970, shortly after a hostile corporate takeover of the Piper Aircraft Corporation in 1969. The Piper family lost direct control of the company, but Piper aircraft continue to be manufactured. Plagued by a variety of management woes and financial problems, Piper Aircraft almost shut down in the 1990's. In 1995, Piper became an employee-owned company and managed to regain some of its lost market share. Now known as New Piper Aircraft, Piper today manufactures a variety of small airplanes, including a single-engine turboprop, the Malibu Meridian, and the twin-engine Saratoga. Still, even today, the name Piper continues to evoke the image of the original bright yellow Piper Cub, the small plane that for many generations of fliers symbolized personal aviation.

Nancy Farm Mannikko

Bibliography

Bowers, Peter. *Piper Cubs*. Blue Ridge Summit, Pa.: Tab Books, 1993. Well researched history of Piper aircraft. Numerous illustrations.

Francis, Devon. *Mr. Piper and His Cubs*. Ames: Iowa State University Press, 1973. An official biography written shortly after Piper's death. Rich in detail, but a little too hero-worshiping in places.

Moore, Don. *Low and Slow: A Personal History of a Liaison Pilot in World War II*. San Antonio, Tex.: San Antonio Heights, 1999. Fascinating memoir of a pilot who flew over Japanese lines.

Piper, William, Jr. *From Cub to Navaho: The Story of the Piper Aircraft Corporation*. New York: Newcomen Society, 1970. History of Piper written by William Piper's son.

Spence, Charles. "They're Not All Piper Cubs," *Aviation History*, November, 1997. Interesting and succinct history of William T. Piper and Piper aircraft.

Triggs, James. *The Piper Cub Story*. Blue Ridge Summit, Pa.: Tab Books, 1978. A concise history with numerous photos and technical drawings. Includes reproductions of pages from the 1941 J-3 Parts Manual.

See also: Aeronautical engineering; Airplanes; Beechcraft; Cessna Aircraft Company; Manufacturers; Pilots and copilots; World War II

Wiley Post

Date: Born on November 22, 1898, in Grand Saline, Texas; died on August 15, 1935, near Point Barrow, Alaska
Definition: A famous and colorful aviator of the 1920's and 1930's.
Significance: Post twice held speed records for transglobal flights, discovered the jet stream, and worked to develop the first pressure suit for stratospheric flight.

During the 1920's, Wiley Post worked in the Oklahoma oil fields. After losing his left eye in an oil-field accident, which led him to adopt his signature eye patch, he used money from an insurance settlement to buy his first airplane. He then performed as a parachute jumper and barnstormer. In 1925, the American humorist Will Rogers hired Post to fly to a rodeo, and the two became lifelong friends. During the late 1920's, Post, flying a TravelAir biplane, was the personal pilot for wealthy Oklahoma oilmen F. C. Hall and Powell Briscoe. Hall bought for Post's personal use a Lockheed Vega 5-C, which Post named *Winnie Mae*, after his daughter.

In the Vega, a streamlined, single-engine plane known for its ruggedness and airworthiness, Post won the 1930 National Air Derby, a Los Angeles-to-Chicago race that made him a national figure. Although the plane's cruise speed was 140 miles per hour, Post's winning time approached 200 miles per hour.

In 1931, Post flew around the world in the *Winnie Mae* with Australian-American aviator Harold Gatty. Traveling a northern route of some 15,000 miles, they set a world record of eight days and sixteen hours, breaking the speed record of twenty-one days set in 1929 by the German airship the *Graf Zeppelin*. Post received the Distinguished Flying Cross in 1932. In July, 1933, Post, flying alone with navigational instruments and an automatic pilot, reduced the time to seven days and eighteen hours, an achievement that earned him the solo record for around-the-world flight and the Harmon International Trophy.

Post took up the challenge of high-altitude flight in 1934, funded by Frank Phillips of the Phillips Petroleum Company. The *Winnie Mae* could not be pressurized, so Post asked the B. F. Goodrich Company to help him devise

Wiley Post poses with the Winnie Mae, *in which he and navigator Harold Gatty completed their around-the-world flight in 1933.* (Hulton Archive)

a pressurized flying suit made of rubberized parachute material, with pigskin gloves, a helmet made of plastic and aluminum, and a liquid-oxygen breathing system. Post first used the suit in a September, 1934, flight over Chicago, in which he also used a supercharger on *Winnie Mae*'s engine to set an unofficial height record of 50,000 feet.

In his high-altitude test flights, Post was the first flier to encounter the jet stream, which he used to his advantage in a May, 1935, flight from Burbank, California, to Cleveland, Ohio. At times, the ground speed on this flight approached 250 miles per hour, and the average ground speed was about 179 miles per hour. However, he failed in four attempts at making a stratospheric flight across the entire continental United States.

Ever the visionary innovator, Post predicted the development of supersonic transports and even space travel. He conducted secret experiments in a high-altitude chamber owned by the U.S. Army and researched the biological rhythms related to pilot fatigue.

In 1935, Post explored flight routes from the West Coast of the United States to Russia. With funding from U.S. airlines, he combined the parts of two planes: the wings of a Lockheed Explorer and the fuselage of a Lockheed Orion. Pontoons were necessary to land in Alaskan and Siberian lakes, and when the desired pontoons did not arrive, Post used a heavier set from a much larger plane.

In July, 1935, Post and Rogers left Seattle, Washington, in this heavy plane, further weighted down with fishing and hunting equipment. Lost in bad weather, they landed in a lagoon near Point Barrow, Alaska. When they tried to take off, the engine failed, and the plane plunged back into the lagoon, killing both men. Post's famous *Winnie Mae* was subsequently sold by his widow to the Smithsonian Institution.

Niles R. Holt

Bibliography

Mohler, Stanley R., and Bobby H. Johnson. *Wiley Post, His Winnie Mae, and the World's First Pressure Suit*. Washington, D.C.: Smithsonian Institution Press, 1971. Contains a considerable amount of detail, photos, and drawings of flight instruments, the pressurized flight suit, and Post's airplanes.

Post, Wiley, and Harold Gatty. *Around the World in Eight Days*. Reprint. New York: Orion Books, 1989. A ghost-written account of Post's first around-the-world trip, with an introduction by Rogers.

Taylor, Richard L. *The First Solo Flight Around the World: The Story of Wiley Post and His Airplane, the Winnie Mae*. New York: F. Watts, 1993. A brief volume intended for younger readers, thoroughly illustrated with photographs of Post and diagrams of the *Winnie Mae*.

See also: High-altitude flight; Record flights; Transglobal flight; *Winnie Mae*

Ludwig Prandtl

Date: Born on February 4, 1875, in Freising, Germany; died on August 15, 1953, in Göttingen, West Germany

Definition: Considered the father of modern fluid mechanics.

Significance: Prandtl's boundary layer equation became fundamental to the study of fluid mechanics. His contributions to turbulence theory include the mathematical foundations for modern wing theory. Although untrained in mathematics, Prandtl was nevertheless able to simplify complex mathematical concepts explaining certain physical phenomena.

Ludwig Prandtl was born in Freising, Germany, in 1875, and studied mechanical engineering in Munich, Germany. After receiving his doctorate from the Munich Technische Hochschule in 1900, Prandtl worked at a factory in Nürnberg, Germany, before becoming professor of mechanics at the Technische Schule in Hannover. In 1904, German mathematician Felix Klein encouraged Prandtl to accept the position of professor of applied mechanics at the University of Göttingen, where Prandtl remained for almost a half-century. Because of Prandtl's groundbreaking work in fluid mechanics, Göttingen developed into an internationally renowned center of aerodynamic research.

Prandtl's 1904 discovery of the boundary layer resolved the issue of fluid friction. Prior to Prandtl's work, scientists had been unable to understand or explain the frictional forces of viscous fluids, especially water and air. Through experiments with a small water tunnel, Prandtl proved the existence of a boundary layer in fluids flowing around a solid structure, such as water in a pipe or air over a wing. He defined the boundary layer as the region of the flow adjacent to the wall of a solid surface, where the viscous effects cause the molecules of the fluid to stick to the wall. Any solid body, such as a boat, airplane, car, or machine part, moving in a viscous fluid, such as water or air, creates a boundary layer around it. Prandtl's theory explained that friction, or drag, at the wall of the solid body is due to the presence of the boundary layer. His breakthrough led to the development of the science of fluid dynamics. The boundary layer theory was initially applied to laminar, or nonturbulent, flows, but Prandtl's later experiments in 1914 demonstrated that the boundary layer also exists in turbulent flows. The boundary layer theory helped scientists design machines and devices to account for the drag that results from the boundary layer.

Prandtl's work on friction drag resulted in his 1918 development of wing theory, which explained the flow of air over airplane wings. The Lanchester-Prandtl wing theory, named for both Prandtl and the British physicist Frederick Lanchester, whose simultaneous work was independent of Prandtl's, calculates the lift on the wing. Prandtl's other numerous contributions include his work in supersonic and subsonic flows and turbulence and in wind tunnel design. Prandtl's contributions to aerodynamics eventually led to manned flight and earned him the title of father of aerodynamic theory. After falling ill in 1952, Prandtl died in Göttingen on August 15, 1953.

Said Elghobashi

Bibliography

Prandtl, Ludwig. *Essentials of Fluid Dynamics, with Applications to Hydraulics, Aeronautics, Meteorology, and Other Subjects*. New York: Hafner, 1952. A technical volume that provides an in-depth look at Prandtl's work in fluid dynamics and other areas throughout his long career.

Schlichting, Hermann. *Boundary Layer Theory*. 6th ed. New York: McGraw-Hill, 1968. A fluid mechanics text with many references to Prandtl and to his students, including a good discussion of his involvement in viscous flow theory, with detailed chapters about laminar and turbulent boundary layers.

Sundaram, T. R. "The Father of Aerodynamics." *World and I* 12, no. 11 (November, 1997). Profiles Prandtl, his early work in airflow modeling, boundary layer theory, and his later career.

See also: Aerodynamics; Airfoils; Forces of flight; Wind tunnels

Propellers

Definition: Rotating airfoils driven by an engine, which provide thrust to an aircraft.
Significance: Propellers were a primary mode of thrust generation for all aircraft up to the development of the gas-turbine engine in the 1940's, and they remain in widespread use, especially on smaller commercial and general aviation aircraft.

History

Propellers have long been recognized as an efficient means of generating thrust. They were popularly used in aircraft design even before being used by Orville and Wilbur Wright to power the Wright *Flyer* in 1903. Leonardo da Vinci sketched propeller designs for helicopters in the 1500's. Early propellers were based primarily on designs used for ships and windmills, but experiments soon found that long, thin airfoils provided better thrust than the shorter, thicker hydrofoil designs used in water.

Nature and Use

The function of a propeller is to create thrust to accelerate an aircraft forward. Although a wing creates lift to overcome an aircraft's weight, a propeller creates thrust to overcome its drag. This thrust keeps an aircraft moving. When the propeller's thrust is equal to the aircraft's drag, the aircraft travels at a constant speed. When thrust is greater than drag, the aircraft accelerates until drag is equal to the thrust. Likewise, when the propeller's thrust is less than the aircraft's drag, the vehicle decelerates until the drag and thrust are equal and the aircraft's velocity becomes constant. Thus, varying the propeller's thrust will change the aircraft's velocity.

In a helicopter, the propeller is turned upward, so that the thrust is generated vertically to overcome the weight of the aircraft. When a propeller is oriented primarily to overcome weight instead of drag, it is usually called a rotor. The engine powering a propeller can be either a conventional piston (reciprocating) engine or a jet (gas turbine) engine. In the latter case, the propeller-and-engine combination is commonly referred to as a turboprop. Turboprops typically derive 95 percent of their thrust from the propeller, while the remainder comes from the jet-engine exhaust.

A propeller may be thought of as a severely twisted wing. In fact, the wings of many aircraft are twisted either to increase or decrease lift on certain portions of the wing by changing the local effective angle of attack. The propeller is twisted for a similar reason. Like an untwisted wing, a propeller could be designed without twist, as some of the first propellers were, but it would create less thrust than would a twisted propeller.

A propeller generates thrust in the same way that a wing generates lift. Instead of moving in a straight line, however, the propeller rotates about a hub that is turned by the engine shaft. A propeller actually traces out the shape of a helix as it travels around in flight. For this reason, propellers are often referred to as airscrews and are also analogous to the propeller screws found on a ship.

Both the rotating and forward movements of a propeller's airfoil have an effect on how much thrust is developed. The velocity at each radial location of the propeller will be different, because the total velocity is the vector sum of the propeller radial velocity and the aircraft velocity. Because the propeller is rotating at a certain rotation rate, the propeller velocity at any distance from the axis of rotation is the rotational speed times the radial distance. Thus, the propeller velocity will be almost zero near the hub and a maximum near the tip. This difference in velocity requires that the cross sections of the propeller's airfoil be twisted so that the chord line has a large angle of attack near the hub and a small angle of attack near the tip, in contrast to the airfoil of a wing that is nearly flat. The propeller's chord line increasingly points in the direction of the aircraft motion, as the propeller airfoil sections progress toward the hub.

The angle between the chord line of the propeller and the propeller's plane of rotation is called the pitch angle. To determine the local angle of attack of a propeller, one uses the propeller's pitch angle at each blade section and subtracts the angle of attack of the incoming relative wind.

Propeller Placement

A propeller can be placed anywhere on an aircraft, either at the nose, tail, wings, or on a pod. In a tractor configuration, the propeller is placed facing forward, usually on the nose, and pulls the aircraft. In a pusher configuration, the propeller is placed facing the rear of the aircraft and pushes the aircraft forward. One design has no real benefit over the other. The tractor configuration is more common, because it allows a better balance of the aircraft's center of gravity about the aerodynamic center of the wing with the engine placed near the nose. Pusher configurations are more common in canard aircraft for the same reason. In a tractor configuration, the slipstream from a propeller is often pushed over the wings, creating a faster flow over that part of the wing. This is sometimes used to generate more lift, but it is not commonly considered in aircraft design.

Propeller Efficiency

The propeller efficiency is a measure of how effectively a propeller transforms the engine power into propulsive power. It is measured by dividing the power output by the power input. The power output is the thrust generated by the propeller multiplied by the aircraft velocity. The power input is the amount of shaft power generated by the engine, measured in horsepower or watts. A propeller that is 100 percent efficient means that all of the power from the engine is transferred directly to the air. No propeller can achieve 100 percent efficiency, however, and is hindered by several factors. The propeller, as it rotates, adds energy to the air, and this energy is lost from the aircraft, because it remains with the air long after the aircraft has passed. Indeed, the most efficient propellers are the ones that take a large amount of air and increase the velocity of the air only slightly. Thus, all things being equal, larger-diameter propellers are more efficient than smaller ones. Also, the drag forces that act on the aircraft as a whole also act on the propeller. These forces include pressure drag, such as separation of the flow over a propeller, and friction drag, in which viscous effects of the air retard propeller motion.

Typical propellers have efficiencies in the 70 to 90 percent range. Fixed-pitch propellers have the lowest efficiency and can drop below 70 percent if they are operating at a velocity for which they were not designed.

Propeller Designs

The Wright brothers and Alexandre-Gustave Eiffel, among others, conducted early experiments on propellers. The Wright brothers were particularly concerned about maximum power output and thrust generation, because their early engines developed very little horsepower. They were able to design propeller blades with an efficiency of up to 70 percent, which was an extraordinary feat for the time. Eiffel, a French engineer and the builder of the Eiffel Tower in Paris, was also an ardent aerodynamicist who performed some of the first detailed wind-tunnel experiments on propellers. He was the first to show that propeller efficiency varied with the propeller's rotation rate, diameter, and aircraft velocity. This parameter is now called the advance ratio and is used in propeller design, optimization, and selection.

Fixed-Pitch Propellers

Propellers can be used on aircraft in several different ways. In the fixed-pitch propeller, the propeller blade has a fixed angle of attack. Although the angle varies along the length of the propeller, the blade has a fixed orientation throughout its flight envelope, meaning that the propeller design has been optimized for a single speed. If the aircraft travels at another velocity, the propeller efficiency is reduced. Fixed-pitch propellers were used on all airplanes up to the 1930's, when variable-pitch propellers were introduced.

Variable-Pitch Propellers

The angle of attack of variable-pitch propellers can be changed by rotating the blade about the hub. This allows pilots to adjust the propellers' relative angle of attack in flight to account for changes in the aircraft and wind velocity. A complex mechanism in the hub allows the pilot to change the propeller pitch in flight, thereby increasing overall performance. When variable-pitch propellers were introduced in the 1930's, propeller efficiency across the range of flight conditions was greatly increased. A major drawback, however, was that as the pitch was altered, the torque on the engine was also changed. This would, in turn, change the rotation speed of the engine, resulting in a lower engine-power output.

Constant-Speed Propellers

Consequently, the constant-speed propeller was introduced in the 1940's. It is a variant of the variable-pitch propeller in which the propeller pitch is changed automatically to keep the engine speed constant and to maximize total power output. Variable-pitch and constant-speed propellers may be feathered in flight during an engine-out scenario to minimize the propeller drag.

To keep the propeller efficiency from dropping, the velocity of the propeller tip must be kept lower than the speed of sound, or Mach 1. If this velocity is exceeded, shock waves form at the tip of the propeller, and the efficiency drops dramatically as the available power is reduced by pressure losses. Shock waves can create other problems, such as severe noise, vibration, and structural damage to the propeller. Because the velocity at the tip is a function of the propeller radius, engine-shaft rotational speed, and aircraft speed, these three factors come into play when determining what size propeller should be used. During the tradeoff analysis of an aircraft design, as the speed of an aircraft increases, the diameter of the propeller decreases.

To generate the same thrust for a smaller-diameter propeller given the same engine speed, an aircraft designer may opt to go with a larger number of propellers. The propeller must be balanced, and two blades are the minimum used. However, any number of blades greater than two may be chosen, as long as the blades are evenly spaced to maintain balance. Increasing the number of propeller blades means that to achieve the same thrust, a smaller diameter can be used. This is sometimes done to avoid the sonic tip speeds that may be encountered with long propeller blades on fast aircraft. Two-, three-, four-, and five-bladed propellers have been commonly used on aircraft throughout the twentieth century.

To overcome the drawback of the sonic tip speed limitation of propellers on some commercial aircraft using turboprops, the use of unducted fan propellers has been proposed. The unducted fan propeller is a many-bladed propeller with short, curved blades that allow craft to overcome the sonic tip concerns that plague high-speed aircraft using traditional propeller designs.

Jamey D. Jacob

Bibliography

Anderson, J. A., Jr. *A History of Aerodynamics and its Impact on Flying Machines*. Cambridge, England: Cambridge University Press, 1997. An exhaustive and well-written history on the science of aerodynamics and how it affected the development of aircraft, including early propeller design.

Milne-Thomson, L. M. *Theoretical Aerodynamics*. New York: Dover, 1958. A classic treatise on aerodynamics that includes detailed analysis of propeller thrust calculations.

Raymer, Daniel P. *Aircraft Design: A Conceptual Approach*. Washington, D.C.: AIAA Press, 1992. An aircraft design guide that includes information on engine and propeller selection and sizing.

Von Mises, Richard. *Theory of Flight*. New York: Dover, 1945. An explanation of the theoretical basis for aircraft flight that includes two chapters on propeller performance and theory.

See also: Airplanes; Forces of flight; Helicopters; Rotorcraft; Turboprops; Wing designs; Wright *Flyer*

Propulsion

Definition: The process of forcing an object to move. The word is also used to refer to the entire system of engines for achieving propulsion in the context of flight vehicles.

Significance: Propulsion is the force that allows aircraft to fly. Aircraft propulsion systems include engines, nozzles, and propellers. Methods of propulsion range from piston engines driving propellers on small airplanes to conceptual models that may use magnetic fields, laser beams, or antimatter to propel spacecraft in the future.

Types of Propulsion Systems

While the machinery is complex, the principles of opera-

The United States' first rocket-assisted airplane takes off on August 12, 1941. The Ercoupe plane was fitted with a solid-propellant 28-pound-thrust JATO (jet-assisted takeoff) booster. (NASA)

tion are common to most propulsion systems. According to Newton's second law of motion, the net force exerted on an object is equal to the rate of change of its momentum. According to Newton's third law of motion, every action (of a force) produces an equal and opposite reaction. For flight in the atmosphere, air is used as the working fluid whose momentum is changed by the propulsion system. The reaction to the resulting force acts on the propulsion system and drives the aircraft forward.

Since momentum is the product of mass and velocity, designers can choose to produce a given increase of momentum by either accelerating a large mass of fluid per second through a small change in velocity, or accelerating a smaller mass of fluid through a large increase in velocity. For flight at low speeds, it is more efficient to do the former. For example, helicopters and propeller-driven airplanes use large rotating blades to capture a large amount of air and accelerate it through a relatively small change in velocity. For flight at high speeds, turbojet and ramjet engines, which usually have small intake areas, add heat to the captured air. This heat is then converted to the work done in accelerating the air through a large velocity change, leaving hot jets of air behind. In effect, a force is exerted on the air by the engine to accelerate it backward from the aircraft. The reaction to this force acts on the engine and hence drives the aircraft forward.

The same principle applies to rocket propulsion, in the atmosphere or in outer space. Rockets generate gas at high pressure by burning chemicals, and this gas escapes at high speed through a nozzle. The reaction to the force used in doing so accelerates the rocket. The key idea is that the engine and the propellant gases are pushing against each other: no other medium is needed to be pushed. In the early days of rocket flight, several experts, including editorials in *The New York Times*, sneered at rocket pioneer Robert H. Goddard for his insistence that rockets could thus work in the vacuum of space, but today such flight is taken for granted.

Piston Engines and Propellers

Early aircraft propulsion systems used piston engines to drive propellers. The revolving blades of the propeller are like rotary wings, producing a force and accelerating the air encountered within the large area swept by the blades. Propellers were termed pusher or puller props, depending on whether they were mounted behind or ahead of the wings. Propellers are highly efficient as propulsion for slow-flying aircraft. Today many short-range aircraft and general aviation aircraft are powered by turboprop engines, where the engine uses the gas turbine principle, but the power generated is used to drive a propeller. For flight at more than about half the speed of sound (Mach 0.5), the speed at the tips of the blades exceeds the speed of sound, and shocks form, generating unacceptable levels of noise and drag.

Solar-Electric Propulsion

Renewed interest in propeller-driven aircraft comes from the idea of continuously flying airplanes in the upper atmosphere using solar power to drive a motor and propeller. The National Aeronautics and Space Administration (NASA) Solar Pathfinder demonstrated ascent to over 80,000 feet using wings covered with solar panels. The energy absorbed from the Sun during the daytime can drive the vehicle to such high altitudes that it can glide all night without coming down too low. Thus automatic, continuously flying aircraft can be propelled using solar power.

Rocket Engines

The earliest evidence of rocket usage is from China, where black-powder rockets stabilized with bamboo poles, perhaps with multiple stages, were used in the twelfth century. The South Indian king Tippu Sultan of Mysore used iron-cased rocket-powered projectiles with 2,400-meter range from 1780 to 1799 in order to protect his nation from British invaders. Using rockets captured from India, Britain's William Congreve developed solid rockets with a 3,000-yard range, used against Napoleon's forces in Bologne in 1806, and in the War of 1812 against the United States. Russia's Konstantin Tsiolkovsky (1857-1935) developed the idea of multistage rockets to escape Earth's gravity in a 1903 paper titled "Isslyedovanye mirovykh prostranstv ryeaktivnymi priborami" ("Exploration of Space with Reactive Devices," 1957) discussing the use of liquid oxygen and liquid hydrogen. American Robert H. Goddard (1882-1945) registered a patent in 1914 for the design of a rocket combustion-chamber nozzle and propellant feed system. He published "A Method of Reaching Extreme Altitudes" in 1919 through the Smithsonian Institute, and conducted experiments with liquid-oxygen and gasoline propellants between 1920 and 1940. In Germany, Hermann Oberth published *Die Rackete zu den Planetenräumen* (1923; the rocket into interplanetary space) and *Wege zür Raumschiffart* (1929; the road to space travel). During World War II, air-launched rocket-powered unguided missiles were used, followed by Russian use of rockets in artillery barrages, and the German V-1 and V-2 ballistic missiles which were launched into Britain. After the war, with German rocket engineers inducted into American and Soviet research organizations, the missile race accelerated. On October 4, 1957, the Soviet Union's Sputnik became the first artificial satellite of Earth, and by 1969, Apollo 11 had taken two men to walk on the Moon and return to Earth.

Solid, Liquid, Cryogenic, and Hybrid Rockets

The simplest rocket engine has a propellant grain of fuel and oxidizer in solid form, ignited at one end. As the solid melts and vaporizes due to the heat, the chemical reaction starts, releasing much more heat. The hot gases reach high pressure in the combustion chamber and exhaust through a nozzle, reaching high velocities. Rocket designers shape the propellant grain (the shape of the interior core of the solid propellant) in various ways to tailor the rate at which the solid material is consumed, thus predetermining how the thrust will vary with time. In general, the thrust of a solid rocket cannot be controlled once it starts, aside from releasing the pressure and thus stopping the combustion: most modern solid propellants do not burn unless the pressure is several atmospheres.

Liquid propellants are stored in one or more tanks, and pumped into the combustion chamber, where the pressure is usually much higher than in the storage tanks. While liquid rockets are more controllable, the pumps often pose failure risks; however, the lack of control of the solid rocket is also a disadvantage. Hybrid rockets use a bi-propellant, where the liquid propellant is metered to flow over a solid propellant grain.

The performance of a propulsion system is characterized by its specific impulse (Isp), which is the thrust developed per second, per unit weight of the propellant consumed, at the standard value of Earth's gravitational acceleration, and expressed in units of seconds. The specific impulse of solid-fueled rockets is limited to about 270 seconds. Liquid-fueled rockets using storable fuels are limited to about 250 seconds. Rockets with cryogenic fuels such as liquid oxygen and liquid hydrogen reach 390 to 450 seconds. Proponents of nuclear thermal propulsion hope to achieve an Isp of 825-925 seconds. Electrothermal propulsion, where the propellant gas is heated by an electric arc, promises 800 to 1,200 seconds; electromagnetic acceleration, 5,000 seconds; and ion propulsion, 10,000 seconds.

High Isp does not tell the whole story, since the higher Isp systems usually required heavy machinery, and produce very small amounts of thrust. The specific impulse of engines in space is proportional to the exhaust velocity of the propellant gas. For a given addition of momentum per unit mass, hydrogen, having the lowest molecular weight, provides the highest specific impulse. An efficient type of rocket engine is the solar-hydrogen engine used in orbit transfer vehicles shuttling between low-Earth orbit and geosynchronous Earth orbits. Here solar energy is focused by a collector to heat hydrogen, which then flows out at high speed through a nozzle.

Nuclear Propulsion

A heat source is crucial to propulsion, and one which generates the most heat with the least expenditure of fuel weight would produce the highest specific impulse. Nuclear reactions satisfy this criterion, but the weight of the shielding needed for the reactor, and the consequences of a crash, have limited their use in flight propulsion. The slow neutron reactors used in ships and submarines proved to be too heavy for use in aircraft, while other designs, which could heat air to high temperatures quickly, operated at temperatures too high for available materials and posed extreme radiation hazards. In the 1950's, an Aircraft Nuclear Propulsion (ANP) project led to several advanced designs for nuclear-powered intercontinental bombers, but none appear to have been flight-tested. Project Pluto, a secret project conducted in Nevada, developed a nuclear-powered ramjet supersonic cruise missile. Small nuclear reactors have been used in deep-space probes such as the Galileo mission, and it is expected that missions to other planets, such as an exploration of Jupiter's atmosphere, will require nuclear propulsion to provide the required specific impulse. Proposed nuclear thermal rockets will heat propellant gas (hydrogen) through the coolant channels of a solid-fuel reactor core at about 3,000 degrees Kelvin, and expand hydrogen through a nozzle.

Ion Propulsion

Ionized gases are accelerated to high exhaust velocity using electromagnetic fields in engines used to produce low thrust, available for station-keeping orbit corrections over long durations on spacecraft. The Boeing 702 Xenon Ion Thruster claims an Isp of 3,800 seconds and thrust of 165 million newtons (by comparison, the Saturn V at liftoff produced over 33 million newtons). The weight of the system required to produce the electromagnetic field has restricted the usage of ion propulsion to low-thrust applications, perhaps until superconducting electromagnets become available for use in such systems.

Air-Breathing Jet Propulsion

For flight in the atmosphere, the effective specific impulse can be increased greatly by using oxygen in the air as oxidizer, and air as the working fluid: air does not have to be added to the fuel cost or vehicle weight. There are three principles of jet propulsion: heat addition to the working fluid is most efficient if the heat is added at the highest pressure possible; the conversion of heat to work is most efficient if the temperature difference is largest; and the thrust is most efficient in driving the aircraft if the exhaust velocity is close to (but greater than) the flight speed.

In the gas turbine cycle, the working fluid is first compressed, then heat is added at constant pressure, and finally work is extracted from the hot, high-pressure fluid as it expands and flows out. Thus, gas turbine engines incorporate a compressor to increase pressure, a combustion chamber to add the heat through a combustion reaction between the fuel and air, a turbine to extract work and run the compressor, and a nozzle to expand the flow out. For large engines used by commercial aircraft, the optimal value of pressure ratio (between the highest pressure after compression and the outside) is as high as 50. At supersonic speeds, the deceleration of the air at the front of the engine itself raises the pressure substantially; the optimum pressure ratio may be only 7. As Mach number increases beyond 2.5, the need for a mechanical compressor vanishes, and ramjet engines can operate. Here the incoming air is decelerated, so that its pressure increases to such large values that mechanical compressors and the turbines to operate them are not needed.

All other gas turbine engines require compressors to increase the pressure of the incoming air, and turbines which drive the compressor and extract work required to run other components including propellers, rotors, and fans. These turbomachines change pressure through several stages. Each stage has a rotor where work is done on the fluid to change its momentum, and a stator, or counter-rotating rotor, to recover the momentum change and convert it into a pressure change. Turbomachine stages may be centrifugal or axial. In centrifugal stages, air comes in near the axis and is flung out pressurized at the periphery. In axial stages, the flow is predominantly parallel to the axis, with rows of blades successively increasing momentum by swirling the flow and recovering the pressure by reducing the swirl.

Turbofans, Turbojets, and Propfans

The first jet engines were turbojets, where all of the airflow went through the same compressor and combustion chamber. The first jet engine was patented in 1930 by Sir Frank Whittle (1907-1996). The PowerJets Model W.1 engine was first tested in April, 1937, and according to Sir Whittle, "made a noise like an air raid siren," sending onlookers running for cover. It weighed 700 pounds and produced 860 pounds of thrust, using a double-sided centrifugal compressor. The first British aircraft to use the engine was the Gloster Meteor, a night fighter which first flew in March, 1943, eventually reaching 420 miles per hour. The first jet-powered flight, however, was on a Heinkel aircraft powered by Hans von Ohain's (1911-1998) axial-compressor turbojet engine in Germany. The first jet fighter took off on July 18, 1942, a Messerschmitt Me-262 fighter piloted by Fritz Wendel of the German Luftwaffe, using a Junkers Jumo 004 turbojet engine producing 2,200 pounds of thrust. Earlier attempts had been made using BMW003 turbojet engines, which used a seven-stage axial-flow compressor and an annular combustion chamber with sixteen burners. Today, centrifugal compressors are used in the turbopumps of rocket engines, while axial compressors are dominant in most aircraft applications. Helicopter turboshaft engines use both centrifugal and axial stages. The thrust-to-weight ratio of modern jet engines has improved to well over 4:1.

Turboprop engines use a small turbine to extract enough work from the hot combustor gases to run the compressor, and a large power turbine to extract most of the work from the air to run a propeller. The propeller is connected through a gearbox to reduce the speed of revolution; this adds considerable weight to turboprop engines. The Soviet Bear long-range bomber used turboprop engines with a pair of counter-rotating propellers on each engine. The design tradeoff between high thermal efficiency (requiring high pressure and temperature) and high propulsive efficiency (requiring a small increase of air velocity from the flight speed) is addressed using bypass or turbofan engines, where a part of the captured air goes through a fan and a nozzle, bypassing the main compressor, combustor, and turbine. The bypass ratio is the ratio of the air bypassing the hot core of the engine to the air which goes through the core and has fuel burned in it. Fighter aircraft turbofan engines use a bypass ratio of approximately 1, while modern commercial aircraft engines, such as the GE90 used on the Boeing 777 and Airbus 340 airliners, use bypass ratios up to 12.

In the 1980's, propfans or unducted fans were explored to bridge the gap between the propeller and the ducted turbofan engine. Using modern computational aerodynamics technology, large fan blades of complex shape were designed to operate with supersonic tip speeds and large pressure rise across each stage. Some designs had counter-rotating rows of fan blades. To increase the capture area, the blades were left without the outer cowling used by turbofan engines. These engines promised large improvements in fuel efficiency for short-haul aircraft, but encountered severe problems of development cost and noise levels high enough to damage the aircraft structure through sonic fatigue.

For air-breathing flight at supersonic speeds, a supersonic inlet must slow down the supersonic flow with minimal losses due to shock waves, so that the fan, compressor, and combustion chamber can operate at subsonic speeds. Inlets vary in complexity from the normal-shock inlet of the early MiG and Sabre fighters, through the movable spike inlets of the MiG-21 or the SR-71, to the multiple-ramp inlets of the F-15 or Concorde. Hypersonic aircraft use the compression across the shock produced by the aircraft fuselage to decelerate, so that engine-airframe integration is vital to such designs. Instead of varying geometry, supersonic flows can also be decelerated and compressed using heat addition (thermal compression). At the other end, nozzles vary from simple convergent nozzles of subsonic aircraft, to the converging-diverging nozzles of fighters with afterburners, to the rectangular nozzles of modern fighters where the thrust can be vectored for maneuvering or vertical takeoff. High-speed aircraft concepts (NASA's X-33, Lockheed's VentureStar, and the Japanese ATREX turboramjet) use the Aerospike or Plug Flow nozzles to enable external variation of the nozzle expansion. Several other types of propulsion devices are being studied by researchers.

In the Mini-Magnetospheric Plasma Propulsion (M2P2) concept developed by Robert Winglee at the University of Washington, jets of heated gas plasma, fired from a spacecraft, interact with the magnetic field generated by the spacecraft to produce a mini-magnetosphere around the craft. The interaction of this magnetosphere with the plasma wind from the Sun (the solar wind) produces forces in a fashion somewhat similar to the interaction of an airfoil shape with flowing air generating lift. This force can be tailored to drive the spacecraft around the solar system at very high speeds. Unlike solar sails, which work better to drive a spacecraft in the inner solar system, M2P2 is seen as an option for travel to the outer planets.

Light Propulsion

Scientists have long speculated that photons could exert pressure on a spacecraft and drive it to speeds approaching the speed of light. Practical systems for focusing high-power lasers onto spacecraft are not yet in use in space. Experiments by Leik Myrabo of Rensselaer Polytechnic Institute and the U.S. Air Force had succeeded, by the year 2000, in lifting small objects to a height of a few dozen meters using ground-based lasers. In extended forms of this concept, the focused laser beam creates an "aerospike" of heated gas ahead of the vehicle, which helps reduce drag as the vehicle is driven up through the atmosphere by a shock created by expanding air beneath the vehicle.

Fusion and Antimatter Propulsion
Scientists hope that in the distant future, power generation by nuclear fusion or matter-antimatter interaction will allow the development of propulsion systems with immense thrust levels and very high specific impulse. For now, such systems remain impractical.

Narayanan M. Komerath

Bibliography
Hill, Philip G., and Carl R. Peterson. *Mechanics and Thermodynamics of Propulsion*. 2d ed. Reading, Mass.: Addison-Wesley, 1992. Comprehensive textbook on gas turbines and rocket propulsion, suitable for undergraduate engineering students.

Hunecke, Klaus. *Jet Engines: Fundamentals of Theory, Design, and Operation*. Osceola, Wis.: Motorbooks International, 1998. A thorough explanation of jet engine mechanics geared toward practical application.

Glenn Learning Technologies Project. NASA Glenn Research Center. (www.grc.nasa.gov/www/K-12/airplane/shortp.html) Expositions of principles, example problems, and animated demonstrations, especially on propulsion.

Marshall Brain's "How Stuff Works." (www.howstuffworks.com/turbine.htm) Concise explanations of a multitude of items in terms of both the systems and their components.

NASA-Marshall Space Flight Center. (www.msfc.nasa.gov) This Web site provides colorful artists' concepts, photographs of current projects, and project information on advanced propulsion concepts.

Turner, Martin J. L. *Rocket and Spacecraft Propulsion: Principles, Practice, and New Developments*. New York: Springer Verlag, 2000. Written by a space scientist for readers without a background in engineering. Covers developments in propulsion systems that may power the next generation of space exploration.

See also: Engine designs; Forces of flight; Robert H. Goddard; Gravity; Helicopters; Hypersonic aircraft; Jet engines; Missiles; National Aeronautics and Space Administration; Hermann Oberth; Ramjets; Rocket propulsion; Rockets; Supersonic aircraft; Turbojets and turbofans; Turboprops; X planes

PSA

Also known as: Pacific Southwest Airlines
Date: From May 6, 1949, to April 8, 1988
Definition: California airline initially limited to intrastate routes to avoid Civil Aeronautics Board (CAB) regulation.
Significance: PSA was the largest airline to fly within one state. The airline had a unique business philosophy, that flying should be fun.

A "Friendly" Airline
Ken Friedkin started Pacific Southwest Airlines (PSA) in San Diego in 1949. Friedkin had run a flight school for the Women's Airforce Service Pilots (WASPs) during World War II. After the war, he wanted to continue training pilots. His flight school was successful, training hundreds of veterans using the G.I. Bill to get an education. By 1948, the school attracted fewer students as most of the veterans completed their education and entered the workforce. Friedkin decided to start a charter service transporting passengers around Southern California. The charter service grew into a scheduled airline, Pacific Southwest Airlines.

On May 6, 1949, the first PSA flight, a DC-3 with twenty-seven passengers, left San Diego's Lindbergh Field bound for Oakland, California, via Burbank. The airfare for the trip was $15.60. The airline flew only on weekends and had very low fares. As a result, PSA attracted a significant number of military personnel, causing some to suggest that its initials stood for the "Poor Sailor's Airline." By 1951, the airline was serving San Diego, Hollywood/Burbank, Oakland, and San Francisco. Because PSA flew only within the state of California, it was able to avoid regulation by the Civil Aeronautics Board.

PSA grew through the 1950's with the inauguration of service to Los Angeles International Airport in August, 1958. Passengers traveled from San Diego to Los Angeles or Burbank for $5.45. Passengers paid $17.26 for the flight from San Diego to San Francisco. In 1959, the airline added three Lockheed L-188 Electra propjets to its fleet. The airline required its stewardesses to wear false eyelashes and bright makeup. PSA would become known for its attractive flight attendants.

"Personality Sells Airlines"
In the 1960's, airline management encouraged crew-passenger interaction. Flight attendants collected tickets on the planes. Flight crews were instructed on how to make conversation with passengers, who were to be treated like

guests in the crewmembers' own homes. By the end of the decade, the airline was dubbed the "Personality Sells Airlines." Ken Friedkin's business philosophy was that flying should be fun. When he died in 1962, his successors at PSA continued his philosophy.

PSA carried more than one million passengers over its four-city route in 1962, earning a profit of $1,368,770. Despite competing with TWA, United, and Western, PSA managed to garner a 50 percent market share. One secret to its success was its stewardesses. PSA was known nationally for its suntanned "California Girl" flight attendants, who wore outfits known as "banana skins." Introduced in 1962, form-fitting outfits zippered all the way up the front. One flight attendant noted that while wearing the outfit, "everything showed."

The airline entered the jet age in 1965 with the purchase of five Boeing 727-100's. The airline added San Jose to its route system in 1966. By the end of the decade, PSA's fleet included one DC-9, one Boeing 727-100, fourteen Boeing 727-200's, and nine Boeing 737-200's.

"Catch Our Smile"

A key element of PSA's corporate culture was adopted when smiles were painted on the aircraft in 1970. Soon all identifying artwork included the smile logo. The "Catch Our Smile" theme defined the airline until USAir purchased it in 1986.

Airline management made some strategic mistakes during the 1970's. In the early part of the decade, the airline launched a diversification campaign called "Fly/Drive/Sleep." PSA would provide passengers with air service, a rental car, and a hotel room. Among PSA's notable purchases was the Queen Mary, anchored in Long Beach, California. The campaign was not a financial success.

The late 1970's marked the beginning of a decade of expansion. PSA began interstate service to Nevada in 1978. The airline experienced tragedy on September 25, 1978, when PSA Flight 182 collided in midair with a privately owned Cessna 172, killing 144 people, including 37 PSA employees. PSA added additional interstate routes in the early 1980's. In 1980, PSA became an international airline with service to Puerto Vallarta and Mazatlan, Mexico. PSA pilots walked off the job for fifty-two days in 1980, causing the airline to cancel flights. More than 9 million passengers boarded PSA flights in 1985. As a result of fare wars, the airline lost $600,000, but the holding company recorded a $26.8 million profit from nonairline ventures in 1980.

The airline industry experienced significant consolidation during a two-year period from 1986 to 1987. PSA management worked to remain independent. In November, 1986, American Airlines purchased Air Cal, PSA's major competitor in California, a sign that PSA would soon be bought. The USAir Group purchased PSA for $400 million in 1987.

Tragedy struck PSA before the airline was completely integrated into USAir. On December 7, 1987, Flight 1771 was in the air between Los Angeles and San Francisco. David Burke, who had recently been fired by USAir, smuggled a gun aboard the plane. He shot the crew and then himself, causing the plane to crash from 23,000 feet into a cattle ranch near Harmony, California. The crash killed forty-four people. This incident was the first to be solved using data from the cockpit voice recorder. PSA's last flight, Flight 1486, departed from San Diego on April 8, 1988.

John David Rausch, Jr.

Bibliography

Davis, R. E. G. *Airlines of the United States Since 1914*. Washington, D.C.: Smithsonian Institution Press, 1972. Examines PSA's early history in light of the development of airline industry in the United States. Includes black-and-white illustrations of PSA planes.

Jacobsen, Meyers K. "'Catch Our Smile' (A History of Pacific Southwest Airlines)." *AAHS Journal* 45, no. 3 (Fall, 2000). Well-written, definitive history of Pacific Southwest Airlines.

Jones, Geoff. *abc USAirways*. Surrey, England: Ian Allan, 1999. A detailed reference work on US Airways that includes a history of PSA.

Labich, Kenneth. "Collision Course." *Newsweek* 92, no. 15 (October 9, 1978). Illustrated examination of the collision of PSA Flight 182 with a Cessna.

Magnuson, Ed. "Nation: David Burke's Deadly Revenge." *Time* 130, no. 25 (December 21, 1987). Detailed discussion of the events leading to the PSA Flight 1771 crash in 1987.

See also: Accident investigation; Air carriers; Airline industry, U.S.; Flight attendants; Flight recorder; US Airways; Women's Airforce Service Pilots

Q

Qantas

Also known as: Qantas Air Ways, Queensland and Northern Territory Aerial Services Limited, Qantas Imperial Airways
Date: Beginning November, 1920
Definition: A leading Australian airline.
Significance: Established in 1920, Qantas is among the oldest airlines in the world. It is arguably the best-known Australian airline and remains famous for its safety record: without a single fatality through the year 2000.

Qantas History

In 1919, former Australian Flying Corps officers W. Hudson Fysh and Paul McGinness accepted an assignment to survey parts of the Australian outback. On August 18, 1919, they began their journey across Queensland and the Northern Territories in a Model T Ford. At that time, few roads cut through this deserted swath of land. As pilots, Fysh and McGinness saw the value in an air service that could link the remote outback settlements to one another.

In Brisbane, Fysh and McGinness approached Fergus McMaster, a wealthy rancher, about their idea. McMaster, who had himself once broken the axle of his car while crossing Queensland's Cloncurry River, needed little convincing. He persuaded several business acquaintances to invest in the two airmen's proposal.

Fysh and McGinness adopted a name for their company: Queensland and Northern Territory Aerial Services Limited, which was abbreviated to QANTAS. The company filed for incorporation on November 16, 1920, with Fergus McMaster listed as chairman.

In 1921, the fleet consisted of two war-surplus planes: an Avro 540K and a Royal Aircraft Factory BE-2E. Keeping the two biplanes aloft proved treacherous: Pieces sometimes fell off in midair. Fysh and McGinness hired their former flight sergeant Arthur Baird as fleet mechanic. Baird proved to be a superb engineer who coaxed 54,000 kilometers out of the planes. The airline flew 871 passengers in 1921.

By 1922, Qantas was running a scheduled airmail service between Charleville and Cloncurry and needed larger aircraft. In 1924, Qantas acquired a four-passenger De Havilland DH-50 for the Charleville-to-Cloncurry run. The enclosed cabin of the DH-50 allowed passengers to forego helmets and goggles for the first time.

In 1926, Baird proposed that Qantas build its own aircraft. The first craft, a DH-50A, was finished in August of that year. It was the first aircraft of its size to be built in Australia under license from an overseas company. Qantas remains the only commercial airline to have built its own planes.

In 1928, Qantas signed a contract for medical flights to the Australian Outback. An available doctor made the difference between life and death for people residing in remote settlements. The contract gave Qantas two shillings, or the equivalent of forty cents, per mile. Arthur Affleck, the regular pilot of the "flying doctors" route, was accompanied by K. St. Vincent Welch, a Sydney surgeon. Together, the two men traveled more than 28,000 kilometers to care for 255 patients in 1928.

In 1929, with extended service to Brisbane, Qantas now covered 2,380 kilometers. This year also marked the airline's first one million miles flown and 10,400 passengers carried. In June, the airline moved its headquarters to Brisbane.

Two years later, Qantas participated in an Australia-to-Burma-to-England airmail run. Qantas cemented its links with British Imperial Airways by registering in Brisbane in 1934 as Qantas Imperial Airways. Qantas and British Imperial each held a half-share in the new airline, and Hudson Fysh was named managing director.

By April, 1935, Qantas carried passengers and mail in a DH-86 on the four-day journey from Darwin, Australia, to Singapore. Demand along this route continued to grow, and by 1938, Qantas introduced Short C-Class Empire flying boats, for which the airline built mooring and fueling facilities in Sydney's Rose Bay. Sydney crowds gathered whenever one of these craft took off or landed. Soon, a Southampton-to-Sydney service with a stop in Singapore debuted.

When World War II broke out in 1939, the Sydney-to-Southampton route became a vital communication link between England and Australia, until Singapore fell to the Japanese in 1942. International passenger services were interrupted until the end of the war. The Australian government commissioned more than one-half of Qantas' airplanes for war service.

In 1943, Qantas participated in a plan to reestablish the England-Australia air route that had been severed by Japanese forces. The plan called for flights between the Swan River in Perth and Koggala Lake in Ceylon (present-day Sri Lanka). The 5,652-kilometer trip across the Indian Ocean would be the longest flight yet attempted. Because enemy aircraft patrolled the waters, radio silence had to be maintained at all times, requiring celestial navigation. The weight of the fuel limited the plane's load to only three passengers and 69 kilograms of diplomatic mail. Passengers were given certificates welcoming them as members of the "Rare and Secret Order of the Double Sunrise," a select group of people who had been in the air for twenty-four hours. By the last flight on July 18, 1945, Qantas had completed 271 successful crossings.

After the war, Qantas modernized its fleet. In 1947, the Australian government bought all remaining shares of Qantas, retaining Fysh as chairman. Two years later, the airline introduced Douglas DC-4 Skymasters on new routes to Hong Kong and Japan. Service to Johannesburg, South Africa, was introduced in 1952. In October, 1953, Qantas took over Australia-to-North America service from British Commonwealth Pacific Airlines, which Qantas eventually absorbed.

Qantas was the first airline outside the United States to buy jet airplanes. Qantas acquired seven Boeing 707-138's between July and September, 1959. Service to the United States began in July, and was extended to London via New York. By October, Qantas offered Sydney-to-London service via India. By 1964, most Qantas routes featured 707's, and the airline began to sell off its propeller-driven fleet.

Qantas, now officially known as Qantas Airways, began operating Boeing 747 jumbojets, which were better suited to long-haul flights, in September, 1971. By 1979, Qantas sold off all its 707's and was now the only airline with an all-747 fleet.

Throughout the 1980's, Qantas flirted with several versions of the Boeing 767. During this decade, routes were retailored to reflect Asia's growing prosperity and demand for air services.

In 1992, the Australian government approved a request for Qantas to buy Australian Airlines and its subsidiaries. The new group was completely privatized. In December of that year, British Airways bought 25 percent of Qantas. For the next several years, Qantas increased capacity along its domestic routes to match rising demand. The airline looks forward to continued domestic and international growth throughout the twenty-first century.

Alexandra Ferry

Bibliography

Bennett-Bremner, E. *Front-Line Airline: The War Story of Qantas Empire Airways Limited.* Sydney: Angus and Robertson, 1944. Reprint. Longreach, Australia: Qantas Founders Outback Museum, 1996. An informative history of Qantas's aerial operations during World War II.

Fysh, Wilmot Hudson. *Qantas Rising: The Autobiography of the Flying Fysh.* Sydney: Angus and Robertson, 1965. Reprint. Longreach, Australia: Qantas Founders Outback Museum, 1996. The autobiography of one of Qantas's founders.

Gunn, John. *The Defeat of Distance: Qantas, 1919-1939.* St. Lucia, Australia: University of Queensland Press, 1988. The story of the early days of Qantas, with illustrations, a bibliography, and an index.

Stackhouse, John. *From the Dawn of Aviation: The Qantas Story, 1920-1995.* Double Bay, Australia: Focus, 1995. A comprehensive history of the airline.

See also: Air carriers; Jumbojets; World War II

R

Radar

Definition: A device or system that transmits radio waves and receives and analyzes their reflections in order to determine the location and speed of objects, such as aircraft.

Significance: Radar is essential for air traffic control, aircraft navigation, various weather observations, and many aspects of modern warfare.

Nature and Use

The word "radar" is an acronym for "radio detection and ranging," where ranging refers to finding the distance to a target. Radar works in a fashion similar to that supposed by the early Greeks for the operation of the eye. The Greeks imagined that rays shot out from a person's eye, and that people saw objects as their personal rays struck those objects and somehow returned information. The concept was one of being able to reach out and touch and feel objects from a distance.

Radar reaches out by sending out a beam of radio waves oscillating electric and magnetic fields. When a radio wave passes a given point, the electric field strength at that point goes up and down in much the same way that the water level at a point on the ocean goes up and down as a water wave passes. The distance between adjacent crests in a radio wave is the wavelength, and the number of waves that pass a given point during one second is the frequency. The frequency multiplied by the wavelength gives the speed of the waves. The speed of radio waves is very nearly the speed of light, 3×10^5 kilometers per second. Light itself is an electromagnetic wave, but it has a much higher frequency than radio waves. At the speed of light, it takes only 2.5 seconds for radio waves to travel to the Moon and back.

Radar Components

A radar set usually consists of a transmitter, a transmitting antenna, a receiving antenna, a receiver, a computer, and a display. Normally, the same antenna is used both to transmit and to receive. The transmitter causes a current to flow back and forth in the antenna, causing radio waves of the same frequency as the current to travel outward from the antenna. When radio waves strike objects, the waves are reflected and absorbed, depending upon the waves' frequency and the properties of the objects. Metals, for example, are particularly reflective. When waves are reflected, a small fraction of the reflected energy may return to the radar antenna as an echo. The receiver amplifies this echo, and then the computer extracts information from the amplified echo and prepares this information to be displayed.

Target Direction, Range, Speed, and Size

A common type of radar, with a revolving antenna, sends out a short burst of waves and listens for an echo. The direction in which the antenna was pointing when it received the echo gives the target's direction, and the time delay between sending and receiving gives the target's distance. If the elapsed time is the time between sending the burst and receiving the echo, then the target's range is one-half the elapsed time multiplied by the speed of radar waves, or about 3×10^5 kilometers per second.

Radar and Air Traffic Control

Radar, essential to air traffic control (ATC), was developed from World War II instruments that sent radio waves from a transmitter and measured the time lapse before the radio signal, reflected from a solid object, returned to a receiver in the instrument. The time lapse told the distance between the target object and the radar.

In the 1950's, more accurate tracking systems and high-power radar able to detect aircraft at long ranges were developed. Amplifiers became available to better serve the power needs of long-range radar. Airborne pulse Doppler radar also was introduced, and Doppler frequency shifts of reflected radio signals led to Doppler radar, detection of moving targets, and useful images of targets, as in weather radar.

During the 1970's and 1980's, advances in digital technology enabled better signal and data processing, the ability to distinguish between different targets, and the ability to measure wind, ocean waves, and other environmental features. Solid-state technology helped to improve radar capabilities still further, and computer technology growth in the 1990's increased the amount of information obtainable from radar.

When the same antenna is used both to transmit and to receive, there must be some way to keep the stronger transmitted signal from completely swamping the weaker return echos. In the pulsed operation just described, this is done by timing. The transmission burst lasts about one microsecond, then the radar listens. The wait time during which the radar set listens for echos before sending out another pulse is keyed to the faintest echo that can be reliably detected. If targets up to 150 kilometers (90 miles) away can be detected, and radar waves can travel this distance and back in one millisecond, the pattern of pulse transmission and listening can be repeated about every millisecond.

When a radar wave is reflected from a moving target, the frequency of the wave changes in a fashion described as the Doppler effect. The target's speed can be determined from this change in frequency. If two targets are at the same distance and have the same radar reflective properties, a brighter echo indicates a larger object. Because radar reflectivity depends upon the shape and composition of the target, a better method to determine size is to send out a series of very short pulses, each lasting only a nanosecond or two. A large target may reflect two or more of these pulses, and the maximum distance between the echos yields the approximate size of the target.

Antennas and Operating Frequency

A simple wire antenna will send radio waves outward in all directions; however, a carefully spaced group of several antennas can concentrate most of the radio waves into a beam. Such antenna groups must be several times the size of the wavelength they broadcast, and they work reasonably well from 3 million to 300 million hertz (cycles per second), or 100-meter to 1-meter wavelengths. The largest radar system in the world is the U.S. Air Force's over-the-horizon backscatter (OTH-B) air defense radar system, built to detect a Soviet bomber attack from thousands of kilometers away but also used to study ocean currents and waves. Each of the six transmitting antennas are 1.1 kilometers long, and the receiving antennas are 1.5 kilometers long. They operate between 5 and 28 megahertz, from 60- to 1.1-meter wavelengths. These wavelengths bounce off the ionosphere, about 200 kilometers above the ground, and reflect back down to the earth's surface.

The need for finer resolution and more portable radar sets eventually led to the development of radar wavelengths only centimeters long. Such short wavelengths can be formed into a searchlight-like beam by reflecting them from a parabolic metal dish. Because the paths of these wavelengths are not bent by the ionosphere, they must have a straight line of sight to the target. However, they will pass through the ionosphere and can be used to track objects in space. Regardless of the type of antenna used, radar beams spread wider as they travel outward from the antenna. The amount of spreading is smaller for shorter wavelengths and for bigger antennas. That is, the narrowest beams are formed, and the finest details can be seen, with radars using the shortest wavelengths and the largest antennas.

The properties of the atmosphere also affect the choice of operating frequency. Atmospheric attenuation is negligible for frequencies up to 1 gigahertz (1 billion hertz). Above 3 gigahertz (1-centimeter wavelength), however, radar absorption by raindrops becomes significant, so weather radars operate at these frequencies. Above 12 gigahertz, clouds begin to absorb the radar waves.

Military Development and Applications

The development of radar was such a natural outgrowth of experiments with radio transmission that it was independently invented and developed by several countries during the 1930's. Probably more than any other device, radar dictated the course of World War II. Even before the war, Great Britain had begun installation of chain home (CH) radar stations along its coasts, with radar antennas on towers up to 110 meters high. Germany began massive bomber attacks on Britain in August, 1940. Chain home radars were so effective at giving warning and allowing the badly outnumbered Royal Air Force (RAF) fighters to position themselves for maximum effect, that by November of that year, daytime bomber attacks had stopped. The CH radar system determined the direction and elevation of an approaching aircraft by comparing the intensity of signals received at different antennas in the chain. When night attacks began the following year, CH radars were used to guide friendly fighters toward enemy bombers until the fighters got close enough to pick up the bombers on the short-range (5-kilometer) radar the fighters now carried. This technique was so successful that night attacks were also stopped.

Radar was also put to other uses. In order to aid radar operators to distinguish between friendly and enemy aircraft, identification, friend or foe (IFF) beacons were developed and used by the Allies. These were small radar receiver/transmitters that broadcast a coded radar signal that identified a craft as friendly when they detected a probing radar wave. Another device, a radar altimeter, is simply a small radar set that sends pulses toward the ground and determines the height from the time it takes for the echos to return. The atomic bomb dropped on Hiroshima in 1945 carried four radar altimeters and was fused to explode when any two measured the height as less than 600 meters (2,000 feet).

Had German submarines been able to cut off the flow of supplies and personnel from the United States and Canada to Great Britain and Europe, the Allied invasion of Europe would have been impossible. At first, the German submarines were very successful in sinking Allied ships, but then the Allies began to hunt the submarines with radar. As submarine losses mounted, the Germans equipped their submarines with radar detectors, and the warning they gained allowed the submarines to be safely hidden underwater by the time attack aircraft arrived.

The British then made one of the most important technological advances of the war, the microwave-cavity magnetron, a device for generating high-power radio waves of 10 centimeters or less. Shorter wavelengths meant radar antennas could be smaller, a great advantage in an aircraft, and smaller targets, such as submarine periscopes, could be detected. The German radar detectors could not pick up the short wavelength the Allies were now using, and the tide turned against them. In 1942, the Germans sank 8,245,000 tons of Allied shipping while losing 85 submarines. In 1944, they sank only 1,422,000 tons, but lost 241 submarines.

Radar Tracking

The familiar weather radar displays distances and directions to radar targets in a maplike image. A moving target such as a storm can be tracked by following its image on the radar screen as its position changes with time. Air traffic controllers use an extension of this method to guide aircraft in the vicinity of busy airports. A sophisticated version of this type of radar is used by the E-3 Sentry, or Airborne Warning and Control System (AWACS) aircraft, a modified Boeing 707 carrying a 9-meter (30-foot) radar dome. When aloft, AWACS can detect low-flying targets more than 375 kilometers (250 miles) away. Special equipment subtracts out the ground clutter that would swamp ordinary radars, thereby allowing AWACS controllers to monitor all the air traffic in the area and to direct friendly aircraft. AWACS assisted in thirty-eight of the forty air-to-air shoot-downs of the 1991 Persian Gulf War.

The efforts of civilian air traffic controllers have contributed to making air travel far safer than automobile travel. Airport surveillance radar (ASR) is a medium-range system that detects and tracks aircraft within about 50 miles of the radar installation. Controllers use this radar as they direct aircraft landings, takeoffs, and flight patterns. Air route surveillance radar (ARSR) tracks aircraft en route between airports. The ARSR-4 uses a wavelength of about 21 centimeters and has a range of about 400 kilometers. It broadcasts a series of pulses that interrogates the radar beacon or transponder carried by all large aircraft. The transponder broadcasts a reply from which the aircraft's identity, range, and direction can be determined. An air traffic controller follows the aircraft's progress and delivers instructions. When the aircraft leaves one controller's sector, it is progressively handed off to controllers in the sectors through which it flies until reaching the destination airport.

Radar sets can be designed to track a target automatically. During the Korean War, the U.S. Army used radar to track mortar shells. A shell follows a parabolic trajectory, and if the radar can follow it for more than one-half of its trajectory, its launch point can be deduced, and artillery fire can be directed against the mortar. The radar dish used could slew, or pivot, quickly in any direction, and a mask partially blocked the center of the radar beam. When the radar locked onto a target, the target was positioned in the center of the beam, where the return echo would be relatively weak because of the mask. If the target drifted from the beam's center, the echo strengthened, and the radar set used this information to move the antenna and keep the target centered. Although a similar scheme can be used to track aircraft, schemes that maximize the echo are more common. In any case, a relatively narrow beam must be used for tracking.

Although mechanical systems can neither move quickly enough to track rockets and nearby fast-moving aircraft nor track multiple targets, phased-array radars can. These arrays consist of hundreds or even thousands of small antenna pods mounted in a regular array on a reflecting surface. Each pod is like a four-leaf clover, with each leaf replaced by a pencil-length rod pointing back toward the reflector at an approximate 45-degree angle. The term "phase" refers to position in the wave cycle. When all of the antennas are in phase, they begin broadcasting the beginning of a wave at the same time, and the radar beam is strongest straight ahead. If, instead, neighboring rows of antennas begin to broadcast at progressively later times, the radar beam will be tilted off to one side. When the radar receives a target echo, a computer can calculate where the target should be a fraction of a second later and direct the beam at that point. It takes only millionths of a second to switch the beam between targets so that a phased array can track one hundred or more targets virtually simultaneously.

The U.S. Air Force maintains Pave Paws radars at Cape Cod, Massachusetts; Beale, California; and Clear Air Force Station, Alaska. "Pave" is an Air Force program name, and

"Paws" is an acronym of phased-array warning system. Each Pave Paws site has twin antennas consisting of 1,792 radiating elements mounted on massive reflecting faces measuring 31 meters across. The primary assignment for these installations is to detect and track intercontinental ballistic missiles or missiles launched from submarines at the United States. The Pave Paws radar beams extend 5,500 kilometers into space and are also used to track satellites.

The heart of the U.S. Navy's Aegis combat system is a 4-megawatt phased-array radar mounted on a special ship that is also equipped with missiles and a Phalanx close-in weapons system (CIWS) for destroying attacking aircraft and missiles.

Countermeasures and Stealth Technology

The crew of an aircraft carrying a radar detector will know whether the craft is being observed. Once alerted, the crew might eject strips of aluminum foil, called chaff. Clouds of chaff appear as new targets on the radar screen and confuse the radar operator. The U.S. Eighth Air Force dropped more than 10 million pounds (4.5 million kilograms) of aluminum foil during World War II. Specially equipped aircraft, such as Ferrets, and later, Wild Weasels, determine the location and frequencies of fire-control radars and jam them by broadcasting radar noise.

Modern radar countermeasures include recording the fire-control radar signals and then beaming them back at the ground installation, thus making false targets appear at various distances and directions. When the aircraft are close enough, pilots can fire high-speed antiradiation missiles (HARMs) that home in on the fire-control radar. This presents the fire-control radar operator with an impossible choice: In order to shoot down the attacking aircraft, the operator must turn on the fire-control radar. However, if the radar is on for more than a few seconds, a HARM can lock in on its beam. In the initial stage of the Persian Gulf War, F-4G Phantom Wild Weasels flew 2,596 sorties and used this technique to devastate the formidable Iraqi air defenses.

Perhaps the best radar countermeasure is to make an aircraft invisible to radar. The radar echos from an air-

A radar receiver locates objects and measures the distance to them by sending out short bursts of radio waves and measuring how long it takes for an echo of the bounced-back wave to return. (Raytheon Company)

craft's rounded fuselage fan out over a broad range of directions, including back toward the originating antenna. Stealth aircraft are made with many flat surfaces that are tilted to deflect the reflected radar beam away from the originating antenna. In order to reduce the radar echo when it is observed from behind, a "W" shape is used for the wing's trailing edge. Right-angled corners such as those between the tail and fuselage of a normal aircraft are eliminated, because they can return strong radar echos. It is such right angles that make highway signs coated with corner reflector crystals appear to light up when lit by a car's headlights. Carbon fiber materials and coatings that absorb radar waves are used extensively. The F-117A Nighthawk can get 90 percent closer to ground-based radar than a normal aircraft before it can be detected. During the opening minutes of the Persian Gulf War, eight Nighthawks followed a wave of Tomahawk cruise missiles and arrived at Bagdad undetected by ground radar. Their presence was announced only by bombs falling on their tar-

529

gets. The massive B-2 stealth bomber first saw combat in Yugoslavia during March, 1999. It carries eight times the bomb load of the F-117.

Charles W. Rogers

Bibliography

Baxter, James Phinney III. *Scientists Against Time*. Cambridge, Mass.: MIT Press, 1968. A popular book about the important inventions of World War II.

Brookner, Eli. "Phased-Array Radars." *Scientific American* 252, no. 2 (February, 1985). A good, basic description of how phased-array radars work.

Jensen, Homer, et al. "Side-Looking Airborne Radar." *Scientific American* 237, no. 2 (October, 1977). A slightly technical description of how terrain-mapping radar works.

Page, Robert Morris. *The Origin of Radar*. Garden City, N.Y.: Anchor Books, 1962. Written for the general public by the Director of Research at the U.S. Naval Laboratory, a scientist who helped develop radar.

See also: Air traffic control; Avionics; Communication; Doppler radar; Gulf War; Instrumentation; Missiles; Nighthawk; Stealth bomber; Stealth fighter; World War II

Ramjets

- **Definition:** A ramjet engine is a jet engine in which the working fluid is compressed solely by the deceleration of the fluid entering the engine.
- **Significance:** Ramjet engines represent the simplest type of air-breathing engines. They are used to power long-range guided missiles, and they also offer the potential to improve the payload and reusability of space launch vehicles.

Principles

Jet engine designs can be understood in terms of the gas turbine cycle. The fluid is first compressed, heat is added at constant pressure, and then work is extracted as the fluid expands. Heat addition is more efficient at high pressure. At high flight speeds, the pressure rise due to the deceleration of air entering the engine is high enough for engine performance, without mechanical compressors. This also removes the need for a turbine to drive the compressor. Since compression depends on a high flight speed, ramjets cannot accelerate from rest, nor produce useful levels of thrust below Mach 0.6. Thus, ramjets are used on vehicles where there is some other propulsion device for the takeoff stage, with ramjet startup occurring at supersonic speeds.

In the theoretical case of the ideal ramjet, air entering at a supersonic Mach number is decelerated through a lossless diffuser. Fuel is added and mixed with the air before it enters the combustor, and then ignited, to complete the fuel-air reaction at constant pressure (no pressure losses) inside the combustor. The heated gas then expands out through a frictionless nozzle, the exhaust Mach number equaling the Mach number ahead of the inlet. This exhaust velocity is higher than the inlet velocity because the exhaust temperature and speed of sound are higher than the inlet values. The thrust of the ideal ramjet is limited by two factors. Firstly, the thrust becomes zero at the Mach number where deceleration of air raises the temperature to the material limits of the engine, preventing further heat addition. Secondly, when the flow velocity reaches the local speed of sound anywhere inside the engine duct, the mass flow rate of air and the amount of heat addition are maximized.

In practice, four other major factors limit ramjet efficiency. The first is that decelerating a supersonic flow usually produces shocks. Drag due to shock losses can be minimized by careful inlet design, but operation over a range of conditions requires variable-geometry inlets, which add weight and complexity. Second, there is a compromise in the burner design. Without flameholders to create zones of slow-moving fluid and turbulence, it is difficult to get the fuel and air to mix and react within the short distance available for a combustor. Increasing the distance usually increases the engine weight, but flameholders and turbulence increase drag. Third, heat addition in any form to a moving fluid entails an irrecoverable loss in the work available from the fluid. The higher the Mach number at heat addition, the greater this Rayleigh line loss. Fourth, the nozzle can rarely be made large enough to enable full expansion of the exhaust to the outside pressure. Solutions to each of these problems can be seen in the various designs of ramjets.

History

French engineer René Lorin is credited with inventing the ramjet in 1913. Practical applications had to wait until the 1940's. Small Lorin-type ramjets were tested atop a Luftwaffe Dornier Do-17Z-2 in early 1942. The Skoda-Kauba SK-P.14 ramjet-powered fighter (early 1945) was built around a 1.5 meter diameter, 9.5 meter long Sanger ramjet. The ramjet duct and two forward fuel tanks occupied much of the fuselage, with the pilot lying prone atop the ramjet in a cockpit located in the aircraft nose. The small unswept wings carried fuel tanks. Booster rockets on a tricycle undercarriage that could be jettisoned enabled takeoff and acceleration to ramjet startup speed. Germany also used ramjet engines to augment the V-1 Doodlebug rocket bombs sent over Britain. Sanger ramjets were also tested with the Messerschmitt Me-262 turbojet fighter and other Luftwaffe aircraft.

Studies using subsonic ramjets at the University of Southern California (USC) in late 1943 led to the 1945 contract to the Glenn Martin company to develop the Gorgon 4 guided ramjet missile. The Gorgon test vehicles had swept wings and tails, designed for Mach 0.7 flight with a range of 50 to 70 miles, with the engine firing for 270 seconds. The full-scale USC supersonic ramjet was tested in August, 1945. The Marquardt Company delivered the first engines for testing to the U.S. Navy, with the first free flight of a supersonic ramjet-powered vehicle on November 14, 1947, off Point Mugu, California. The National Advisory Committee for Aeronautics (NACA) used the F-23 Ramjet Research Vehicle in tests at their Wallops Island facility from 1950 to 1954. The two 1,000-pound-thrust engines of the F-23 used acetylene fuel, reaching Mach 3.12 and an altitude of 159,000 feet. In 1959, a French experimental aircraft set a speed record of 1,020 miles per hour using ramjet engines. Meanwhile Soviet designer Mikhail Bondaryuk developed a kerosene-fueled ramjet stage for the EKR launch vehicle in 1953 and 1954, producing 1,250 pounds of thrust, with a specific impulse (Isp) of 1,580 seconds. This engine was studied for an experimental winged cruise missile, which formed the basis for the later Burya missiles.

On August 29, 1947, the McDonnell XH-20 "Little Henry" helicopter first flew, powered by ramjet engines at its rotor tips. While this concept eliminated the need for a countertorque system such as a tail rotor, it was too noisy to be a practical helicopter propulsion device. At the turn of the twenty-first century, a ramjet-powered spinning disc was being developed as an efficient power-generation device. With these two exceptions, all ramjet applications have been for high-speed flight. Ramjets are thought to be useful for flight at up to Mach 18, with advances in materials and fuels.

Ramjet-Powered Missiles

The British Bloodhound and SeaDart series, the U.S. Navy's Mach 2.7 Talos, which could carry a 5 kiloton nuclear warhead, the Soviet SA-6, and the Indian Akash are examples of surface-to-air missiles which use a solid-fueled rocket boost, followed by ramjet-powered acceleration. The BAe Meteor beyond visual range air-to-air missile (BVRAAM) uses a solid-fueled variable-flow rocket-ramjet engine. The ramjet engine enables the thrust to be distributed and controlled over a longer duration, widening the range of parameters within which the missile has a high probability of destroying its targets. Ramjet air-to-surface missiles include the Russian KH-31/AS-17 Krypton. In 1955, the U.S. Navy launched and then canceled full-scale development of the Triton, a ramjet-powered, Mach 3.5, 21,600-kilometer-range, submarine-launched cruise missile. France has deployed the ramjet-powered, air-launched, nuclear-armed, Mach 3.5, 300-kilometer-range ASMP cruise missile. Newer programs are the U.S. Fasthawk Mach 4 booster-ramjet cruise missile to replace the Tomahawk, and the CounterForce Mach 4-6 surface-to-air missile (SAM).

Turboramjets and Ramrockets

Most missiles which use ramjets are actually rocket-ramjets or ramrockets. They use a rocket booster either as a separate stage or as an integral part of the engine. At liftoff, the intake is closed or blocked by fuel, and the vehicle operates as a rocket. As the rocket propellant grain burns down, the intakes are opened, and a combustion chamber formed for the ramjet to start operating. In some missiles, the ramjet engines are separate strap-ons which do not operate fully until the rocket booster stage is expended. High-speed aircraft use engines which operate partially as ramjets. For example, the SR-71 Blackbird has engines which start as turbine engines. At high altitudes and speeds, larger air intakes open, allowing air to bypass the fan and operate as a ramjet. The Japanese ATREX project developed an expanding air turboramjet engine. In this concept, liquid hydrogen fuel was used to precool the incoming air before sending it through a fan (at takeoff) or around the fan at high speeds. Combustion was conducted in subsonic flow. A tip-turbine operated in the high-speed bypass flow to recover work to be used to run the liquid hydrogen turbopump. A plug nozzle was used, where the flow adjusted itself to be optimally expanded as the external conditions changed.

Hypersonic Ramjets

The vehicles discussed above are mostly limited to publicized Mach numbers below 3.5. The ramjet also offers several advantages as a propulsion system for space launch vehicles and hypersonic missiles. Without complex turbomachinery, the engine can be quite light, offer an unobstructed airflow path, and can use a wide variety of fuels, ranging from cryogenic hydrogen to storables like kerosene and methane. However, major problems face engine designers. Above Mach 4, shock losses suffered in decelerating the flow to subsonic speeds for combustion may exceed the Rayleigh line losses of heat addition to a supersonic stream. The pressure rise incurred in deceleration to subsonic speeds would demand heavy casings, and the temperature rise is such that further heat addition would melt the burner. Improvements in materials can yield only limited gains, because most fuels would decompose and not release heat at very high temperatures. For these reasons, supersonic-combustion ramjets (scramjets) are being developed in several countries, including the United States, Russia, Britain, Europe, Japan, and India. In these designs, the fuel is mixed into a supersonic airstream and the heat added by reaction until the Mach number comes down close to unity. The technology for air liquefaction, where oxygen is recovered from air at the lower altitudes and stored in liquid form for rocket flight at high altitudes, appears to be key to making these into viable space launch engines.

In the 1960's, scramjet research produced a few designs, such as those by Aerojet General, which showed positive net thrust (more thrust than drag) at hypersonic Mach numbers in wind tunnel tests. Such engines injected the fuel in jets perpendicular to the supersonic airstream, enabling fast mixing, albeit with high drag. Antonio Ferri's "thermal compression" idea removed the need for variable geometry. The X-15 project, intended to study scramjet operation, was canceled before testing full-scramjet mode. In the mid-1980's, NASA, the U.S. Air Force, the U.S. Navy, Britain, France, Germany, and Japan each conducted large programs directed toward different vehicle concepts. Best-known among these was the National Aerospace Plane (NASP) project announced by President Ronald Reagan, with the French Hermes, German Sanger, and British HOTOL springing up concurrently. When American funding for NASP dried up in the mid-1990's, citing difficulties with supersonic fuel-air mixing, all these programs dropped from public view, citing high cost. Scramjet engines have since been developed for missile applications. A November, 1991, test lasting 130 seconds near Baikonur Cosmodrome in Kazakstan is reported to have taken a scramjet on a SAM booster to Mach 8. The Russian GELA hypersonic experimental flying testbed, believed to be an air-launched strategic cruise missile, was shown at Moscow in 1995. The Mach 6-10 Hyper-X program, the Boeing/NASA X-43, and a DARPA scramjet program are examples. The Johns Hopkins Applied Physics Lab reported success with a dual-combustor ramjet which proved operation of a scramjet engine up to Mach 6 with JP-10 storable liquid hydrocarbon fuel.

Nuclear Ramjets

The heat addition in the ramjet need not be chemical. In the 1950's, the U.S. Air Force's Project Pluto developed a Mach 3 ramjet-powered missile where the flow was heated to over 2,500 degrees Fahrenheit by a fast neutron nuclear reactor. The missile would carry nuclear weapons and loiter around the periphery of the Soviet Union in tense times. In a nuclear war, these 150,000-pound "Doomsday Missiles" were to dash supersonic at low altitudes (500 feet) and deliver their 50,000-pound payloads to their targets. After dropping bombs, the missiles were to cruise back and forth across the Soviet Union indefinitely, destroying property with the shock waves created by their passage, and contaminating everything with radiation from their engines. The nuclear ramjet engine was tested in the Nevada desert. The danger of the missile going out of control during flight testing and cruising back and forth across the United States ensured the project's cancellation.

Robert W. Bussard described an interstellar ramjet. The vehicle would create a magnetic field and capture hydrogen ions (protons) occurring in space. Nuclear fusion of these protons would heat the gas and propel them through a nozzle. The critical speed needed for ramjet startup was estimated to be about 6 percent of the speed of light, and the inlet diameter was of the order of 6,000 to 10,000 kilometers. Lasers were proposed to ionize hydrogen ahead of the inlet. There is debate whether the protons would actually enter the engine, and would sustain fusion.

Narayanan M. Komerath

Bibliography

Anderson, J. D. *Hypersonic and High Temperature Gas Dynamics*. Reston, Va.: American Institute of Aeronautics and Astronautics, 2000. Graduate-level engineering textbook with historical introductions.

Glenn Learning Technologies Project. NASA-Glenn Research Center. (www.grc.nasa.gov/www/K-12/airplane/shortp.html) These Web pages provide expositions of principles, example problems, and animated demonstrations.

Hill, Philip G., and Carl R. Peterson. *Mechanics and Thermodynamics of Propulsion*. 2d ed. Reading, Mass.: Addison-Wesley, 1992. Comprehensive textbook on gas turbine and rocket propulsion, suitable for undergraduate engineering students.

Ordway, Frederick I., III, and Ronald C. Wakeford. *International Missile and Spacecraft Guide.* New York: McGraw-Hill, 1960. Description of early development of missiles and ramjet engines, with data.

See also: Engine designs; Forces of flight; Robert H. Goddard; Gravity; Helicopters; Hypersonic aircraft; Jet engines; Missiles; National Aeronautics and Space Administration; Hermann Oberth; Rocket propulsion; Rockets; Supersonic aircraft; Turbojets and turbofans; Turboprops; X planes

Raptor

Also known as: F-22
Date: First flew on September 7, 1997
Definition: Next-generation air superiority fighter.
Significance: The F-22 is expected to become the predominant fighter plane in the world when it becomes operational in 2005, and supporters argue that it will guarantee the U.S. Air Force dominance over potential enemies through at least 2040.

Evolution of the Raptor

First conceived in the midst of the Cold War arms race with the Soviet Union, the F-22 grew out of U.S. fears that future Russian fighters might prove superior to the F-15 Eagle. Experts called for the creation of an advanced tactical fighter in 1981, and after competition between various manufacturers the Air Force awarded Lockheed Martin a contract to build the plane in 1991. Assembly of the first test model began in 1994, the aircraft flew for the first time in 1997, and in 1999 the Air Force approved a low-rate production plan that would put eight Raptors into advanced flight testing by the end of 2001. The Air Force hoped to purchase 339 F-22's and to form the first operational Raptor squadron in 2005.

Capabilities

Although the F-22 is fully capable of attacking ground targets with precision, its primary mission is to destroy enemy aircraft at either close or long range under any weather conditions. It incorporates a number of advanced technologies, including a stealth airframe design which utilizes flattened surfaces and special materials to make the aircraft difficult to detect with radar. The Raptor is powered by two revolutionary Pratt & Whitney F-119-PW-100 engines, which allow it to fly for extended periods at supersonic speed (beyond the speed of sound) without using its afterburner. An afterburner essentially pumps raw fuel into the flame of a jet engine, generating great thrust and speed in exchange for a great increase in fuel consumption. This ability to supercruise allows the Raptor to fly farther and faster while using less fuel than any jet fighter to date. In addition, the F-22 uses thrust vectoring, in which the nozzle of each engine moves to help the plane turn, climb, or dive, to greatly enhance maneuverability. The F-22 also has an integrated avionics suite in which all the computers on the plane, such as weapons, radar, and flight control, function well together, with a central integrated processor one hundred times more powerful than the computers on the space shuttle. These technologies allow the single pilot of an F-22 to see enemy aircraft at long range and destroy them with very little risk of being detected, or to close with and eliminate adversaries in a close-range dogfight under any circumstances. They represent an enormous advance over previous aircraft.

Weapons

The F-22 carries a 20-millimeter Gatling gun and air-to-air missiles or ground-attack ordnance in an internal weapons bay which reduces drag and enhances stealth characteristics. Extra weapons or fuel tanks may be carried on external racks if necessary, though this arrangement makes the aircraft more visible to enemy radar. A normal weapons load would include six radar-guided AIM-120 medium-range air-to-air missiles or two AIM-120's and two GBU-32 joint direct attack munitions (JDAM). In either case, the Raptor could also carry two AIM-9 Sidewinder short-range air-to-air missiles on its wingtips.

The Future of the Raptor

Supporters of the F-22 point to its unparalleled capability and argue the United States should make the aircraft operational as soon as possible. They maintain that the current fleet of Air Force F-15 Eagles and F-16 Fighting Falcons are old and increasingly difficult to maintain, and that advances in computers, radar, and surface-to-air missiles make existing U.S. aircraft more and more vulnerable to the air defenses of potential enemies.

Critics counter that cost overruns and production delays have made the F-22 the most expensive fighter plane in history, and that the end of the Cold War and the diminishing aerial threat posed by other nations means the United States can delay production of the aircraft for at least a decade. They point to current estimates which place the cost of the entire Raptor program at approximately $62.7 billion for 339 planes (or $187 million each), and to studies which show that F-15's and F-16's will remain superior to the aircraft of any potential adversary through perhaps 2014. They suggest that Raptor production be delayed while the Air Force purchases additional aircraft based on current designs, and then accelerated when the threat posed by possible enemies is commensurate with the Raptor's cost. No matter who wins this argument, the Raptor seems certain to enter service in at least limited numbers between 2005 and 2007.

F-22 Specifications
The Raptor's length is 62 feet, 1 inch, and its height is 16 feet, 5 inches, with a wingspan of 44 feet, 6 inches. Its maximum takeoff weight is 60,000 pounds, although its normal takeoff weight is yet to be determined. Its maximum cruise speed is Mach 1.5 (one-and-a-half times the speed of sound) or better, with an absolute maximum speed of Mach 1.7. Its maximum altitude is 50,000 feet, although its range is not yet known. The plane has two Pratt & Whitney F119-PW-100 engines, each rated at approximately 35,000 pounds of thrust.

Lance Janda

Bibliography
Aronstein, David C., Michael J. Hirschberg, and Albert C. Piccirillo. *Advanced Tactical Fighter to F-22 Raptor: Origins of the Twenty-first Century Air Dominance Fighter.* Reston, Va.: American Institute of Aeronautics and Astronautics, 1998. A richly detailed technical history of the origins and development of the F-22 from the early 1980's to the present.

Pace, Steve. *F-22 Raptor: America's Next Lethal War Machine.* New York: McGraw-Hill, 1999. An accessible overview of the F-22 aimed at general aviation enthusiasts.

Sweetman, Bill. *F-22 Raptor.* Osceola, Wis.: Motorbooks International, 1998. This brief work emphasizes photographs and provides highlights of the F-22's history and capabilities.

See also: Air Force, U.S.; Eagle; Fighter pilots; Jet engines; Lockheed Martin; Military flight; Supersonic aircraft

Reconnaissance

Definition: The military exploration of enemy territory to gain strategic information.

Significance: Aerial reconnaissance was one of the earliest military uses of aircraft and remains a vital tool for military intelligence gathering.

History and Development
Aerial reconnaissance was the first mission of combat aviation, from which all other combat missions were outgrowths. Since their humble beginnings in World War I (1914-1918), when pilots flew over battlefields looking for the enemy, reconnaissance aircraft, their sensors, and their missions have evolved in directions that would have been unimaginable to those pioneers in their flimsy aircraft over no-man's-land.

By the late twentieth century, the most frequently used battlefield reconnaissance aircraft were scout helicopters, such as the OH-58, which fly at low altitudes, following the terrain to minimize their vulnerability. These aircraft look for artillery targets and information for the divisional intelligence staff and flush out victims for attack helicopters. High-performance fighters are unsuited for these vital and dangerous missions, which require aircraft that can move slowly enough to find targets as small as a single vehicle or group of soldiers and can hover over the battlefield long enough to make a difference.

At an echelon above the battlefield scouts are high-performance reconnaissance aircraft, generally modified fighter aircraft. In World War II (1939-1945), they tended to be stripped-down versions of the fastest aircraft available, such as the F-5, a modified P-38 Lightning, or the De Havilland Mosquito. Their speed and high-altitude performance usually allowed them to evade pursuit and to avoid flak. Two primary missions of high-performance reconnaissance aircraft during this period were finding targets for strategic bombers and reporting on the results of bombing raids.

With the introduction of satellites and more specialized strategic reconnaissance aircraft, the modified fighter declined in prominence and now primarily supports the intelligence-gathering needs of the theater commander. Thus, the modified fighter reconnaissance aircraft no longer has the best available airframe. In recent decades, aircraft types have remained in service for reconnaissance long after they have been replaced as fighters. A prime example, the RF-4C Phantom, flew reconnaissance missions for the U.S. Air Force for more than a decade after the F-4 fighter was retired from the active inventory. Although these aircraft can mount a variety of sensors, including side-looking airborne radar (SLAR), their primary tool is usually photography.

During the Cold War, the modified fighter was phased out of strategic reconnaissance missions. Because it had never been feasible to send a modified fighter deep into the interior of the Soviet Union, this region remained a total mystery to the West at the start of the Cold War. During the early 1950's, nations of the North Atlantic Treaty Organization (NATO) routinely learned about new Soviet weapons systems only after they had been paraded across Moscow's Red Square on the May Day holiday. The first effective U.S. attempt to address this problem was the U-2, a low-speed, high-altitude aircraft with a ceiling of 70,000 feet. Stategists hoped that the U-2 would fly high enough to avoid any possibility of intercept. The U-2 succeeded at its mission from 1956 until 1960, when an SA-2 brought one down with disastrous political consequences.

The next stage in the development of strategic reconnaissance aircraft was the SR-71. Its existence was first made public in 1964, and it officially remains the fastest airplane in the world. To this day, the SR-71 has never been successfully intercepted, and it remains outside the altitude and speed envelopes of the most capable surface-to-air missiles.

During the late 1940's, it was realized that the most effective solution to the strategic reconnaissance problem was the Earth-circling satellite, but it was many years before the technology was implemented. In August, 1960, a satellite, launched under the name Project Corona, took the first photograph from space. By the 1970's, both the United States and the Soviet Union had routinely deployed a broad array of surveillance satellites. Satellites initially used cameras, which would jettison their film after their mission was completed. A recovery aircraft would then snag the film capsule in midair as it drifted down to Earth.

With time, further sensors have been added to satellites to include infrared and electronic intercept capabilities, and encrypted satellite downlinks have removed the need for midair recovery of falling film canisters. Satellites, however, continue to be hindered by their predictable and difficult-to-change orbits and by their limited ability to see targets that are obscured by the effects of clouds and other atmospheric conditions.

The Intelligence Process

Aerial reconnaissance, although extremely important, is not the only tool available to the intelligence analyst. Intelligence can be described as a mosaic, in which each aerial image, communications intercept, or spy report is a piece. Although each piece, in itself, might not reveal much information, when placed in the context of all other intelligence from all other available sources, the pieces come together to form a coherent picture. Each intelligence source has its own complementary strengths and weaknesses.

Human Intelligence

Human intelligence (HUMINT) is information gained from human beings: spies, prisoners of war, scouts, or combatants in contact with the enemy. In an airborne context, human intelligence usually consists of spot reports of visual sightings by pilots or observers. On the modern battlefield, with video feeds to ground stations becoming increasingly common, the line between human intelligence and imagery intelligence has become somewhat blurred.

Imagery Intelligence

Imagery intelligence (IMINT) has always been the aircraft's forte. Imagery has traditionally involved photography, and although photographic imagery remains an important tool, technology has added additional tools to the IMINT toolbox. Infrared, electro-optic video, and radar also produce images that can provide valuable intelligence and see things that conventional photography cannot.

The aerial photograph provides a powerful intelligence tool. It freezes in time an image that can be minutely examined. The exact make and model of enemy equipment, the strength and deployment of enemy forces, the condition of roads and other lines of communication, the output of industrial plants, and the effectiveness of prior attacks can all be determined through aerial photography.

Photographic intelligence does have weaknesses, however. It cannot be gathered through obstructions such as clouds or smoke. It freezes a single instant in time, allowing detailed analysis, but may miss something that happened an instant before or after, and it may lack the context of a moving image.

There are three forms of aerial photographic image: the vertical, the oblique, and the panoramic. The vertical image is taken from directly over the target. It provides a constant scale, which can be determined from the focal length of the camera and altitude of the platform. It is the preferred format, but because it requires the camera platform to fly directly over the target, it can be a bit too dangerous in a high-threat environment.

An oblique image is taken at an angle from the target. It covers a good deal of ground and is much safer to take. While it gives definition to tall objects, such as radio aerials, it also allows terrain to mask possible targets. Because it does not provide a constant scale, measurements taken from it are far less precise. In addition, only the first one-third of the image is generally usable, whereas the rest of the image is captured at too flat an angle for any meaningful interpretation.

The U-2 spy plane piloted by Francis Gary Powers was shot down over the Soviet Union on May 1, 1960, becoming one of the most notorious reconnaissance planes in history. (NASA)

The panoramic image is a combination of the vertical and oblique images. It covers a vast area below the platform and off to both sides and combines the strengths and weaknesses of vertical and oblique.

Infrared Imagery

Infrared imagery (IR) provides an effective and deadly addition to the aerial reconnaissance toolbox. IR sees electromagnetic radiation at a wavelength lower than visible light, which is radiation that is produced by heat.

IR works most effectively when the difference between the heat of the targets and the ambient temperature is high. IR is far less effective at high noon than it is at midnight. At night, the ambient temperature usually drops well below the heat of human bodies and vehicle engines. When the differential is high, hot targets appear as glowing objects on a dark background.

In the 1980's, forward-looking infrared (FLIR) was widely deployed. FLIR provides cueing for other intelligence assets and also works as a lethal target-acquisition tool for attack helicopters and low-altitude fighter-bombers. FLIR operates in real time and can capture movement as well as heat. If a target is both hot and moving, it will be detected.

Although FLIR can see much that conventional photography cannot, it cannot see through anything that absorbs or dissipates radiated heat, such as thick fog, rain, or solid obstacles.

Radar

Side-looking airborne radar (SLAR) has greatly expanded the vision and range of the aerial observer. The resolution has been improved to the point where individual buildings, roads, woods, and even vehicles can be reliably located. Added to these advantages is SLAR's ability to use Doppler measurements to determine which of the returns is currently moving. These moving target indicators (MTIs) mean that mass ground targets such as armored regiments can be picked out and targeted in real time.

The U.S. Air Force has invested in a new class of battlefield surveillance aircraft based on various forms of SLAR. The mission of the joint surveillance target attack radar system (Joint STARS) is to fly parallel to the front line and look deep into the enemy's rear for large-scale enemy movements and targets of opportunity. When teamed with the airborne warning and control system (AWACS), which uses radar to watch the skies deep into the enemy's rear, the U.S. Air Force sees the battlefield in three dimensions, making it extremely difficult for any conventional modern army to operate without being under constant attack by aircraft, long-range artillery, and rockets.

Radar can see through darkness, fog, clouds, and all but the heaviest weather. It can also see through camouflage and any sort of obstacle that is not dense enough to stop radio waves. It also provides location information that is accurate enough for immediate targeting.

The weakness of radar is that it behaves in a way that is different enough from familiar visible light that its ability to identify targets is very limited. The shape of a radar return can vary according to the angle at which it strikes a target. Although much effort has been expended toward making radar blips more descriptive, none so far has been reliable. Objects smaller than a B-52 can be identified no more precisely than as probable armored vehicles or possible radars.

Signals Intelligence

In addition to imagery, aircraft make excellent platforms for devices that collect and analyze the signals from communications systems, radars, or other devices broadcasting electromagnetic radiation into the atmosphere. Signals intelligence (SIGINT) consists of communications intelligence (COMINT) that intercepts and locates radio communications and electronic intelligence (ELINT), which is the location and identification of non-communication emitters, primarily radars.

The Future

The turn of the twenty-first century has brought a revolutionary change in the nature of aerial reconnaissance. The reconnaissance pilot "alone, unarmed, and unafraid" has become increasingly rare. The future, and to a large degree, the present of aerial reconnaissance lies with the uninhabited aerial vehicle (UAV). Systems such as the U.S. Army's Predator system are taking over the mission of battlefield reconnaissance. Using a combination of video and the Global Positioning System (GPS), they provide battlefield intelligence staffs with real-time intelligence information and accurate targeting without risking the lives of pilots.

The next stage of aerial reconnaissance is the replacement of many large radar and SIGINT platforms with long-endurance UAVs such as the Global Hawk. The long-range strategic mission will soon be performed by high-altitude uncrewed aircraft that will fly three times faster than the SR-71. These superfast UAVs, with their ability to fly on demand and address specific targets rather than follow fixed orbits, may eventually render the spy satellite obsolete.

New-generation UAVs carry sensors that will change the way imagery is collected and analyzed. Intelligence analysts will be able to interpret an image while the aircraft is still over the target, and advancements in digital image enhancement are making imagery even more useful. The future belongs to real-time sensors on a variety of aerial platforms (mostly uncrewed) networked to computerized command centers.

Walter Nelson

Bibliography

Stanley, Roy M. *To Fool a Glass Eye: Camouflage Versus Photoreconnaissance in World War II*. Washington, D.C.: Smithsonian Institution Press, 1998.

Vaughn, David, et al. *Capturing the Essential Factors in Reconnaissance and Surveillance Force Sizing and Mix*. Santa Monica, Calif.: RAND Project Air Force, 2000.

See also: Balloons; Communication; Fighter pilots; Military flight; Radar; Satellites; Uncrewed spaceflight; Uninhabited aerial vehicles; World War I; World War II

Record flights

Definition: Flights that surpass previous performance achievements.

Significance: Since the earliest days of human flight, pilots have attempted to fly faster, higher, longer distances, and longer periods of time than their predecessors. This competitive attitude has created the impetus to improve aircraft technology, and feats that were once remarkable become commonplace features of commercial aviation.

The desire to "push the envelope" of aircraft performance has provided the impetus to improve aircraft technology since the eighteenth century, from hot-air balloons to solar-powered aircraft. Record keepers usually compare the performances of aircraft of comparable weight and engine type.

Record flights

Turboprop Landplanes with Takeoff Weights of 3,000 to 6,000 Kilograms

On September 1, 1988, Einar Envoldson flew a Burkhart Grob Egrett-1 to a record altitude of 16,329 meters without a payload. Propulsion consisted of one Garrett TPE-33 1-14A 750-shaft horsepower engine. During that same flight, over a course in Greenville, Texas, Envoldson also set a record in altitude in horizontal flight without a payload of 16,238 meters.

On March 31, 1994, Werner Kraut of Germany set a record in altitude with a 1,000-kilogram payload of 15,552 meters. He flew a Burkhart Grob G-520 Egrett over Mindelheim, Germany.

On December 13, 1985, Sergei Gorbik of the Soviet Union set a record altitude of 6,150 meters with a 2,000-kilogram payload. He flew an Antonov An-3 powered by one 1,450-horsepower IX-TBD2O engine. On that same flight, Gorbik set another record for the greatest mass carried to a height of 2,000 meters: 2,375 kilograms. He flew over Podkievscoe Airfield, Soviet Union.

On April 16, 1985, Charles E. "Chuck" Yeager of the United States and Renald Davenport set a record in time to climb to a height of 3,000 meters: 1 minute, 48 seconds. They flew a Piper PA-42-1000 Cheyenne 400LS aircraft powered by two 1,000-shaft horsepower Garrett TPE-3 31-14 engines over Portland, Oregon. On that same flight, the pilots set a record of time to climb to a height of 6,000 meters of 3 minutes, 43 seconds, and to 9,000 meters of 6 minutes, 34 seconds. They also set a record of time to climb to a height of 12,000 meters of 11 minutes, 8 seconds.

On May 22, 1982, Joachim H. Blumschein of Germany set a speed record over a closed circuit of 100 kilometers without a payload of 571.43 kilometers per hour. He flew a Gulfstream Commander 695/980 powered by two 717.5-shaft horsepower Garrett TPE-33 1-10-501 engines over Leine, Germany. During the same flight, he set a record for speed over a closed circuit of 500 kilometers without a payload of 571.43 kilometers per hour. He also set records for speed over a closed circuit of 1,000 and 2,000 kilometers without payload of 572.08 kilometers per hour and 569.85 kilometers per hour, respectively.

On March 21, 1983, Joe Harnisch of the United States and David B. Webster set a speed record for eastbound flight around the world of 490.51 kilometers per hour. They flew a Gulfstream Commander 695A powered by two 820-horsepower Garrett TPE 33 1-501K engines. Their course began in Elkhart, Indiana, and extended across Goose Bay, Canada; Keflavik, Iceland; Vienna, Austria; Cairo, Egypt; Luxor, Egypt; Sharjah, Iran; Colombo, Sri Lanka; Singapore; Manila, Philippines; Agana, Guam; Wake Island; Midway Island; Honolulu, Hawaii; and San Francisco, California.

Turboprop Landplanes with Takeoff Weights of 6,000 to 9,000 Kilograms

On June 16, 1966, James F. Peters of the United States set a record in altitude in horizontal flight without a payload of 9,753 meters when he flew a Grumman OV-1C Mohawk over Calverton, Long Island, New York. The aircraft was powered by two 1,160-ESHP Lycoming T-53-L-7 engines.

On December 12, 1985, Vladimir Lysenko of the Soviet Union set an altitude record with a 1,000-kilogram payload of 6,100 meters. During the same flight, he set another record by reaching the same altitude with a 2,000-kilogram payload. He flew an Antonov An-3 powered by one 1,450-horsepower TBD-20 engine over Podkievscoe Airfield in the Soviet Union.

Turboprop Landplanes with Takeoff Weights of 9,000 to 12,000 Kilograms

On August 30, 1993, William G. Walker and Wyatt C. Ingram of the United States set a record of altitude reached without a payload: 10,892 meters. They flew a Marsh S-F3T Turbotracker powered by two 1,645-shaft horsepower Garrett TPE 331 engines over a course in Santa Rosa, California. During that same flight, they set a record for time to climb to a height of 3,000 meters of 3 minutes, 40 seconds, and speed over a closed circuit of 100 kilometers without payload of 454.53 kilometers per hour.

Turboprop Landplanes with Takeoff Weights of 12,000 to 16,000 kilograms

On May 7, 1982, Marina Popovitch and Galina Kortchuganova, both of the Soviet Union, set a record of altitude without payload of 11,050 meters. They flew an Antonov An-24 powered by two 2,820-horsepower AN24 engines over Podkievscoe Airfield in the Soviet Union.

On May 11, 1982, the same two pilots set a record of altitude in horizontal flight without payload of 10,920 meters in an Antonov An-24 powered by two 2,820-horsepower engines, again over Podkievscoe Airfield.

On February 16, 1976, Canadians Thomas E. Appleton, W. E. Pullen, and Harry Hubard set a record for time to climb to a height of 3,000 meters of 2 minutes, 13 seconds. They flew a De Havilland Canada DHC-5D Buffalo powered by two 3/33-ESHP engines over Downsview,

Canada. During the same flight, these crew members also set a record for time to climb to a height of 6,000 meters of 4 minutes, 27.5 seconds, and time to climb to a height of 9,000 meters of 8 minutes, 3.5 seconds.

Turboprop Landplanes with Takeoff Weights of 16,000 to 20,000 Kilograms

On December 17, 1991, Matt Klunder and Pete Tomczak of the United States set a record for speed over a closed 100-kilometer circuit without a payload of 600 kilometers per hour. They flew a Grumman E2-C Hawkeye powered by two 5,250-horsepower Allison T56-A-427 engines. During the same flight, the crew set a record for speed over a closed 100-kilometer circuit with 1,000-kilogram payload of 600 kilometers per hour and one of speed over a closed 100-kilometer circuit with 2,000-kilogram payload of 600 kilometers per hour.

On December 19, 1991, Matt Klunder and Steven Schmeiser of the United States set a record for altitude in horizontal flight without payload of 12,150 meters. They flew a Grumman E2-C Hawkeye powered by two 5,250-horsepower Allison T56-A-427 engines. They flew over Patuxent River Naval Air Station in Maryland. During the same flight, they set a record for altitude with a 1,000-kilogram payload of 12,518 meters.

On May 19, 1993, Gideon Singer and Kjell Nordstrom of Sweden set a record for time to climb to a height of 3,000 meters of 2 minutes, 26 seconds. They flew a Saab 2000 powered by two 2,100-horsepower Allison T2100 engines. During the same flight, they set a record for time to climb to a height of 6,000 meters of 4 minutes, 45 seconds, and to 9,000 meters of 8 minutes, 1 second.

Turboprop Landplanes with Takeoff Weights of 20,000 to 25,000 Kilograms

On December 18, 1991, Eric Hinger and Steven Schmeiser of the United States set a record for altitude with a 2,000-kilogram payload of 12,178 meters in a Grumman E2-C Hawkeye powered by two 5,250-horsepower Allison T56-A-427 engines, over Patuxent River Naval Air Station in Maryland.

On November 5, 1985, Petr Kirichuk and Alexandre Tkachenko of the Soviet Union set a record of altitude with a 5,000-kilogram payload of 11,230 meters in an Antonov An-32 powered by two 5,180-ESHP Am-20 engines. They flew over Podkievscoe Airfield, Soviet Union.

On July 7, 1982, Marina Popovitch and Galina Kortchuganova of the Soviet Union set a record for greatest payload carried to a height of 2,000 meters of 8,096 kilograms. They flew an Antonov An-24 powered by two 2,820-horsepower engines over Podmoskovnoe Aerodrome in the Soviet Union.

Turboprop Landplanes with Takeoff Weights of 25,000 to 35,000 Kilograms

On October 28, 1985, Alexandre Tkachenko and Vladimir Lysenko of the Soviet Union set a record for altitude with 1,000-kilogram payload of 11,120 meters in an Antonov An-32 powered by two 5,180-EHPS engines. They flew over Podkievscoe Airfield in the Soviet Union. During the same flight, they set a record altitude of 10,890 meters with a 2,000-kilogram payload.

On November 4, 1985, Petr Kirichuk and Alexandre Tkachenko of the Soviet Union set a record for altitude with a 5,000-kilogram payload of 10,510 meters in an Antononov An-32 powered by two 5,180-EHPS engines. They flew over Podkievscoe Airfield in the Soviet Union. During the same flight, they set a record for the greatest mass carried to a height of 2,000 meters of 7,256 kilograms.

Turboprop Landplanes with Takeoff Weights of 45,000 to 60,000 Kilograms

On April 20, 1999, Arlen D. Rens, Lyle H. Schaffer, and Timothy L. Gomez of the United States set a record for speed over a closed 1,000-kilometer circuit without a payload of 637.58 kilometers per hour. They flew a Lockheed Martin C-130J powered by four 4,700-horsepower AE engines over Dobbins Air Force Base, Georgia.

On March 22, 1991, Evgenii Bistrov and Alexei Marenkov of the Soviet Union set five records for speed over a closed 1,000-kilometer circuit of 587.53 kilometers per hour for an aircraft without a payload, with a 1,000-kilogram payload, with a 2,000-kilogram payload, with a 5,000-kilogram payload, and with a 10,000-kilogram payload. They flew an Antonov AN-12 powered by four 4,250-horsepower AI engines over Jasmine Aerodrome, Akhtubinsk, Soviet Union.

Turboprop Landplanes with Takeoff Weights of 100,000 to 150,000 Kilograms

On October 5, 1989, Igor Malychev and M. M. Bachkirov of the Soviet Union set four altitude records. The first was of 12,265 meters without a payload. The second, third, and fourth also reached 12,265 meters with payloads of 1,000, 2,000, and 5,000 kilograms. They flew a VP-021 (TU-95) powered by four 15,000-EHP Kuznetov engines over the Jasmine Aerodrome, Akhtubinsk, Soviet Union.

On September 26, 1989, V. E. Mossolov and I. A. Tchalov of the Soviet Union set multiple speed records over a closed 1,000-kilometer circuit of 807.37 kilometers per hour without a payload and with 1,000, 2,000, 5,000, 10,000, 15,000, 20,000, 25,000, and 30,000-kilogram payloads. They flew a VP-021 (TU-95) powered by four 15,000-horsepower HK engines.

Turbojet Landplanes

On May 17, 1975, Piotr Ostapenko of the Soviet Union set a record for time to climb to a height of 30,000 meters of 3 minutes, 10 seconds. He flew an E-266M powered by two 14,000-kilogram RD engines over the Podmoskovnoe Aerodrome in the Soviet Union.

On March 23, 1988, Nikolai Sadovnikov of the Soviet Union set a record for time to climb to a height of 15,000 meters of 1 minute, 10 seconds. He flew a P-42 powered by two 13,600-kilogram P-32 engines over the Podmoskovnoe Aerodrome in the Soviet Union.

On May 7, 1987, Vladimir Tersky and Yuri Resnitsky of the Soviet Union set a record for distance over a closed circuit without landing of 20,150.92 kilometers. They flew an Antononov An-124 powered by four 23,4000-kilogram D-1 8T engines.

On August 31, 1977, Alexandr Fedotov of the Soviet Union set a record for altitude without a payload of 37,650 meters. He flew an E-266M powered by two 14,000-kilogram RDF engines over the Podmoskovnoe Aerodrome in the Soviet Union.

On July 25, 1973, Fedotov set one record of altitude with a 1,000-kilogram payload of 35,230 meters and one for altitude with a 2,000-kilogram payload of 35,230 meters. During this flight, he flew an E-266 powered by two 11,000-kilogram PD engines.

On July 20, 1983, Sergei Agapov and Boris Veremei of the Soviet Union set altitude records of 18,200 meters with 10,000, 15,000, 20,000, 25,000, and 30,000-kilogram payloads. They flew a 101 aircraft, known in the military as the Tu-144, powered by four 20,000-kilogram Model 57 engines over Podmoskovnoe Aerodrome in the Soviet Union.

On October 29, 1959, Boris Stepanov and Boris Lumachev, both of the Soviet Union, set altitude records of 13,121 meters with 35,000, 40,000, 45,000, 50,000, and 55,000-kilogram payloads. They flew a 102M powered by four 13,000-kilogram D.15 engines over Podmoskovnoe Aerodrome in the Soviet Union.

On July 26, 1985, Vladimir Tersky and Alexandre Galounenko of the Soviet Union set altitude records of 10,750 meters with 160,000, 165,000, and 170,000-kilogram payloads. They flew an Antonov AN-124 powered by four 23,4000-kilogram Lotarev D-18T engines over the Podmoskovnoe Aerodrome in the Soviet Union.

On June 27, 1988, James C. Loesch and Howard B. Greene of the United States set a record for the greatest mass carried to a height of 2,000 meters of 405,656 kilograms. They flew a Boeing 747-400 powered by four 56,000-pound P&W 4056 engines over Moses Lake, Washington.

On November 18, 1998, Bryan Galbreath of the United States set a record for the greatest mass carried to a height of 15,000 meters of 1,503 kilograms. He flew a Lockheed Martin U-2 powered by one 16,500-pound F118 GE1O1 engine over Palmdale, California.

On April 8, 1973, Alexandr Fedotov of the Soviet Union set a record for speed over a closed 100-kilometers circuit without a payload of 2,605.10 kilometers per hour. He flew an E-266 powered by two 11,000-kilogram RD engines over Podmoskovnoe Aerodrome in the Soviet Union.

On July 27, 1976, Adolphus Bledsoe of the United States set a record of 3,367.22 kilometers per hour for speed over a closed circuit of 1,000 kilometers both without a payload and with a 1,000-kilogram payload.

On July 13, 1983, Sergei Agapov and Boris Veremei of the Soviet Union set speed records of 2,0351.55 kilometers per hour for speed over a closed circuit of 1,000 kilometers with 5,000, 10,000, 20,000 and 30,000-kilogram payloads. They flew a 101 (military Tu-144) powered by four 20,000-kilogram 57 engines over Podmoskovnoe Aerodrome in the Soviet Union.

On September 24, 1981, G. Volokhov and A. Turumine of the Soviet Union set records of 962 kilometers per hour for speed over a closed circuit of 1,000 kilometers with 40,000, 45,000, 50,000, 55,000, 60,000, 65,000, 70,000, 75,000 and 80,000-kilogram payloads. They flew an Ilyushin IL-86 powered by four 13,000-kilogram Kuznetzov engines over Podmoskovnoe Aerodrome in the Soviet Union.

On January 12, 1961, Henry J. Deutschendorf of the United States set records of 1,708.82 kilometers per hour for speed over a closed circuit of 2,000 kilometers with 1,000 and 2,000-kilogram payloads. He flew a Convair B-58A Hustler powered by four GE J-79-SA 15,000-pound engines over Edwards Air Force Base in California.

On April 7, 1994, Michael S. Menser of the United States set a record of 964.95 kilometers per hour for speed over a closed circuit of 10,000 kilometers without a payload. He flew a Rockwell B-1B powered by four F101-GE-102 12,000-pound engines from Grand Forks, North Dakota, to Mullan, Indiana, via Monroeville, Alabama.

On August 26, 1995, Russell F. Mathers and Daniel G. Manuel of the United States set records of 884.26 kilometers per hour for speed over a closed circuit of 10,000 kilometers with 1,000, 2,000, and 5,000-kilogram payloads. They flew a Boeing B-52H powered by eight P&W TF-33 17,100-pound engines over Edwards Air Force Base in California.

On June 3, 1995, Douglas L. Raaberg, Ricky W. Carver, Gerald V. Goodfellow, and Kevin D. Clotfelter of the United States set a record for speed around the world, eastbound, with refueling in flight, of 1,015.76 kilometers per hour. They flew a Rockwell B-1B powered by four GE F101-GE-102 30,780-pound engines.

On October 28, 1977, Walter H. Mullikin, Albert A. Frink, and W. Beckett, Jr., of the United States set a record for speed around the world over both of the earth's poles of 784.31 kilometers per hour. They flew in a Boeing 747 SP powered by four P&W JT9D-7 46,150-pound engines, from San Francisco, California, via the geographical north pole, London, Capetown, South Africa, the geographical south pole, and Auckland, New Zealand.

Gas Balloons

On September 8, 1984, Coy Foster of the United States set a record distance of 695.74 kilometers in a gas balloon over 250 cubic meters or less when he flew from Plano, Texas, to Lee's Summitt, Missouri.

On July 1, 1922, Georges Cormier of France set a record distance of 804.17 kilometers for a gas balloon of 400 to 600 cubic meters volume when he flew from Paris, France, to Muszen, Germany.

Oliver Griffin

Bibliography

Baker, David. *Flight and Flying: A Chronology.* New York: Facts on File, 1994. A comprehensive almanac of aviation history.

Gunston, Bill, ed. *Aviation Year by Year.* Updated ed. New York: Dorling Kindersley, 2001. Written for enthusiasts and the general public alike, covers the history of aviation through the year 2000 with articles, photographs, and timelines.

Jane's All the World's Aircraft, 2001-2002. New York: Franklin Watts, 2001. The standard reference for current aviation.

See also: Airplanes; Experimental aircraft; High-altitude flight; High-speed flight; Hypersonic aircraft; Pilots and copilots; Supersonic aircraft; Test pilots; Transatlantic flight; Transcontinental flight; Transglobal flight; Turbojets and turbofans; Turboprops

Reentry

Definition: The action of reentering the earth's atmosphere after space travel.

Significance: The study of reentry and the aerodynamics associated with the high-speed penetration of a planetary atmosphere allow humans to understand the nature of spaceflight.

History

Since 1830, small groups of scientists have studied meteors, natural objects entering Earth's atmosphere at high speed. Their studies have ranged from chemical analyses of recovered meteors to speculations about the physical changes that might take place during the meteor's high-speed passage through the atmosphere. However, when the technology became available to send manufactured objects outside the atmosphere, various engineering disciplines such as aerothermodynamics, high-temperature materials science, and trajectory analysis were developed.

Reentry Bodies

A craft that is built to withstand reentry into the earth's atmosphere is known as a reentry body (RB). The engineering requirements that must be met by any reentry body design depend upon the purpose of the reentry body. For example, a reentry body containing an astronaut must be able to soft-land. Such a reentry body must not only survive the environment of passage through the atmosphere, but also impact the earth at a very low vertical speed. For a reentry body such as the space shuttle, there is the additional requirement that the landing occur at a specific location. In other cases, such as that of the early Mercury capsule, a soft landing in the ocean was all that was required. For military weapons, a soft landing may be of no importance.

The most fundamental aspect of reentry bodies is their overall material requirements. In physics, the unit of measurement for energy is the joule. About 1,054 joules are required to raise the temperature of 1 pound of water 1 degree Fahrenheit. A material is vaporized when it passes from a solid to a gas. About 60,000,000 joules are required to vaporize 1 kilogram (2.2 pounds) of carbon. Nearly all other materials require less energy to be vaporized. A little more than 2,000,000 joules are required to vaporize 1 kilogram of water, for example. The kinetic energy, or the energy of motion, of a typical reentry body just entering the atmosphere might be 30,000,000 joules. Therefore, if all the reentry body's kinetic energy were converted to heat or thermal energy, the entire reentry body would vanish, unless it were made entirely of carbon.

The fact that many reentry bodies survive to make soft landings indicates that a significant amount of energy is dissipated in some way other than the vaporization of the reentry body itself. Some of the kinetic energy, turned into heat, is radiated or conducted into the air surrounding the reentry body. This energy changes the chemical makeup of the air by changing its molecules. The process of changing a molecule by the application of high temperature is called disassociation.

The amount of heat absorbed by the reentry body and the amount absorbed by dissociation depends upon the reentry body's speed; it also depends upon the reentry body's altitude, because the gases that make up the atmosphere vary with altitude. In addition, the reentry body's shape also strongly influences the amount of heat it absorbs. A blunt shape is very effective in directing the heat away from the reentry body.

The accompanying figure illustrates some of the important parts of the flow about a typical reentry body. This figure assumes that the observer is stationary with respect to the reentry body. Consequently, the flow of air is moving from the left to the right. An important way of describing such flows is with the term Mach number, or the ratio of the speed of the flow to the speed of sound at the point in flow. The speed of sound varies with the temperature and the temperature varies throughout the flow region. The speed of the flow approaching the reentry body is much greater than the speed of sound. A very strong shock wave, identified in the accompanying figure by the term "bow shock," is formed. This shock wave is detached from the reentry body and stands ahead of the reentry body into the oncoming flow. The distance between the shock wave and the body is called the standoff distance.

In region A, between the reentry body and the bow shock wave, the speed of the flow is less than the speed of sound. The stagnation point is where the flow is brought to rest. In the vicinity of the stagnation point, the heat flow to the reentry body is the greatest. Therefore, the reentry body is often covered with a carbon heat shield in region A. Much of the flow in region A passes into region B. The flow that passes into region B increases in speed, finally equaling the speed of sound. The line called the sonic line shows where this transition from a speed lower than to a speed higher than the speed of sound occurs. In region A the speed is less than the speed of sound, in region B the speed is greater than the speed of sound. Some of the flow in region A goes into what is called the boundary layer.

Somewhere beyond the maximum thickness of the reentry body is a series of weak pressure waves called expansion waves, which bring the flow from the higher-pressure region B to the lower-pressure region C. The pressure in region C is slightly higher than that external to the bow shock wave. The region outside of the bow shock wave is unaffected by the presence of the reentry body until it encounters the bow shock.

The body shown in the accompanying figure has the shape of a teardrop with the blunt end facing the oncoming flow. A very thin layer forms around the reentry body where the friction of the air becomes important. This layer is called the boundary layer when it is in contact with the reentry body and the shear layer when it continues past the reentry body. Fluid friction comes about when adjacent layers of air have greatly different speeds. Fluid friction is illustrated by the following simple experiment: If one rubs the heel of one's hand rapidly along the surface of a desk, one becomes aware of a warmth in that part of the hand contacting the desk. The desk acts as one

Flow Field Regions of a Reentry Body

layer of fluid, and the heel of the hand acts as an adjoining layer. Because one layer is moving rapidly relative to the other, heat is generated in much the same way as in reentry. In this experiment, the mechanical energy of forcing the hand over the desk against friction is converted into heat energy, raising the temperature of the outside of the hand. The region where fluid friction is important is known as viscid, and the region where friction is unimportant is known as inviscid.

The air in direct contact with the reentry body must come to rest relative to the reentry body, whereas the air at a short distance from the reentry body has a speed greater than the speed of sound. Therefore, the fluid experiences a rapid change in speed over a small distance. Therefore, friction becomes a predominant part of the fluid motion in the vicinity of the reentry body. This friction force generates heat, which can cause vaporization of the surface of the reentry body.

The vaporization of the surface of the reentry body is often called ablation. The material forming the surface of the reentry body changes directly from a solid to a gas. The products of vaporization, usually compounds of carbon and oxygen, enter the flow near the body. Because vaporization requires heat energy, the reentry body is deliberately designed to sacrifice a portion of its surface to prevent heat from penetrating into the interior of the reentry body.

In region C, all the flow has about the same speed, and friction effects are rather insignificant. Just behind the reentry body is a small region where the flow seems trapped and is being pulled along by the reentry body. The shear layer from around the body comes to a small area called the neck, beyond which there is an expansion of the flow into a wake. The wake has a core region, where friction effects are significant, and an outer region, where the flow is essentially inviscid. Whereas the friction in the wake core cannot affect the reentry body, it does provide a means by which the trajectory of the reentry body can be detected from the ground.

The shape of the reentry body does affect the size of the wake and the chemical activity within the wake, and therefore the ability of a ground station to detect or track the reentry body. The flow field produces a great amount of heat, which must be controlled by selecting the shape and materials of the reentry body. In addition, the flow field produces drag. The magnitude of the drag forces in some cases can be one hundred times the weight of the reentry body. A crewed reentry body must be designed in a shape that will avoid such high drag loads. It has been found that very blunt bodies, rather than streamlined bodies, limit the peak drag forces.

Reentry Body Control

A reentry body can be controlled by altering the trajectory or path that it follows as it moves through the atmosphere. The two major reasons for controlling a reentry body are first, to reduce its speed and, second, to direct it to an impact or landing site on Earth. An impact, or high-speed Earth encounter, results in destruction of the reentry body, a landing, or low-speed Earth encounter, allows recovery of the reentry body intact.

The aerodynamic forces on a reentry body are those of drag and lift. Drag, identified as the force in the direction of the velocity, tends to reduce the velocity. Lift acts at right angle to the velocity and therefore changes the direction of the velocity.

Small gas jets applied to the body, similar to those of the Mercury capsule, can make small but significant changes to the direction of the velocity. Such controls are used well outside of the atmosphere to limit the side forces during reentry. Expandable flares can also be used to increase drag and slow down the reentry body.

A versatile control system is the split windward flap. This control consists of two side-by-side flaps that have the appearance of rectangular paddles. When the flaps are extended at equal angles, they cause a pitching of the reentry body; when they are extended at unequal angle, they cause the reentry body to roll as well.

The space shuttle is controlled much like a high-performance airplane with a rudder and a combination of elevator and ailerons called elevons.

Another method of controlling a reentry body is by bending or canting its nose, or front part. The reentry body's center of gravity may also be moved laterally by moving an object within the reentry body. Lift can then be developed in a preferred direction, similar to the way hang glider pilots move the gliders' center of gravity, and thereby change direction, by moving their own weight.

Reentry bodies operate in flight conditions that make great demands upon the vehicles' materials and shape. Heat loads threaten to vaporize a large part of the structure. In addition, the structure must support aerodynamic loads that can reach values as high as one hundred times the weight of the reentry body. With a human crew aboard, heat and aerodynamic loads must be very carefully managed to ensure integrity right down to a soft landing.

Frank J. Regan

Bibliography

Baker, David. *The History of Manned Space Flight*. New York: Crown, 1981. A thorough history of most crewed spaceflight up to space shuttle flights, with discussion of reentry problems and engineering solutions spread throughout the book.

Martin, John J. *Atmospheric Reentry.* Englewood Cliffs, N.J.: Prentice Hall, 1966. An engineering text with some introductory material that may be accessible to those without a strong background in physics.

Regan, Frank J., and Satya M. Anandakrishnan. *Dynamics of Atmospheric Reentry.* Reston, Va.: American Institute of Aeronautics and Astronautics, 1992. An engineering text with overview introductory sections requiring no extensive background in mathematics or physics.

See also: Aerodynamics; Crewed spaceflight; High-speed flight; Orbiting; Spaceflight; Supersonic aircraft; Uncrewed spaceflight

The Apollo 11 space capsule reenters Earth's atmosphere. (NASA CORE/Lorain Valley JVS)

Hanna Reitsch

Date: Born on March 29, 1912, in Hirschberg, Germany; died on August 24, 1979, in Frankfurt am Main, Germany

Definition: Germany's best-known female pilot during and after World War II.

Significance: Reitsch tested aircraft for the Luftwaffe during the war and set more than forty records for powered and motorless flight.

Hanna Reitsch began her career by learning to fly gliders in 1930, becoming the protégé of the influential glider instructor Wolf Hirth. In May, 1933, riding the rising air of a storm cloud, she set a new world altitude record for gliders. After gaining certification and experience as a glider instructor, she was chosen in 1934 to be a glider test pilot for the German Institute for Glider Research. She tested newly developed dive brakes, demonstrating controlled terminal-velocity dives. These brought her to the attention of Ernst Udet, perhaps the most famous World War I pilot. Through Udet's efforts, she became the first German woman to win the honorary title of Flugkäpitan, or flight captain.

With Udet's assistance, Reitsch began testing the Luftwaffe's latest fighters and bombers in 1937. That year, she was among a group of five pilots who made the first glider flights over the Alps. In 1938, she was sent to the United States to demonstrate glider aerobatics at the Cleveland Air Races. In 1942, she was the first German woman to win the Iron Cross, an honor that gained her access to the experimental Me-163 rocket-powered airplane.

Fiercely patriotic, Reitsch in 1943 organized with two friends a suicide bomber squadron to turn the tide against the Allied march. She performed tests on a piloted version of the V-1 rocket in 1944. In the closing days of the war, Hitler requested in his bunker the presence of Reitsch's friend General Robert Ritter von Greim, whom Reitsch accompanied. After von Greim was wounded by Russian gunfire, Reitsch took command of his airplane. Although she wanted to die with Hitler, he commanded her to fly von Greim to where he could take command of the Luftwaffe. Reitsch flew the last German plane out of Berlin in late April, 1945, before it was seized by the Russians.

Reitsch was captured and interned for fifteen months by the U.S. Army, during which time she gave testimony about Hitler's last days. When permitted by the Allies, she returned to her first love, gliding. In 1953, she gained a bronze medal at the World Gliding Championship in Spain, as the sole woman competitor. In 1957, she won a bronze medal at the German glider championships and set two women's altitude records. She helped establish the national school of gliding in Accra, Ghana, beginning in

1962. Only a few months after her last flight, in 1979, she died of a heart attack.

W. N. Hubin

Bibliography
Lomax, Judy. *Hanna Reitsch: Flying for the Fatherland.* London: John Murray, 1988. A comprehensive biography of Reitsch, from original sources, with details of her family, her unswerving patriotism, her personality, and her postwar activities.
Piszkiewicz, Dennis. *From Nazi Test Pilot to Hitler's Bunker.* Westport, Conn.: Praeger, 1997. A useful, recent biography from a longer perspective, concentrating on Reitsch's wartime activities.
Reisch, Hanna. *The Sky My Kingdom.* Translated by Lawrence Wilson. Mechanicsburg, Pa.: Stackpole Books, 1997. A translation of Reitsch's autobiography *Fliegen, mein Leben* (1955).

See also: Aerobatics; Airplanes; Experimental aircraft; Gliders; Luftwaffe; Test pilots; Women and flight; World War II

Rescue aircraft

Date: First utilized by the U.S. Coast Guard in 1920
Definition: Aircraft capable of rescuing individuals in distress either on land or at sea.
Significance: Quick response and the ability to access remote or geographically difficult terrain allow rescue aircraft to assist individuals that have been stranded, are in need of medical attention, or are in danger from problems such as forest fires or high seas.

U.S. Coast Guard Rescues

In 1920, the U.S. Coast Guard borrowed several Curtiss HS-2L flying boats from the Navy and began the first air rescue operations out of the former naval base at Morehead City, North Carolina. The following year, the station was closed due to a lack of funding. Four years passed before Lieutenant Commander C. G. von Paulsen convinced officials that the Coast Guard needed aircraft to prevent the smuggling of alcohol during Prohibition. The U.S. Congress appropriated $152,000 for the Coast Guard to purchase three Loening OL-5 amphibians and two Chance Vought UO-4's, which were stationed at Gloucester, Massachusetts, and Cape May, New Jersey.

Although law enforcement remained the primary function of the Coast Guard, pilots also executed rescue operations. During the 1920's, the number of seafaring vessels increased and the Coast Guard received more and more calls for assistance. By 1928, the number of rescues had increased to a level that justified the creation of an aviation section, under the command of Commander Norman Hall. The Coast Guard purchased five General Aviation Flying Life Boat PJ-15's and two Douglas Dolphin RD-2's capable of landing on rough seas to perform rescue operations.

Over the next few years, the Coast Guard engaged in numerous rescue operations. Although the aircraft were capable of taking off from water, sometimes the seas were too rough and the plane and pilot were stranded along with the victims. Some of the aircraft were later recovered, including one plane, the *Arcturus*, which washed ashore with the pilot and the little boy he was sent to rescue still on board. During the Great Depression, the secretary of the Treasury, Henry Morgenthau, transferred the aviation department of the Customs Service to the U.S. Coast Guard and then persuaded Congress to designate Public Works Administration funds for the purchase of forty-two additional planes and the establishment of six air stations.

During World War II, the U.S. Coast Guard defended the coast of Greenland and in the process engaged in many rescue operations during snowstorms and in frozen areas. In 1943, the Coast Guard formed an Air Sea Rescue Squadron in San Diego, California, and within two years, the agency had 165 aircraft and operated out of nine air stations. The extreme weather conditions of the Arctic required the development of the Northrop YC-125 Raider that could land on short, uneven runways. The first of the Raiders were delivered to the Air Force in 1949, but within a few years the planes were declared surplus.

By 1945, the importance of the air rescue operations had led to the use of helicopters. After two aircraft attempted and failed to rescue nine members of the Royal Canadian Air Force who had crashed in Labrador, the Coast Guard shipped an HNS-1 helicopter to Goose Bay, Labrador, where it was reassembled and flown to the crash site by Lieutenant August Kleisch, who successfully retrieved all the survivors. The post-World War II period witnessed a dramatic increase in the number of rescues conducted by the Coast Guard, with helicopters providing the quickest method of extricating people from dangerous situations. With the ability to hover between objects in close proximity, such as trees and telephone lines, the helicopter provided the maneuverability necessary to perform the delicate operations.

During the Vietnam War, the U.S. Coast Guard participated in search-and-rescue operations that commenced in 1968. Assigned to the Thirty-seventh Aerospace Rescue and Recover Squadron at Da Nang, Vietnam, more than seven thousand pilots rescued marines under fire from enemy forces. During the 1980's, the Coast Guard utilized Sikorsky HH-52 Seaguards, HH-52's, and Aerospatiale HH-65 Dolphins, as well as the now-retired amphibian Sikorsky HH-3F Pelican helicopter. By 2000, the Coast Guard continued to rely primarily on the HH-65 for its search-and-rescue operations.

U.S. Air Force Rescues

The Air Force used the Sikorsky R-6A Hoverfly II, designed primarily for observation, as a rescue aircraft beginning in 1944. The helicopter, with a main rotor diameter of 38 feet and a length of 38.25 feet, was equipped with capsules on each side of the fuselage that could be used to carry litters for medical evacuation. Capable of flying at speeds up to 96 miles per hour with a range of 305 miles, the Hoverfly II also carried 650 pounds of bombs and continued to be used throughout World War II.

During the Korean War, the primary helicopter used by the Air Force for search-and-rescue missions was the Sikorsky YH-5A Dragon Fly. The YH-5A, built with a main rotor diameter of 48 feet and capable of reaching speeds of 90 miles per hour with a range of 280 miles, rescued United Nations troops from behind enemy lines and evacuated wounded personnel from the front lines. The Sikorsky UH-19B Chickasaw rescue helicopter was also used during the Korean War. Equipped with a 400-pound capacity hoist mounted above the door and an external sling with a 2,000-pound limit, the Chickasaw was used mainly for rescue and medical evacuation. Capable of traveling at 112 miles per hour, the aircraft has a range of 330 miles and is able to carry 8,400 pounds. The large cargo area allows for the evacuation of several people at once.

By 1952, the Chickasaw was joined by the Vertol CH-21B Workhorse on rescue missions. Originally designed to transport troops, the aircraft was modified to carry twelve litter patients. The Workhorse had a longer range than the Chickasaw, being able to fly 400 miles at speeds of 132 miles per hour, making evacuation quicker. In 1958, the U.S. Air Force Tactical Air Command received the first Kaman HH-43B Huskie helicopter. The Huskie was used in Vietnam for both aerial firefighting and for rescuing downed pilots. Capable of being airborne within sixty seconds, the helicopter reaches speeds of 120 miles per hour and has a range of 185 miles. The aircraft is manned by two rescuers or firemen, who use foam pushed down by the backwash of the rotors to clear an area large enough to extricate trapped persons. The Air Force purchased over 175 Huskies at a cost of $304,000 each.

In 1955, Bell Helicopter introduced the UH-1P Iroquois that would later be known as the Huey. Used in Vietnam as a medical evacuation aircraft, with enough room for eleven passengers or six littered patients, the Huey also flew as an armed gunship. The Huey was the first Air Force helicopter capable of cruising on one engine. The maximum speed for the Huey was 140 miles per hour, with a range of 330 miles at altitudes below 24,830 feet. Each aircraft cost $273,000. The Hueys replaced the Huskies in 1970.

Another rescue helicopter used by the U.S. Air Force is the Sikorsky CH-3E. The CH-3E, nicknamed the Jolly Green Giant, was modified for combat rescue and is fully armored, has defensive armaments on board, and is equipped with self-sealing refueling tanks and a rescue hoist. It also has the ability to refuel while in flight. The CH-3E has a rotor diameter of 62 feet, a length of 73 feet, and weighs 22,050 pounds when loaded. The aircraft is armed with two .50-caliber machine guns. With a maximum speed of 177 miles per hour and a range of 779 miles with external fuel tanks, the three-man crew flies missions at altitudes of 21,000 or less. Each costs $796,000.

In addition to rescue helicopters, the U.S. Air Force has also relied on various airplanes for medical evacuation or extrication. One of the earliest airplanes used for rescue was the Cessna O-1G Bird Dog. Although designed for reconnaissance, the Cessna O-1G, with a top speed of 150 miles per hour and range of 530 miles, rescued many downed pilots and trapped military personnel.

By the time the Vietnam conflict reached its apex in the late 1960's, the Air Force relied on the North American OV-10A Bronco. Designed for combat support and equipped with four 7.62-millimeter machine guns in fuselage sponsons and 3,600 pounds of mixed ordinance carried externally, the Bronco performed rescue missions and was capable of transporting two litter patients and a medical attendant. The key characteristic of the aircraft was that it was capable of short takeoffs and landings. Each aircraft cost $480,000 and had a maximum speed of 281 miles per hour and a much longer range of 1,240 miles. With a wingspan of 40 feet, length of 41 feet, 7 inches, and height of 15 feet, 1 inch, the aircraft flew at altitudes below 26,000 feet.

During World War II, the U.S. Army, Navy, and Air Force used different versions of the Consolidated OA-10 Catalina aircraft. The Catalina had twin engines and was a parasol-mounted monoplane with a flying boat hull, retractable tricycle landing gear, and retractable wingtip floats. Used primarily for amphibious rescues, the Catalina was instrumental in saving the lives of hundreds of pilots. The aircraft, nicknamed the Dumbo, had a wingspan of 104 feet, weighed 36,400 pounds fully loaded, was armed with two .50-caliber machine guns in the waist and two .30-caliber machine guns, with one located in the bow and the other in the rear tunnel, and carried 8,000 pounds of bombs. Each aircraft cost $50,000 and had a maximum speed of 184 miles per hour, a range of 2,325 miles, and a service ceiling of 22,400 feet.

On June 9, 1945, the first Grumman OA-12 Duck joined the sea-rescue aircraft of the U.S. Air Force Air Rescue Service and performed numerous over-water rescues. With a 39-foot wingspan, the Duck had a maximum speed of 188 miles per hour and a range of 780 miles. Each airplane, capable of flying to altitudes of 20,000 feet, cost $69,000.

The most versatile of the rescue airplanes is the Grumman HU-16B Albatross, with a design that allows for operation from land, water, snow, or ice. The first Albatross flew on October 24, 1947. During the Korean War, the Air Force used the Albatross to rescue U.N. forces along the coast and behind enemy lines. In 1962, the Air Force received 297 of the airplanes and assigned most of them to rescue duty in Vietnam. Since the 1960's, the Air Force has relied on helicopters as the primary aircraft for rescue operations. Working with civilian authorities through the Aerospace Rescue and Recovery Service, these rescue aircraft and their crews save hundreds of lives a year.

Cynthia Clark Northrup

Bibliography

Green, Michael. *Air Rescue Teams*. Mankato, Minn.: Capstone Books, 2000. An easy-to-read description of the men, aircraft, and equipment used for aerial rescues by the Coast Guard and the Air Force. The training team members receive and the current and future of rescue aircraft is also discussed.

Holden, Henry. *Black Hawk Helicopters*. Berkeley Heights, N.J.: Enslow, 2001. The author examines the effectiveness of the Sikorsky Black Hawk helicopter. In addition to combat operations the helicopter performs numerous rescue missions, primarily for medical evacuation.

Schreiner, Samuel Agnew. *Mayday! Mayday! The Most Exciting Missions of Rescue, Interdiction, and Combat in the Two-Hundred-Year Annals of the U.S. Coast Guard*. New York: D. I. Fine, 1990. A collection of real-life adventures showing the Coast Guard in action. Written for the general reader.

United States Coast Guard. *Air Search and Rescue: Sixty-three Years of Aerial Lifesaving—a Pictorial History, 1915-1978*. Washington, D.C.: Author, 1978. A pictorial history of air rescues performed by the U.S. Coast Guard. Interesting accounts for the general reader.

See also: Firefighting aircraft; Helicopters; Rotorcraft; Vertical takeoff and landing

Manfred von Richthofen

Date: Born on May 2, 1892, in Breslau, Germany (now Wrocław, Poland); died on April 21, 1918, near Vaux-Sur-Somme, France
Definition: The most famous fighter ace of World War I.
Significance: Von Richthofen, best known as the "Red Baron," and leader of the "Flying Circus" air fighter group, was the most famous fighter pilot of World War I. Most of his air-combat operations manual, written shortly before his death at age twenty-five, remains valid.

Early Years

Born in 1892, Manfred Freiherr von Richthofen was the eldest son of a family of the lesser nobility of Silesia and heir to a Prussian military tradition. He grew up at the turn of the twentieth century in an atmosphere comparable to that of an English country squire. Von Richthofen did not choose a career, but rather had one chosen for him. His father packed the boy off at the age of eleven to the German military school at Wahlstatt. Von Richthofen was not a good student, but he proved to be athletically gifted. After passing cadet school at Wahlstatt, he went to the Royal Military Academy in Lichterfelde, near Potsdam, an important military center.

The Fighter Pilot

In 1911, von Richthofen became a lieutenant in the First Uhlan Cavalry Regiment of the Prussian Army, fighting in Russia during World War I and participating in the invasion of Belgium and France. After the cavalry lost its importance as a fighting force in the era of trench warfare, von Richthofen joined the infantry. He then transferred to the Imperial Air Service and entered combat as a fighter pilot in September, 1916.

An important role model and teacher to von Richthofen was Captain Oswald Boelcke, who, until he was overtaken by von Richthofen, was Germany's greatest ace, with forty victories in aerial combat. It has been said that Boelcke was the father and teacher of combat pilots, whereas von Richthofen developed his mentor's methods to the highest degree of mastery. Von Richthofen was present in his fighter on October 28, 1916, when Boelcke was killed in an aerial collision with another plane.

The Flying Circus

Von Richthofen eventually became commander of Fighter Group I, known officially as Jagdgeschwader I (JG I). JG I was officially chartered on June 26, 1917, by the Kogenluft, the German Air Service Headquarters. Because of its fancifully decorated triplanes, JG I came to be known as the "Flying Circus." Von Richthofen's own triplane was painted red, a color he had favored for his previous fighter planes. Von Richthofen thus became known as the "Red Baron."

The JG I comprised four fighter units. To weld his group into what became the most notoriously feared air-fighting formation in history, von Richthofen chose his subordinate leaders with great care. He was a shrewd judge of character and chose men whom he felt were capable of leadership yet could follow his instructions and orders. With his subordinates' assistance, he would coordinate the motions and mass the forces of the JG I at whatever target he deemed appropriate.

Under von Richthofen's leadership, the Flying Circus became a very successful fighter group. One of the most successful days in JG I's history was March 27, 1918. During that day, JG I carried out 118 sorties, and had 39 inconclusive air combats and 13 successful combats. Von Richthofen had his seventy-first, seventy-second, and seventy-third victories. He was eventually credited with shooting down a total of eighty enemy aircraft, making him the top ace of World War I.

The Legend

The precise circumstances of von Richthofen's death remain unclear. Von Richthofen was reputedly shot down on April 21, 1918, by Captain A. Roy Brown, a Canadian ace flying in the Royal Air Force (RAF). It has been said that von Richthofen disobeyed one of the basic tenets of his air combat operations manual and stayed in pursuit of an enemy plane too long, while Captain Brown's plane came up behind him. However, it is possible that von Richthofen may have been killed instead by ground fire from Australian troops. Brown died in Ontario, Canada, in March, 1944, without ever categorically claiming that it was he who shot and killed von Richthofen.

After the end of World War I, von Richthofen's remains were first transferred to a large German military cemetery at Fricourt. In 1925, the remains were exhumed, and a formal state funeral was held in Berlin with President von Hindenburg present. Von Richthofen was then interred with some of Germany's greatest heroes in the *Invalidenfriedhof* in Berlin. In 1976, von Richthofen was once again exhumed and reinterred, this time in a family plot in Mainz in western Germany.

Dana P. McDermott

German World War I ace Manfred von Richthofen's squadron became known as Richthofen's Flying Circus because of the gaudy colors that members painted their planes; Richthofen's own fondness for painting his plane red led to his being nicknamed the "Red Baron." (Hulton Archive)

Bibliography

Franks, Norman, and Alan Bennett. *The Red Baron's Last Flight: A Mystery Investigated.* St. Catharine's, Ontario: Vanwell, 1998. A study and analysis of Manfred von Richthofen's last flight, which ended in his death, and the actual circumstances of what happened during the battle.

Franks, Norman, Hal Giblin, and Nigel McCrery. *Under the Guns of the Red Baron: The Complete Record of Von Richthofen's Victories and Victims Fully Illustrated.* Boston: Grub Street the Basement, 1999. This history recounts each of von Richthofen's eighty enemy kills. It also contains a short biography of the pilots and a description of the death of the Red Baron himself. It includes rare photos of aircraft and squadrons.

Kilduff, Peter. *The Illustrated Red Baron: The Life And Times of Manfred von Richthofen.* London: Arms & Armour Press, 1999. A comprehensive summary of Richthofen's career, mentors, comrades, aircraft, and opponents.

_____. *Richthofen: Beyond the Legend of the Red Baron.* New York: John Wiley & Sons, 1993. This volume traces the development of German fighter aviation from early single aircraft aerial ambushes to the massed attacks of the JG I, the battle force that von Richthofen developed into a highly effective air weapon. It examines von Richthofen as air fighter, leader, and strategist and tries to find the truth behind the myths that have surrounded von Richthofen since 1918. Included are personal writings by the Red Baron, his own air combat operations manual, and observations from his comrades, admirers, and enemies.

See also: Dogfights; Fighter pilots; Fokker aircraft; Triplanes; World War I

Eddie Rickenbacker

Date: Born on October 8, 1890, in Columbus, Ohio; died on July 23, 1973, in Zurich, Switzerland

Definition: A decorated World War I American air ace who returned home to enter business, founding an automobile company and, later, an airline.

Significance: Rickenbacker exploited the fame he enjoyed as a decorated air ace in World War I to popularize air travel and airmail. As manager of Eastern Air Lines for many years, he helped develop many of the features of air travel now taken for granted.

Edward Vernon "Eddie" Rickenbacker, the third of eight children, entered the world of work as a boy, first by selling newspapers and then by moving to jobs in a glass factory, a foundry, a brewery, a shoe factory, and a monument works. He became interested in automobiles, and, at age sixteen, he was hired by Lee Frayer, a race-car driver and auto company executive who introduced him to the world of automobile racing. By 1912, Rickenbacker was working with auto designer Fred Dusenburg and entering races on his own. In 1914, he set a world speed record at Daytona Beach, Florida.

Rickenbacker became interested in aviation after an aircraft-designer friend, Glenn Martin, took him on a flight in 1916. He was further intrigued by flying after meeting some Royal Air Force (RAF) fliers on a trip to England later that year.

When the United States entered the war in 1917, Rickenbacker volunteered for service, becoming a driver for General William "Billy" Mitchell. Soon he was able to persuade Mitchell to assign him to flight training, and he joined the Ninety-fourth Aero Pursuit Squadron near Toul, France. He had spent fewer than three weeks in training.

World War I Fighter Ace

During 1918, Rickenbacker's flying skill steadily improved, and he began to shoot down enemy planes with increasing frequency. In October of that year, Rickenbacker scored fourteen victories. Although there is controversy over his exact wartime total of downed aircraft, it was certainly at least twenty-four, including four balloons. Rickenbacker survived 134 aerial battles and logged more combat hours than any other American pilot. These achievements made him famous when he returned home, promoted to the rank of major. Rickenbacker was awarded the French Croix de Guerre in 1918 and the Congressional Medal of Honor in 1930.

Business Career

After the war, Rickenbacker declined numerous offers to endorse products or to go act in motion pictures and returned to the automobile industry as president of the Rickenbacker Motor Company. After a bold start in 1922, the company went bankrupt in 1925, leaving its namesake deep in debt. Undaunted, Rickenbacker bought a controlling interest in the Indianapolis Motor Speedway, wrote a book about his war experiences, and even authored a syndicated comic strip. His primary occupation was as a sales manager for General Motors. Even with all these activities, he still found time to travel the country giving speeches on aviation and its future. He urged many city governments to consider building municipal airports.

In 1934, Rickenbacker became general manager of Eastern Air Lines. Under his management the airline added routes and became the first profitable airline in the United States. Stewardesses tended to passengers during each flight, and pilots were provided with up-to-date navigational instruments. Eastern also started its own meteorology division and instituted regular medical checkups for pilots. Maintaining a close relationship with Donald Douglas, Rickenbacker bought planes from Douglas Aircraft, and made a record-breaking flight from California to New Jersey in the new Douglas airliner, the DC-1.

World War II Achievements

Always an advocate for air travel and military air power, Rickenbacker traveled all over the country to give talks. Early in 1941, on a trip to Atlanta, he was seriously hurt in a plane crash and required months of surgery and physical therapy. The United States was now involved in World War II, and Rickenbacker, when he was well, was sent by the War Department on special missions. He gave inspirational talks to pilots and recommended improvements in aircraft and procedures. He traveled to England, where he met with Prime Minister Winston Churchill and was entrusted with supreme commander of the Allied Expeditionary Force Dwight D. Eisenhower's planning documents for the invasion of North Africa, which he brought back to Washington, D.C.

In October, 1942, on a mission to New Guinea, the plane carrying Rickenbacker and a crew of seven ran out of fuel and crashed in the Pacific Ocean. Using three small rubber rafts, the men managed to survive for twenty-four days with virtually no shelter, water, or provisions. Only one man died; the others kept alive by drinking rainwater and by eating small fish and a gull they caught with their bare hands. At the end of this unprecedented ordeal, the survivors were spotted by a navy pilot and rescued. Prodded by Rickenbacker, the Navy made many modifications to the survival gear carried in planes, increasing the size of the rafts and providing for sails and solar water

Eddie Rickenbacker was the United States' top ace in World War I, with twenty-six kills. (Hulton Archive)

stills. During the remainder of the war, many other servicemen benefited from these steps.

After the war, Rickenbacker rejoined Eastern Air Lines, but was never as successful in business as he had previously been. He was gradually eased out of management and retired in 1964, but he continued to speak and write until his death in 1973, on a trip to Switzerland.

John R. Phillips

Bibliography

Gurney, Gene. *Flying Aces of World War I*. New York: Random House, 1965. Stories of heroism for young readers.

Rickenbacker, Edward V. *Fighting the Flying Circus*. New York: Frederick Stokes, 1919. A memoir of the men who flew with the Ninety-fourth Aero Pursuit Squadron in World War I, with many harrowing accounts of air battles.

_____. *Rickenbacker*. Englewood Cliffs, N.J.: Prentice Hall, 1967. An autobiography completed six years before Rickenbacker's death, with photographs of the author with other aviation celebrities, including Amelia Earhart, Orville Wright, Jimmy Doolittle, and others.

_____. *Seven Came Through*. Garden City, N.Y.: Doubleday, 1943. Rickenbacker tells how he and his seven companions survived for twenty-four days on rubber rafts in the Pacific Ocean after a plane crash during World War II.

See also: Airline industry, U.S.; Fighter pilots; World War I; World War II

Sally K. Ride

Date: Born on May 26, 1951, in Encino, California

Definition: An astronaut for the National Aeronautics and Space Agency (NASA) and the first American woman in space.

Significance: As the first American female astronaut, Ride illustrated the potential of women in space. As a mission specialist, she demonstrated the importance of scientists who could conduct experiments in space.

Sally Kristen Ride was born on May 26, 1951, in Encino, a suburb of Los Angeles, California. In 1968, she enrolled at Swarthmore College in Pennsylvania as a physics major, but left after three semesters to concentrate on tennis after winning a national collegiate tennis tournament. After a few months, she reassessed her potential and decided against tennis as a professional career. She returned to her studies at Stanford University and completed an undergraduate program with a double major in physics and English. She continued her studies in physics at Stanford, earning a master's degree. While completing work on a doctorate in astronomy and astrophysics at Stanford, she was attracted by NASA's call for astronauts. In 1977, she entered astronaut training as a mission specialist with a group of thirty-five successful applicants, including six women. She completed her doctorate in 1978.

Shortly after earning her doctorate, Ride reported to the Lyndon B. Johnson Space Center outside Houston, Texas, to begin the intensive training required of mission specialists. As she worked her way toward a flight assignment, Ride worked on the design of the remote arm used on the space shuttle to deploy and retrieve satellites and was part of the ground team for the second and third flights of *Columbia*.

Ride's chances at flight came in 1983 and in 1984 when she flew on *Challenger* for a total of more than 343 hours. The June 18, 1983, flight earned her the distinction of being the first American woman in space and the youngest person ever in orbit. While on these flights, Ride tested the remote arm and oversaw the onboard science experiments. Other scheduled flights were canceled after the explosion of the *Challenger* in 1986. Ride was the only astronaut to serve on the commission that investigated the explosion.

Ride retired from NASA in 1987 to join Stanford's Center of International Security and Arms Control. In 1989, she became the director of the California Space Institute and professor of physics at the University of California, San Diego. She later left academia to enter private business. She became interested in science education and, in 2000, resigned as president of space.com, a World Wide Web site devoted to education and the space industry, to spend more time and effort promoting improvements in science education. Ride's personal crusade is to encourage women to enter math and science disciplines.

Kenneth H. Brown

Bibliography

Camp, Carole A. *Sally Ride: First American Woman in Space*. Berkeley Heights, N.J.: Enslow, 1977. A well-constructed biography written for young adults.

Ride, Sally K. *Leadership and America's Future in Space*. Washington, D.C.: United States Government Printing Office, 1987. In this report of a government commission established following the *Challenger* explosion,

Ride set forth principles to get NASA's mission back on track.

Ride, Sally K., and Susan Okie. *To Space and Back*. New York: Morrow Avon, 1989. Written for a young audience, this book shares Ride's personal experiences from her orbital flights.

See also: Astronauts and cosmonauts; Crewed spaceflight; Johnson Space Center; National Aeronautics and Space Administration; Space shuttle; Spaceflight; "Vomit Comet"; Women and flight

Rocket propulsion

Description: The movement of a device by the ejection of matter, without the need for taking on ambient air for combustion.

Significance: Rocket propulsion permits the application of rockets both inside and outside the atmosphere, in space, or under water.

Most rockets exhaust propellant at high velocities and temperatures. The propellant is produced at high pressure through the release of chemical, nuclear, or electrical energy to the working fluid. In outer space, the propellant escapes from the rocket chamber to a high-exit kinetic energy in proportion to its available energy per unit mass. This explains why the reaction of low molecular weight fuel, such as liquid hydrogen, with liquid oxygen can produce an effective exhaust velocity almost twice that of rockets using solid fuel mixed with oxidizer crystals. Newton's second law shows that rocket thrust is the product of the effective exhaust velocity multiplied by the mass flow rate. Thus the higher the "effective" exhaust velocity, the lower the mass of propellant required for a given mission. Future long-range space missions may be based on electric, nuclear, or solar energy to increase the effective exhaust velocity up to ten times, thereby reducing required propellant mass by a factor of ten. A quick estimate of a rocket thrust is to multiply the rocket chamber pressure by the smallest flow area of the exhaust nozzle, called the throat.

Common rockets contain at least the following components: engine, nozzle, propellant storage, payload, airframe, and guidance and control devices. Payloads vary widely and include spaceships, instrument packages for upper atmosphere observations, warheads on missiles, artillery projectiles, and fireworks.

History

As early as 600 C.E., the Chinese manufactured black powder, a mixture of charcoal, sulfur, and saltpeter, for use as rocket propellant. In the year 1232, the Chinese used rocket-propelled fire-arrows successfully to defend their towns against hordes of invading Mongols. In the early eighteenth century, Sir William Congreve developed a sophisticated military missile, known as the Congreve rocket, which provided the "rocket's red glare" observed by Francis Scott Key in 1812 at Fort McHenry.

The first liquid fuel rocket, propelled by hydrogen and oxygen, was designed in 1903 by the Russian scientist Konstantin Tsiolkovsky. Physicist Robert H. Goddard was the first in the United States to succeed in launching a liquid fuel rocket using oxygen and gasoline on March 16, 1926. Within 2.5 seconds, Goddard's rocket gained an altitude of about 40 feet and a speed of 60 miles per hour.

The Soviet Union was the first nation to achieve spaceflight, with the Sputnik 1 satellite on October 4, 1957, and with the pilot Yuri Gagarin's flight on Vostok 1 on April 12, 1961. The next crewed spaceflight was made by the United States one month later, on May 5, 1961, in Mercury capsule *Freedom 7*, piloted by astronaut Alan Shepard. In the 6-by-6-foot capsule, Shepard experienced a gravity load of 7 g's (seven times his weight) during launch and a gravity load of 1 g during recovery. Rocket flight has remained a continual challenge to crews.

At the end of the twentieth century, rockets had already launched the space shuttle more than one hundred times. Rocket technology development in the last half-century has made a major impact on modern space exploration and warfare strategies. Examples of such technology include the nearly 3,000,000-pound-thrust solid booster rockets developed for the space shuttle and the approximately 100,000 horsepower required by the turbine-driven pumps to pressurize the liquid hydrogen and oxygen for each of the three shuttle main engines. Improving materials and thrust-level control throughout the burn period is an ongoing technical challenge.

Rocket Science

Rockets have been developed for many different purposes and therefore differ widely in dimension, takeoff weight, thrust, range, propellant type, pressure, and temperature. The combustion process itself pressurizes solid fuel rockets, making solid fuel rockets more simple than liquid fuel rockets and capable of higher thrust levels. In the case of the space shuttle, two solid booster rockets are used to launch the vehicle, each with almost 3,000,000 pounds of thrust. Their function is to accelerate the shuttle as quickly

Basic Rocket Propulsion

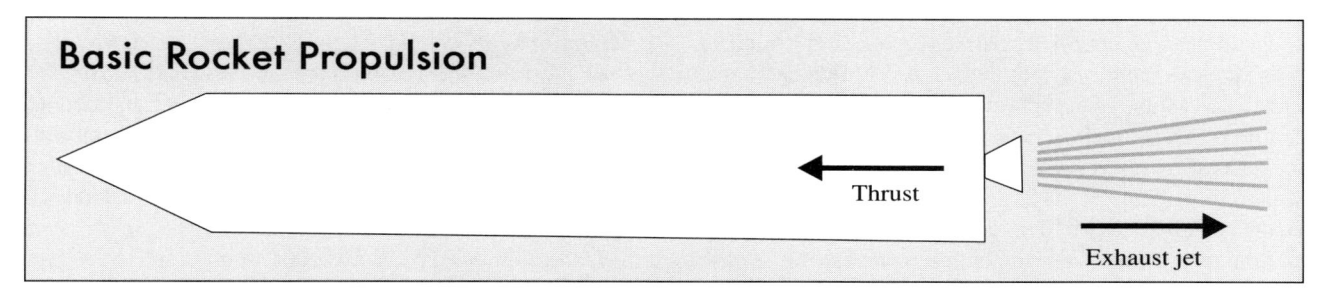

(Diagram: rocket with arrow labeled "Thrust" pointing left and arrow labeled "Exhaust jet" pointing right)

as the crew can tolerate to near orbital velocity. From then on, the liquid fuel space shuttle main engines (SSME) continue to provide thrust with almost twice the effective exhaust velocity but only about one-seventeenth the thrust level. Typical fireworks rockets have burn times of only seconds and therefore require exceptionally high acceleration rates or thrust-to-weight ratio. Air-pressure-driven, water-type toy rockets have low exhaust velocities, similar in magnitude to the nozzle velocity of a garden hose.

The most important difference between rockets and jet engines is that rockets do not need to take in air, whereas jet engines require air for combustion and temperature control with mass-flow rates of up to one hundred times that of their fuel-flow rate. Because jet engines must ingest air, they can only operate below 100,000 feet altitude. However, rockets can operate anywhere inside and outside the atmosphere, even under water.

The rocket nozzle is used to accelerate the propellant to high exit velocity. To keep this nozzle small and therefore lightweight, the propellant must be generated at high pressure inside the rocket chamber. The corresponding smaller exit area also minimizes the nozzle thrust loss from ambient air pressure. The use of a low molecular weight propellant at high temperature increases the effective exhaust velocity, thus minimizing the required propellant mass-flow rate.

The most energetic chemical propellants are produced by the combustion of liquid hydrogen with liquid fluoride as the oxidizer. This mixture generates a combustion temperature of 7,200 degrees Fahrenheit and nozzle gas velocities of up to 15,400 feet per second. Less corrosive is a combination of liquid hydrogen with liquid oxygen, which produces a combustion temperature of 5,400 degrees Fahrenheit and nozzle gas velocities of up to 14,600 feet per second.

To pressurize these liquid propellants, very high-horsepower turbopumps are used. For example, the SSME requires both fuel and oxidizer pumps of a delivery pressure of around 8,000 pounds per square inch. With their combined-flow rate of approximately 1,000 pounds per second, this requires almost 100,000 horsepower for pumping per engine.

In contrast, a solid fuel rocket is much more simple to operate and therefore less expensive, as it does not need a pump to pressurize its combustion chamber. To understand the pressurization process, one must realize that the maximum amount of mass-flow which can escape through a rocket nozzle is directly proportional to gas density or pressure inside the chamber. Prior to ignition, the rocket chamber is at ambient pressure. The solid propellant inside is typically a mixture of oxidizer crystals, such as ammonium perchlorate, combined in a synthetic rubber binder, which serves as fuel. The fuel inner surface geometry is designed to adjust the combustion rate and thereby provide the desired thrust/time characteristics. When this solid surface is ignited, the amount of hot gas produced exceeds that escaping out the nozzle. Therefore, gas mass accumulates inside the rocket chamber and increases the gas pressure. This pressure rise continues until it is high enough to allow as much gas to escape out of the nozzle as is being generated inside the combustion chamber. In a fireworks rocket, this operating pressure is reached within a fraction of a second.

Some small liquid-propellant rockets can be operated without a pump, if the fuel and oxidizer are pressurized by a container of high-pressure inert gas. An even more basic liquid rocket uses a monopropellant, such as hydrogen peroxide. This liquid, when brought into contact with a catalyst, transforms into a 1,000-degree-Fahrenheit steam-and-oxygen gas that makes a good propellant.

Liquid propellants have the advantage over solids in that the exhaust velocity is higher and that thrust is controllable with a valve. Thrust control can also be obtained by combining a liquid oxidizer with a solid fuel, which is termed a hybrid engine. Hypergolic propellants such as nitric acid and hydrazine spontaneously combust upon contact, thereby eliminating the need for an igniter.

Rocket staging is an important technology used to increase payload capacity. The dropping off of empty fuel and oxidizer containers reduces weight and drag, which, in turn, reduces the thrust required in the subsequent stage. The disadvantage of rocket staging in launching the space shuttle is that retrieving and refurbishing the solid booster rocket casings adds several months to the launch turnaround time. This means many units are needed for a frequent launch schedule. The cost associated with this arrangement is the main reason for current research efforts to develop a space shuttle replacement in the form of a single-stage-to-orbit vehicle. In such a vehicle, the weight savings normally achieved by the staging process must be replaced by reducing the amount of oxidizer carried on board, necessitating takeoff with an air-breathing jet engine instead of a rocket. The switch to rocket propulsion cannot occur until after the vehicle reaches a speed of Mach 10. Then, a nonstaged rocket is sufficient to continue into orbit. Such an air-breathing jet engine is called a supersonic combustion ramjet, or scramjet, and its technology as yet remains nonoperational.

Long-range space missions in orbital trajectories represent flight in a zero-gravity environment for a majority of the mission. In those cases, a very small thrust supplied over a long time period can be made more fuel-efficient than can the use of chemical rockets. The energy for this type of rocket is supplied by either nuclear or solar energy. Electric energy can be used to heat gas to temperatures of up to 10,000 degrees Fahrenheit in an electric arc and produce a very high exit velocity. Ion rockets are even more propellant efficient. They accelerate charged particles in an electric field to exhaust velocities up to ten times those possible in chemical rockets.

International cooperation in rocket launch systems expanded at the end of the twentieth century. Near Moscow, the Russians have built more than 10,000 rocket engines. Based on the Russians' experience, Lockheed Martin placed an order for 101 type RD-180 rocket engines. The RD-180 is a single-engine rocket, producing up to 933,400 pounds of thrust and using two combustion chambers, each with its own steerable nozzle. It burns a kerosene-oxygen mixture, with up to 1 ton of oxygen per second at maximum thrust. It can be throttled back to 40 percent thrust level for accurate trajectory control. These rockets were planned for used in the U.S. Atlas III Program, designed to put 9,000 pounds of payload in Earth geosynchronous orbit.

Other applications of rocket technology are in the airbags used for passenger safety in modern automobiles. These bags are filled with the exhaust gases from a small solid rocket, which is ignited when the vehicle experiences a collision.

John L. Loth

Bibliography

Oates, Gordon C. *Aerothermodynamics of Gas Turbine and Rocket Propulsion*. Reston, Va.: American Institute of Aeronautics and Astronautics, 1997. An electronic text on the aerodynamic principles of aircraft turbines and rocket engines, featuring a bibliography and index.

Sutton, G. P. *Rocket Propulsion Elements*. 7th ed. New York: John Wiley & Sons, 2001. A comprehensive text on the workings of rocket engines.

Turner, Martin J. L. *Rocket and Spacecraft Propulsion: Principles, Practice, and New Development*. New York: Springer, 2000. A text covering the science of rocket propulsion in spaceflight.

See also: Robert H. Goddard; Jet Propulsion Laboratory; Microgravity; National Aeronautics and Space Administration; Rockets; Russian space program; Spaceflight

Rockets

Definition: Entirely self-contained projectiles or vehicles that are self-propelled by jets of gas.

Significance: Because they are self-propelled and self-contained, rockets are capable of operating independently of any outside support equipment. Furthermore, because rockets do not need to take in air to operate, they are capable of operations outside of Earth's atmosphere.

Nature and Use

A rocket is propelled forward by a jet of material coming from one of its ends. This jet is generally hot gases resulting from burning fuel in the rocket. The fuel is burned in a combustion chamber and the exhaust gases are expelled from the rocket. Frequently the exhaust gases are directed using a nozzle. Forcing the gases to be expelled in one direction pushes the rocket in the other direction. The amount of force pushing on the rocket as a result of expelling the jet of gas is called thrust.

An important consideration for a rocket is its thrust-to-weight (TTW) ratio. The higher a rocket's TTW, the greater its acceleration. If a rocket has a TTW of less than one, it cannot lift off vertically from the surface of a planet or moon, though it can still fly horizontally with the aid of wings. As a rocket burns fuel, it has less mass and, thus, less weight. As the mass of the rocket decreases, its TTW increases. Rockets, therefore, tend to accelerate faster the longer they burn, unless the thrust is reduced. The Saturn V rocket that carried the Apollo missions to the Moon had an initial TTW of 1.25. The space shuttle was designed with a TTW of approximately 1.5.

A rocket is an entirely self-contained system. Jet engines also rely on the expulsion of hot gases in order to achieve thrust; however, jet engines take in air that mixes with the fuel and burns to provide the exhaust gases. Rockets, in contrast, carry everything they need with them and do not need to take in air to mix with the fuel. Depending on the fuel and the rocket design, rockets sometimes carry oxygen or another chemical that acts as an oxidizer to combine with the fuel in order to make it burn. The fuel and oxidizer taken together are called the rocket propellant. Other rockets contain self-oxidizing fuel, sometimes called a monopropellant, which does not need to be mixed with anything in order to burn. A few advanced rocket designs are able to expel gases without burning fuel at all and, thus, do not need an oxidizer to mix with the propellant.

Different propellants burn with different efficiencies and release different amounts of energy. As a consequence, not all combinations of propellants yield the same thrust even when used in the same rocket. Rocket engineers characterize the efficiency of a rocket propellant by its specific impulse. The specific impulse of a rocket propellant is determined by dividing the thrust provided by the propellant by the weight of propellant consumed per second. The amount of thrust produced depends not only on the propellant used, but also on the rocket design. Thus, the specific impulse of a propellant is valid only for that propellant used in a particular rocket, hence it is specific to the rocket.

Applications

Rockets have many uses. Some rockets are used in conjunction with other propulsion sources to provide additional thrust. Such rockets are called booster rockets. Some rockets are designed to carry cargo or scientific instruments. Anything carried by the rocket that is not part of the rocket itself is called the payload of the rocket. Many military rockets carry a payload of a bomb or other explosive weapon. In such cases, the rocket is called a missile, and the payload is called a warhead.

Rockets have been used with aircraft, either as the sole propulsion system or as strap-on boosters used to achieve extra thrust needed for heavy aircraft to lift off on short runways. The main use of rocket-assisted takeoff is for military transports that need to take off from airfields with runways that are too short to allow for takeoff with conventional engines.

Because rockets can continue to accelerate for as long as they have propellant, they are useful for achieving very high speeds. Such high speeds are needed to achieve orbit around Earth or to leave the vicinity of Earth. Rockets used to launch vehicles into space are called launch vehicles. Furthermore, because rockets are self-contained, they can operate outside of Earth's atmosphere. All spacecraft use rockets for propulsion.

Sometimes rockets are used to propel other rockets. In such cases, the combined rockets are called multistage rockets. The first rocket is known as the first stage and is often called the rocket booster.

Types of Rockets

Rockets are often classified by the type of fuel that they use. Early rockets used a fuel composed of a paste made from gunpowder. Many modern rockets use a fuel that is a solid chemical. These are called solid-fueled rockets or, occasionally, simple solid rockets. Solid-fueled rockets have an advantage in that the fuel is often easy to manufacture and can be cast into the rocket casing itself. A single piece of solid fuel is called a grain or charge. The shape of the grain can be adjusted to yield different specific impulses as needed. The shape can even be adjusted to yield a different thrust at different times after the grain is ignited. Furthermore, solid fuel is often stable at normal environmental temperatures, and the rocket can be left fully fueled until needed. A disadvantage, however, is that once ignited, solid fuel burns by itself and cannot be easily controlled. A solid-fueled rocket is nearly impossible to turn off once it is ignited, and the amount of thrust cannot be much changed from the initial design considerations taken into account during rocket construction. Once the propellant of a solid-fueled rocket is ignited, it generally has to continue burning until it is all gone.

In 1926, the American physicist Robert H. Goddard designed and built a rocket that used a liquid rather than a solid propellant. The initial liquid propellant consisted of gasoline and liquid oxygen. Since that time, many other liquid propellants have been used. A major advantage of liquid-fueled rockets is that the amount of thrust can be easily controlled by simply adjusting valves that govern the amount of propellant that goes into the combustion chamber. Furthermore, liquid-fueled rockets can be turned off at any time by simply shutting off the propellant control valves. Most liquid-fueled rockets can even be turned on again by opening the valves again after they have been shut off. Although some liquid propellants need an ignition source to start burning the fuel, a few mixtures of fuel and propellant simply begin to burn on contact. These self-igniting fuels are called hypergolic propellants. Although liquid-fueled rockets have some clear advantages over solid-fueled rockets, there are some serious disadvantages. Many liquid propellants are cryogenic liquids that must be kept at extremely low temperatures. These cryogenic fluids generally cannot be stored for extended periods of time in the rocket. The rocket, therefore, can only be fueled shortly before use. Furthermore, most liquid propellants are extremely dangerous to transport and to store. Liquid-fueled rockets tend to have complex valve and control systems and, thus, are usually more complicated to design and more expensive to construct than are solid-fueled rockets.

Most rocket designs require the burning of either solid or liquid fuels to provide the source of hot gas and energy that expels a jet of gas that powers the rocket. A few rocket designs do not require burning of the propellant to provide the exhaust jets needed to power the rocket. One such design would employ a reservoir of compressed gas, which would be released and expelled from the rocket. Alternately, the compressed gas could force another propellant, such as water, from the rocket. Some toy rockets are of this extremely simple and inexpensive design. A major disadvantage of this design, however, is that it is very inefficient and cannot provide very much thrust for very long.

Another rocket design calls for the use of a nuclear reactor to heat gases to cause them to be expelled from the rocket. Such nuclear-powered rockets are extremely efficient and powerful. A few nuclear-powered rocket motors have been constructed and tested on the ground or in very short flights, but, due to safety concerns, none have been used in extended flight.

Another technology used to provide the jet of gases is the acceleration of charged atoms or molecules, called ions, with electric fields. The ions are ejected from the rocket in the direction in which the electric field accelerated them. Ion-drive rockets are quite economical. The electric fields can be generated using solar power, and almost any gas can be used as a propellant. The major disadvantage of an ion rocket is that the gas must be very diffuse for the system to work, and this results in very low thrust. The thrust, however, can be sustained for extended periods, resulting in very high speeds after long periods of operation. Because ion-driven rockets have a very low thrust, they cannot be used to launch a vehicle into space, but they can be used once a rocket is already in space.

Parts of a Rocket

Different rocket designs obviously require different components. Some of the most complicated and diverse rockets are liquid-fueled rockets. There are general similarities among most liquid-fueled rockets, however. The bulk of the rocket's volume holds tanks storing the propellant. For most propellants, there must be separate tanks for the fuel and the oxidizer. The location of the tanks does not really matter, but generally the oxidizer tank is located forward of the fuel tank. This placement allows for a shorter path for the fuel to travel from the tank to the rocket motor. If the rocket is designed to operate within the atmosphere, the rocket body may have fins that help stabilize the rocket in flight, but a true rocket does not use the fins as wings to fly. Some rockets are guided rockets, able to steer while in flight. The mechanisms for guidance and steering are also located within the rocket body. Generally, a rocket's control mechanism is located away from the rocket motor in order to minimize any damage to the guidance system from the rocket motor's heat or vibration.

The rocket motor consists primarily of the combustion chamber, which is where the propellant is burned. The rest of the rocket motor is generally composed of valves and plumbing to deliver the propellant and to mix the fuel and oxidizer as efficiently as possible. Frequently, because the fuel and oxidizer are cryogenic fluids, the fuel lines carry the propellant past the combustion chamber before injecting the fuel into the chamber. This has the advantage of helping to cool the combustion chamber and warm the fuel, generally resulting in a more efficient burning process.

Most rockets contain a nozzle to help direct the exhaust gases from the combustion chamber. A nozzle is not strictly necessary, because a properly designed combustion chamber tends to direct the exhaust gases away from the chamber as a jet through an opening at one end of the chamber. The exhaust gases, however, tend to expand as soon as they are out of the combustion chamber and the jet of exhaust gas becomes less directional after leaving the combustion chamber. A nozzle will direct the gas jet in the desired direction. The more directional the jet of gas leaving the rocket motor, the higher the thrust that the rocket motor will have. Thus, a properly designed rocket nozzle is an important part of a rocket motor. The most efficient type of nozzle is the bell-shaped Venturi nozzle, which is narrow at the point where it connects to the combustion chamber and flares out to a much larger diameter farther from the combustion chamber. Some nozzles are fixed in position, whereas others are capable of tilting slightly, thus changing the direction of the jet of gases and, consequently, the direction of the rocket's thrust. Such movable rocket nozzles are important in guided rockets. For rockets designed to operate outside Earth's atmosphere, the motion of the rocket nozzle is the chief mechanism for steering the rocket.

Solid-fueled rockets are more simple in design than are liquid-fueled rockets. Both types of rocket have similar rocket bodies and nozzles; the main difference between the two types is in the design of the combustion chamber and the propellant storage. Often, the solid-fueled rocket contains a single grain of fuel. The combustion chamber is often located inside the grain, with the grain itself forming the walls of the combustion chamber. As the grain burns, the combustion chamber expands outward. Alternately, the grain fills the combustion chamber and burns from one end to the other. This is generally a less efficient design. The design and shape of the grain can be adjusted to yield variable thrust according to a predetermined formula, but the thrust variations are determined by the manufacture of the grain and cannot be changed after the rocket is ignited.

The Physics of Rockets

One of the fundamental laws of physics is the law of conservation of momentum. Momentum is defined as the mass multiplied by velocity. The conservation of momentum law says that the total momentum of a system does not change unless an external force acts on the system. Rockets operate using this principle. Jets of material streaming away from one end of the rocket carry momentum. This may be thought of as negative momentum since it is in a direction opposite to the direction of the rocket's flight. As a consequence, the rocket must have momentum in the opposite, or positive, direction. The sum of the two yields zero. As the jet of gas leaves the rocket carrying negative momentum, the rocket must have an increase of positive momentum. This means that the rocket must increase its forward speed as the rocket's mass decreases.

Thus, the more mass that is expelled from the rocket, the more momentum it carries. Likewise, the faster the mass leaves the rocket, the more momentum that it carries. The rate at which negative momentum is carried from the rocket determines the thrust of the rocket. For a highly directional jet of gas from a rocket, the thrust is given by the first rocket equation:

$$F = Ru$$

In this equation, F is the thrust, u is the speed at which the jet of gas leaves the rocket, and R is the rate of propellant used, measured in mass per time.

As a rocket continues to burn, its mass decreases, and, thus, the acceleration increases if the thrust remains constant. The final speed of a rocket operating outside of the influence of other forces can be determined by the second rocket equation:

$$v_f = v_i + u \times \ln\left(\frac{m_i}{m_f}\right)$$

In this equation, v_f is the final rocket velocity, and v_i is the initial rocket velocity. The ln indicates the natural logarithm function. The initial rocket mass is given by m_i and the final rocket mass is given by m_f. The u term represents the exhaust velocity of the gas as it leaves the rocket.

Both of these equations describe idealized rockets. Real rockets are generally not ideal, and, thus, modifications to the equations must be made. Generally, the adjustments to the equations are to yield an effective thrust less than the thrust determined from the first rocket equation and to yield a final velocity less than that determined by the second rocket equation. These equations, therefore, provide the maximum thrust and maximum possible final velocity for a rocket. The goal of rocket engineers is to construct rockets that are as close to ideal as possible.

Much of a rocket consists of storage space for the propellant. After propellant has been used, the portion of the rocket used in storing the propellant becomes dead weight. As indicated in the second rocket equation, if the final mass were reduced, then the final velocity could be increased. This mass reduction could be accomplished by jettisoning the propellant storage spaces. Rather than building rockets that jettison used propellant storage areas, rockets are often designed to propel other rockets, called stages. The first rocket, or first stage, fires until it has used up its propellant. After the first stage has finished using its propellant, it drops off, and the second stage begins operation. A rocket can have as many stages as needed. However, the difficulty and expense of designing and constructing multiple stages, each with its own rocket motors, makes it generally economically unfeasible for a rocket to have more than two or three stages.

Raymond D. Benge, Jr.

Bibliography

Jeppesen Sanderson. *Aviation Fundamentals*. 3d ed. Englewood, Colo.: Jeppesen Sanderson, 1991. Chapter 12 of this textbook for beginning private pilots is an excellent overview of rockets and rocket propulsion.

Miller, Ron. *The History of Rockets*. New York: Franklin Watts, 1999. A book written for young readers, chronicling the history of rockets.

Neal, Valerie, Cathleen S. Lewis, and Frank H. Winter. *Spaceflight: A Smithsonian Guide*. New York: Macmillan, 1995. A nice overview of spaceflight, with a good description of rocket basics and a history of rocket development.

Turner, Martin J. L. *Rocket and Spacecraft Propulsion: Principles, Practice, and New Developments*. New York: Springer Verlag, 2000. A rather technical and thorough description of rockets.

See also: Wernher von Braun; Forces of flight; National Aeronautics and Space Administration; Orbiting; Propulsion; Rocket propulsion; Spaceflight

Roll and pitch

- **Definition:** Roll is the angular motion of an airplane about its centerline, a line of equal distance between the wings through the fuselage. Pitch is the angular motion of an airplane about a line from wingtip to wingtip perpendicular to its centerline.
- **Significance:** Roll is important because pilots can use this motion to direct the lift on the wings and change the path of the airplane; by pitching the airplane, the pilot can change the magnitude of the lift on the airplane. For example, in setting up an airplane for a landing, the pilot must continually redirect the lift force to keep the airplane aligned with the runway. In landing, changes to the pitch angle can make small changes to the lift force and therefore alter the descent rate of the airplane.

Ailerons and Elevators

The primary airplane controls that generate roll are the ailerons, which are located on each side of the wing and are identified as the left and right ailerons. Both ailerons are of the same size and are located at the same distance from the centerline of the airplane. These controls are essentially the same in both expensive, high-performance general aviation jets and low-performance training airplanes. In both, each aileron is attached to its corresponding wing by a hinge. The ailerons deflect upward and downward about the hinge line. When one aileron deflects upward, the other aileron deflects downward. The pilot deflects the ailerons by moving the control wheel. If the control wheel is rotated counter-clockwise, the left aileron moves upward and the right aileron moves downward.

This movement is in contrast to that of the elevator; both right and left elevators move together. The elevator is the primary control for changing the pitch angle or the angle that the centerline makes with the horizontal. The pilot deflects the elevator by moving the control wheel or stick backward and forward. Rearward movement of the wheel raises the elevator and therefore the nose of the airplane.

Rudders

Even though the ailerons are the primary roll control, the rudder is often moved with the ailerons in making turns. The rudder moves the nose of the airplane in the direction of the lower wing. However, movement of the rudder also can affect the airplane roll. In a turn (to the left, say), the aileron on the left wing is raised and the aileron on the right wing is lowered. In this aileron position, the rudder is moved to the left. This rudder movement pushes the tail to the right and therefore the nose to the left. The force on the tail due to the rudder deflection is shown pointed to the right. A force at the tail to the right will push the nose of the airplane to the left. Since this force due to the rudder is to the right and above the centerline of the airplane, the result is an initial rolling action opposite to that resulting from the aileron movement. Therefore even though the rudder is required to move left to help turn the airplane to the left, there is a secondary effect as soon as the rudder is applied, which detracts from the rolling motion of the ailerons.

However, because the rudder forces the nose to the left, in spite of its contrary rolling effect, the nose is moved to the left of the direction of the oncoming air. This deflection produces a cross-flow coming from the right to the left for the left turn.

Airplane wings are designed with a slight upward bend. This bend is called a wing dihedral, and the angle that the wing makes with the horizontal is called the dihedral angle. As a result of both dihedral angle and cross-flow, the right wing has a slight increase in upward flow, and the left wing has a slight decrease in upward flow. The result is that the lift on the right wing is increased and the lift on the left wing is decreased. The result is a roll angle, left wing down and right wing up, that is in the same direction as that caused by the deflection of the ailerons. The rudder initially causes the airplane to roll in a direction opposite to that of the ailerons; however, the yawing motion of the rudder causes a cross-flow to develop, and that flow, along with the built-in dihedral angle, causes the airplane to roll in the proper direction for the turn: left wing down for turn to the left, right wing down for turn to the right.

An airplane can, however, have an excessive amount of dihedral, the result of which would be that wind gusts from the left or right would cause a rolling motion that would increase with the dihedral angle. The airplane would have an unpleasant rocking motion in response to even small gusts.

As has been pointed out, the rudder can cause the airplane to roll, but the ailerons can cause the airplane to yaw. The aileron can cause the airplane to yaw because there is always a drag associated with lift. If lift is increased, then the drag is increased. When the right aileron is deflected downward, the lift increases on the right wing. At the same time, the left aileron is moved upward, decreasing the lift on the left wing. Thus, there is an increase in drag on the right wing and a decrease in drag on the left wing, which will cause the nose of the airplane to swing to the right. Because the ailerons are moved to turn to the left, the yaw that results from aileron deflection is called adverse yaw. The main purpose of the rudder is to counteract this adverse yaw. When the airplane rolls to the left, the nose-right adverse yaw of the ailerons is countered by moving the rudder left.

The primary roll control on an airplane is managed by the ailerons, one on each wing. The pilot controls airplane roll by rotating the control wheel in the direction of the desired roll. Aileron deflection produces an adverse yaw, which is countered by the rudder. Pitch is controlled by movement of the elevator, moved in turn by the pilot by a backward, or nose-up, and forward, or nose-down, movement of the control wheel.

Frank J. Regan

Bibliography

Raymer, Daniel P. *Aircraft Design: A Conceptual Approach.* 3d ed. Reston, Va.: American Institute of Aeronautics and Astronautics, 1999. A highly recommended, comprehensive, and up-to-date book on airplane design, directed at the engineering student, but featuring many sections requiring little more than high school algebra.

Stinton, Darrel. *The Design of the Airplane.* New York: Van Nostrand-Reinhold, 1985. An excellent introduction to airplane design.

Taylor, John W. R. *The Lore of Flight.* New York: Crescent Books, 1974. A massive, well-illustrated, oversized book featuring nontechnical descriptions of airplanes and spacecraft, and covering controls and cockpit instruments.

See also: Aerodynamics; Ailerons and flaps; Airplanes; Flight control systems; Forces of flight; Rudders; Stabilizers; Tail designs; Wing designs

The F-15B is equipped with nozzles that allow it to control both pitch and yaw. (NASA)

Rotorcraft

Also known as: Rotary-wing aircraft

Definition: Any aircraft that uses a rotor, or rotating wings, to provide the craft's lifting force.

Significance: Rotorcraft, the first aircraft able to perform short and vertical takeoffs and landings, continue to comprise the majority of all short takeoff and landing (STOL) and vertical takeoff and landing (VTOL) aircraft.

Rotary- Versus Fixed-Wing Aircraft

All aircraft can be divided into two general categories: fixed-wing aircraft and rotary-wing aircraft, or rotorcraft. The principal difference between the two types of aircraft is the method used to provide the lifting force that allows the aircraft to fly. Fixed-wing aircraft use large, stationary wings to provide the required lift. The lift on the wings is generated by pulling the entire aircraft through the air with some type of propulsion system, such as propellers or jet engines. Rotorcraft, on the other hand, are equipped with at least one rotor, made up of a set of two or more rotating wings, that provides the lift that the aircraft needs to stay aloft. The lift on each of the rotating wings is generated as the rotor spins through the air, around the rotor shaft. As a result, the rotor can generate lift without the entire aircraft necessarily having to be in motion.

Types of Rotorcraft

The two most common types of rotorcraft are the helicopter and the autogiro. Helicopters and autogiros are similar in that they both have large-diameter rotors that provide lift for the aircraft in all flight conditions. Helicopters are used in a large number of civilian and military applications. Civilian applications include airborne ambulance, police surveillance, news gathering, fire fighting, logging, heavy construction, intracity passenger transportation, tourism, cargo transportation, and search and rescue. Military applications include troop transport, logistical support, combat air support, and combat search and rescue. Autogiros, in contrast, have few commercial or military applications and are flown mainly by sport aviators.

Virtually all other rotorcraft can be broadly grouped into a category called tilting proprotor aircraft. These aircraft include the tilt-shaft/rotor, tilt-prop, tilt-wing, and tilt-rotor aircraft. All have two or more rotors, which provide either lift or propulsive force by tilting to a vertical position for vertical flight and to a horizontal position for forward flight. In vertical flight, the rotors provide all the lift necessary to keep the aircraft aloft in takeoff, landing, and hover. In forward flight, wings perform that function, and the rotors provide propulsive force. With the exception of the V-22 Osprey, a tilt-rotor aircraft, tilting proprotor aircraft have never progressed beyond the prototype stage.

Helicopters

Helicopters can be distinguished from other rotorcraft by the fact that their rotors have a fixed orientation relative to the aircraft fuselage and simultaneously provide lift and propulsion. On a helicopter, engines provide the power that drives the rotation of the rotor. Most modern helicopters have either one or two rotors that provide lift and propulsive force. The maximum forward speed of a helicopter is limited by the fact that the rotor (or rotors) must provide both propulsion and lift. Under high-speed flight conditions, the vibratory forces on the rotor blades become extreme, thereby limiting the top speed of the helicopter. In order to increase the top speed, some helicopters, known as compound helicopters, have been equipped with auxiliary propulsion, such as propellers or jet engines.

Helicopters have been built in a variety of configurations. The most common configuration is the single-rotor helicopter, which has a single main rotor for thrust and pitch and roll control and often has a smaller tail rotor that provides directional control. Another common configuration is the tandem helicopter, which has two large rotors, one near the forward end of the helicopter and the other near the aft end. This configuration is particularly well suited for the transport of heavy cargo, because the two rotors can accommodate large changes in the aircraft's center of gravity.

Less common configurations include the coaxial and side-by-side helicopters. The coaxial helicopter has two counterrotating rotors that share a common mast. Side-by-side helicopters also have two rotors, but one is located on the right side of the aircraft and the other is located on the left side. A variant of the side-by-side helicopter is the synchropter, on which the two rotors are placed close together so that they intermesh.

The concept for the helicopter has been around since the Chinese top, which predates the Roman Empire. Leonardo da Vinci also considered the possibility of vertical flight. However, like the airplane, the helicopter did not become a practical concept until the invention of the internal combustion engine. Significant developments in the direction of a practical helicopter began to be achieved not long after Orville and Wilbur Wright flew their first airplane in 1903. Men such as Emile and Henry Berliner, Raoul Pescara, Louis-Charles Breguet, Heinrich Focke, and Anton Flettner made major contributions to the development of the helicopter. Although some give credit to Igor Sikorsky for building the first successful helicopter, the VS-300, others argue that the Focke-Wulf Fw-61 was the world's first practical helicopter. At the same time, other individuals, including Arthur Young, Frank Piasecki, and Stanley Hiller, were developing their own designs.

After World War II ended, a number of companies began designing and building helicopters. The most successful were Sikorsky, Bell, Piasecki (later Boeing), Kaman, and Hiller. During the Korean War, the use of helicopters for medical evacuation showcased the usefulness of helicopters and spurred further developments. Among the most important developments was the introduction of the turboshaft engine. Later, during the Vietnam War, the role of helicopters was expanded to include troop and cargo movement and attack missions. The expanded uses for the helicopter led to more developments that resulted in modern helicopters.

Autogiros

Autogiros look very much like helicopters, except that they typically have only one rotor. The rotor on an autogiro also has a fixed orientation relative to the fuselage, but, in contrast to that of the helicopter, the autogiro's rotor provides only lift. Propulsive force is provided by an auxiliary power source, such as a propeller. In addition, the rotation of the rotor is driven not by an engine, but by the air that passes through the rotor disk as it is dragged through the atmosphere by the aircraft. This behavior is similar to that of a maple seed, which spins as it falls from the tree. Because the rotor requires the aircraft's forward motion in order to rotate, the autogiro can neither take off nor land vertically, nor can it hover. It is a short takeoff and landing (STOL) vehicle.

Autogiro development began in about 1920 and was considered a viable alternative to the helicopter until the development of Sikorsky's helicopter. The father of the autogiro is Juan de la Cierva of Spain. After building two unsuccessful aircraft, Cierva flew his first successful autogiro in 1923. In the United States, the Pitcairn and Kellett Aircraft Companies were principally responsible for the development of the autogiro. Operating under a license from Cierva, they cooperated with Cierva in developing his original design. Cierva used conventional aircraft controls to fly his autogiro. By 1932, control was achieved by tilting the rotor with respect to the fuselage, eliminating the need for all aircraft controls except the rudder. Also, early autogiros started their rotors by taxiing around on the ground. Later models were equipped with a geared connection to the engine.

Tilting Proprotor Aircraft

The principal reason for the development of tilting proprotor aircraft was to overcome the inability of helicopters to fly at high forward speeds, while retaining the ability to hover, take off, and land vertically. A comparison of the rotors of helicopters and autogiros to those of tilting proprotor aircraft shows that the latter have much smaller diameters. Tilting proprotor aircraft also have wings and vertical and horizontal tail surfaces like those of conventional fixed-wing aircraft.

Tilt-shaft/rotor aircraft were the predecessors of the modern tilt-rotor aircraft. This rotorcraft was able to take off and land vertically, as well as hover, by virtue of the fact that its rotors could pivot to provide lift for takeoff, landing, and hover, as well as propulsive force in forward flight. Stationary wings provided the required lift in forward flight. The first tilt-shaft/rotor aircraft was the Model 1-G, which was built by the Transcendental Aircraft Corporation and became the first such aircraft to successfully make the transition from hover to forward flight in December, 1954. The rotors on the Model 1-G were located at the ends of the wings, and the engine that provided power to them was located in the fuselage. The Model 2 followed the Model 1-G and was tested from 1956 to 1957. Bell Helicopter Company, which had been working on a similar concept since 1951, introduced the XV-3 in 1955. Two prototype aircraft were eventually built and flew many flight tests. The XV-3 was similar in design to the Model 1-G, which was not surprising because aircraft engineer Robert Lichten played a major role in the design of both aircraft.

The concept for the tilt-prop aircraft was similar to that of the tilt-shaft/rotor aircraft, except that the diameter of the tilt-prop rotors was smaller, like a large propeller. Only two aircraft of this type were ever built, both of which were built by Curtiss-Wright and called the X-100 and the X-19. The X-100 had two tilting props at the ends of a stationary wing. The X-19 had four tilting props, two at the ends of the main wing and two at the ends of a smaller wing at the tail of the aircraft.

The tilt-wing aircraft was another variant of the tilting proprotor aircraft. As with the others, the orientation of the rotors could be changed from horizontal to vertical, so that the aircraft could both hover and fly at high forward speeds. However, on a tilt-wing aircraft, the rotors were rigidly attached to the wing, and the entire wing pivoted. The first tilt-wing aircraft was the Vertol 76 (VZ-2), which first flew in 1958. Hiller Aircraft then built and flew the X-18 in 1959. The two most successful tilt-wing aircraft, the LTV-Hiller-Ryan XC-142 and the Canadair CL-84 Dynavert, appeared in the mid-1960's. In 1964, the XC-142 became the largest vertical takeoff and landing aircraft to fly. Five prototypes were built, but all eventually crashed or were otherwise accidentally destroyed.

Similar in configuration to other tilting proprotor aircraft, the tilt-rotor appears to be a fixed-wing aircraft with large propellers attached to nacelles at the tips of the wings. The engines that provide the power to turn the rotors are located in the nacelles. In 1975, Bell Helicopter Company began the development of the XV-15 tilt-rotor research aircraft. Two prototype aircraft were built, and the first successful flight with conversion to forward flight took place in 1977. Since that time, the XV-15 has performed hundreds of hours of research flight testing and flight demonstrations. The unprecedented success of the XV-15 led directly to the development of the Bell-Boeing V-22 Osprey, the first operational tilt-rotor aircraft.

Donald L. Kunz

Bibliography
Campbell, J. P. *Vertical Takeoff and Landing Aircraft*. New York: Macmillan, 1962. Overview of aircraft developed with vertical takeoff and landing capabilities.

Gabelhouse, C. *Helicopters and Autogiros, A Chronicle of Rotating-Wing Aircraft*. London: Scientific Book Club, 1967. A history of rotorcraft, including both helicopters and autogiros.

Hirschberg, M. J. *The American Helicopter, An Overview of Helicopter Developments in America, 1907-1999*. Arlington, Va.: ANSER, 2000. A historical account of twentieth century helicopter developments, with pictures and descriptions of many different designs.

Lindenbaum, B. L. *V/STOL Concepts and Developed Aircraft: A Historical Review*. Dayton, Ohio: University of Dayton, 1982. A historical review of concepts for vertical/short takeoff and landing aircraft, including descriptions of research aircraft.

Muson, K. *Helicopters and Other Rotorcraft Since 1907*. London: Macmillan, 1968. A historical account of helicopter development.

See also: Apache helicopter; Bell Aircraft; Firefighting aircraft; Gyros; Helicopters; Military flight; Osprey helicopter; Rescue aircraft; Vertical takeoff and landing

Royal Air Force

Also known as: RAF
Date: Founded in 1918
Definition: The military air force of one of the world's most powerful countries.
Significance: The Royal Air Force is credited with halting Adolf Hitler's campaign to invade Britain in 1940, and has since taken part in many of the United Kingdom's and the British Commonwealth's military actions.

The Royal Air Force is the airborne fleet and pride of the United Kingdom. The history of this air fleet dates as far back as 1880 when balloons were first used in British military maneuvers at Aldershot. Britain's first military air unit, the Air Battalion of the Royal Engineers, was founded in 1911, and one year later, the Royal Flying Corps (RFC) was constituted. Three days after the assassination of the Austro-Hungarian Archduke Ferdinand, which sparked World War I, the Royal Naval Air Service (RNAS) was formed from the naval wing of the RFC. These two branches of the British military constituted Britain's air force throughout most of World War I. Finally, on April 1, 1918, the Royal Air Force was founded by reamalgamating the RNAS and RFC. The RAF was engaged in several small wars between the two World Wars, but it was World War II that offered the service the opportunity to show their true prowess.

The Battle of Britain
The RAF particularly distinguished itself in 1940 during the Battle of Britain and prevented a German invasion. The German dictator Adolf Hitler saw England as a key target to be taken for his own designs. The Battle of Britain began its first phase of defense against the German aggression in August and September of 1940, when the fall of France had left Britain exposed to immediate German invasion. This period also forms what has been referred to as the most dangerous period of the war. England had scarcely enough equipment to arm two divisions, but the Prime Minister, Winston Churchill, raised the fighting spirit in the people and particularly among the RAF pilots who were called on night after night to fight in the skies over England. His famous words regarding the absolute need for victory are well known: "We shall defend our island whatever the cost may be, we shall fight on the beaches, we shall fight on the landing grounds, we shall fight in the fields and in the streets, we shall fight in the hills; we shall never surrender!"

Hitler's plan for Operation Sea Lion, the German code name for their planned invasion of Great Britain, called for heavy use of the German Luftwaffe air fleet. In order to achieve a successful invasion, it was necessary for the Luftwaffe to gain control of the airspace above the English Channel and, geographically, the southern portion of England. In the first phase of the Battle of Britain, the Luftwaffe attempted to destroy the Royal Air Force and its bases. Initially it seemed as if the Luftwaffe had a better advantage and would be successful in their battle for control of British airspace and indeed Britain itself. The British credit the determination and courage of the Royal Air Force pilots who fought the Germans in the air as one of the key factors that led to the success of the Royal Air Force. The RAF also greatly benefitted from a newly developed radar warning system. While the British suffered great damage and loss of life from the continued air raids and attacks from the Luftwaffe, the Germans suffered severe losses as well. Home defenses were prepared that had strengthened coastal areas, and local militia volunteers supported the RAF in any way they could. Later called the Home Guard, their ranks swelled to about half a million and worked for the defense of the country, as well as helping the RAF in any way possible.

It was generally assumed that Hitler had a grandiose scheme for Operation Sea Lion, but in truth there was no such plan. The Germans had hardly thought beyond the defeat of the French government, simply assuming that once France had been conquered and occupied—knocked out of the war, as it were—the British would see the folly of further armed resistance and capitulate. In actuality, it was not until May, 1940, that Hitler began to formulate thoughts about the invasion of Britain, and not until approximately July that preparations for a landing in England began to take shape. Such a plan required naval power and a command of critical airspace. Churchill and his war advisory ministers faced what he termed the "hateful decision" that the French fleet could not fall into German hands to be used against England, and thus, after a long and heated debate with the war ministers, knowing that superiority at sea was their only serious advantage, British warships began a bombardment and destruction of French naval fleets in Oran, Nigeria, and Dakar, French West Africa.

At the same time, Germany increased and intensified their air raids against Britain. Furious at the British for not capitulating and surrendering, Hitler issued orders for an all-out campaign, with orders to seek out and destroy the Royal Air Force, their bases, and the British aircraft industry itself. For approximately three weeks in late August and early September, 1940, an average of one thousand Luftwaffe planes were over Britain daily. Their targets were airfields, known factories, suspected radar stations, and the famed docks of East London. The Germans had successfully used a technique called Blitzkrieg, or "lightning war," whereby they invaded by sea, land, and air. They could not use the Blitzkrieg successfully to land in England, but they did indeed blitz from the skies day after day, night after night, in an attempt to wear down the pilots, people, and government of King George VI.

Initially, the RAF was unorganized, and there was doubt they could hold against the German onslaught. However, by the first week of September, the RAF grew in strength and sheer determination as the pilots flew round the clock to keep the Germans from gaining critical air superiority. By mid-September, 1940, the RAF was displaying greater effectiveness and efficiency in the air, and were downing two Luftwaffe planes for every one British loss. Thus, the German attempt to invade England was a dismal failure and cost them dearly. Hitler finally conceded that his Operation Sea Lion plans were in defeat and postponed and eventually cancelled further land or sea plans to invade England. He was forced to disperse the shipping units poised for the invasion, and by the end of September, 1940, the British government felt safe in assuming that there would be no invasion of their island homeland.

The Germans continued heavy night raid bombing, as defenses were rendered more difficult at night because of darkness and cloud cover. Hitler moved to systematically destroy any identifiable center of British industry. Particularly during the winter of 1940-1941, London was under constant bombardment from the Luftwaffe. On the night of December 8-9, 1940, more than four hundred Luftwaffe bombers blitzed London, inflicting great damage. Other industrial areas, including Coventry, Birmingham, Plymouth, and Liverpool, suffered the same heavy air attacks. In June, 1941, Hitler diverted his attention to Russia, which diminished the pressure on England and its Royal Air Force. Ultimately, just a handful of courageous pilots had saved the island, and Prime Minister Churchill gratefully thanked the Royal Air Force pilots, saying that "never had so many owed so much to so few."

There were great odds against the RAF, but one of their main advantages was their planes. The German planes were heavy and could only fly for a limited time without returning to refuel. The planes were also big and bulky, making changes in flight pattern and maneuvering difficult, if not impossible. The RAF flew in smaller planes, the Spitfire and Hurricane fighters. While these are the most popularly known planes, there were others that fought in

Two Hawker Hurricane Mark I fighter planes take off on August 15, 1940, to fight in the Battle of Britain. (Hulton Archive)

the Battle of Britain and throughout the war, such as the Gloster Gladiator and the Bristol Blenheim. The British aircraft gained advantage from their ability to dart and dive around, above, and below the heavier Luftwaffe planes. It was hard for the Germans to hit such moving targets. The British planes were lighter and smaller, and ultimately proved far more efficient in the long run. There are restoration programs underway to restore some of the original Spitfire and Hurricane planes.

The Modern RAF

Today, the Royal Air Force is a viable fleet of aviation power. Their training is world-renowned and intense. The Battle of Britain is not forgotten as pilots and career service personnel train in various schools and branches of the Royal Air Force. They are the air defense system of the United Kingdom and the Commonwealth, incorporating other Commonwealth nation units among their own, training together in a common cause of defense and international friendship. In May, 2001, the British Ministry of Defense announced plans to incorporate New Zealand's top combat pilots after that country decided to scrap the Royal New Zealand Air Force's fighter squadrons. Anticipating what may be the largest ever influx of New Zealand airmen into the Royal Air Force since World War II, the Ministry of Defense is nonetheless looking to fill their many vacancies, primarily for pilots, but also for necessary support personnel such as doctors and engineers. The Royal Air Force has indicated its willingness to pursue any enquiry received from the New Zealand service. Ironically, the Royal Air Force has been suffering an outflow of pilots despite greater and special financial incentives to remain in RAF service. New Zealand's termination of its fighter squadrons comes at a beneficial time for the RAF, affording the RAF the opportunity to recruit fully trained pilots who could easily assimilate the RAF's culture and traditions. Planning to sell off its fighter planes and equipment, New Zealand's fleet could easily supply the shortages the Royal Air Force is facing in planes and helicopters.

Present career training in the Royal Air Force includes such specific and demanding work as the air battle combat support course. This particular course is done in four phases, which culminate in war games. Run twice a year for two intensive weeks, each class is limited to eighteen students, who must demonstrate the ability to withstand the class. Other classes include the air electronic warfare course, an intensive aerosystems course, an air battle staff course, and an air electronic warfare course.

Senior RAF personnel study joint targeting and missions, joint air weapons systems, senior officers air warfare, and targeting and battle damage assessment. If one takes the aerosystems course, the phases contain such topics as platforms and weapons, navigation, electronics and communications, information systems, sensors, and integrated systems. With a long history behind it, the Royal Air Force remains one of the strongest air force fleets in the modern world.

Pamela M. Gross

Bibliography
James, T. C. G. *The Battle of Britain.* Portland, Oreg.: Frank Cass, 2000. The RAF's official history of its defining moment.
Nesbit, Roy Conyers. *RAF: An Illustrated History from 1918.* Thrupp, Gloucestershire, England: Sutton, 1998. Published to commemorate the RAF's eightieth anniversary, this history, written by a well-known aviation writer, covers all the service's main's campaigns. Profusely illustrated.
Royal Air Force Web Site. (www.raf.mod.uk./rafhome.html) This site will provide many links for various types of information about the RAF. Various links navigate an amazing network of information, including extensive bibliographies and technical aircraft information.

See also: Battle of Britain; Luftwaffe; Military flight; Radar; World War II

Rudders

Definition: Large, vertical, moveable, flaplike devices attached to the vertical stabilizers on most aircraft, or movable vertical fins on a missile.
Significance: The rudder is the primary device used to yaw, or steer the nose of the aircraft to the left or right, in a turn or to counteract the yaw resulting from aileron use in certain cross-control maneuvers.

An aircraft's or a missile's rudder, a flap or a wing-shaped surface mounted at or near the craft's rear, serves a purpose similar to that of a rudder on a ship. When the rudder is deflected to one side or the other, it produces a force and a resulting moment, or yaw, about the vehicle's center of gravity. The force rotates the vehicle in the same direction as the deflection of the rudder.

Because rudders have been used for centuries to steer ships, early airplane designers naturally assumed that they could be used to steer airplanes. However, these designers often failed to anticipate the roll of the aircraft that resulted from the use of the rudder. When the rudder causes an airplane to yaw, it causes one wing to travel slightly more quickly through the air than the other and, hence, to produce more lift, which subsequently causes the airplane to roll in the direction of the turn. This roll was a problem with early airplanes, which flew very close to the ground, and required the use of ailerons and similar devices to control the resulting roll. Through experimentation, early aviators learned that the most successful turns are coordinated turns, made using a combination of rudder and ailerons.

On wingless missiles, the rudder is the only device used to make the vehicle turn. A missile's rudder yaws the missile such that it flies at an angle to the airflow and develops a side-force on its body, or fuselage. This side-force produces the needed acceleration along the turn radius to carry the missile through the desired turn.

Turns
Airplane turns are more complex and require more than the use of a rudder. As noted above, when the rudder is deflected, the fuselage yaws, and the wings develop different lift forces. The wing on the outside of the turn develops a larger lift than does the wing pointing into the turn. The difference in lift between the wings results in a roll of the fuselage, which tilts or rotates the lifting force of the wings into the direction of the turn. Because the lifting force of the wings is much greater than the forces on any other part of the airplane, it is the tilted lift that provides the force to turn the airplane. When the turn is properly coordinated, the combination of yaw caused by the rudder, roll caused by the ailerons, and the slight increase in thrust will produce just the right amount of lift to balance the weight of the aircraft, so that the aircraft can make the turn without losing altitude.

Engine Loss
The rudder must also be used to keep the airplane from yawing or turning when a multiengine airplane loses one of its engines. When a multiengine plane encounters an engine-out situation, the rudder must be used to produce enough yaw to counteract the effect of having more thrust on one side of the airplane than on the other. For this reason, multiengine airplanes have much larger rudders than do single-engine airplanes.

Landings
Another common use of the rudder is to cross-control an airplane, especially in its approach to landing. In an ideal

landing, the atmospheric wind would be blowing straight down the runway. In the real world, the wind is often at an angle to the runway and, when landing or taking off, the pilot must adjust the flight of the plane to account for the crosswind. On takeoff, this is done by allowing the plane to yaw into the wind as soon as it leaves the ground and by flying away in a straight line extending from the runway centerline with the airplane turned somewhat into the wind in a slightly sideways motion. The approach to landing can be made in the same manner, with the plane yawed into the wind; at some point, the pilot must align the fuselage with the runway before the wheels touch down, so the aircraft can be properly controlled on the ground. To do this, the pilot uses the rudder to yaw the airplane until it is parallel to the runway and uses the ailerons to keep the wings level. This use of rudder and aileron is the opposite of that used in a turn and is referred to as cross-control.

The rudder is controlled on most aircraft by cables or hydraulic lines connected to pedals on the floor of the cockpit. The pilot presses the right rudder pedal to move the rudder and, thus, the nose of the aircraft, to the right, or presses the left rudder to rotate left. Modern airliners and fighters use power-augmented hydraulic or electrical systems to connect the rudder pedals to the rudder, and the rudder is often connected to an automated control system which will allow control of the airplane by a computer system.

James F. Marchman III

Bibliography

Barnard, R. H., and D. R. Philpott. *Aircraft Flight*. 2d ed. Essex, England: Addison Wesley Longman, 1995. An excellent, nonmathematical text on aeronautics. Well-done illustrations and physical descriptions, rather than equations, are used to explain virtually all aspects of flight.

Docherty, Paul, ed. *The Visual Dictionary of Flight*. New York: Dorling Kindersley, 1992. A profusely illustrated book showing the parts and the details of construction of a wide range of airplane types, old and new. An outstanding source of information about what airplanes and their parts really look like.

Stinton, Darrol. *The Design of the Airplane*. London: Blackwell Science, 1997. An outstanding reference on the design of all types of aircraft. Slightly technical but well written and illustrated.

See also: Aerodynamics; Ailerons and flaps; Airplanes; Flight control systems; Forces of flight; Landing procedures; Roll and pitch; Stabilizers; Takeoff procedures.

Runway collisions

Definition: Unplanned contact between aircraft while on an airport runway or inadvertent contact between an aircraft and a ground vehicle, pedestrian, obstruction or animal while on an airport runway.

Significance: Runway collisions are among the greatest hazards of aviation.

The world's most deadly aviation accident, the collision of two fully loaded Boeing 747's, occurred in 1977 on a foggy runway at Tenerife Airport, Canary Islands. In this incident, the captain of a KLM jumbojet, in a hurry to take off and suffering from a profound loss of situation awareness, accelerated down the runway directly into a Pan American jet taxiing in the opposite direction. In the ensuing carnage, 583 people were killed and nearly all of the survivors were injured to a significant degree.

Causes

The threat of runway collisions has increased along with the growth of air travel around the world. Since World War II, commercial aviation has steadily grown, dramatically so during most of the 1990's. In the United States, air travel grew four times more quickly than any other form of ground transportation, pushed by the introduction of jet aircraft into commercial service on a large scale in the early 1960's. By the year 2000, some 600,000 pilots had made almost 70 million takeoffs and landings at 450 different American airports. Alarmingly, the rate of runway collisions, incidents, and near-misses has exceeded the rate of growth of air travel, even throughout the 1990's, exhibiting a 75 percent increase between 1993 and 1999, according to the Federal Aviation Administration (FAA).

Despite unparalleled airline passenger volume growth, the actual number of runways in the United States has diminished during this time, due, in large part, to extremely strict noise and environmental pollution regulations. As a result, more operations have been crowded onto fewer runways, taxing the abilities of pilots and air traffic controllers alike. This situation remains largely unresolved, with a particularly hazardous combination of large, complex airports and inexperienced pilots, who are common during times of industry growth.

Human Factors

Except for the rare instance of an aircraft colliding with an animal crossing a runway, the cause of most runway collisions is human error, on the part of pilots, air traffic controllers, or a combination thereof. Such collisions are said to involve human factors.

Air traffic controllers have the primary responsibility of providing safe separation for all forms of traffic at large, busy airports. On infrequent but regular occasions, controllers fail in this mission, due to workload, loss of situation awareness, faulty procedure design, or simple short-term memory loss. Such was the case in 1991 at Los Angeles International Airport, where a USAir 737 landed on top of a Skywest turboprop commuter, which had been directed by a controller to stop on a dark runway awaiting clearance for takeoff. Momentarily distracted by a third aircraft, the controller then cleared the USAir jet to land, without ever directing the Skywest aircraft to take off. Thirty-four people died in the resulting collision.

For both pilots and air traffic controllers, two elements contribute heavily to human-factor errors: a loss of situation awareness and miscommunication. Loss of situation awareness occurs when perception and reality are incongruent, especially with regard to location. To a large degree, this is due to poor or zero visibility, because sight is by far the most dominant sense. With impaired vision, usually due to darkness, fog, obstruction, or sun glare, the ability of pilots and controllers to develop a mental picture of the locations of all relevant aircraft and vehicles is significantly decreased. This leads to participants acting on imperfect information, which, in aviation, can have deadly consequences.

Communication problems repeatedly cause human-factor errors. Except in infrequent instances, in which light-gun signals are used, all operational aviation is coordinated by radio. The quality of radio communications on the frequencies used in aviation is markedly inferior to that of other forms of electronic communication, such as telephone or television, and is subject to static, interference, garble, and outright transmitter or receiver failure. Difficulties can also arise from controllers speaking at a rapid-fire rate, from pilots' unfamiliarity with an airfield, from passengers or crewmembers asking questions of the pilot, and from poorly marked taxiways. The opportunity for misunderstanding is multiplied when controllers and pilots do not speak the same native tongue, forcing one or both of them to speak a second language.

Preventing Runway Collisions

In-flight safety has improved steadily since World War II, to the extent that, according to the FAA, ground operations have become the most dangerous phase of flight. With this in mind, and with the memory of the Tenerife disaster still fresh, FAA officials aggressively attacked the issue of runway safety throughout the 1990's. In 1991, 1995, and again in 1998, the FAA developed action plans to address specific issues relating to safer ground operations. The agency also made the reduction of runway accidents and incidents its highest priority, with the goal of markedly reducing occurrences each year. To this end, the National Runway Safety Program Office, formerly known as the Runway Incursion Program Office, was created in 1996 as part of the FAA to focus and coordinate resources and efforts. Four areas were targeted for improvement: management and procedures, airport signs and surface markings, technology, and runway incursion awareness efforts.

Management and Procedural Changes

Recognizing that confusion, usually due to miscommunication or complex instructions, was often a root cause of runway safety incidents, the FAA took steps to clarify the instructions provided to pilots and required more confirmations from pilots of critical elements of information. Additionally, new restrictions were placed on pilots conducting land and hold-short operations, air traffic control procedures used to expedite the flow of arriving and departing aircraft at airfields with intersecting runways.

Signs and Surface Markings

Another effort to reduce confusion and to increase situation awareness was to develop more visible and easily recognizable airport signage and markings. Hold-short lines on a taxiway mark the limit of travel toward a runway with specific clearance to cross or enter it. It is essential that these lines are easily seen and recognized. The FAA mandated that all airports double the size of these lines and provide a black background to improve contrast and visibility. In cooperation with the Aircraft Owners and Pilots Association, the FAA examined the possibility of using an anamorphic projection, or unequal magnifications along two perpendicular axes, to create a sort of three-dimensional painted hold-short line. The FAA also examined the possibility of using a stop light system, similar to those used at European airports, to prevent inadvertent runway incursions.

Enhanced Technology

The FAA has invested heavily in technology improvements to solve runway safety problems. Because many problems arise when controllers cannot readily see the aircraft and vehicles they are controlling, typically in fog, snow, or dark conditions, beginning in the early 1990's, contracts were issued for the development of a ground-scan radar system. This project combined what is essentially a land-oriented version of air traffic control radar with a sophisticated software system called the Airport Movement Area Safety System (AMASS). The system was designed to be used at large airports to automatically alert controllers to impending conflicts in enough time for corrective actions to be taken. Initial results were disappointing. The system was labeled as being over budget, over schedule, and ineffective, criticisms leveled at the FAA on a number of projects during this period. The first AMASS unit was installed at San Francisco, California, in September, 2001, with thirty-three other airports to follow. A simpler and less costly version, ASDE-X, was to be provided to smaller airports, but most U.S. airports would not benefit from either program.

Runway Incursion Awareness

The FAA has long recognized that training and education are effective ways to address human-factors issues, and that policy was extended to the runway collision problem. Reaching air traffic controllers was relatively easy, because they are almost all FAA employees and could thus be scheduled for training as necessary. Controllers received training on new equipment, were educated about the scope and scale of the runway safety problem, and were taught new techniques to address specific issues, especially those involving communication and clarity.

Addressing human-factors issues with the 600,000 pilots utilizing U.S. airports was a more difficult task. Airline pilots could be provided relevant education by their corporate training departments, but teaching general aviation pilots, who constitute the bulk of active aviators in the United States, was more challenging. Taking advantage of the requirement that pilots obtain refresher training every two years, the FAA encouraged flight instructors to promote heavily runway safety awareness. Student pilots received similar instruction as part of their initial training. Through newsletters, safety seminars, and booths at aviation conventions, the FAA spoke directly to pilots on the subject of runway safety. The FAA was aided in this effort by nonprofit aviation organizations, such as the Air Safety Foundation and the Flight Safety Foundation, whose missions are to improve the safety of all forms of air transportation.

Part of the FAA's agenda was to step up enforcement actions. Increasingly, pilots found there was no such thing as an inconsequential runway incursion. Violations were met with fines, pilot certificate suspensions, or mandatory retraining. Repeat or flagrant offenders could expect more than one of the aforementioned actions.

Specific Runway Safety Instruction

The FAA, flight instructors, and the nation's aviation schools identified a number of steps that pilots could take to reduce the possibility of a runway safety compromise.

The first step was to increase visibility. It was recommended that pilots use rotating beacons, landing and taxi lights, and strobe lights while operating on the airport surface, even in the daytime. The degree of illumination should be based on environmental conditions.

A second step involved communications. Unclear or ambiguous instructions should be clarified so that both pilots and air traffic controllers achieve a shared mental model of the situation. Critical elements of information must be repeated back to the controller to ensure that a message has not only been heard but also understood. A sterile cockpit, that is, one in which no extraneous conversation takes place in the presence of the crew, is vital for keeping a cockpit free of distractions.

A third step recommended that pilots taxi accurately. This is best achieved by the pilot having in hand an airport diagram, essentially a road map of the airfield, while the taxi is underway. If a diagram is not available or uncertainty still exists, a "progressive taxi," involving turn-by-turn sequential instructions from a ground controller, may be requested.

Pilots should also know and abide by taxiway and runway markings and signs. Airport signs and markings are standardized throughout the United States, making this job easier.

Pilots should always confirm runway alignment. More than one pilot has landed or taken off on the wrong runway, creating an obvious safety hazard. This error can be remedied by confirming the runway number and cross-checking with the compass.

Lastly, a pilot's most important actions should always be to look, listen, and talk. Communication helps all flight participants achieve a shared mental model that is vital to situation awareness.

Cass D. Howell

Bibliography

ASF Runway Safety Program. (www.aopa.org/asf/runway_safety/). Part of the Air Safety Foundation effort to reduce runway accidents by providing highly relevant operational pilot information, this Web site features a three-module, interactive program designed to teach pilots about runway safety

Craig, P. A. *The Killing Zone: How and Why Pilots Die.* New York: McGraw-Hill, 2001. An analysis of National Transportation Safety Board investigations of all types of aircraft accidents, written for pilots and nonpilots alike and providing detailed explanations of trends and human-factors issues.

Gero, D. *Aviation Disasters*. 3d ed. Somerset, England: Patrick Stephens, 2000. An encyclopedia of every commercial aviation crash that took at least eighty lives. An excellent source of reference information, illustrated with diagrams and photographs.

See also: Accident investigation; Air carriers; Airline industry, U.S.; Commercial flight; Federal Aviation Administration; KLM; Jumbojets; Landing procedures; Military flight; National Transportation Safety Board; Pan Am World Airways; Safety issues; Takeoff procedures; Taxiing procedures; Training and education

Runways

Definition: Facilities on airfields that accommodate aircraft takeoff and landing operations.

Significance: Runways are the last part of the airport that an aircraft uses before reaching the sky and the first part of the airport an aircraft uses upon landing at its destination.

Design Characteristics

The earliest runways were nothing more than small grass or dirt strips that provided room for small aircraft to land or take off. Although thousands of small runways used by small and light aircraft still exist, the heavier aircraft employed by commercial air carriers require large paved runways for their operations. The design of airport runways involves many factors that allow aircraft to perform takeoff and landing operations within aircraft performance specifications and local environmental conditions.

Runway Length

One of the most important characteristics of a runway is its length. Runways must have sufficient length to accommodate aircraft takeoffs and landings. Larger and heavier aircraft tend to require longer distances and, thus, longer runways, in order to accelerate to a speed high enough for liftoff. Small aircraft may require only 500 feet of runway length, whereas the largest commercial aircraft may require nearly 12,000 feet, more than 2 miles, of runway to take off. In addition to aircraft specifications, runways located at higher elevations and in warmer climates tend to be longer, as aircraft need longer distances to take off in the thinner air of hot climates and high elevations. In addition to greater runway length requirements, larger aircraft tend to require runways of greater width, so that landing gear wheels can fit on the runways. Runway widths range from as few as 50 feet to more than 200 feet. Runways are also built with shoulders, similar to those of roads, and safety areas to make sure that there are no obstructions that will be in the way of any aircraft operations.

Runway Orientation

The direction, or orientation, in which a runway is located is another important characteristic. Aircraft perform better when taking off or landing into a wind, called a headwind, than when taking off with a tailwind, with the wind behind the aircraft, or with a crosswind, with the wind blowing across the side of the aircraft. Therefore, runways are oriented so that aircraft can take off or land into the preferred wind direction. Runways that are oriented in the direction of the prevailing winds are called primary runways. Runways that are oriented in the direction of less frequent winds are called crosswind runways. Because smaller aircraft are more sensitive to crosswinds, airports that accommodate smaller aircraft tend to have multiple crosswind runways, oriented in several different directions. Airports serving larger aircraft tend to have more primary runways all oriented in the same direction, called parallel runways.

Runway Pavement

The type and amount of surface material, called pavement, used to build the runway is yet another important runway characteristic. Runways accommodating heavier aircraft tend to be constructed out of thick, rigid pavements, such as concrete. Runways accommodating smaller aircraft tend to be built out of more flexible pavements, such as asphalt. If a runway pavement cannot support the weight of an aircraft, the aircraft will not be able to perform a smooth takeoff or landing.

Signage, Lights, and Markings

Runways may be operated with a variety of associated lights, signs, and markings. A runway is named by the numbers painted on each runway end. The numbers on each end of a runway describe the direction relative to magnetic north. For instance, an airport runway named 09-27 is a runway that runs east 90 degrees from magnetic north to west 270 degrees from magnetic north. Other markings on runways include centerlines and lines that help pilots make accurate landings. Some runways also have electronic landing aids that aircraft use to make precision landings in inclement weather. These runways are called instrument runways. Depending on the type of landing aids and the type of markings on the runway, the runway may either be a precision-instrument or a non-precision-instrument runway. Runways are often also equipped with edge lights, centerline lights, and approach lights, to help pilots make accurate landings at night.

The runway threshold is defined as the beginning of the usable part of the runway for aircraft landing. Often, runways have displaced thresholds, identified by white arrows, before the threshold, to provide extra runway length for aircraft departures. Sometimes, runways have relocated thresholds, identified by yellow chevrons, which provide extra runway length for emergency landings. Relocated thresholds are not for use during normal aircraft takeoff and landing operations.

Runway Capacity

Airports often have more than one runway to handle the large numbers of aircraft that land over a period of time. Both government rules and the physical properties of flight limit the number of aircraft that can use a runway during a given period of time. The typical capacity, or maximum number of aircraft that can use a runway, is approximately sixty operations per hour. At busy airports, where more than sixty aircraft depart or land over the course of an hour, parallel runways are often operated. Government rules dictate how far apart these runways must be for them both to be used simultaneously. In cloudy, or instrument flight rules (IFR), conditions, for example, parallel runways must be 4,300 feet apart, or nearly three-quarters of a mile, in order to be used simultaneously. This is one reason why the world's largest airports take up a large amount of land.

Seth B. Young

Bibliography

Horonjeff, R., and F. McKelvey. *Planning and Design of Airports*. 4th ed. New York: McGraw Hill, 1994. The definitive text on airport planning and design, providing an engineering-oriented approach to runway characteristics.

Federal Aviation Administration. *Airport Design*. Washington, D.C.: U.S. Department of Transportation, Federal Aviation Administration, 1994. A guide to the design and management of airports, including runways.

Kazda, Antonín, and Robert E. Caves. *Airport Design and Operation*. New York: Pergamon, 2000. An encyclopedic examination of the design, construction, and management of airports, with illustrations, bibliographical references, and an index.

See also: Airports; Commercial flight; Landing procedures; Pilots and copilots; Runway collisions; Safety issues; Takeoff procedures; Taxiing procedures; Training and education; Vertical takeoff and landing

Russian space program

Date: Beginning in 1945
Definition: The Russian space program was one of two successful attempts to travel into outer space. Starting in 1945, the Soviet Union developed sophisticated scientific and technological expertise that allowed it to make significant accomplishments in space exploration.
Significance: The Russian space program played an important role in extending humankind's knowledge of outer space. The technological and scientific accomplishments of this great endeavor also had a significant impact on the international struggle known as the Cold War.

Russia has had a long and significant role in the history of space exploration. Most historians of science designate Konstantin Tsiolkovsky as the father of modern spaceflight. In the first decade of the twentieth century, Tsiolkovsky produced a ground-breaking theoretical study on the possibilities of traveling in space. The essay, "Issledovanie mirovykh prostanstv reaktivnymi priborami" (1903; exploration of cosmic space with reactive devices), published in the journal *Naootchnoye Obozreniye* (scientific journal), described the methods to be employed to develop vehicles that would carry human beings into outer space.

Tsiolkovsky was both a technological visionary and a social utopian. He perceived spaceflight as the instrument to free humankind from the drudgery of earthly existence. He viewed the power to conquer the law of gravity as a metaphor for the human race's ability to liberate itself by embarking on a new historical epoch of limitless possibilities. The connection among science, technology, and political and social philosophy within Russian culture played an important role in the development of Soviet technological policy.

Unfortunately, Tsiolkovsky's ideas were constrained by the autocratic regime of Czar Nicholas II and the economic, political, and social instability it fostered. This cultural turmoil led to Russia's disastrous defeat in World War I and the subsequent Bolshevik Revolution. The modern history of Russian spaceflight begins in this politically explosive era. From the ascension of Lenin to the construction of the Soviet space station Mir, the Russian space program would be linked to and directed by changes in the accepted political doctrine of Communist totalitarianism.

Early Communism and Space Theory

The intellectual foundation of communism was laid on the philosophy of Karl Marx, who did not consider himself a political philosopher in the classical sense but insisted that his ideas were based upon scientific principles. Technology would be the instrument used to establish Marx's new utopian society. In 1917, Vladimir Ilich Lenin, the leader of the Communist Party, accepted these ideas in the abstract, but the practical problems of reconstructing a wartorn nation drove Lenin to compromise his adherence to strict Marxist-Leninist theory in favor of economic recovery. Lenin's famous statement, "Electrification plus Soviet power equals socialism," set the tone for his national recovery program.

From this emphasis on science and technology, a technological elite developed whose expertise was used to create a new socialist order. Many of these technologists were influenced by the works of Tsiolkovsky, especially by his utopian vision based upon space travel. The Soviet scientific community during the 1920's adopted a research and development program focusing upon the possibilities of space exploration, and two influential works were published during this decade. Yuri Kondratyuk's book *Zavovevanie mezhplanetnykh prostorov* (1929; *The Conquest of Interplanetary Space*, 1997) and Nikolai A. Rynin's work *Mezhplanetye Soobschchicheniia* (1927-1932; *Interplanetary Flight and Communication*, 1970-1971) had a significant impact on the technologists around the world who were working on the possibilities of spaceflight.

Technology Under Stalin

Soviet society drastically changed with the death of Lenin and the ascension of Joseph Stalin to power. In Stalin's purges, technological expertise became secondary to ideological purity, and he launched a nationwide attack against the "elite experts"; many of them suffered the same fate as their military and political counterparts. Stalin's concentration on making socialism safe in Russia had an important impact on Soviet space research. The utopian vision of a socialist cosmos was declared unimportant at a time when the Soviet Union needed to construct a competitive industrial and military sector in order to protect its borders from both its fascist and democratic rivals.

The aeronautical expertise that had been focused on spaceflight during the 1920's was now directed toward the construction of a world-class air force. During the 1930's, the Soviet Union made great strides in aeronautical engineering, generating a confidence among Russia's military leadership that its air force was among the best in the world. This optimism was shown to be unfounded when the German Luftwaffe soundly defeated the Soviet air force during the Spanish Civil War.

Stalin reacted with reprisals against the Russian aeronautical engineering establishment. Many of the Soviet Union's finest rocket scientists were sent to the gulag (a series of camps for political prisoners) and released only after the German invasion of 1941. Among these prisoners was Sergei Korolev, who became the driving force behind the postwar Soviet space program, working on the development of military rockets for the defense of the Soviet Union.

World War II and the Early Cold War

Two major scientific developments of World War II had a lasting impact on the Russian space program. In the last months of the war in the European theater of operations, the Nazis attempted to change the strategic direction of the conflict by introducing a new super weapon, the V-2 rocket. The German industrial sector was too damaged to mass-produce this weapon in the numbers needed to change the outcome of the war, but all of the Allied nations, including the Soviet Union, recognized the potential of this revolutionary new delivery system. The Russians expended considerable resources and energy to capture as many German rocket scientists as possible. The new technology became even more important after the United States successfully used two atomic bombs to force the Japanese to surrender in August, 1945.

The breakdown of the wartime alliance due to Soviet expansion in Eastern Europe brought on the Cold War. Once again, Stalin focused upon the defense of the "Motherland," but this time he accepted the connection between rocket science and the protection of the Soviet Union. A new generation of Soviet rockets was produced through the combined efforts of German and Russian scientists. With the successful detonation of an atomic bomb in 1949 and a hydrogen bomb in 1953, the Soviets accelerated their research in an attempt to create an accurate, uncrewed delivery system for these new weapons of mass destruction. After Stalin's death in 1953, the direction of Russian rocket technology once again focused on space travel.

The Sputnik Era

The Khrushchev era catapulted the Soviet Union into a position of prominence in the area of space exploration. Nikita Khrushchev was a true intellectual child of Marxist-Leninist thought and believed in the compatibility of socialist and scientific truth. Like Tsiolkovsky, he envisioned a utopian state that would reap the benefits of increased productivity based upon science and technology. He extended this idea of universal brotherhood to the entire universe when the Soviet Union successfully launched Sputnik, the first artificial satellite, on October 4, 1957. Khrushchev believed this great scientific and technological accomplishment confirmed both the power of Russian science and the inevitability of communism because it showed that the communist system had created the conditions and the environment for great scientific advancement.

Sputnik had an impact on Khrushchev's foreign policy that went far beyond the technological strategic implications of United States-Soviet relations. This dramatic event also captured the attention of the newly independent nations of Africa, Asia, and the Middle East. An important aspect of the Cold War was the struggle between the democratic and communist camps to win the allegiance of this important segment of the world community. When Sputnik went into orbit, most of the leading nations of the Third World issued press communiqués praising the achievements of the Soviet scientific community. Many seemed convinced that the socialist model, based upon the universal ideal of a one-world community sharing equally the benefits of human knowledge, was responsible for such great accomplishments.

Khrushchev also used the image of Soviet scientific prowess to challenge the theory that war was inevitable between the capitalist and communist nations. Russia's seeming ability to accurately target the United States helped to create the reality of mutual assured destruction, which Khrushchev believed would reduce the likelihood of a third world war.

Khrushchev's confidence in this new strategic doctrine established a sense of security among the nations of Western Europe that bordered the Soviet Empire, and it upset an already strained relationship between the Soviet Union and the ultraradical People's Republic of China. Mao Zedong embraced the Leninist doctrine that power would have to be taken from the capitalist nations through the use of force. As a result of Sputnik, the Chinese believed that the Soviet Union had the ability to bring down the capitalist West. Mao was not deterred by the possibility of widespread death and destruction. He believed a new socialist order would rise from the dust and inaugurate a utopian epoch. He had no concept of the fact that the dust of the old civilization would contain deadly levels of radiation with a half-life of ten thousand years. Khrushchev refused to adopt Mao's radical strategy, an attitude that helped create the Sino-Soviet split.

The success of the Russian space program also caused considerable tension between Khrushchev and the Soviet military establishment. Khrushchev believed that a new strategic doctrine that reflected recent accomplishments in space technology was necessary if the Soviet Union was to reach the ultimate economic goal of universal material prosperity. Khrushchev desperately wanted to reduce the size of the military in order to redirect money and resources into the domestic economy. He created a Seven-Year Plan that proposed increasing both agricultural and industrial output. The military perceived these cuts as unwarranted and dangerous, and it vigorously opposed his plan. At the same time that the Soviet leader proposed massive cuts in conventional forces, he approved a large budget for important research into the development of spy satellites. Khrushchev knew the United States was far more advanced in this field; he recognized that if the Soviet Union hoped to maintain some sort of military parity, significant progress would have to be made in this all-important area. This action exacerbated his problems with the military, which recognized that introducing this new technology could also mean a further reduction in the military budget.

The Space Race

Khrushchev's plan to reduce both world tensions and the size of the Russian military rested upon the image of Soviet scientific and technological superiority. A potentially dangerous aspect of this situation was the absolute importance of staying one step ahead of the accomplishments of the United States.

On November 4, 1957, the Soviet Union launched Sputnik 2; this spacecraft carried Laika, a Russian dog that was the first living creature to be placed into orbit. These successes set the stage for the greatest era of human space exploration. Russia's first crewed project, Vostok, had to reflect both Soviet scientific strength and the proposed egalitarian nature of the communist system. Yuri Gagarin had all the attributes necessary for this space spectacular. He was a highly intelligent, handsome test pilot from one of Russia's elite units. Politically, Gagarin was made to order. He was born in the Russian hinterland, grew up in a log cabin, and was the son of a poor artisan. The success of his magnificent flight on April 12, 1961, seemed once again to validate the inherent strength of the Soviet system.

The Russian space program soon scored another propaganda victory on June 16, 1963, by launching the first woman into space, and like Gagarin, she fit the Marxist model perfectly. Valentina Tereshkova was a simple factory worker whose lack of scientific training and expertise would be emphasized to show once again the power of Soviet science. Soviet propaganda would describe how the innate strength of the socialist model based upon the power of technology would one day create a utopian society.

When intelligence reached the Soviet Union that the United States was planning to launch two astronauts into space, Khrushchev reacted by pressuring Sergei Korolev to strike first by launching a capsule containing three men. The Russian space program had already started to develop plans for a vessel that could carry more than one cosmonaut. Initially the program was designated Soyuz, but in 1961 it was only in the earliest stages of development. To meet the deadline set by Khrushchev, the Russians had to modify the Vostok capsule at great risk to the three cosmonauts. All but essential equipment was removed, and they had to fly without the protection of their outer spacesuits as well, in order for three men to fit inside what was supposed to be a one-person vehicle. On October 12, 1964, Voskhod 1 was launched and placed into orbit. It returned the three cosmonauts safely to earth in what was perceived to be the next example of Soviet dominance of outer space. On March 18, 1965, the crew of Voskhod 2 again impressed the world when Aleksei Leonov made the first space walk, remaining outside his capsule for twelve minutes while orbiting 128 miles above the surface of Earth.

The Soviet Moon Program

Sergei Korolev had developed a plan to land cosmonauts on the lunar surface that consisted of three major stages. The Vostok and Soyuz programs were to provide the Soviets with the necessary experience and information concerning both the effect of spaceflight on human beings and the skills needed to successfully complete a sophisticated lunar mission. This would be followed by a program designated Luna, which would consist of a series of reconnaissance missions to familiarize the cosmonauts with the surface of the moon. Finally, the N-Program would be the Russian equivalent of the American Apollo Program, which would transport three cosmonauts to the moon.

Two important events occurred in the mid-1960's that would forever change the direction of the Soviet lunar program. On January 14, 1966, Sergei Korolev died of complications resulting from his years as a prisoner in Stalin's gulag. Korolev's great intelligence, formidable power, and universal respect among Russia's scientific elite had enabled him to push his fellow space scientists to achieve at levels unmatched by any other members of the space establishment. The problems that resulted from his death were compounded by the political demise of Nikita Khrushchev. In pursuit of his new socialist order, Khrushchev had alienated too many powerful interest groups, especially the Soviet military. When widespread agricultural and industrial failure was combined with the military and political embarrassment of the Cuban Missile Crisis, Khrushchev was removed from office.

Khrushchev was replaced by Leonid Brezhnev, a Stalinist hardliner whose political philosophy was far more practical than that of Khrushchev. He inherited a very inefficient economy that already had to balance the military expenditures of the world's largest army with the growing consumer expectations of Soviet society. Brezhnev's strategic view differed significantly from that of Khrushchev. He believed that if the Soviet Union continued an extensive military buildup, the United States by the early 1980's would find it necessary to begin to accommodate to Russian international demands.

The Soviet Space Program in Decline

On September 12, 1970, after the success of the Apollo Program, the Russians attempted to salvage some international respect by landing an uncrewed vehicle on the lunar surface. Luna 16 extracted soil samples to be studied back on Earth. A second moon mission on November 17, 1970, saw a Soviet Lunokhod lunar rover explore the surface of the Moon. However, these two missions actually reflected the underlying weakness of the Russian space program.

In the 1980's, the United States established its clear supremacy in outer space. The year 1981 saw the successful flight of the space shuttle that displayed a level of space technology decades beyond the capabilities of the Soviet Union. The Soviet Union attempted to maintain some respectability by concentrating its resources on an extensive space station program. Instead of competing against the United States in the arena of space travel, the Soviets decided to focus on creating a permanent working environment that would provide space-based laboratories for scientific research.

Soviet premier Mikhail Gorbachev attempted to institute a series of reforms that would revitalize the Soviet economy and provide an economic foundation for the development of a new generation of technology that would allow the Soviet Union to once again compete in space with the United States. Instead of reinforcing the communist system, *glasnost* and *perestroika* set in motion a chain of events that brought down the Soviet Union. Initially there was great optimism about a future democratic Russia operating within a structure where both material goods and ideas flowed freely. Unfortunately, this dream was not realized, and Russia fell into economic and political chaos. In 1996, the new Russia ranked eighteenth out of the top twenty nations in expenditures on space technology. By the turn of the century, a series of disasters ravaged the space station Mir and in the end turned the broken spacecraft into a metaphor for the collapse of the Russian space program.

Richard D. Fitzgerald

Bibliography

Burrows, William E. *This New Ocean*. New York: The Modern Library, 1999. A comprehensive one-volume history of spaceflight that provides a detailed chronological account of the age of space exploration.

Harford, James. *Korolev: How One Man Masterminded the Soviet Drive to Beat America to the Moon*. New York: John Wiley and Sons, 1997. An unique and interesting look inside the Soviet space establishment as seen through the life of Russia's most important space scientist.

Heppenheimer, T. A. *Countdown: A History of Space Flight*. New York: John Wiley & Sons, 1997. An excellent one-volume history of spaceflight that describes the economic, social, and political impact of the space age.

McDougall, Walter A. *The Heavens and the Earth: A Political History of the Space Age*. Baltimore: The Johns Hopkins University Press, 1985. An outstanding political history of the space race that describes the important linkage between the events of the Cold War and the American and Soviet space programs.

See also: Astronauts and cosmonauts; Crewed spaceflight; Yuri Gagarin; Spaceflight; Sputnik; Valentina Tereshkova; Konstantin Tsiolkovsky; Uncrewed spaceflight

Burt Rutan

Date: Born on June 17, 1943, in Portland, Oregon
Definition: The best known, most creative, most prolific, and most influential late twentieth century aircraft designer.
Significance: Rutan revolutionized aircraft design with his tail-first, canard airplanes and his all-composite homebuilt and commercial aircraft. His best-known design, the *Voyager*, was the first aircraft to fly around the world without refueling, in December, 1986. Mostly through his Scaled Composites firm, he has designed forty new types of aircraft as well as a catamaran, a space-load launcher, a gondola, and a car body. His futuristic-looking prototypes have been used in a number of Hollywood motion pictures.

Born into an airplane-involved family, Elbert Leander "Burt" Rutan began to design and build award-winning model airplanes while still a teenager. He made his first solo flight at sixteen years of age, and his ability to look at aircraft design from a pilot's viewpoint has been an important factor in the success of his many airplane designs.

In 1965, Rutan received a bachelor of science degree in aeronautical engineering from California Polytechnic University, where his thesis won a national award from the American Institute of Aeronautics and Astronautics. After graduating from college, he took a job as a civilian flight test project engineer at the Air Force Flight Test Center at Edwards Air Force Base, California, and began working on his first homebuilt, the VariViggen, inspired by the canard XB-70 bomber and the canard Saab Viggen fighter.

In 1972, Rutan left the Air Force to work in development and flight testing for a homebuilt kit manufacturer. Two years later, in June, 1974, he established the Rutan Aircraft Factory to develop and sell homebuilt aircraft plans. Rutan's second homebuilt design, the VariEze, introduced in 1975, was a very efficient canard homebuilt that revolutionized homebuilding. The VariEze's moldless composite construction of fiberglass-covered foam did not require specialized skills or tools to build and produced smooth, sculpted surfaces. The longer-range follow-up, the Long-EZ, set many distance records, including for around-the-world flights, and remains one of the most popular homebuilt aircraft. A powered glider, the Solitaire, and a push-pull, twin-engine canard, the Defiant, were his last designs for homebuilders.

In April, 1982, Rutan founded the Scaled Composites firm to develop research prototypes for government and industry. Scaled Composites firm has produced such well-publicized aircraft as the *Voyager*, the Pond Racer, the AD-1 skew-wing aircraft for NASA, the Beechcraft Starship prototype, the Advanced Technology Tactical Transport, the Triumph business jet, the Ares close air support airplane, the *Proteus* high-altitude aircraft, and the Boomerang. The firm is competing in the first private race to space: a race to develop a practical, reasonably inexpensive, reusable flight vehicle for short flights out of the atmosphere for future space tourists.

Over the course of his career, Rutan has received many awards, including Outstanding Design Awards from the Experimental Aircraft Association, the Presidential Citizen's Medal, the Collier Trophy, the Chrysler Award for Innovation in Design, and the British Gold Medal for Aeronautics. In 1995, he was inducted into the National Aviation Hall of Fame.

W. N. Hubin

Bibliography

Downie, Don, and Julia Downie. *The Complete Guide to Rutan Aircraft*. 3d ed. Blue Ridge Summit, Pa.: Tab Books, 1987. Discusses the development of the VariViggen, VariEze, Long-EZ, Grizzly, Defiant, Solitaire, Starship, and Voyager.

Lennon, Andy. *Canard: A Revolution in Flight*. Hummelstown, Pa.: Aviation, 1984. A useful discussion of the history and aerodynamics of canard-type aircraft, from ultralights and homebuilts to high-speed aircraft.

Rollo, Vera Foster. *Burt Rutan: Reinventing the Airplane*. Lanham, Md.: Maryland Historical Press, 1991. A well-written biography of Burt Rutan through 1990, including his background and his career.

Yeager, Jeana, and Dick Rutan, with Phil Patton. *Voyager*. New York: Alfred A. Knopf, 1987. The story of the *Voyager*'s record-breaking flight around the world, piloted by Jeana Yeager and Rutan's brother, Dick.

See also: Airplanes; Experimental aircraft; Military flight; Model airplanes; National Aeronautics and Space Administration; Test pilots

Safety issues

Definition: Aspects of the airline industry that affect the number of accidents and incidents, as well as the continuing effort to reduce this number as much as possible.

Significance: Because millions of people travel every year for both business and pleasure, safe air travel is vital to passengers, businesses, and economies of the world.

Statistics

The aviation industry has a remarkable safety record. The total number of fatalities on board commercial jets in the years from 1959 to 1999 is less than one-half the annual U.S. automobile fatality rate. However, because so many people can be affected by one incident, aviation accidents make headline news. Although the airlines' safety record is impressive, continuous efforts by the aviation industry, the federal government, and the airlines are aimed at reducing the accident rate to zero.

Statistics from the Boeing Company show that the ten-year commercial jet airplane accident rate from 1990 to 1999 was less than one accident per one million departures of scheduled air carriers. Even this statistic does not tell the whole story, however, because fatal injuries were not present in all of those aircraft accidents. Although accidents are very rare occurrences, reducing the accident rate remains important. If the number of departures doubled from ten million to twenty million annually and the rate of accidents remained the same, there would be an increase in the number of aircraft accidents.

Many organizations, both public and private, are actively involved in research to prevent safety problems before accidents occur. The National Aeronautics and Space Administration (NASA) is very involved in funding basic research into new technologies and cockpit displays to prevent accidents both on the ground and in flight. The NASA Aviation Safety Program is a partnership with the Federal Aviation Administration (FAA), the Department of Defense (DOD), aircraft manufacturers, airlines, and universities. Their collective efforts have contributed significantly to the reduction of the number of aircraft accidents.

Human Factors

Research reveals that more than 70 percent of all airline accidents can be attributed to human error, including that of pilots, air traffic control personnel, airport employees, and others. Government and industry officials have been implicated in some accidents because of delays in implementing certain safety warning devices. However, flight crews are ascribed with the majority of the errors that result in accidents. Aviation researchers are actively involved in determining how best to relieve this problem.

The discipline of human factors in aircraft operations has become focused not only on the causes of accidents but also on the best ways to incorporate lessons learned from them into the aviation system. Rarely does a single event result in an aircraft accident. Research has shown that most accidents can be blamed on a series of uncorrected errors, intervention at any point in which would likely have disrupted the pattern and prevented the accident. Although aircraft operations attempt to make corrections based on lessons learned, the implementation of such procedures remains a complex issue involving many personalities, agencies, airlines, manufacturers, and governments.

Human Performance

Accidents are rarely caused by a deliberate disregard of procedures. They are more generally caused by a series of uncorrected mistakes or by the development of a situation in which people become overwhelmed or find their capabilities are inadequate for the situation. Human performance in an accident or serious incident should be measured in terms of what could normally be anticipated and under what circumstances could a reasonable degree of correct performance have been expected from the persons involved.

Many aspects of human performance must be considered when evaluating crew behavior. Work experience, working conditions, skill, fatigue, low blood sugar, reduced oxygen, and use of medicines, drugs or alcohol can all affect a person's capabilities. Environmental conditions, such as noise, vibrations, motion, and visual cues may also affect a person's ability to perform. The least measurable aspect of one's capability is one's psychological state. At any given time, one's emotion, awareness, memory, attention, complacency, boredom, judgment, perceptions, and attitude are all significant contributors to an individual's psychological capability. The level and quality of interaction with others associated with the flight will affect the tenor of the entire experience.

Crew Resource Management

Research into an aircraft accident reveals the specifics of the event and most often assigns the blame to the flight crew. Nevertheless, the question of why qualified, demonstratively competent, highly trained, medically fit, well-paid professionals failed to perform the job correctly, resulting in an accident, continues to demand an answer. In 1983, the National Transportation Safety Board (NTSB) established its Human Performance Division to place an emphasis on answering that question.

Investigations into crew behavior and organizational cultures reveal that the personalities of the individuals involved have a direct bearing on the flight crew's general attitude. In the early days of commercial flight, the captain was considered the indisputable boss, and the other crewmembers were required to follow the captain's orders. Although this hierarchical approach was the norm and expected, especially because most of the airline pilots at the time had been retired from the military, post-accident analysis revealed that if a subordinate crewmember had been more assertive, the accident chain might have been disrupted.

A new concept of crew interaction was adopted by United Air Lines in the 1980's and became known as crew resource management (CRM). CRM challenged the paradigm of the captain-as-boss and introduced the concept of teamwork for decision making. It was a revolutionary idea at the time, and airlines holding the traditional view of cockpit authority were reticent to embrace this concept.

In 1989, United Air Lines Flight 232, whose pilot was able to land a hopelessly crippled DC-10 and saved the lives of half the passengers, forever changed the perception of CRM training from an interesting concept to an indispensable part of crew training. The crew's remarkable teamwork was identified by the captain as the result of the CRM training that he and his fellow pilots received.

The CRM concept is now the accepted norm and required by federal regulations. Airline management uses CRM training as an opportunity to intervene in a broad class of poorly defined problems. Line-oriented flight training (LOFT) is a curriculum of real-time simulator exercises that introduce situations to flight crews that enable them to practice their CRM skills and receive comments on their performance from the instructor. This broad-scale approach to social communication-based behaviors and attitudes is in marked contrast to the previous norm of a top-down captain-copilot relationship. CRM teaches the value of using all members' experience to solve a problem, even though the captain maintains the legal authority to make final decisions.

The success of CRM training has extended beyond cockpit crews. Airlines have discovered that cabin crews can also play a significant role in enhancing flight safety. Flight attendants, when included in preflight briefings by the captain, feel that their role in the safety of the flight is recognized. This inclusion contributes to the healthy tone of the flight and increases the likelihood that cabin crews would intervene in instances where communication between the cabin and cockpit was necessary.

Training

Training is the single best method of ensuring airline safety. Airlines spend millions of dollars each year to evaluate pilot performance and to teach corrective actions and procedures based on current research.

Training instructs pilots how to perform their tasks. Procedures are designed to dictate the manner in which tasks are implemented by the flight crew, ground crew, and others with direct input to the flight. Training programs, standardization of procedures, quality control, and printed materials such as manuals and checklists are used by all airlines for the safe operation of flight. The prevention and elimination of human error through successful training programs is a vital safety step.

Checklists

The purpose of checklists has been to alleviate the burden of pilots from trying to remember all the steps necessary to configure the aircraft for various flight regimes. The use of standardized checklists began about the time of the U.S. Airmail Service and evolved to a complex written list of actions to be performed, a system which has not changed in concept from those early days despite the modern computerized checklists.

The checklist is a critical tool for ensuring safe and consistent flight operations. Consistent, accurate use of the checklist is a safeguard to ensure that the aircraft is properly configured, operations are completed sequentially and efficiently, and the aircraft is prepared for flight.

The FAA's Federal Aviation Regulations (FARs) require the checklist to include a starting engines check, a takeoff check, a cruise configuration check, an approach check, an after-landing check, and a shutdown check. The FARs also require a checklist for the emergency operations of fuel, hydraulic, electrical, and mechanical systems and instruments and controls, as well as engine inoperative procedures and any other emergency procedures necessary for a safe flight.

Significant research has been conducted in the area of checklist design and usage. The determination of which items should be included, their sequence, redundancy, action and verification, and by whom the checking should be done, is complex. Checklist presentation—on paper, electronically, or mechanically—will vary among airlines and aircraft types.

Role of Technology

Since the 1950's, continuing improvements in aircraft and engine design have significantly reduced the number of accidents based on these factors. High-bypass engine reliability, aircraft design, warning devices, and automation have all had a significant effect on reducing the airline accident rate.

Several major improvements in aircraft systems and technology contribute to the safety record of the industry. These include ground proximity warning devices, traffic alert and collision avoidance systems (TCAS), and new cockpit computers and displays that provide updated weather and flight status information directly to the cockpit.

Ground Proximity Warning System

The introduction of the ground proximity warning system (GPWS) has significantly reduced the number of accidents involving controlled flight into terrain since its introduction in the 1970's. Controlled flight into terrain occurs when an airworthy aircraft, under the control of the flight crew, is flown unintentionally into terrain, obstacles, or water, usually with no prior awareness by the crew. Because controlled flight into terrain accidents represent the leading cause of aircraft hull losses annually, this safety device is particularly relevant. The GPWS system uses radar altimeter and aircraft configuration information to alert the flight crew of impending terrain. An advanced design, enhanced GPWS (E-GPWS) takes advantage of satellite Global Positioning System (GPS) technology and cockpit computer technology in third-generation aircraft to combine traditional GPWS with terrain mapping and GPS location information. E-GPWS is expected to reduce or eliminate the number of controlled flight into terrain accidents attributable to the flight crew's loss of situational awareness.

Traffic Alert and Collision Avoidance Systems

In the decades following World War II, the steady increase in the number of flights by airlines and general aviation aircraft increased the likelihood of midair collisions, especially in the congested airspace over cities. In 1978, a Pacific Southwest Airlines Boeing 727 collided with a single-engine Cessna 172 over a populated area of San Diego, California, resulting in many deaths. In 1986, an Aeromexico DC-9 collided with a single-engine Cherokee over Cerritos, California. The aftermath of this accident and the memory of the 1978 midair accident motivated the FAA and the airlines to develop a technology to augment vision and assist pilots in detecting and avoiding other aircraft. This research led to the development and implementation of traffic alert and collision avoidance systems (TCAS). This system displays other transponder-equipped aircraft within a specified radius. TCAS II, implemented a few years later, gives pilots resolution advisories (RA) either to descend or to climb in order to avoid a collision. Since 1993, TCAS II has been required on all passenger aircraft with more than thirty seats. Commuter aircraft with from ten to thirty seats are required to be equipped with TCAS I.

Pilots widely and readily accept TCAS, finding it an indispensable cockpit tool. TCAS enhances pilots' situational awareness and assists the visual location of aircraft advisories issued by air traffic control.

Weather

Because weather is such an integral part of aviation, improvements in severe weather information, prediction, and depiction have a significant relevance to improving the safety and comfort of flight. Thunderstorms, although easy to detect, have associated hazards, such as lightning, turbulence, heavy precipitation, icing, wind shear, and microbursts, that are more difficult to see and predict. These hazards are most dangerous when the aircraft is low to the ground, as in takeoff and landing. On-board weather detection systems enable pilots to see the thunderstorm and avoid its associated hazards.

Turbulence

Aircraft encounters with turbulence result in upsets and injuries every year. Turbulence accounted for 103 injuries on board commercial aircraft in the period from 1990 to 1999. Although turbulence is not uncommon in flight, the severity of turbulence ranges from uncomfortable to fatal. Types of turbulence include convective turbulence, mountain range turbulence, and clear-air turbulence.

Convective turbulence occurs in localized, vertical air movements. The most hazardous types are usually associated with thunderstorms. Mountain range turbulence, as the name implies, occurs when wind blows across rugged hills or mountains, creating updraft on the windward side and strong downdrafts on the lee side. Lenticular clouds that form on the lee side of a mountain range and cumulus-looking rotor clouds that form parallel to the ridge line of a mountain are indicators of strong winds and occasionally severe downdrafts and associated turbulence.

Clear-air turbulence is rough, bumpy air that sometimes buffets an airplane in a cloudless sky. It is usually found above altitudes of 15,000 feet and is often located near the jet stream winds. It is associated with a drastic change in wind direction, speed, air temperature, and horizontal or vertical wind shear. Research into the detection and avoidance of clear-air turbulence is important to reduce the injuries and fatalities on board aircraft.

Microburst and Wind Shear

Microburst and wind shear are atmospheric phenomena that have been implicated in several major airline accidents. Investigations into these crashes and computer simulations of the events have led to specific training procedures for pilots to escape from these extremely hazardous winds.

Low-level wind shear alerting system (LLWSAS) is a system of anemometers implemented in select airports to give air traffic tower controllers information on wind direction and speed at different locations on the airport. If the wind direction and velocity exceed a predetermined parameter, an alarm will sound in the tower. Timely dissemination of the wind directions and velocities to the pilots help them prepare for or avoid encounter with a wind shear.

Runway Incursions

Crowded skies inevitably lead to crowded airports. Increased congestion at major airports has consequences on the ground as well as in the airspace above. Although it is a rare occurrence, the ground collision of aircraft accounts for the worst aviation disaster in history: that which occurred between two fully loaded Boeing 747 jumbojets in Tenerife, Canary Islands, in 1977. From 1995 to 2000 there was a 60 percent increase in near-collisions on the ground, according to the NTSB.

The FAA places a high priority on the reduction of the number of runway incursions. New methods for pilots to determine their exact location on the airport in low-visibility or night situations are being researched. Improved airport markings, assessing new technologies, strategic plans for foreign air carrier pilot awareness, training, and review of pilot/controller communications phraseology are among the issues being explored to mitigate this safety problem.

Veronica T. Cote

Bibliography

Boeing Commercial Airplane Group. *1999 Statistical Summary Airplane Safety*. Seattle, Wash.: Boeing, 2001. A detailed description of accidents and incidents in table and chart form from 1959-1999.

Hawkins, Frank H. *Human Factors in Flight*. 2d ed. Brookfield, Vt.: Ashgate Publishing, 1987. An in-depth textbook on pilot performance and behavior, based on academic sources of knowledge and practical operation of aircraft.

Krause, Shari S. *Aircraft Safety, Accident Investigation, Analysis, and Applications*. New York: McGraw-Hill, 1996. A reference book with analysis of accidents caused by human factors, weather, midair collisions, and mechanical failure and their applications to the field.

O'Hare, David, and Stanley Roscoe. *Flightdeck Performance: The Human Factor*. Ames: Iowa State University Press, 1990. A well-researched, technical book on accidents and their causes.

Wells, Alexander T. *Air Transportation: A Management Perspective*. 4th ed. Belmont, Calif.: Wadsworth, 1999. A textbook covering all major topic areas in the air transportation field.

See also: Accident investigation; Air carriers; Air traffic control; Airline industry, U.S.; Avionics; Cockpit; Communication; Federal Aviation Administration; Flight attendants; Instrumentation; Landing procedures; National Aeronautics and Space Administration; National Transportation Safety Board; Pilots and copilots; Runway collisions; Runways; Takeoff procedures; Taxiing procedures; Training and education; Weather conditions; Wind shear

Antoine de Saint-Exupéry

Date: Born on June 29, 1900 in Lyons, France; died on July 31, 1944, near Corsica

Definition: The literary voice of early aviation and an inspiration for many would-be fliers.

Significance: Saint-Exupéry, through his writing, reflected the romance and mystery of aviation and promoted flying among his early twentieth century readers.

Antoine de Saint-Exupéry, whose classic story The Little Prince *(1943) reflected his lifelong fascination with flying.* (Hulton Archive)

Antoine de Saint-Exupéry was the eldest son of a provincial, aristocratic family. His father's early death in 1904 made the family dependent on relatives. This background shaped Saint-Exupéry's character to an enormous extent. The commanding French lead in early aviation during his formative years was the primary external influence on his life.

At age twelve, Saint-Exupéry experienced his first airplane flight and began taking flying lessons in 1921. By 1922, he had become a second lieutenant and pilot in the French army reserves. In 1926, he began flying airmail from France to Spain, before the airmail service rapidly expanded into Africa and South America. Becoming an industry legend, Saint-Exupéry was soon in charge of operations, first in Morocco and then in Argentina.

The Great Depression of the 1930's and events in France caused the collapse of the airmail business in 1932. To support himself financially, Saint-Exupéry turned increasingly to writing, flying only sporadically. He worked briefly as an industrial test pilot and then made an abortive attempt to set a record by flying to Saigon. He crashed in the Libyan desert and walked for four days before encountering a camel caravan. French newspapers made much of the story and its hero. A later goodwill tour of the Americas likewise ended in a crash, this time in Guatemala.

Saint-Exupéry was in the United States when France fell to the Nazis, but he returned to his army reserve position and began flying reconnaissance. His unit was demobilized after Dunkirk (1940), and Saint-Exupéry spent the next three years in New York. When the unit was remobilized in Africa, he was reassigned to it, this time flying the new Lockheed P-38 Lightnings in reconnaissance. With the successes of the Allied landings at Normandy on D day, June 6, 1944, operations moved to Corsica, and it was from Corsica that Saint-Exupéry made his last flight. The Cape Corse radar tracked him into southern France but never spotted his return. Nothing more is known of his death.

Saint-Exupéry was much more than a pilot. He held several patents for aviation improvements, but his writings are remembered as his main achievements. His first book, *Courrier sud* (1929; *Southern Mail*, 1933) was published just before he went to Argentina. It was followed by *Vol de nuit* (1931; *Night Flight*, 1932) and *Terre des hommes* (1939; *Wind, Sand, and Stars*, 1939). These two books won major prizes and a reputation for their author as a major literary talent. *Pilote de guerre* (1942; *Flight to Arras*, 1942) and *Le petite prince* (1943; *The Little Prince*, 1943), probably his best-known work, followed. All but the last drew heavily on tales from his life as a pilot. *Vol de nuit* proved to be a major factor in recruitment for the French air force early in the war.

John A. Cramer

Bibliography

Cate, Curtis. *Antoine de Saint-Exupéry: His Life and Times*. New York: Paragon House, 1990. A compendious but not always well-documented biography.

Robinson, Joy D. M. *Antoine de Saint-Exupéry*. Boston: Twayne, 1984. A short biography focused on Saint-Exupéry's writing.

Shiff, Stacey. *Antoine de Saint-Exupéry*. New York: Alfred A. Knopf, 1994. A detailed biography.

See also: Airmail delivery; Airplanes; Military flight; Pilots and copilots; World War II

Alberto Santos-Dumont

Date: Born on July 20, 1873, in Palmira, Brazil; died on July 24, 1932, in Guarujá, Brazil
Definition: The designer and pilot of the first truly dirigible balloon and the first airplane in Europe.
Significance: A flamboyant early twentieth century advocate of lighter-than-air flight, Santos-Dumont built and flew airships in Paris before mastering heavier-than-air flight and becoming the first European builder of airplanes.

Alberto Santos-Dumont was born in an outlying district in Brazil in 1873, the seventh and last child of a civil engineer and his wife, who soon afterward became the nation's most wealthy coffee plantation owners. The death of his father in 1892 left Santos-Dumont financially secure, allowing him to pursue an eclectic scientific and technical education in Paris while indulging his passion for automobiles. After reading a book about a famous aerial expedition to the North Pole that had ended in tragedy, the mechanically gifted young man turned his attention to ballooning. Seeking out the book's authors, two Parisian balloon manufacturers, he persuaded them to build a small vehicle to his specifications, and he rapidly became expert in handling free spherical balloons. By 1898, however, he was experimenting with powered lighter-than-air craft, building, testing, and often crashing successively more sophisticated models that were designed to be far more maneuverable than Henri Giffard's steam-powered dirigible of almost a half-century earlier. For nearly fifty years, advances in dirigible technology had been nonexistent. Santos-Dumont became single-minded in his desire to overcome all obstacles, using his financial resources, assembling a talented group of mechanics, and taking upon himself all the physical risks involved with testing his concepts.

Winning the Deutsch Prize

In April, 1900, the financier Henri Deutsch de la Meurthe announced a prize of 100,000 francs to go to the first person who could navigate an aerial trip from the Parc d'Aérostation of the Aéro Club de France in St. Cloud, near Paris around the Eiffel Tower and back to the Parc d'Aérostation in less than thirty minutes without landing, a feat which would require an average speed of 14 miles per hour. Santos-Dumont alone was in a position to accept the challenge. On July 13, 1901, his airship number 5 flew the circuit in forty minutes before sinking into a tree. Two weeks later, the repaired vehicle met a similar fate in an encounter with a hotel facade. On October 19, 1901, a new airship, 33 meters in length and equipped with a 20-horsepower engine, completed the task in a few seconds over the stipulated time, but was fast enough to garner the prize.

Santos-Dumont was already a familiar, if solitary, figure in Paris, a fastidious dresser whose somber visage, slight frame and nerves of steel augmented his status as premier conqueror of the air. His mastery of powered ballooning had gained him international fame, and during a visit to the United States in 1902, he was sought out by Thomas Edison and Samuel P. Langley.

The Airplane Builder

Over the next few years, Santos-Dumont continued to design new airships, building his own station for them at Neuilly St. James. In 1904, however, he became interested in heavier-than-air flight. The following year, he teamed up with Gabriel Voisin to build an ungainly looking "canard-type" airplane, with a rectangular, fabric-covered fuselage and tail unit forward of the main wing with its propeller in the rear. Its wings, which resembled large box kites, were attached at a pronounced dihedral angle, providing lateral stability. A 50-horsepower engine propelled the craft through the air. Attached to the leading end of the fuselage was a small boxlike device that pivoted both vertically and horizontally, the sole means of control during flight. The pilot stood in a wicker basket directly in front of the engine. On October 23, 1906, the craft flew for a distance of some 60 meters, the first successful European airplane flight. On November 12 of the same year, it flew 220 meters, managing to stay aloft for more than 20 seconds.

To a Europe that knew nothing of Orville and Wilbur Wright's triumph at Kitty Hawk three years earlier, Santos-Dumont's new accomplishment was heralded as another technological first, rivaling his previous feat in controlled aerial navigation in 1901. Soon, former associates such as Henri Farman and Louis Blériot were breaking Santos-Dumont's records, but only Wilbur Wright's flying exhibitions in a biplane during a 1908 visit to France finally disabused objective observers of Santos-Dumont's claim to the first flight. Yet the Brazilian aeronaut continued to contribute to the airplane's evolution: His lightweight *Demoiselle* (dragonfly), first tested in 1909, could attain a speed of 70 miles per hour and was easy to control.

In 1910, Santos-Dumont suddenly gave up designing and flying and sold his entire fleet of vehicles. In March of that year, he was diagnosed with multiple sclerosis, and its inevitable sentence of gradual physical debilitation often tempted him to despair. His dark moods were further exacerbated during World War I by a sense of responsibility for the deaths caused by aerial warfare. He lectured on three continents about the use of aircraft in peace and war, often sounding a distinctly pacifist note.

The last two decades of Santos-Dumont's life offer few milestones beyond the occasional honors bestowed on him—particularly by the country of Brazil, which idolized him as its most famous citizen—for his pioneering work and a chronicle of rootless travel between Europe and South America. His efforts at invention, notably with proposed ornithopters, were only parodies of his former audacious triumphs, and he gradually receded from public view. Even a planned festive trip to Brazil in 1928 ended in disaster when a seaplane sent out to greet his arriving ocean liner plunged into the sea in front of his eyes, killing all passengers, among whom were many of the nation's leading intellectuals.

In 1931, Santos-Dumont returned permanently to Brazil, but the country's descent into civil war hastened his physical and mental decline. On July 23, 1932, after witnessing an aerial bombing raid carried out by government forces against fellow Brazilians, he took his own life.

David M. Rooney

Bibliography

Page, Joseph A. "Brazil's Daredevil of the Air." *Americas* 45, no. 2 (March/April, 1993). A profile of Santos-Dumont, his career in early aviation, his aircraft designs, and his education.

Santos-Dumont, Alberto. *My Airships: The Story of My Life*. 1904. Reprint. New York: Dover, 1973. An unabridged republication of the English translation originally published in 1904 by Grant Richards in London of the inventor's own *Dans l'air*, an ebullient account of Santos-Dumont's exploits, written at the height of his popularity.

Wykeham, Peter. *Santos-Dumont: A Study in Obsession*. New York: Harcourt Brace, 1963. A superbly written biography that situates Santos-Dumont within Paris's *belle époque*.

See also: Airplanes; Balloons; Buoyant aircraft; Dirigibles; Heavier-than-air craft; History of human flight; Kites; Lighter-than-air craft

SAS

Also known as: Scandinavian Airlines System
Date: Founded as a consortium in 1946
Definition: SAS, a major international airline, was formed by three national Scandinavian air carriers.
Significance: SAS is a unique major airline in that it is a consortium of three airlines under one brand. SAS has a global route network and a good reputation for safety, technical standards, and service.

History and Organization

Scandinavian Airlines System (SAS) is a major international airline. Its headquarters are in Stockholm, Sweden. Three national Scandinavian air carriers, through a consortium agreement, established the airline. The carriers were Det Danske Luftfartselskab (DDL), the Danish airline; Det Norske Luftfartselskab (DNL), the Norwegian air carrier; and AB Aerotransport (ABA), the Swedish airline. On September 17, 1946, *Dan Viking*, the first DC-4 painted in SAS's colors, made its premier flight from Stockholm's Bromma airport to New York via Copenhagen, Prestwick, and Gander. The flight took twenty-seven hours. By November 30, SAS had inaugurated its second route, to Rio de Janeiro and Montevideo.

In 1947, SILA (from Sweden), DDL, and DNL operated to North and South America under SAS's colors. DDL, DNL, and ABA operated their own domestic and European services and all three had plans to open routes to the Middle East, Asia, and Africa. The three airlines had difficulties in developing their traffic, hampered by heavy restrictions on travel and how much currency people were allowed to bring with them. The three carriers often offered parallel services, and passengers were few.

In 1948, on the initiative of the Swedish government, privately owned SILA and state-owned ABA were merged on a fifty-fifty ownership basis and named ABA. An agreement was made with DDL and DNL to coordinate European traffic. The cooperation agreement was called ESAS (European SAS) and Copenhagen was made the operational center. All aircraft used by ESAS were painted in SAS colors, and offices abroad were merged. ESAS did not provide the economies of scale that had been anticipated and the three companies struggled with major financial problems.

In September, 1949, the Norwegian Department of Transport urged DNL to withdraw from ESAS. Instead of a complete collapse of the cooperation, a new SAS Consortium comprising the total traffic of the three companies was established. On February 8, 1951, ABA, DDL, and DNL ceased to exist as independently operating airlines. Their share of the new consortium remained three-sevenths, two-sevenths, and two-sevenths, respectively. Ownership of each of the three companies was distributed fifty-fifty among government and private interests.

Corporate Activities

SAS as of 2001 operated scheduled passenger, freight, and mail flights between nearly one hundred cities in about fifty countries. The company also offered tour and catering services, and operated hotels in Scandinavia, Greenland, and the rest of the world under the SAS Radisson brand. Since 1990, SAS has owned and operated its own flight academy as a subsidiary company. The SAS Flight Academy is headquartered at Arlanda Airport in Stockholm and is responsible for training pilots, cabin attendants, and mechanics for SAS and other airlines. SAS Media, founded in 1972, is also a subsidiary of SAS. The company has offices in Stockholm and Oslo employing forty-one people, with an annual turnover in 2001 of $10 million.

The airline operates a fleet of several types of aircraft, most of them made in the United States. In addition to the Boeing B-767-300 ER, which is used for its long-haul flights, SAS operates for its short- and medium-haul flights the Boeing B-737-600, 700, and 800 series, the McDonnell Douglas (Boeing) MD90-30, the McDonnell Douglas (Boeing) MD-81-82 and -83, the McDonnell Douglas MD-87, the McDonnell Douglas DC-9, the Dutch-made Fokker F-50 and F-28, the Swedish-made SAAB 2000, and the Canadian De Havilland Q-400.

The SAS route system is built around nonstop flights to and from the Scandinavian capitals and offers its customers a global traffic system. This is a hub-and-spoke network, which attempts to provide customers with convenient and efficient travel connections between continents, countries, and towns.

A notable first in flight operations for SAS took place on February 24, 1957, when a SAS DC-7C took off from Copenhagen to Anchorage and Tokyo. Simultaneously, another SAS DC-7C departed from Tokyo. At 9:10 P.M. the two aircraft met over the North Pole. By tying together the southern route and the polar route, SAS was the first airline to fly over the pole and around the world.

Events in SAS History

1946: SAS, a consortium of three Scandinavian airlines, AB Aerotransport (ABA), Det Danske Luftfartselskab (DDL), and Det Norske Luftfartselskab (DNL), is formed for the purpose of joint transatlantic service.

1947: Daily flights are scheduled between Stockholm, Sweden, and New York City.

1952: SAS introduces tourist class fares costing 25 percent less than previous standard fares.

1957: With the inauguration of SAS's pioneering Copenhagen-Anchorage-Tokyo polar route, flying time to Japan is reduced from fifty-two to thirty-two hours.

1965: SAS introduces its SASCO electronic airline reservations system.

1971: The airline takes delivery of its first Boeing 747.

1979: SAS inaugurates business-class service on its transatlantic flights.

1980: SAS takes delivery of its first Airbus A300.

1988: SAS establishes a cooperative agreement with Continental Airlines.

1991: With delivery of its fiftieth MD-80 aircraft, SAS becomes the world's largest MD-operating airline carrier outside the United States.

1996: SAS forms an alliance with Lufthansa.

1997: SAS joins the Star Alliance with Lufthansa, United Air Lines, Air Canada, and Thai Airways. All SAS flights are made nonsmoking flights.

1999: SAS presents a new corporate image, with redecorated aircraft and redesigned uniforms.

Alliances

In an attempt to solve some of the problems connected with SAS's geographic position in the far north, in an area with a relatively sparse population, SAS entered into agreements with a number of airlines having strategically better locations as early as the 1950's. Among those were Austrian Airlines, Thai Airways International, and Gamsa of Mexico. In order to keep down the costs for training, maintenance, and equipment for their newly acquired Boeing B-747's, SAS entered into the KSS (for the initial letters of each partner) agreement with Swissair and KLM in 1971.

In May, 1995, a strategic alliance with Lufthansa was signed, and implemented on February 1, 1996. This agreement was the impetus for Scandinavian Airlines System to found, along with Lufthansa, Air Canada, Thai Airways International, and United Air Lines, the Star Alliance in 1997. In subsequent years, membership grew to include Air New Zealand, ANA (Japan), Ansett Australia, Austrian Airlines, British Midland, Lauda Air (Austria), Mexicana Airlines, Singapore Airlines, Tyrolean Airways (Austria), and Varig Brazil. The Star Alliance grew significantly and by mid 2001 it encompassed fifteen airlines and a network of 130 countries and 815 destinations, making it the world's largest alliance.

In addition to its Star partners, SAS has cooperated with several other airlines. The cooperation encompasses, among other things, code-share flights and the participation in each other's frequent flier programs. In the Scandinavian market, SAS offers a comprehensive network together with its regional partners Cimber Air, Widerøe, Skyways, Air Botnia, and Maersk. SAS is also regional partners with Estonian Air in the Baltic and Spanair in Spain. All in all, SAS can offer more than eight thousand departures daily to over 815 destinations in 130 countries. SAS has proven that through cooperation, three relatively small nations are able to create an airline of international magnitude.

Triantafyllos G. Flouris

Bibliography

Groenewege, Adrianus D. *The Compendium of International Civil Aviation*. 2d ed. Geneva, Switzerland: International Air Transport Association, 1999. A comprehensive directory of the major players in international civil aviation, with insightful and detailed articles.

Weimer, Kent J. ed. *Aviation Week and Space Technology: World Aviation Directory*. New York: McGraw-Hill, 2000. An excellent introductory guide on all global companies involved in the aviation business. The information is very basic but very essential as a first introduction to each company.

See also: Air Canada; Air carriers; Fokker aircraft; Lufthansa; MD plane family; Singapore Airlines

Satellites

Definition: Objects gravitationally bound to and orbiting about larger bodies.

Significance: Artificial satellites permanently stationed in space perform many important economic, military, and scientific missions. Uncrewed artificial satellites are the chief instrument of space exploration and provide the only means of obtaining permanent utilization of space.

Virtually all objects in space are satellites of one body or another. Satellites range in size from galaxies such as the Large and Small Magellanic clouds in orbit about the Milky Way to microscopic flakes of paint in low-Earth orbit that have eroded from artificial spacecraft. In practice, the word satellite is reserved for uncrewed spacecraft in Earth orbit. Crewed spacecraft are usually referred to individually by name, such as the International Space Station. Nonfunctional objects of artificial origin are regarded as orbital debris. Natural satellites of stars are more properly referred to as planets, while natural satellites of planets are more properly referred to as moons.

Satellites travel on elliptical trajectories called orbits, which are freely falling paths determined by the local gravitational field. Although satellites are indeed falling, they are also traveling sideways at extremely high speeds, on the order of 7 kilometers per second (5 miles per second) at 200 kilometers altitude (130 miles). The combination of free fall and high lateral velocity creates a closed trajectory that carries the satellite around Earth repeatedly.

The point on the orbit nearest to the earth is called the perigee; it is also the point at which the satellite has the greatest velocity. The point farthest away is called the apogee. That is also where the satellite velocity is least. If space were a perfect vacuum, satellites would orbit forever, but the atmosphere has no distinct end, and gradually fades away with altitude. Satellites orbiting at altitudes from 200 to 600 kilometers (130 to 400 miles) encounter enough residual atmosphere to create significant aerodynamic drag. Over the months, these low-Earth-orbit satellites lose energy and decrease in apogee until the apogee equals the perigee and the orbit is a circle. The satellites then drop closer to Earth on a spiral path, accelerating as they do so. Eventually, they enter regions where the atmosphere is too thick for them to continue in orbit. Aerodynamic drag becomes so strong that all of the satellite's energy is converted into heat in a matter of minutes. The air around the satellite becomes hot enough to glow, and exposure to the heat burns up the satellite.

Satellites orbiting below 200 kilometers (130 miles) reenter Earth's atmosphere in a matter of months. Those orbiting above 600 kilometers (400 miles) seldom reenter.

Satellites are classified according to user (commercial, military, or scientific) and according to mission (communications, remote sensing, or experimentation and measurement). Commercial satellites belong to private businesses. Military satellites support military operations. Scientific satellites perform experiments or make measurements in support of scientific research.

A satellite is only one part of a space mission's architecture, an assembly which consists of the satellite, the launch system necessary to place it in orbit, the ground support system necessary to control the satellite and communicate with it, and a data analysis and information management system to exploit the data gathered by the satellite.

The Satellite Design Process

The satellite design process begins with the delineation of the satellite mission. A mission to photograph Earth from space, for example, might be expressed in terms of the goal that all areas of Earth between 45 degrees north latitude and 45 degrees south latitude be photographed with sufficient clarity that objects as small as 10 meters across can be imaged clearly. This requirement immediately eliminates all orbits of less than 45 degrees inclination and makes the orbital altitude of the satellite heavily dependent on camera quality: high-resolution cameras will be able to fulfill the requirement from greater altitudes than low-resolution cameras. In this way, the mission is expressed in the form of a set of requirements for orbital altitude, inclination, life span, launch date, and other needs which the satellite must fit.

A satellite is composed of the payload and the support bus. The payload consists of those components which perform the primary mission of the satellite. Component choice is driven by the best fit of available hardware to mission requirements. The components chosen will in turn determine payload parameters such as mass and volume, and payload demands such as power consumption, data storage and transmission, and attitude control.

The bus contains various systems to support the payload and provide electric power, thermal control, attitude control and propulsion, communications, and structural support. Bus components must be chosen that are capable of filling all of the payload demands as well as supporting the bus itself.

Total mass and volume are determined once payload and bus design are complete. Total mass and volume together with orbit requirements determine the choice of launch vehicle.

No satellite design process is complete without the development of ground sites. Ground sites monitor the status of the satellite and issue commands as necessary to maintain proper function or to correct anomalies in function. Ground sites receive data sent down by the satellite, process the data into a form intelligible to the user, and deliver it. Ground site personnel continually track the satellite, noting inevitable changes in orbit and issuing predictions for future passes within range of the ground site.

Power

The power system provides the electric power needed to operate electrical and electronic components. Solar cells are usually the primary source of power, converting sunlight to electricity. What is not immediately required for satellite operations is stored in rechargeable batteries for later use. The power requirements of the payload and bus together determine the size of power system components. Solar cells must have enough area to collect all the power needed by the satellite plus more to provide a margin of safety. Because solar cells degrade over time in the harsh space environment, they must be built larger than initially required to guarantee that enough capability remains after years of degradation to continue operating the satellite. The number and size of batteries must be sufficient to meet the voltage and current demands of the payload and bus.

Power consumption must be carefully managed on board satellites. Consumption of electricity inevitably generates heat, which cannot easily escape in the vacuum of space and becomes a challenge for the thermal control system. Batteries build up internal pressure when charging and are in danger of bursting and destroying the satellite if overcharged. On the other hand, batteries that discharge too deeply are in danger of dying completely. Also, electronic components that lose power or receive too little voltage (an undervoltage condition) may cease operating or undergo an uncommanded reset when normal conditions return. Power system conditions such as voltage, current, and temperature are monitored at critical locations with the results transmitted to satellite operators on the ground.

Satellites

Thermal Control

The thermal control system maintains proper temperature throughout the satellite. It removes heat from components in danger of overheating from electric power consumption or exposure to the Sun, and provides heat to components in danger of freezing from exposure to the cold vacuum.

Attitude Control and Propulsion

The attitude control system maintains the satellite in the proper orientation required for the satellite to fulfill its mission. Communications satellites must have antennas permanently pointed toward Earth's surface, for example, while the Hubble Space Telescope must be constantly looking at the object being photographed.

The simplest type of attitude control system is none at all; the satellite is allowed to tumble uncontrollably. This requires the use of antennas that broadcast in all directions at once, so that communication with the ground is never interrupted. This also means that most of the broadcast power is wasted on transmissions into empty space and that only a small fraction of the power reaches the ground. This is acceptable only for the simplest types of low-Earth-orbit satellites.

Oblong satellites can be oriented so that the long axis points toward Earth and couples to tidal gravitational forces to provide gravity gradient stabilization. Once gravity gradient stabilization is achieved, the satellite will permanently present one face toward Earth, where cameras, remote sensing instruments, and communications antennas may be advantageously mounted. Gravity gradient stabilization is usually achieved by building a telescoping boom into the satellite structure, which deploys when the proper orientation is obtained. When extended, the end of the boom closest to Earth feels the strongest gravitational field and is continually pulled downward. That continuous downward pull keeps that end pointed toward Earth.

Active attitude control systems include momentum wheels and control moment gyroscopes. Momentum wheels are spun up in one direction so that the satellite will spin in the opposite direction in reaction. Three momentum wheels mounted in three perpendicular directions provide attitude control about any rotation axis. When the spin axis of a control moment gyroscope is altered, complicated reaction forces are created that may be used to rotate the spacecraft. Both of these systems have the virtue of reorienting the satellite without consuming propellant.

Active attitude control requires the satellite to have some knowledge of its orientation with respect to the outside world. The location of the Sun can be determined through the use of sensors that respond to visible light to indicate which side of the spacecraft is facing the Sun and which is in shade. Earth sensors respond to infrared radiation from the comparatively warm Earth. Star sensors look for the light from very bright stars. Stable platforms controlled by gyroscopes maintain a constant orientation regardless of the rotation of the spacecraft.

Communications

The communications system keeps the satellite in contact with the ground support system and moves data and commands to and from the satellite. The communications system includes transmitters and receivers, data encoders and decoders, data storage and retrieval elements (memory), and antennas. High-gain directional antennas carry the maximum amount of data with the minimum amount of power, but must be accurately pointed toward the reception site. This requires additional equipment to control the pointing of the antenna and maintain communications lock. The antenna may move itself, or the attitude control system may be tasked to reorient the entire satellite.

Orbital speeds of the order of 7 kilometers per second (5 miles per second) create significant shifts in the frequency of radio waves transmitted or received by satellites. Frequency goes up as the satellite approaches a ground site and falls as the satellite recedes, a phenomenon known as the Doppler shift. The ground site must continuously adjust frequency of both transmission and reception so that communication is continuous and no information is lost.

Most satellites are in range of a ground site for only ten minutes or less at a time and only during the infrequent occasions when their orbit takes them over the ground site location. Data collected at other times must be stored on board for relay to the ground during the next pass.

Structure

The structural system holds the parts of the satellite together and protects the components of the satellite from the high accelerations and intense vibrations experienced during launch. Structures range from simple frames to hold the components of the satellite in place to complicated mechanical systems folded and stowed during launch that must unfold and extend instruments upon deployment. The structure must not respond resonantly to vibrations generated by the launch vehicle or the satellite will shake itself to destruction. Special composite materials and honeycomb construction keep structural members lightweight without sacrificing strength.

Satellite Construction and Testing

The high costs of launch and the inability to make repairs on malfunctioning satellites demand high reliability and long operational lifetimes. Both are expensive and difficult to achieve. Altogether, these requirements force satellite designers and builders to make every attempt to make the satellite perfect the first time and every time. Components are extensively tested individually, and each system is tested and retested as new components are added. Complete systems are tested individually, and then tested and retested as they are linked into the final satellite assembly. Finally, the complete satellite is tested and retested under conditions simulating spaceflight as closely as possible.

The quest for perfection begins at the component level. Items for use in satellites must meet rigorous requirements. Materials cannot emit water vapor or volatile organic compounds in a vacuum. They must not chemically break down, degrade, or darken under exposure to ultraviolet light or atomic oxygen. Electronic parts and components must not be susceptible to ionizing radiation. Electrical systems must not be susceptible to the build-up and discharge of static electricity.

Complete satellite assemblies must survive a harsh launch environment. Launch vehicle accelerations can produce the equivalent of eight to ten times normal weight in the satellite. Rocket exhaust plumes generate strong vibrations and intense noise that can vibrate poorly constructed assemblies to destruction. Satellites therefore undergo vibration testing on massive shake tables that realistically simulate the launch vibration environment. After vibration testing, the satellite is placed in a vacuum chamber and run through heating and cooling cycles that mimic what the satellite will encounter in space.

All stages of satellite construction are extensively documented. Even after all this testing, satellites fail on orbit. Since a failed satellite cannot be retrieved for study, the only way to analyze what went wrong is to review the documentation and deduce the cause of the failure. A complete and thorough record of the design and construction process is essential.

Tracking Satellites

The U.S. Space Command (USSPACECOM) catalogs and tracks every object in Earth orbit greater than 10 centimeters (4 inches) in length with ground-based radar and electro-optically enhanced telescopes. Continuous space surveillance allows U.S. Space Command to predict when and where a decaying space object will reenter Earth's atmosphere in order to prevent an innocent satellite or inert piece of debris from triggering missile-attack warning sensors of the United States or other countries upon reentry. It also charts the present position and anticipated motion of space objects, detects new manmade objects in space, and determines their country of origin. An extremely important function of space surveillance is to inform the National Aeronautics and Space Administration (NASA) of the identity and path of objects that may endanger the space shuttle.

The space shuttle deploys a satellite by means of a robotic arm. (NASA)

End-of-Life Operations

Space is becoming crowded. The Soviet Union launched Sputnik 1, the first artificial Earth satellite, in October, 1957. The United States launched its first satellite, Explorer 1, in January, 1958. Both have long since decayed and burned during reentry. The oldest satellite still in orbit is Vanguard 1, launched in March, 1958. As of June 6, 2001, U.S. Space Command reported 2,728 satellites in orbit, while 2,569 other satellites had undergone orbital decay and burned on reentry since 1957.

Satellites still in orbit degrade in the harsh space environment, shedding small particles of debris, such as paint flecks and pieces of thermal blanket. In extreme cases, old satellites are completely destroyed when aging batteries burst or leftover propellant spontaneously explodes. As of June 6, 2001, U.S. Space Command reported 6,150 pieces of debris in orbit that were 10 centimeters or greater in length. Satellites in low-Earth orbit run a significant risk of collision with a piece of orbiting debris. At collision velocities on the order of 10 kilometers per second (about 7 miles per second) even a tiny fleck of paint can do significant damage.

In an effort to slow the rate at which new debris is being created, satellite designers routinely include end-of-life planning in the satellite design process. At end-of-life, batteries are disconnected from solar panels to prevent destructive overcharging, and any unused pressurized liquids or gases are vented into the vacuum. The last few gallons (or pounds) of propellant are consumed in an orbital adjustment burn which either forces low-Earth-orbit satellites to reenter the atmosphere and burn up, or moves higher-altitude satellites to disposal orbits where they do not present a hazard to other spacecraft.

Observing Satellites

Satellites shine by reflected light and are visible to the naked eye for a short time just before sunrise and just after sunset. During these periods, the background sky is dark enough for dim objects to be seen by observers on the ground, but satellites passing overhead are still illuminated by the sun. There are so many satellites in orbit that every morning and evening, several pass over virtually every location on Earth. Satellites of the Iridium group of communications satellites have large, highly polished solar panels that can be extremely bright when the sun is reflected in them. Sightings of so-called Iridium flares are extremely common.

Billy R. Smith, Jr.

Bibliography

Heavens Above. (www.heavens-above.com) Provides easy-to-use information about satellite passes, both morning and evening, for almost every location on Earth. The user inputs either a place name or latitude and longitude information, and the Web page returns pass predictions for all visible satellites for the coming days. Star maps showing the start, stop, and path of the pass are also available. High-visibility objects, such as the International Space Station and Iridium flares, are specifically noted.

Maral, Gerald, and Michel Bousquet. *Satellite Communications Systems: Systems, Techniques, and Technology.* 3d ed. New York: John Wiley & Sons, 1998. Offers a detailed analysis of satellite communication system construction and operation.

Montenbruck, Oliver, and Eberhard Gill. *Satellite Orbits: Models, Methods, Applications.* New York: Springer Verlag, 2000. A textbook on orbital mechanics covering all aspects of satellite orbit prediction and determination.

U.S. Space Command. (www.peterson.af.mil/usspace/index.htm) The U.S. Space Command Web site provides links to the current satellite box score and satellite space catalog.

See also: National Aeronautics and Space Administration; Orbiting; Propulsion; Spaceflight; Sputnik; Uncrewed spaceflight; Vanguard Program

Saturn rockets

Date: First flight (SA-1) on October 27, 1961; last flight (SA-210) on July 15, 1975

Definition: A family of heavy-lift rockets that culminated with the Saturn V Moon rocket used in the Apollo Program.

Significance: The Saturn rockets were the first U.S. rockets truly designed from their inception as space rockets and not as adaptations of existing intercontinental ballistic missiles. The Saturn V rockets were the largest and most powerful rockets ever built.

History

In the late 1950's, adaptations of existing intercontinental ballistic missile (ICBM) technology led to the development of the Atlas and Thor missiles and the Juno and Jupiter rockets. These rockets could be adapted to launch small payloads into Earth orbit, as demonstrated when a Jupiter C rocket developed by rocketry pioneer Wernher von Braun at the U.S. Army Ballistic Missile Agency (ABMA) successfully launched the United States' first Earth-orbiting satellite, Explorer 1, on January 31, 1958.

Even before Explorer 1 was launched, it had become apparent that existing rockets could only orbit fairly small payloads. Development was underway for the Atlas rockets, but von Braun foresaw a need for a launch vehicle designed to lift heavy payloads into space. This new rocket was to be a successor to the Jupiter rocket and was tentatively designated as the Jupiter V, though it was often referred to as the "super Jupiter."

The Jupiter V project was approved in part because the Soviet Union had already developed very large rockets capable of lifting into orbit payloads far larger than those of any U.S. rocket at that time. Soon after ABMA began development of the Jupiter V at its site near Huntsville, Alabama, it became apparent that the new rocket would be of a totally new design and not merely an adaptation of the Jupiter rocket. Von Braun proposed that the name of the new rocket be "Saturn," because that was the next planet from the Sun after Jupiter. The name was agreed to, and so from then on, the Jupiter V rocket under development was called the Saturn I rocket. The Saturn rocket would be able to lift into Earth orbit payloads far greater than those of any other U.S. rocket. Von Braun, however, was planning ahead. He proposed a new rocket, based on existing technology, that would be able to boost a payload to the Moon and back. The tentative name for this proposed new rocket was Nova. The Nova rocket, von Braun reasoned, would need nearly 12,000,000 pounds of thrust. This would require a first stage with more than fifty of the then-most powerful rocket engines.

The Advanced Research Projects Agency (ARPA), associated with ABMA, began test-firing of the engines for the first stage of the Saturn rocket in late 1958. The Saturn project was nearly canceled in June, 1959, when the U.S. Department of Defense decided that it did not really need a heavy-lift vehicle after all. ABMA was told to stop working on both Saturn and Nova. The initial proposed need for the development of the Saturn had been to launch orbiting communications satellites. It was found that such satellites would not be as heavy as had been thought. However, the National Aeronautics and Space Administration (NASA), the civilian space agency created in 1958, was very interested in both the Saturn and Nova rockets. Eventually, a deal was worked out to transfer von Braun, his rocket development team, and most of ABMA to the jurisdiction of NASA. The ABMA site in Huntsville became the Marshall Space Flight Center.

Work began immediately on the first of the Saturn rocket family, the Saturn I. During development of Saturn I, new engine technology was being developed that allowed modifications to the Saturn I. The improved rocket, designated the Saturn IB, was capable of lifting far heavier payloads. The Saturn I was never used except as a technological development stage toward later rockets.

The exact design of the Nova rocket would depend upon the mission characteristics and requirements of a crewed Moon program. In 1962, NASA's Office of Manned Space Flight decided to use a lunar orbit rendezvous mission, in which a small lander, rather than the entire rocket, would descend to the lunar surface and then return to a mother ship orbiting the Moon. This method would require a rocket slightly smaller than von Braun's proposed Nova rocket. It became apparent that the Saturn rocket program could be adapted and significantly enhanced to yield a rocket of specifications nearly like those of Nova. This new rocket, which was ultimately built, was designated the Saturn V rocket.

Saturn I

The Saturn I rocket was designed as a two-stage rocket. The upper stage would use liquid hydrogen as fuel and liquid oxygen as oxidizer. The first stage used kerosene (RP-1) and liquid oxygen. Liquid hydrogen is more energetic as fuel than kerosene but is harder to handle. Furthermore, hydrogen is lighter than kerosene, making it ideal for the upper-stage fuel. Kerosene, however, requires less storage space than does liquid hydrogen. Additionally, the rocket would be more stable with a heavier first stage, so kerosene was deemed the best fuel for first stage use.

The first stage of Saturn I, designated S-I, used eight H-1 engines, developed by the Rocketdyne Division of North American Aviation. Each engine provided 188,000 pounds of thrust. The four inboard engines were fixed in position, and the four outer engines were gimbaled, or suspended, to change direction slightly in order to steer the rocket. A decision was made to use existing Mercury and Jupiter propellant tanks to save development costs. The larger Jupiter tank was used for liquid oxygen. Clustered around it were four Redstone rocket oxygen tanks and four Redstone fuel tanks filled with kerosene. This clustering approach ensured that the fuel would not slosh around inside the large tank but made the plumbing of the system difficult. Although the first few S-I stages were constructed in-house by ARPA, the sheer magnitude of the project led to the selection of the Chrysler Corporation's Space Division as a contractor to build the remaining S-I stages.

The Saturn I upper stage, designated S-IV, was constructed by Douglas Aircraft. Nearly two thirds of the S-IV was used by the liquid hydrogen tanks. Liquid hydrogen and liquid oxygen must be kept extremely cold, and so the propellant tanks were heavily insulated. This insulation, however, would be very heavy, and the lighter the stage, the higher the payload that could be delivered to orbit. North American Aviation devised a honeycomb aluminum insulation that was both very light and very strong. The honeycomb aluminum actually became stronger when cooled, so it was used to boost the strength of the propellant tanks, allowing the tank walls to be made thinner so that the tanks could be lighter. To power the S-IV stage, six Pratt & Whitney RL-10 engines were used, each providing 15,000 pounds of thrust.

Ten successful missions, beginning on October 27, 1961, were flown with Saturn I rockets. The first three involved the first stage only, with a dummy payload in place of the second stage. The last Saturn I rocket was launched July 30, 1965.

Saturn IB

The Saturn IB was essentially an upgrade of the Saturn I. Rocketdyne upgraded the H-1 engines to 200,000 pounds of thrust for the Saturn IB first stage, designated S-IB. Additionally, the dimensions of the first stage were slightly altered to couple with the redesigned upper stage. The S-IB had onboard computers and guidance systems intended to be used on the later Saturn V rockets. The rocket's computers were constructed by International Business Machines (IBM). Although they were used for only a few minutes, they had to monitor a very large number of operations of the rocket.

The Saturn IB's second stage, the S-IVB, was completely redesigned. The S-IVB used a liquid hydrogen and liquid oxygen propellant system and was powered by a single J-2 engine developed by Rocketdyne. The J-2 engine, with 200,000 pounds of thrust, provided the S-IVB with more than double the thrust of the S-IV used on Saturn I. The S-IVB was also configured to receive a collar on its top end to mate with payloads expected of the Apollo Program.

The first Saturn IB flew on February 26, 1966. Only four test flights were made with Saturn IB before the first crewed flight, Apollo 7, on October 11, 1968. Apollo 7 demonstrated the effectiveness of the Apollo spacecraft in an Earth-orbital mission. From this time until 1973, when the Apollo Program was canceled after the Apollo 17 mission, all remaining Apollo missions would use the Saturn V rocket. The Saturn IB, however, was used for three more missions in 1973 to launch Apollo capsules. The final launch of a Saturn IB was on July 15, 1975, when an Apollo capsule was launched to rendezvous with a Soyuz spacecraft launched by the Soviet Union.

Saturn V

In order to achieve the necessary thrust for a lunar mission, Rocketdyne developed the F-1 engines used in the Saturn V first stage. The F-1 engines burned 40,000 gallons of kerosene per second and provided a thrust of 1,600,000 pounds each. Each F-1 engine provided about the same thrust as the entire Saturn IB first stage. The Saturn V first stage was designated S-IC, and it was a complete redesign of the earlier first stages. Five F-1 engines were used. The center engine was fixed, and the outer four engines were gimbaled to steer the rocket. No other rocket had ever been constructed to match the 8,000,000-pound thrust of the S-IC. The S-IC, constructed by Boeing, was 33 feet in diameter and 138 feet in length. It contained enough kerosene and liquid oxygen in two giant tanks to fill more than fifty railroad tank cars.

The second stage of the Saturn V was a new design, designated the S-II. The S-II used five Rocketdyne J-2 engines. The S-II, constructed by North American Aviation, was also 33 feet in diameter and 81.5 feet in length. The S-II used liquid hydrogen and liquid oxygen as a propellant. The upper part of the S-II mated with a flared collar that fitted the more narrow third stage of the Saturn V.

The Saturn V's third stage was the venerable S-IVB stage that had been used as the second stage to the Saturn IB. On top of the S-IVB was the payload for the Saturn V. For the Apollo missions, the payload had consisted of the Lunar Module, the Command Module, and the Service Module. The Service Module contained power systems for the Command Module and a rocket designed to return the Apollo spacecraft back to Earth from the Moon. On top of the Command Module was an escape tower that held rockets designed to lift the Command Module off of the Saturn V in the event of a catastrophic failure during launch. The total height of the rocket was 364 feet, and its total weight was more than 6,000,000 tons when fully fueled and ready for liftoff.

A total of fifteen Saturn V rockets were constructed. The first two launches on November 9, 1967, and April 4, 1968, were unmanned test missions. December 21, 1968, however, a Saturn V launched Apollo 8 on a trip around the Moon and back to Earth. On July 16, 1969, a Saturn V rocket, designated SA-506, launched Apollo 11, which was the first manned landing on the Moon. The last lunar mission was rocket SA-512, which launched Apollo 17. Only one other Saturn V rocket was launched. On May 14, 1973, SA-513 launched a modified S-IVB as Skylab, the first U.S. space station. The two remaining Saturn V rockets were never used, and became displays at the Kennedy Space Center and at the Johnson Space Center.

Raymond D. Benge, Jr.

Bibliography

Bilstein, Roger E. *Stages to Saturn: A Technological History of the Apollo/Saturn Launch Vehicles*. Washington, D.C.: Government Printing Office, 1996. An authoritative and thorough, though readable, description of the entire Saturn project from first conceptions to the program's spinoffs.

Braun, Wernher von. "Saturn the Giant." In *Apollo Expeditions to the Moon*, edited by Edgar M. Cartright. Washington, D.C.: Government Printing Office, 1975. An excellent description of the Saturn rockets for the layperson, written by the lead designer himself.

Heppenheimer, T. A. *Countdown: A History of Space Flight*. New York: John Wiley & Sons, 1997. A very readable history of space exploration, with a section on the Apollo lunar exploration.

Kennedy, Gregory P. *Rockets, Missiles, and Spacecraft of the National Air and Space Museum*. Washington, D.C.: Smithsonian Institution Press, 1983. A very good, though brief, description of the H-1 and F-1 rocket engines.

See also: Apollo Program; Wernher von Braun; Crewed spaceflight; Robert H. Goddard; Johnson Space Center; Missiles; National Aeronautics and Space Administration; Orbiting; Rocket propulsion; Rockets; Spaceflight; Uncrewed spaceflight

Seaplanes

Also known as: Float planes, flying boats
Definition: Aircraft that are capable of taking off and landing on bodies of water.
Significance: Seaplanes allowed aircraft to fly across large bodies of water, allowing for transoceanic passenger and freight service.

History

The development of water-based aircraft, or seaplanes, as they are called, was a natural outgrowth of the development of flight. In the early years of aviation, almost the only places where sufficiently long "runways" for takeoff and landing existed were along various bodies of water. Because almost one-half of the populations of the United States and Western Europe lived within close proximity to the coastline, the development of water-based flight became important.

Over the years, long over-water, or transoceanic, flights became a natural part of the transportation infrastructure. Yet, in many cases aircraft did not have the range to fly across the entire ocean nonstop. The development of seaplanes allowed for craft that could stop at islands or other harbors to refuel, do maintenance, or wait for improved weather before continuing on their way. Seaplanes also opened remote areas to travel, as they could land or take off on lakes, rivers, or harbors without requiring shore-based facilities.

The military, by the 1930's, had taken a great interest in seaplanes. Naval vessels used catapult-mounted planes as forward scouts and observers. They could be landed on the sea and recovered back aboard ship for reuse. Seaplanes were also used for search and rescue by the military. They not only had long over-water flight capability, but also could set down on the water's surface to pick up people. Some of these planes were also armed and used to hunt submarines, to lay mines, or to bomb torpedoes.

These uses, coupled with the dramatic increase in the number of flight passengers and the opening of regular transatlantic and transpacific mail routes in the years prior to World War II, led to the development of a number of different seaplane designs. Designers at Dornier, Sikorsky, Martin, Boeing, Grumman, and Consolidated all contributed to the variety of seaplanes available for both military and civilian use.

Types

Seaplanes have been designed and built as two distinctly different types of aircraft. The first type, float planes, are essentially land-based aircraft modified for water takeoffs and landings. Float planes could be fitted with a single float under the fuselage and wingtip floats under the wings. Other aircraft manufacturers adapted their plane designs with twin floats under the hull. Manufacturers such as Cessna, DeHavilland, Grumman, and others have successfully adapted their aircraft to the rough conditions of water takeoffs and landings. These aircraft are prized for their ability to give access to remote areas. They are used for search and rescue and backcountry expeditions and as supply planes and tourist vehicles. Some are twin-engine planes, and others are single-engine planes. Due to the conditions of rough water, spray, and low visibility, however, all float planes have high-wing designs.

The second type of seaplanes, flying boats, have the rounded hull shape of a boat. The fuselage is designed so that it floats in, and not above, the water like float planes. This type of aircraft may also be equipped with wing floats. Flying boats are generally multiengined aircraft, with either two, three, or four engines. The number of engines depends upon the size of the plane and the range it is designed to fly over water. Flying boats also have a high-wing design, required not only by rough water, spray, and low visibility, but also by the fact that these planes land on their hulls in the water.

Seaplanes

Commercial Aviation

The interwar years and, to some degree, the years during World War II, were a time of great success for commercial enterprises operating flying boats. One of the first companies to undertake long-haul, transoceanic service was Imperial Airways, formed in 1924 by the merger of four small companies, Handley Page Transport, Instone Air Line, Daimler Airway, and British Marine Air Navigation. Imperial's goal was not only to unite the British Empire through air travel, but also to carry mail throughout the empire. Imperial Airways flew a number of different craft on its routes. In the early years, it flew small Supermarine Sea Eagle craft of the biplane style, with two wings placed one above the other and a single engine in between, with the propeller facing the rear. Sea Eagles were about 37 feet long, with a single Rolls-Royce 350-horsepower engine capable of flying at 93 miles per hour for all of its 200-mile cruising range.

Imperial Airways eventually expanded its service to include routes from England to Egypt, Australia, India, Kenya, South Africa, and Hong Kong. By the late 1930's, Imperial was flying Short S-23 flying boats. These were known as C-class boats, and all had names beginning with the letter "C," such as Cabot, Clio, Canopus, Coorong, and Cambria. C-class boats were very large vessels with a take-off weight of nearly 40,000 pounds. They had four 910-horsepower engines, which gave them a top speed of almost 200 miles per hour over their 1,500-mile cruising range.

During this same period, another airline was establishing seaplane service in the United States also using flying boats. In 1927, Juan Terry Trippe merged a number of small airlines to create Pan American Airways, known as Pan Am. The airline flew primarily from the United States to points of call in Central and South America. When in 1928, the Foreign Air Mail Act, also known as the Kelly Act, began to allow U.S. commercial air carriers to be paid to carry United States mail overseas, Pan Am seized this opportunity to enlarge its fleet. The first vessels added were S-38 flying boats built by Sikorsky Aero Engineering Corporation.

As business expanded, Pan Am became America's "official" airline. Although the U.S. government did not have financial investments in any airline, it was able and willing to help Pan Am compete against foreign state-run airlines such as Air France or Lufthansa. By 1931, Pan American had added the larger S-40 series to their fleet. These were the first of the Pan Am "Clippers" and carried thirty-two passengers.

By 1932, the S-42 series of vessels had begun to appear, and Pan American was looking to fly not only North, Central, and South American routes but also transatlantic and transpacific routes. S-42 aircraft were powered by four

Boeing's 314A Clipper was one of the most famous seaplanes, carrying seventy-four passengers and a crew of ten. (Library of Congress)

700-horsepower Hornet radial engines and were capable of a 1,200-mile range. Although these craft turned out to be effective on the transatlantic run, they could not get all the way to Hawaii.

In 1935, the first of the real long-range flying boats were delivered to Pan Am for their Pacific service. The Martin 130 "China Clippers" were powered by four 950-horsepower Wasp engines, giving them a speed of 160 miles per hour and a cruising range of more than 4,000 miles. The first transpacific trip, from San Francisco, California, to Manila, the Philippines, took approximately 60 hours of flying.

By 1939, Pan Am had started to take delivery of the Boeing 314A, with a length of 106 feet, a wingspan of 152 feet, and a takeoff weight of 84,000 pounds. The four 1,600-horsepower Wright Cyclone engines could push the aircraft at 180 miles per hour for a cruising range of 3,700 miles. The first of these planes to fly was the "Dixie Clipper," capable of carrying seventy-four passengers and a crew of ten. The Boeing 314A did not have wingtip floats for stability but instead had sponsons on the lower portion of the hull.

Military Aviation

Imperial Airways and Pan American Airlines were not the only beneficiaries of the new types of flying boats. The militaries of numerous countries were also involved in the design and manufacture of a variety of seaplanes.

German manufacturers designed and built a number of aircraft during this period. The Heinkel and Blohn und Voss companies both designed float planes and flying boats for the German military. Another successful designer and manufacturer of flying boats was Dornier. The Wal was a workhorse for Lufthansa in the 1920's and 1930's. In 1929, the Dornier DO-X made its maiden voyage from Lake Constance in Switzerland. It was the largest craft ever built at the time, with a wingspan of 157 feet, a length of 131 feet, and a weight of 48 tons. It was powered over a 1,000-mile range by twelve 600-horsepower engines.

During this time both Italy and France produced a number of flying boats. Both the Italian Macchi company and the French Latecoere company produced a number of designs. British companies such as Felixstowe, Sea Eagle, Iris, and Short all produced a number of designs for the Royal Navy during this period. Short, in particular, produced the Sunderland series, 85-foot-long craft with a 112-foot wingspan. The four 1,050-horsepower engines pushed the vessel's 58,000-pound takeoff weight at 205 miles per hour over its 2,700-mile range.

In the United States, the Consolidated, Grumman, Sikorsky, Martin, and Boeing companies all contributed designs to the U.S. Navy's flying boat fleet. Some of these designs, such as the Martin Mariner (PBM-3D), were used primarily as submarine hunters because of their 2,400-mile range.

During World War II, more than six thousand flying boats and float planes were produced by the United States, Russia, England, and Germany. This is a very large number of aircraft, but of the total, 3,290 of those were of one series, the Consolidated PBY series. The PBY-5 became known as the Catalina. The Catalina was 63 feet long with a wingspan of 104 feet. The twin 1,200-horsepower Pratt & Whitney engines drove the 34,000-pound aircraft at 190 miles per hour over its 4,000-mile range. These were some of the most versatile aircraft built for military service. They served as submarine hunters, coastal patrols, mine layers, search-and-rescue craft, and personnel carriers. They were built in a number of nations throughout the war.

The war years marked the end of an era for flying boats. The development of a large number of long-range aircraft and the building of the large number of airfields with runways capable of handling these planes made most flying boats obsolete. Some navies, including that of the United States, continued to develop flying boat prototypes for a number of years, but none of these were deployed to the fleet.

Contemporary Uses of Seaplanes

There remain places in the world so remote and with so little infrastructure that they are still serviced by seaplanes such as the Grumman Widgeon. The Widgeon is small, with a 31-foot length, a 185-mile-per-hour top speed, and a 1,00-mile range.

More recently, flying boats have made a comeback of sorts. They are not used for passengers or freight. Instead they are used, with special scoops attached, as firefighting aircraft. These vessels swoop down low over a lake or other body of water and scoop up a large volume of water and then return to the fire site to drop their water "bomb" on the fire.

Robert J. Stewart

Bibliography

Conrade, Barnaby, III. *Pan Am: An Aviation Legend.* Emeryville, Calif.: Woodford Press, 1999. An excellent history of the long-lasting airline, with much material on the use of seaplanes and some outstanding photographs.

Munson, Kenneth. *Flying Boats and Seaplanes Since 1910*. New York: Macmillan, 1971. A history of seaplanes that includes the major manufacturers in both the United States and Europe, with well-done color drawings and cutaways.

Oliver, David. *Wings over Water: A Chronicle of Flying Boats and Amphibians of the Twentieth Century*. Edison, N.J.: Chartwell, 1999. A well-written history of seaplanes, with color photographs.

See also: Airplanes; Firefighting aircraft; Manufacturers; Military flight; Rescue aircraft

707 plane family

Definition: The dominant family of passenger planes made in the twentieth century.

Significance: The Boeing 707 was the first U.S. commercial jet airplane to be introduced. It was followed by eight more advanced airplanes, and by the end of the twentieth century the 707 family dominated the commercial jet aircraft market.

The Boeing 707 Family

The family of jet commercial transport planes developed by the Boeing Company began in 1952, when the company gambled nearly $16 million on a prototype airplane. It was a success and led to a family that grew to over eight thousand airplanes by the turn of the century. By the year 2000, about 65 percent of the world's commercial jets were members of the 707 family.

The first 707 was not a pioneer. The British Comet, built by the De Havilland Aircraft Company, blazed the trail of commercial jet travel. With a prototype built in 1949 and a first production plane in 1951, the Comet took advantage of the experiences learned by the aircraft industry during World War II. These experiences were not good enough, however. A series of disastrous crashes brought production of Comets to an end in the 1950's. Most of the Comet crashes were traced to design faults, especially with respect to the integrity of the fuselage covering.

The Comet crashes had damaged the public's and the airlines' confidence in jet travel and Boeing realized that it would have to reestablish that enthusiasm before being able to successfully introduce its 707. An extensive period of testing and publicity about safety eventually led to public acceptance, and soon jet travel became the mode of preference, especially for long-distance flights where the jet's extra speed was important to passengers. The 707 jets succeeded in cutting travel time approximately in half compared to even the fastest propeller planes, such as the Douglas DC-7, the last of the great prop planes.

By the year 2000, the 707 family had grown to nine different named models, most of which had several different versions. The evolution was driven by two considerations: the different requirements of short-range, medium-range, and long-range markets, and the need for improved performance in terms of load capacity, fuel efficiency, noise abatement, and passenger convenience.

The Dash 80

First conceived in 1952, the prototype of the 707 was completed in 1954 and had its first flight that summer. Nicknamed the "Dash 80," this plane was never sold by the company but was kept for demonstrations and various tests. It was eventually retired in 1972, when it was presented to the Smithsonian Air and Space Museum. It spent several years parked in Arizona and then was returned to the Boeing Company. In 2000, it was still to be seen on the tarmac at Boeing Field in Seattle, waiting for the construction of a new Museum of Flight facility to allow it to be on public display.

The Dash 80 still looks like a modern airplane. Its design formed the pattern that dominated the commercial aircraft industry for fifty years, a remarkable record. With its sweptback wings, sleek nose, and numerous small windows, its appearance was a hit with both passengers and airlines. Its performance was also impressive. It broke a long series of records for both speed and distance. In 1957, for instance, the Dash 80 flew from Seattle to Baltimore nonstop in just 4 hours and 48 minutes, with an average speed of 612 miles per hour. Its logbook records three thousand hours of flying, all of it for testing and demonstration.

The 707's

After the extensive and well-publicized test flights of the 707 prototype, the public and the world's airlines were ready for the first 707's to fly. Pan American World Airways, then one of the premier intercontinental carriers, ordered the 707 early and began its inaugural flights in 1958. Its first flight, between New York and Paris, was such a success that 707's were put into service by most large airlines as soon as the planes could be delivered. In the following year, Pan American introduced the first scheduled around-the-world jet service with its 707's, and the jet age had begun. The first 707 model, called the 707-120, was an excellent plane for medium to long flights, but with a range of only about 4,000 miles, it was considered better for transcontinental flights than for intercontinental. In the late 1950's, 707's were scheduled by several airlines for coast-to-coast service. For the Los Angeles-to-New York route, for example, 707's could cut travel time from more than ten hours to only about five hours. Their use for longer distance travel, however, was restricted by their limited range, which necessitated intermediate stops for such flights as from San Francisco to Tokyo.

In response to this special need, Boeing developed a longer-distance model of the 707 called the 707-320 series, popularly known as the 707 Intercontinental. With a range of 6,000 miles, a larger fuselage, and more powerful engines, the Intercontinental quickly became the most commonly used airplane for long flights, especially transoceanic ones. Many national airlines of the Western world adopted the Intercontinental for its longer flights, and its familiar sleek outline was graced by the insignias of dozens of airlines, such as Air France, Lufthansa, BOAC (later renamed British Airlines), and Qantas.

It was almost impossible to fly in a 707 at the beginning of the twenty-first century. Most of them have been retired or converted to freighters. An example of an especially long-lived 707 is the plane that was used by Air Zimbabwe until well into the 1990's. It was a favorite of tourists to Victoria Falls until it was replaced by newer Boeing airplanes.

The 720

The 1960's saw the Boeing 707 and its Douglas rival, the DC-8, take over most of the long-distance air routes of the Western world. Shorter routes, however, still saw smaller planes in common use, especially because the 707 had a large capacity and required a long runway. For that reason, a new model of the 707 was introduced that was somewhat smaller and that was efficient for use on medium-range flights. Called the 720, it had essentially the same design as the 707 and offered passengers the same comfort and speed as its larger sibling.

The 720 was used, for instance, for the north-south routes along the West Coast by Western Airlines, where its characteristics were well matched to the needs.

The 727

The popularity of the 707 and its similarly sized competitors, the Douglas DC-8 and the Convair 880, demonstrated passenger preference for jet travel. However, these big planes demanded long runways and large airports. In spite of attempts to expand airport facilities rapidly, most commercial airports were just too small to handle the jets. In response to this problem, the 727, a smaller, three-engine jet, was developed. With newly designed wing flaps, the 727 could take off remarkably steeply and could land slowly, fitting onto smaller runways. The first 727 was put into service in 1964 by United Air Lines, which flew that one plane continuously for twenty-seven years. The last 727 was built in 1984, at which time 727's were being used by nearly one hundred different air carriers and were carrying 150 million passengers per year. Near their peak in 1995, the 727's had flown over four billion passengers on short-to medium-range commercial flights.

As wide as the 707, the 727 began as a much shorter and lighter airplane. Early models had a gross weight of 170,000 pounds, which increased to 210,000 pounds for the later versions. The cabins were roomy and, with the engines behind almost all passenger seats, the interior was relatively quiet, both features that helped the plane's popularity. A total of 1,832 of the 727's were built.

Although the 727 had several variants, there were only two main models, the 727-100 series and the 727-200 series. Included was a convertible version that could carry passengers, freight, or a combination of the two. The 727-200F, for instance, carries nearly 60,000 pounds of freight. As the 727's aged, many were converted to freighters, carrying considerable amounts of mail and express packages.

The 737

By the end of the twentieth century, the Boeing 737 had become the most popular commercial airplane of all time. It had been delivered to airlines throughout the world, including Eastern Europe and Asia, which previously had not been notable customers of American airplane companies. By the year 2000, this airplane had carried over six billion passengers, equivalent to the total population of the world.

The 737 started as the "little cousin" of the 727, intended for shorter flights and even smaller airports. The first planes were delivered in 1967 to Lufthansa, and thirty-five years later, the 737 was still being built and delivered to airlines over the world. As in the case of the 727, Boeing used high-lift devices to provide steep takeoffs and slow landings, making the 737 a particularly versatile plane as far as runways were concerned. It had two wing-mounted engines and thus used less fuel than three- or four-engine planes. It soon became the workhorse of many commercial airlines, making frequent and fuel-efficient short hops to serve a wide range of communities.

As an example of the common use of 737's, Aloha Airlines of Hawaii has an all-737 fleet, most of which are devoted to the short (less than an hour) trips between the islands. In the year 2000, Aloha 737's flew more than one thousand flights per week, carrying about five million passengers in the year.

As of 2001, there were nine different models of the 737. The first, the 737-100, carries ninety-nine passengers when used as a one-class airplane, with six-abreast seating and a central aisle. It has an 87-foot wingspan and a fuselage only 95 feet long, giving it a squarish appearance. Each engine can develop 14,000 pounds of thrust for a maximum takeoff weight of 110,000 pounds. Its cruising speed at 35,000 feet is 575 miles per hour and its range is 2,160 miles, although it is primarily used for much shorter flights.

Responding to airline requests, Boeing soon introduced the 737-200 series, with a fuselage that is 6 feet longer than that of the 737-100 and a carrying capacity of 124 passengers when used as a one-class airplane. This series was followed by the 737-300, which was longer yet and had a wingspan of 95 feet. Its range is 2,595 miles. Improvements in fuel efficiency, noise abatement, and speed led to the introduction of the 400 and 500 series, and then Boeing made several additional design changes and introduced the Next Generation 737's, the 600 to 900 series. The 737-900, introduced in 2001, can carry 189 passengers, almost twice as many as the 737-100. The plane, originally designed for short-haul flights, was by 2001 being used for transoceanic flights, as between California and the Hawaiian Islands. It has a 274,200-pound takeoff weight and a range of 3,160 miles. In wingspan and fuselage length, the 900 is about 30 feet bigger than the 100.

The 747

In the mid-1960's, the aircraft industry realized that the potential of commercial jet transport included scales of plane size and capacity that would be vastly different from past experience. Pan American World Airways conceived of planes that could carry at least twice as many passengers as the 707 and could travel nonstop over twice the distance. Working with Boeing engineers, Pan Am promoted the idea of the "superjet." It took nearly five years to bring that idea to fruition.

Under the leadership of chief engineer Joseph Sutter, Boeing designers put together a plan for an airplane that could carry over four hundred passengers and that could fly nonstop for more than 5,000 miles. To ensure the building of such a revolutionary new craft, Pan Am ordered twenty-five of them in 1966. As no existing facility could hold such a giant airplane, Boeing had to build an entire new plant, choosing a site north of Seattle near the small city of Everett, Washington. This plant was said to be the largest building in the world.

The first superjet, named the 747-100, was completed in 1968. It was first shown to the aviation world at the Paris Air Show in 1969. This plane, named the *City of Everett*, is still in service, being used by the company for various tests of new equipment, and is destined for the Museum of Flight in Seattle, Washington. The characteristic look of the 747, with its forward hump, was the result of a two-deck design in which the cockpit and a passenger cabin were located above the main floor. This idea was not entirely new; Boeing's pre-jet-era passenger plane, the Stratocruiser, had two decks, incorporating a lower passenger deck, usually used as a passenger lounge, below the main cabin.

The first commercial flight of the 747 occurred in January, 1970, when Pan American flew its first 747 nonstop from New York to London. In the next thirty years, over 1,200 747 superjets were built, flying 33 billion miles in airline service. Most were delivered to non-U.S. airlines for service on long-range international flights. By the year 2000, over 2.2 billion passengers had flown on 747's.

Four different versions of the 747 were developed in the first thirty years, called versions 100, 200, 300, and 400. Each of these included various special versions, such as freighters, combis carrying both freight and passengers, and convertibles, which allowed airlines to convert from freight to passengers depending on needs such as seasonal demands. The freighters were given hinged noses to allow large objects to be loaded easily. Each version incorporated new features, including increased capacity, better fuel efficiency, and more modern (digital) avionics. For example, the 747-300, introduced in 1982, added about forty-four passenger seats by having an extended upper deck.

The 747-400 has a wingspan of 211 feet and a length of 232 feet, making it about as large a plane as airports can handle. Its tail rises above the tarmac as high as a six-story building. The interior of the cabin is 20 feet wide, making room for ten economy class seats abreast. In a two-class configuration, the 747-400 can carry 524 passengers over a range of 8,430 miles. Each of its four engines develops about 63,000 pounds of thrust so that it can take off with a gross weight of nearly one million pounds.

The 757

The Boeing 757 is a medium-range airplane that was designed to take the place of older jets, such as the 727, by providing a plane that could serve airline hubs efficiently, being capable of flying either short or medium-range flights. It has two engines and a single-aisle interior, with six-abreast seating in the main cabin. With a larger capacity than the 727 (it can carry 239 passengers in a two-class configuration), its improved aerodynamical design and high-bypass-ratio engines mean a quieter aircraft and a fuel savings of about 40 percent per seat.

The cockpit is fully digital, with a flight management control system that provides automatic control and guidance of the plane from just after takeoff to final approach. This system is designed for maximum efficiency, taking into account all flight and aircraft conditions en route. The cockpit design is the same as that of the 767, so that pilots certified for one can fly the other.

By the end of 2000, more than one thousand of the 757's had been built. Included was a freighter version that had no passenger windows or doors, but instead a large cargo door on the starboard side of the cabin.

The 767

In 1978, United Air Lines expressed the need for a modern wide-body jet that would be highly fuel-efficient for long-distance flights but smaller than the 747 when it ordered thirty of the not-yet-built Boeing 767 airplanes. The first 767 was finished in 1981. It had longer, thicker, and less swept-back wings compared to earlier jets, and it introduced a new feature, raked wingtips, all of which increased the plane's flying efficiency. With two aisles, it could accommodate seven-abreast seating in economy class, with a passenger count in the two hundred to three hundred range, depending on seating arrangements. The 767 became popular for intercontinental flights, as it was approved for two-engine flights that would take it as far as three hours from the nearest runway. In the year 2000, the 767 was the most common airplane flying the busy North Atlantic route, outnumbering all other jets combined.

In 2001, there were three 767 models: the 200, 300, and 400 series. The 200 is 159 feet long, the 300 is 21 feet longer, and the 400 has an overall length of 201 feet. Combined, more than eight hundred of the three models had been built by 2001.

The 777

During the final decades of the twentieth century, the airplane industry's emphasis turned to issues of efficiency and passenger comfort. Manufacturers worked to develop more spacious cabins, more fuel-efficient engines, and more lightweight construction materials. At the same time, computers were extensively employed to control both operations and performance monitoring, while modern communication and navigation systems were installed as well. The Boeing 777 became that company's best example of a plane ready for the twenty-first century. There are five different models of the 777, a two-engine plane that was intended to bridge the gap between the 747 and the 767. The first, the 777-200, was certified in 1995. It has a passenger capacity of four hundred in a two-class configuration. Its two-aisle cabin is designed to give passengers more room than earlier jets. There is built-in flexibility in the cabin: lavatories, overhead storage units, and galleys can be moved readily when configuration changes are needed.

The 777-200 is a large plane. Its wingspan is a full 200 feet and its length is 209 feet. It has a maximum takeoff weight of 545,000 pounds and a maximum range of 5,600 statute miles, allowing it to fly, for example, from San Francisco to Tokyo nonstop. There is an extended-range model that has the capability to fly almost 8,500 statute miles. The 777 was certified to fly as far as three hours from the nearest airport.

The 777-300 model was introduced by Cathay Pacific Airways in 1998. It is thirty-three feet longer than the 777-200 and can carry 479 passengers in a two-class configuration. Its range is 6,600 statute miles. Two new models, the Longer Range 777-200 and 777-300, will be introduced in 2003. The LR777-200 will have a range of 9,750 statute miles, the longest distance that any two-engine passenger plane can fly nonstop.

The 717

Not originally part of the 707 family, the Boeing 717's ancestor was the popular Douglas DC-9, a fuselage-mounted twin-engine jet designed for short- and medium-range flights. Completely redesigned by Douglas's successor, McDonnell Douglas, in 1995, the plane was first called the MD-95. When Boeing merged with McDonnell Douglas in 1997, the plane's name was changed to the Boeing 717. It has a usual capacity of 106 seats and a range of 1,500 statute miles.

Paul Hodge

Bibliography

Bowers, P. *Boeing Aircraft Since 1916*. 2d ed. Columbus, Ohio: Funk and Wagnalls, 1993. A comprehensive description of Boeing planes, starting with the mail plane built in Boeing's boathouse in 1916 and including both military and civilian airplanes.

Norris, Guy, and Mark Wagner. *Modern Boeing Jetliners*. Osceola, Wis.: Motorbooks International, 1999. With an emphasis on the later 700 series of planes, this thorough book includes rare photos of the production of the planes as well as good illustrations of the finished products. The BWB (Blended Wing Body) design is included.

Redding, R., and B. Yenne. *Boeing, Planemaker to the World*. 2d ed. San Diego, Calif.: Thunder Bay Press, 1997. A very well-illustrated history of the company with an emphasis on airplanes, but including also helicopters, hydrofoils and Boeing's aerospace products.

See also: Airplanes; Boeing; Jet engines; Jumbojets; Manufacturers; Tail designs; Wing designs

Alan Shepard

Date: Born on November 18, 1923, in East Derry, New Hampshire; died on July 21, 1998, in Monterey, California
Definition: The first American astronaut to fly in space.
Significance: Shepard flew the first U.S. manned space flight in 1961 and became the only Mercury astronaut to walk on the Moon.

Alan Bartlett Shephard, Jr., was born to Colonel Alan B. Shepard and his wife in East Derry, New Hampshire. He graduated from Pinkerton Academy in Derry and spent a year studying at Admiral Farragut Academy in Toms River, New Jersey, prior to his acceptance into the United States Naval Academy.

Shepard pursued flight training after World War II, earning his wings in 1947. Completing U.S. Naval Test Pilot School training in 1950, he remained at the school, participating in high-altitude research, flight operations development for a naval in-flight refueling system, F2-H3 Banshee testing for carrier deployment, and angled carrier-deck development.

After two tours of duty in the Pacific aboard the USS *Oriskany*, Shepard returned to the Naval Test Pilot School to fly F-3H Demon, F-8U Crusader, F-4D Skyray, F-11F Tiger, and F-5D Skylancer aircraft. Shepard achieved instructor status there, but five months later entered the Naval War College in Newport, Rhode Island, graduating in 1958.

After the National Aeronautics and Space Administration (NASA) began screening military files for potential astronauts, Shepard's test-pilot career singled him out as a prime candidate. In April, 1959, Shepard was one of the seven astronauts selected for Project Mercury. The Mercury astronauts worked cooperatively on all aspects of Project Mercury but competed for flight assignments. In 1960, NASA picked Shepard, John Glenn, and Virgil "Gus" Grissom to train for a suborbital Mercury-Redstone mission.

Alan Shepard undergoes a flight simulation test preparatory to his Mercury flight in 1961. (NASA)

Although the Soviets had beaten the Americans into space by launching Yuri Gagarin into orbit on April 12, 1961, NASA moved forward with Project Mercury. Shepard lifted off on May 5, 1961, inside his *Freedom 7* spacecraft strapped atop a Redstone missile. Shepard was exposed to high g forces and five minutes of weightlessness. The spacecraft achieved a 116-mile altitude before splashing down in the Atlantic 302 miles from Cape Canaveral.

Three years later, Shepard was grounded by Meniere's syndrome, an inner-ear condition capable of inducing nausea, ringing ears, and vestibular disturbances. He was reassigned to Astronaut Office management. In 1969, Shepard underwent surgery that corrected his condition, and, within six months, he had gained command of Apollo 14.

The Apollo 14 mission launched on January 31, 1971, with Shepard, Stuart Roosa, and Edgar Mitchell. Shepard and Mitchell touched down Lunar Module *Antares* in the Fra Mauro region, deployed scientific instruments on the lunar surface, and collected samples during two moonwalks. Shepard hit two golf balls before leaving the surface. After 33 hours, Shepard and Mitchell lifted off the Moon to rejoin Roosa. Apollo 14 splashed down in the Pacific on February 9.

In 1974, Shepard retired from the Navy and NASA. He enjoyed subsequent success in the business world, helping found the Astronaut Scholarship Foundation. Diagnosed with leukemia in 1997, Shepard valiantly fought the disease and expected to join the other surviving Mercury astronauts to witness their colleague Glenn fly aboard space shuttle *Discovery* in late 1998. However, Shepard's condition worsened, and Shephard died on July 21, 1998, three months before Glenn's mission.

David G. Fisher

Bibliography

Carpenter, Scott M., et. al. *We Seven*. New York: Simon & Schuster, 1962. Describes Project Mercury from the viewpoint of the astronauts.

Shepard, Alan, and Deke Slayton, with Jay Barbree and Howard Benedict. *Moon Shot: The Inside Story of America's Race to the Moon*. Atlanta: Turner, 1994. A history of NASA's race for the Moon from two astronauts' viewpoints.

Slayton, Donald K., and Michael Cassutt. *Deke! U.S. Manned Space: From Mercury to the Shuttle*. New York: Forge, 1994. A chronicle of the early days of the space program, written by an astronaut involved with selection and training of crews.

See also: Apollo Program; Crewed spaceflight; Yuri Gagarin; John Glenn; Mercury project; National Aeronautics and Space Administration; Navy pilots, U.S.; Spaceflight; Test pilots

Igor Sikorsky

Date: Born on May 25, 1889, in Kiev, Russia; died on October 26, 1972, in Easton, Connecticut
Definition: Russian-American aeronautical engineer, aircraft manufacturer, and inventor best known for developing the helicopter.
Significance: Sikorsky's introduction of controlled-pitch rotor blades was instrumental to the development of the modern helicopter.

Igor Sikorsky was born in 1889 to educated parents who were both physicians, although his mother did not practice professionally. His formal training began in 1903, when he enrolled at the Russian Naval Academy in St. Petersburg. His interest in education led him to leave the service in 1906 and to enroll at the Polytechnic Institute in Kiev. At the age of twenty, Sikorsky built his first helicopter, which would not leave the ground. In 1911, he set a record by flying for thirty minutes at 70 miles per hour in the S-5, a plane he had designed himself. In 1913, at the request of the Russian Army, he designed and built the world's first four-engine, dual-controlled airplane, which served as a bomber in World War I.

A strong anti-Bolshevist, Sikorsky left Russia after the Revolution of 1917 and made his home in the United States. He became a U.S. citizen in 1928. He originally joined in business with a group of Russian immigrants building airplanes, but the business failed. In 1923, he started over, forming the Sikorsky Aero Engineering Corporation, which built "flying boats" for Pan American's transoceanic flights and fifty-six "aerial yachts" for wealthy clients. After the stock market crash of October, 1929, his once-wealthy clients could no longer meet their payments, ending his independent company, which became a division of the United Aircraft Corporation. Sikorsky continued to head the division until his retirement.

In 1939, Sikorsky developed the VS-300, the first helicopter with controlled-pitch blades. This innovation turned out to be instrumental in making helicopters practical. Although early helicopter models were used in World War II after 1944, they came of age during the 1950's. Sikorsky also designed a patrol bomber, known as the Flying Dreadnought, for the U.S. Air Force's use in World War II. Sikorsky continued to be a vital part of the company even after his 1957 retirement at the age of 68. He consulted on design and on business matters and was at his desk the day before his death at 83 years of age.

Kenneth H. Brown

Bibliography

Cochrane, Dorothy. *The Aviation Careers of Igor Sikorsky*. Seattle: University of Washington Press, 1989. Follows Sikorsky's development through his varied roles in the aircraft industry.

Delear, Frank J. *Igor Sikorsky: Three Careers in Aviation*. New York: Bantam, 1992. A biography that focuses on the place Sikorsky holds in the early development of aircraft.

Sikorsky, Igor. *Story of the Winger-S*. Reprint. Temecula, Calif.: Reprint Services, 1995. Sikorsky's autobiography, written in 1938, which chronicles his development as an aircraft designer and builder.

Singapore Airlines

Also known as: Singapore International Airlines, Malayan Airways
Date: Founded in 1947 as Malayan Airways
Definition: A major international airline and the national flag carrier of Singapore.
Significance: Singapore Airlines is internationally recognized as one of the world's leading carriers. The company has achieved record growth and financial health through careful planning and management.

History

Singapore International Airlines is a major international airline headquartered in Singapore. It is owned by the state of Singapore (54 percent) and private investors (46 percent). Singapore Airlines was formerly known as Malayan Airways. Malayan Airways was founded in May, 1947, at which time it first operated a twin-engine Airspeed Consul between Singapore, Kuala Lumpur, Ipoh, and Penang. As passenger demand grew, so did the airline. By 1955, the airline had a fleet of Douglas DC-3's. The creation of the Federation of Malaysia in 1963 prompted two name changes for the airline, first to Malaysian Airways and then, three years later, to Malaysia-Singapore Airlines (MSA). The second name change was in deference to the carrier's joint shareholders, the governments of Malaysia and Singapore.

MSA came to an end in October, 1972, giving birth to two new airlines: Malaysia Airline System (now called Malaysia Airlines), headquartered in Kuala Lumpur, and Singapore Airlines, headquartered in Singapore. In 1972, Singapore Airlines operated a fleet of ten aircraft and commanded a route network that covered twenty-two cities in eighteen countries. It began immediately to modernize its fleet of aircraft and improve customer service standards for its customers. By 2001, the airline was internationally recognized as one of the world's leading carriers, frequently wining customer service awards in international competitions. The route network spans over ninety cities in more than forty countries. The company has pioneered some of the flight service amenities that have become standard throughout the industry, such as complimentary headsets and free drinks, and their amenities are some of the best available, such as their revolutionary interactive entertainment system.

Fleet

In 2001, Singapore Airlines operated an all-wide-body fleet of modern aircraft. It is the world's largest operator of Boeing 747-400 aircraft. It also operates the Airbus A340-300E and has placed firm orders for the A340-500, the Airbus A310-300, and Boeing 777-200 and 300. Singapore Airlines has placed firm orders with Airbus and has taken options on the Airbus A380-800 double-deck super transporter. Silk Air, a wholly owned subsidiary of Singapore Airlines also based in Singapore, operates a fleet of Boeing 737's. Silk Air has an extensive regional network to some of Southeast Asia's resorts and lower-load-factor cities. Other subsidiaries of Singapore Airlines include SIA Engineering Company and Singapore Airport Terminal Services.

Alliances

Singapore Airlines has been a member of the Star Alliance since 1999. Lufthansa, along with Air Canada, SAS, Thai Airways International, and United Air Lines founded the Star Alliance in 1997. In subsequent years, membership grew to include Air New Zealand, ANA, Ansett Australia, Austrian Airlines, British Midland, Lauda Air, Mexicana Airlines, Tyrolean Airways, and Varig Brazil. As of 2001, the Star Alliance encompassed fifteen airlines and a network of 130 countries and 815 destinations, making it the world's largest airline alliance.

Safety

Singapore Airlines and its subsidiary, Silk Air, have had one hijacking, which took place in 1991, as well as two significant accidents. On December 20, 1997, Silk Air Flight MI185, a jetliner heading from Jakarta to Singapore, crashed outside the southern Sumatran city of Palembang. On board the Boeing 737-300 were ninety-seven passengers and seven crew, all of whom died. The reason for the crash remained unclear for a long time as there was apparently nothing wrong with the aircraft, the weather was clear, and the aircraft crashed while in cruise, without reporting anything out of the ordinary. After more than a year of investigation, it was concluded that the plane had crashed as a result of "unlawful interference," possibly a murder-suicide on the part of the captain.

Singapore Airlines Flight SQ006, carrying 159 passen-

> ### Events in Singapore Airlines History
>
> **1947:** Singapore Airlines' predecessor, Malayan Airways, flies between Singapore and the Malayan cities of Kuala Lumpur, Ipoh, and Penang.
> **1955:** The airline develops a fleet of DC-3 aircraft.
> **1963:** In response to national political changes, Malayan Airways is renamed Malaysian Airways.
> **1966:** The airline's name is again changed, to Malaysia-Singapore Airlines (MSA) to reflect its governmental owners.
> **1972:** After MSA ceases operations, Malaysia Airlines and Singapore Airlines continue as individual national flag carriers.

gers, crashed soon after takeoff at Taipei's Chiang Kai Shek Airport, on October 31, 2000. Taiwanese authorities investigating the crash released a factual data report concluding that airport officials had not properly marked a closed runway. The Singapore Airlines jumbojet mistakenly tried to use the closed runway and slammed into construction debris, bursting into flames and killing eighty-three people. In addition, one runway light was broken and another was not bright enough when the Los Angeles-bound plane tried to take off during a fierce rainstorm caused by an approaching typhoon. The captain's decision to continue with the takeoff despite the weather and his commencing the takeoff on the wrong runway were contributing factors to the accident.

Triantafyllos G. Flouris

Bibliography

Groenewege, Adrianus D. *The Compendium of International Civil Aviation.* 2d ed. Geneva, Switzerland: International Air Transport Association, 1999. A comprehensive directory of the major players in international civil aviation, with insightful and detailed articles.

Weimer, Kent J. ed. *Aviation Week and Space Technology: World Aviation Directory.* New York: McGraw-Hill, 2000. An excellent introductory guide on all global companies involved in the aviation business. The information is very basic but very essential as a first introduction to each company.

See also: Accident investigation; Air carriers; Lufthansa; Safety issues

Skydiving

Definition: Recreational and competitive sport parachuting, which arose from early twentieth century barnstorming and military parachuting. Skydivers jump from aircraft, high buildings, or cliffs, or are towed by speedboats

Significance: Skydiving is excellent recreation, lowering tension and providing good exercise. It is also a highly appreciated spectator sport.

Parachuting, originally conceptualized in the fifteenth century by Leonardo da Vinci, became skydiving (or sport parachuting) using steerable parachutes about five centuries later. The first parachute was developed in the eighteenth century by Louis-Sébastien Lenormand. It was a canopy, strengthened at the edge and using rigging to hold an underslung passenger basket. It was tested with animal passengers. At the end of that century the first human parachutist, André-Jacques Garnerin, used a modified Lenormand chute. Nineteenth century barnstorming parachutists used Garnerin's modified chutes to parachute from balloons. To hone the thrills for spectators, folded and packaged canopies were developed. An outstanding chute was the Broadwick coat pack, worn attached to jackets and held to balloons by static lines designed so that, as parachutists fell, their weight pulled against the line and caused the canopy to open.

In 1912, in Ohio, the first aircraft parachute jump—from 1,500 feet—was made by Captain Albert Berry. High aviator mortality in World War I led Leslie Irvin and Floyd Smith to design a parachute escape system for the U.S. Air Force. Because aircraft that were falling out of control were unsuitable platforms for static-line systems, Smith and Irvin built free-fall packs with ripcords that let pilots control the chute opening. By the end of World War II, 100,000 aviators had been saved by parachutes, and paratroopers were routinely sent into battle.

Basics of Sport Parachuting

In the 1950's, parachute modifications led to steerable chute canopies and people began to parachute for fun. Soon, changes in chute shape allowed good horizontal movement, fine motion control, and soft, precise landings. In 1954, "blank gore" modification removed a panel (gore) from the hemispherical parachute canopy and used escaping air to provide some thrust and direction via pulled steering lines attached to the gore bottom. Then, placing L-shaped slots in the rear of the canopy increased ability to "hold" the wind.

In 1961, Pierre Lemoigne designed the first really steerable parachute, leading to ram-air chutes, inflatable flying wings which hugely increase canopy control. They are rectangular, and inflation of their double surfaces (skins) produces the wing shape. Control is obtained by means of low-porosity canopy material; devices enabling the maximum use of canopy air; steering toggles to turn, brake, and control descent rate; and useful shroud-canopy connection systems at the front and rear of the chute. Overall venting arrangements of sport parachutes thus allow skydivers to fine-tune their descents after the canopy opens.

In skydiving, a jump is usually made from a slow-moving plane flying at altitudes from 10,000 to 12,000 feet. "Free fall" is sustained down to 2,000 to 2,500 feet above the ground before opening the parachute. Free-fall maneuvers are accomplished by controlling body position.

Skydiving events include jumping for style, landing accurately, and performing in teams. Early contests in the 1930's involved only accuracy in landing on a target. The first world championship in skydiving was in Yugoslavia in 1951. It involved contestants from five countries. After this event, world championship contests were scheduled every two years, under the auspices of the Fédération Aéronautique Internationale (FAI). Currently, thirty-five countries participate in world championship contests. The U.S. Federal Aviation Administration (FAA) regulates all skydiving in U.S. competitions. Governance is by the International Parachuting Committee of the FAI, as represented by the U.S. Parachute Association. American competitive skydiving events occur every year.

In jumping for style, the parachutists are required to perform their stunts (called aerobatic maneuvers), such as back turns, in the shortest time possible during free fall, and are judged on their aerobatic form, not on landing site. In accuracy jumping events, competing parachutists seek to land as close as possible to the center of a circular target, set on the ground. In team events, members perform maneuvers such as baton passing or forming circles or other geometric figures (all called "relative work"). Each competing team attempts to form the largest number of patterns in the time available to them. In "canopy relative work," team members link together and perform figures after their parachutes have opened.

In all competition jumping, the sport parachute is opened at an altitude designated by FAI judges. The way in which contestants leave the delivery aircraft is likewise predetermined. In most recreational skydiving, jumpers carry an altimeter, which indicates rate of descent and tells them when to open the chute. Two new forms of sport parachuting are BASE (an acronym for building, antennae, span, Earth) and parasailing. In BASE jumping, the parachutist leaps from a very high structure such as a building or a cliff. In parasailing, the parachute is linked to and towed by a long line attached to a moving speedboat. The boat's forward motion both lifts and tows the parachutist.

Sport Parachute Construction and Use

A skydiving parachute is manually opened with a ripcord after free fall, and the jumper rides it down to the ground. Each parachute is contained inside a knapsacklike harness container (a rig). In addition to the rig, other equipment includes altimeters, jumpsuits, helmets, and goggles. Most parachutes used are ram-air chutes, named for the way in which they open and fly. The first commercial ram-air canopies, developed in the 1970's, and more modern canopies use the same flight theory. The canopy leaves the rig and the weight of the jumper causes it to inflate into a shape resembling an aircraft wing or airfoil. The canopy holds its airfoil shape because of two-skin (two-layer) construction, with the top and bottom skins joined at the rear (trailing edge) and ends.

The front, the parachute's leading edge, is open to the air. The canopy is divided into pockets or cells. Suspension lines between the skydiver and the canopy are shorter at the leading edge than at the trailing edge, causing the airfoil to tilt forward and move downward. Air is thus rammed into the cells and, as the jumper and chute move forward, the leading edge divides the air it meets so that air moves over the top skin faster than the air flowing under the lower parachute skin. This leads to lower pressure on the top surface than the bottom and creates lift force, the mechanics that create flight. The canopy flies enough to make descent to the ground relatively slow. However, the lift is not large enough to allow for ascent.

Canopy materials have changed frequently during the history of skydiving. Early canopies, later modified for sport parachute use, were made of silk. This gave them a small rig volume compared to the cotton or linen used by nineteenth century parachutists, while providing the strength and elasticity needed for fast opening. Silk was replaced with more durable and damp-resistant nylon soon after nylon was discovered in the 1930's. Most nylon in contemporary skydiving is the "ripstop" used in many garments. Ripstop resists tears because it is woven as many tiny squares, so that damage in any single square is contained within it. Shrouds (lines) that attach the jumper to the canopy need to combine strength and elasticity. Dacron, Kevlar, and zero-porosity (ZP) nylon are used to increase strength and reduce total rig weight for skydiver comfort. The greater the canopy porosity, the faster air passes through and the faster the chute falls. Use of ZP nylon slows fall by allowing little air through the canopy.

Vertical (straight-ahead) ram-air flight is achieved by means of steering toggles situated above the chutist's right and left shoulders, into which the hands are inserted. The toggles connect to shrouds (suspension lines) in the canopy's trailing edge and act like ailerons. Equal downward pull on both toggles distorts the trailing edge to slow the canopy's vertical movement and descent rate, if the pull is not too radical. If, however, both toggles are depressed to waist level, full braking occurs, airspeed becomes negligible, and descent rate increases as the canopy loses its ability for lift. Turning a chute also uses the steering toggles.

With one toggle depressed and the other unmoved, a full turn is produced in the direction of pull because the side of the canopy that is pulled slows down while the other side remains flying at speed. To land, a sport parachutist faces into the wind because opposing airflow slows the parachute somewhat, making it easier to land on one's feet. However, it does not affect descent rate, and this must be reduced if a hard landing is to be avoided. In order to slow descent rate and forward speed, a parachutist identifies the wind direction and turns directly into the wind by smoothly and quickly pulling down both toggles. This converts the canopy's forward speed, for an instant, to lift, during which time the sport parachutist steps down onto the ground. Maneuvering is complex and takes practice. However, student skydivers usually have the basics down after four to six hours of individual instruction.

Sanford S. Singer

Gravitation, Gravity, and Parachutists

Gravity is the force of attraction Earth exerts upon objects on or near it. Gravitation is one of the four basic forces that control the interactions of matter. The law of gravitation was formulated by the English physicist Sir Isaac Newton in 1684. Newton's law states that the gravitational attraction between two bodies is proportional to the product of the masses of the bodies ($mass_1 \times mass_2$) and it is inversely proportional to the distance between them. The force of gravitation is tiny. For example, between two spherical objects each of mass 1,000 grams and separated by 1 meter, the gravitational force is only 3.3 millionths of a gram. (For these purposes, the terms mass and weight have equivalent meanings.)

The force of gravity, measured as the amount of acceleration that the force of gravitation gives to an object falling to Earth's surface, is 9.8 meters (32 feet) per second squared. Thus, neglecting air resistance, a body falling freely toward Earth's surface increases its speed of fall at a rate of about .5 mile per minute squared. It is this deadly acceleration due to gravity that a parachute counters. The parachute canopy uses the pressure difference across it to maintain the necessary inflated parachute shape for this purpose. The pressure difference is caused by a mass of air trapped inside the canopy and the movement of the air outside of the canopy. The shape of the parachute causes it to experience tension forces only. Hence, the very strong fabric (such as nylon) of which parachutes are made maintains parachute integrity during use.

Bibliography

Barrett, Norman S., and Simon Ward. *Skydiving*. London: Watts, 1987. A nice book on skydiving from the European point of view.

Donaldson, Chris. *Skydive: Sport Parachuting Explained*. Marlborough, England: Crowood Press, 2000. Describes the sport of skydiving, its history, equipment, training, and advanced skills, with a useful glossary and many illustrations.

Greenwood, Jim. *Parachuting for Sport*. Blue Ridge Summit, Pa.: Tab Books, 1978. Describes the evolution of parachuting from its beginnings until well into the development of skydiving.

Meeks, Christopher. *Skydiving*. Mankato, Minn.: Capstone Press, 1991. A solid, well-illustrated book covering many aspects of skydiving.

Poynter, Dan. *Parachuting: The Skydivers's Handbook*. 8th ed. Santa Barbara, Calif.: Parachuting Publications, 2000. A thorough handbook on parachutes, parachuting, and skydiving.

See also: Air shows; Barnstorming; Parachutes; Wingwalking

Skywriting

Definition: An aviation technique in which an oil-based liquid is added to an airplane's exhaust system, creating words or images with the resulting bright white smoke against a clear blue sky.

Significance: In the days before television, advertisers used skywriting to promote their products to a wider audience. Skilled pilots created mile-high messages against a clear blue sky over racetracks, fairgrounds, and any other place where a large number of people were expected to gather.

History

British war pilot J. C. Savage was the first to write an aerial message in the skies over England, in 1922. In the fall of that year, Captain Allen J. Cameron brought skywriting to the United States when he wrote "Hello U.S.A." in the sky over New York City. An advertising executive for the American Tobacco Company saw the message and signed Cameron to a $1,000-per-day contract to promote the cigarette company.

A skywriter leaves a reminder of the holiday, Valentine's Day, above downtown Los Angeles, California. Skywriters use a special paraffin-based additive in their exhaust to create long-lasting smokelike letters or shapes in the sky. (AP/Wide World Photos)

Since the early days of aviation, one of skywriting's biggest advertising advantages has continued to be the attention it attracts. After people on the ground see a skywriting message begin to form, they are driven by curiosity to stop and watch. Advertisers hire skywriters to create messages over beaches, fairgrounds, racetracks, and anywhere else they are guaranteed a large audience for their messages.

Method

In skywriting, both timing and planning are crucial. Paraffin or some other nonpolluting oil-based fluid is vaporized in the 1,500-degree heat of the aircraft engine to create white smoke, which is then discharged under pressure. Letters are drawn at slightly different altitudes, which allows pilots to see what they have already drawn as they proceed. This method also allows pilots to complete their message without disrupting the letters already in place. Pilots will often use roads or railroad tracks to ensure that their skywriting follows a straight line. Letters average 1 mile high, and, on a clear day, they can be seen from a distance of up to 30 miles away. Depending on the weather conditions, skywriting messages will remain in the sky for up to twenty minutes.

Skywriting is performed at altitudes ranging from 7,000 to 17,000 feet, depending on temperature. On warm days, skywriting must be done at higher altitudes, because the temperature drops 3.5 degrees for every 1,000 feet of altitude. Each letter takes approximately twenty seconds to create. Skywriting works best in a cloudless sky with no more than a moderate wind.

A modern version of skywriting is called skytyping, in which five to seven planes fly in parallel across the sky in perfect unison. The message is written as smoke generators in each plane produce short, sharp puffs that expand after they are released, leaving a continuous line of dots in the sky. Using a master control panel in the lead plane to synchronize the smoke generators, the vapor is released in specific sequences, creating the letters in much the same manner in which dot-matrix printers create images on paper.

P. S. Ramsey

Bibliography

Brown, David. "Big Ads in the Sky." *Westways* 78, no. 1 (January, 1986): 34-37. A brief article on the modern use of skywriting in advertising.

Klemin, Alexander. "Handwriting on the Sky." *Scientific American* 128 (May, 1923): 323. A classic article about early use of skywriting in advertising, describing the chemical processes and techniques involved.

McConnell, B. M. "Story of Skywriting." *St. Nicholas* 55 (April, 1928): 439-441. An early article about the history and technique of skywriting.

Patiky, Mark. "Smoke Signals." *Air Progress* 46 (April, 1984): 41-49. An illustrated article about skywriting.

See also: High-altitude flight; Weather conditions

Sopwith Camels

Date: First entered combat in 1917
Definition: A leading British fighter plane of World War I, the Camel was a rotary-engined, single-seat fighter biplane.
Significance: The Sopwith Camel was one of the most successful British fighter planes in World War I, and one of the war's most successful fighters of any nationality. More enemy aircraft were downed by Camels than by any other Allied airplane during the war. The air forces of Australia, the United States, France, Belgium, and the British Navy flew the Camel.

The Air War in France

The air war over the western front in France during World War I saw the development of military aircraft from unreliable observation and artillery-spotting platforms to specialized attack and defense systems. Fighter aircraft soon were developed from existing planes or designed from scratch to bring down enemy observation, spotting, and bombing craft. Great Britain was, in 1917, in need of an effective fighter plane to combat several superior German aircraft, as well as to overcome the losses from the so-called Bloody April of 1917, a period in the air war that had seen many German fighter airplanes preying successfully on slower and less effective Allied fighter and observation planes.

Predecessors

Sopwith had a number of aircraft in World War I, many of them quite successful. The Sopwith Tabloid, an early single-seat tractor-engine design, was employed early in the conflict and became famous for bombing German zeppelin sheds at Cologne and Düsseldorf. Later planes, such as the Two-Seater, nicknamed the "1½ Strutter," for the formation of the wing struts, saw combat in 1916. Sopwith also built a triplane (similar, but not identical, to the popular German Fokker triplane, which was supposedly based on the Sopwith design) and later the popular Sopwith Pup, which gave decent performance (more than 90 miles per hour) with a very low-powered engine (an 80-horsepower Le Rhone). The Pup was a stable aircraft and pilots enjoyed flying it. The Camel, which entered service in mid-1917, was considered by some to be a refinement and improvement of the Pup. If so, it was an extensive one.

The Camel

The Camel's distinguishing characteristics were the humplike sheet metal covering the two machine guns directly in front of the pilot, which gave the craft its nickname, and the pronounced dihedral (the angle away from horizontal) of the lower wings. In addition, it had a much more powerful engine and more powerful armament: two machine guns either both in front of the pilot, synchronized to shoot through the propeller blades, or, in some cases, one synchronized gun and another machine gun mounted on the upper wing above the pilot. Compared to modern warplanes, the Camel was rather small. The wingspan was only 28 feet; the length of the craft was almost 19 feet. From the ground to the top of the upper wing was only 9 feet. Fully loaded with pilot and ammunition, the plane weighed about 1,500 pounds. In an era when the ability of the craft to stay in the air was measured in terms of endurance rather than a specific range of miles, the Camel could spend 2.5 hours in the air, and traveled at a maximum speed of 113 miles per hour—a very good speed for that time. Like most World War I aircraft, it was built of a wooden framework for the fuselage and wings, with fabric stretched over the plane and then stiffened and tightened with airplane dope. The wings were braced to the body with wooden struts and rigging wires. Like all World War I aircraft, it had fixed landing gear carrying inflatable rubber tires. The cockpit was small and cramped. Over 5,700 Camels were built, including marine versions that could take off from launching ramps erected on large warships; these versions had a folding fuselage for stowage aboard ship.

The Reputation

Two things are said of the Camel today: it was an effective "killer" of enemy aircraft, and it also had a bad habit of killing its own inexperienced pilots. As for the latter, the Camel's bad reputation was partially deserved and difficult for it to shake. The powerful Bentley, Le Rhone, or

The Sopwith Camel was one of the best-known fighter planes of World War I. (Hulton Archive)

Clerget rotary engine, which was mounted only a few feet ahead of the pilot, created from 110 to 150 horsepower, as well as a great deal of torque in the direction that the engine and propeller were spinning. As the craft still weighed less than a ton when loaded, such a significant amount of weight (guns, pilot, and engine) at the front of the plane meant that turns in the direction of the engine's spin were considerably faster than turns in the opposite direction. Novice pilots could quickly find themselves out of control, especially when turning immediately after takeoff. Eventually, pilots became used to (and were warned of) this tendency and the Camel went on to great success; however, given that mishaps unrelated to combat cost the lives of over three hundred Camel pilots, the problem was more than passing.

The Result
Even with its early reputation, the Sopwith Camel was eventually to become, along with other British fighters such as the SE-5A and the two-seat Bristol Fighter, one of the distinguishing aircraft of the British aerial forces during World War I. Difficult to learn to fly, yet very capable in the hands of a competent pilot, the Camel helped the British forces achieve domination of the skies over the western front during the final years of World War I. Pilots flying the Camel in British and other air services shot down 1,294 enemy aircraft, while just over four hundred pilots died in combat while flying the Camel. This is a very high kill ratio, made even more impressive when it is realized that this was all accomplished from July, 1917, when the Camel entered service, to the end of the war in November, 1918—only sixteen months. The structural and design elements that made the Camel hard to learn to fly also made it extremely maneuverable, and it was especially fast in turns.

Famous Camel Pilots
Many pilots flew the Camel, and many became extremely effective, becoming aces—denoting that they had shot down five or more enemy aircraft. Perhaps the most famous was Canadian William Barker, who, while flying for

the Royal Flying Corps and later the Royal Air Force, downed fifty enemy planes, forty-six of them in the same Sopwith Camel, and who eventually won the Victoria Cross. Kenneth Unger was the highest-scoring American ace who flew the Camel, with fourteen victories, and American Field Kindley, who also flew the Camel, shot down twelve. No list of Camel pilots would be complete without mentioning Canadian Roy Brown, who flew a Sopwith Camel and shot down ten aircraft; his last victory being over the "Red Baron," German ace Manfred von Richthofen.

Aftermath

Within a few years after the war, most Camels were scrapped; very few survive. One, which was flown by Field Kindley, is on display in the United States at the Aerospace Education Center in Little Rock, Arkansas. Interestingly, in the 1960's, the Camel again reached the world's attention with the cartoon character Snoopy, the big-nosed beagle in Charles M. Schulz's *Peanuts* comic strip, whose fantasy exploits in his Sopwith Camel fighting the "Red Baron" delighted millions.

Robert Whipple, Jr.

Bibliography

Aerodrome, The. "Aces and Aircraft of World War I." (www.theaerodrome.com) A detailed Web site devoted to World War I aviation, including a concise description of the Camel, its specifications, and brief history.

Aerospace Education Center. "Sopwith Camel F-1." (www.aerospaced.org/permart/sopwith.htm) A Web site on the only surviving original Sopwith Camel, built between 1917 and 1918, in the United States.

Angelucci, Enzo, ed. *The Rand-McNally Encyclopedia of Military Aircraft, 1914-1980*. Chicago: Rand-McNally, 1981. An exhaustive illustrated guide to all military aircraft from 1914-1980, with discussion, illustrations, and technical specifications.

Jane's Fighting Aircraft of World War I. Reprint. London: Studio, 2001. The definitive reference work on aircraft for the years from 1914 to 1919.

Tallman, Frank. *Flying the Old Planes*. New York: Doubleday, 1973. Contains an account of a modern flight in a Sopwith Camel, written by the pilot, an antique aviation pioneer.

Whitehouse, Arch. *The Years of the Sky Kings*. New York: Doubleday, 1959. An account of the development of aerial combat in World War I, written by a pilot who flew in the Royal Flying Corps through most of World War I.

See also: Airplanes; Biplanes; Dogfights; Fighter pilots; Manufacturers; Military flight; Manfred von Richthofen; Royal Air Force; World War I

Sound barrier

Definition: A wall of superimposed sound waves along the leading edge of an aircraft traveling at the speed of sound in air.

Significance: When an aircraft punches through the sound barrier and travels at supersonic speeds, it creates a continuous pressure wave that reaches the ground as a sonic boom.

Doppler Effect

The Doppler effect, discovered by Austrian physicist Christian Johann Doppler in 1842, is the change in the observed frequency of a wave, of sound or light, for example, due to relative motion between the observer and the wave source. When observer and source approach each other, the emitted frequency of the waves is measured to be higher, due to the velocity of approach; the greater the relative speed, the greater the frequency shift. When the source and observer are receding from each other, the emitted frequency is measured to be lower, in direct proportion to the velocity of recession.

Although the Doppler effect applies to all types of waves, it is particularly noticeable for sound waves. When an ambulance speeds by, for example, the pitch, or frequency, drops noticeably. The effect is most easily explained by considering water waves on a placid pond created by a small insect jiggling its legs. The insect's movement creates a pattern of equally spaced concentric rings; each ring represents the crest of a wave traveling outward from the insect at constant speed. If the insect is traveling toward the left while jiggling its legs, the wave pattern is distorted; the rings are no longer concentric, but the centers of consecutive waves are displaced in the direction of motion. Although the insect has not changed the frequency with which it jiggles its legs, an observer at a position toward the insect's left encounters a higher frequency of waves because the waves are compressed in the direction of motion. An observer at a position to the insect's right perceives a lower frequency of waves. The waves are spread farther apart because the insect is moving away from the observer.

Although sound waves are invisible and spread into three dimensions, the same principle applies. When a source of sound approaches, the perceived frequency, or pitch, is higher than the emitted frequency, and the opposite is true for a receding source.

Wave Barrier

If the insect discussed above were to swim across the water at the same speed as the velocity of water waves while continuing to jiggle its legs at a constant frequency, the wave crests would be superimposed on one another directly in front of the insect rather than moving ahead of it. This wall of water may be considered a wave barrier, because the insect would have to exert considerable effort to swim over this barrier in order to travel at a speed greater than the wave velocity. However, after the insect had surmounted the barrier by exceeding the wave velocity, the water ahead would be smooth and undisturbed.

When an aircraft travels at the speed of sound in air, it also encounters a barrier of superimposed sound waves. The compression waves are stacked up along the leading edge of the aircraft, requiring some additional thrust for the aircraft to punch through. After the plane exceeds the velocity of sound, however, there are no further barriers to inhibit additional acceleration; the airplane may travel at supersonic speed.

Shock Waves

As the jiggling insect travels through water with a speed greater than the wave velocity, it produces the pattern in which each consecutive wave crest, represented by a circle, is located outside the previous crest. The wave crests overlap to form larger crests. This small wall of water, called a bow wave, has a solid "V" shape.

When an aircraft flies at a supersonic speed, the overlapping spherical sound waves form a cone of air pressure that grows in size until intercepted by the ground. This thin conical shell of compressed air is termed a shock wave. Just as a person floating in a tranquil lake will be hit by the bow wave of a speed boat traveling faster than the speed of water waves, people on the ground will be struck by the shock wave of a supersonic aircraft. This wave, called a sonic boom, is heard as a sharp cracking thunderclap.

Sonic Booms

The sound of a subsonic aircraft is perceived by a listener on the ground as a continuous tone. The shock wave produced by a supersonic airplane, consisting of many superimposed waves, occurs like an explosion in a single burst. Both processes consist of a burst of high-pressure air that creates a loud, unpleasant noise. In actuality, the shock waves produced by supersonic aircraft create a double sonic boom; the shock wave from the bow of the plane is a pulse of increased pressure that is followed a fraction of a second later by a negative-pressure pulse from the trailing edge of the aircraft. Overall, the pressure wave has the general appearance of the letter "N." This pressure shock wave is produced during the entire course of a supersonic flight and not only during the time when it passes the sound barrier, as is mistakenly believed. Because the width of the sonic boom trail is about 20 miles, and its length is the flight path, sonic booms can create considerable problems. First, there is the annoyance factor of people being startled or awakened by the loud, explosive noise. Because of sonic booms' intense and rapid pressure changes, sonic booms can destroy property in inhabited areas. Broken windows and structural damage are not uncommon. Finally, sonic booms can be problematic even in uninhabited regions; they have been known to topple rock structures in national parks.

Brief History of Supersonic Flight

The speed of sound at sea level is 760 miles per hour. The speed of sound decreases with increased altitude, so that at 50,000 feet, sound travels at 660 miles per hour. Because the wall of pressure termed the sound barrier differentiates subsonic from supersonic flight, the speed of sound is defined as a velocity of Mach 1. Mach 2, then, would be twice the speed of sound, and so on.

Although several attempts were made in the early 1940's to exceed the sound barrier, early jet planes of the period were not powerful or sturdy enough to succeed. When an aircraft reaches Mach 1, strong local shock waves form on the wings, and the flow of air around the plane becomes unsteady. As a result, the airplane is subjected to severe buffeting that interferes with the plane's stability and renders it difficult to control. In 1943, U.S. aeronautical engineers began working on the first airplane specifically designed to surmount these problems and withstand the tremendous air pressure of Mach 1 in order to obtain supersonic flight. This goal was realized on October 14, 1947, when Captain Charles E. "Chuck" Yeager of the U.S. Air Force smashed through the sound barrier in a Bell X-1 rocket plane. Although many supersonic flights at ever-increasing speeds were made over the next decade, the speed never exceeded Mach 2.5, because friction caused by the rapidly moving air overheated the outer shell of the airplanes.

Using jet engines specifically designed for supersonic flight, the North American F-100 Super Sabre jet fighter became the first jet capable of flying at supersonic speeds in level flight. The first supersonic bomber, the Convair B-58 Hustler, became operational in 1956. By 1963, the

X-15 rocket plane was able to fly 67 miles above the earth's surface at a speed exceeding Mach 6. The world's first supersonic transport (SST) plane, the Tupolev Tu-144, was tested by Soviet pilots in 1968. Britain and France jointly constructed the Concorde SST, which was designed to fly at Mach 2 and began commercial service in 1969. Since that time, however, the number of supersonic flights has been limited due to the high cost of fuel and the problems of sonic booms. In the United States, commercial supersonic flights are now restricted to transoceanic flights.

George R. Plitnik

Bibliography

Anderson, John D. *Introduction to Flight: Its Engineering and History*. New York: McGraw-Hill, 1978. An introductory text that considers the theoretical questions of aerodynamics, including the design and construction of airplanes planned for different purposes.

Dwiggins, Don. *Flying the Frontiers of Space*. New York: Dodd, Mead, 1982. A readily accessible history of American experimental aircraft from 1947 to the early 1980's.

Kerrebrock, Jack. *Aircraft Engines and Gas Turbines*. 2d ed. Cambridge, Mass.: MIT Press, 1992. A technical description requiring some familiarity with physics or engineering of the power plants necessary for supersonic flight.

Kryter, K. D. *Noise and Man*. New York: Academic Press, 1970. This work includes a complete description of sonic booms, their effects on people and structures, and the potential sonic hazards of SST overland flights.

Strong, W., and G. R. Plitnik. *Music, Speech, Audio*. Provo, Utah: Soundprint, 1992. An easy-to-read introduction to the science of acoustics that contains a complete explanation of the physics of the Doppler effect and sonic booms in easy-to-understand descriptive terms.

See also: Aerodynamics; Aerospace industry, U.S.; Concorde; Doppler radar; High-speed flight; Hypersonic aircraft; Mach number; Supersonic aircraft; Andrei Nikolayevich Tupolev; X planes; Chuck Yeager

Southwest Airlines

Date: Founded in 1971
Definition: A major U.S. carrier.

Significance: Southwest is a leading short-haul, low-fare carrier in the southwestern United States.

In the early 1970's, Herb Kelleher and Rollin King were growing frustrated with short-haul flights in Texas and the Southwest. Kelleher and King believed that flights were not only too expensive but also not frequent enough to accommodate the needs of business travelers. The two decided to target this niche, and Southwest Airlines was born. On June 18, 1971, Southwest inaugurated service with flights between Houston, Dallas, and San Antonio. Southwest has since grown into a major U.S. carrier, with revenues in excess of $1 billion yearly, employing more than thirty thousand workers and operating more than 2,700 flights a day.

History

In 1971, Southwest Airlines inaugurated service among three Texas cities: Dallas, Houston, and San Antonio. At this time, Houston flights took off and landed in Houston Intercontinental Airport (now called Bush Intercontinental). Many passengers disliked Houston Intercontinental because it was located 23 miles north of downtown, entailing a 40-minute drive to take a 45-minute flight. Because of passenger frustration, Southwest in 1972 transferred all flights originating or terminating in Houston to Houston's Hobby Airport, a mere 7 miles from downtown.

The next year, 1973, marked Southwest's first profitable year. At this time, Southwest applied to the Texas Aeronautics Commission (TAC) for permission to extend service to the Rio Grande Valley.

During 1974, Southwest carried its one-millionth passenger. This year also marked a capital outlay for the company as it remodeled its Houston terminal by adding two new boarding gates and departure lounges, at a cost of $400,000.

The TAC did not approve Southwest's request to provide service to the Rio Grande Valley until 1975. The commission permitted four roundtrips to the valley via the Harlingen Airport each business day. The TAC must have been satisfied with Southwest's flights because in 1976, the commission gave Southwest clearance to fly to Austin, Corpus Christi, El Paso, Lubbock, and Midland/Odessa.

Several milestones for Southwest occurred in 1977: the airline carried its five-millionth passenger, and Southwest stock was listed on the New York Stock Exchange as "LUV."

Several organizational changes happened during the following year. After Lamar Muse stepped down as president, Herb Kelleher filled in as interim president, CEO, and chairman of the board. Later in the year, Howard Putnam was unanimously elected president and Chief Executive Officer. Kelleher stayed on as permanent chairman of the board.

Southwest Airlines continued to grow, and in 1979, the airline extended service to the first city outside of Texas: New Orleans, Louisiana.

> ## Events in Southwest Airlines History
>
> **1971**: Southwest Airlines inaugurates service within Texas, between the cities of Dallas, Houston, and San Antonio.
> **1973**: Southwest applies to the Texas Aeronautics Commission (TAC) to extend service to the Rio Grande Valley and completes its first profitable year.
> **1974**: Southwest carries its one-millionth passenger.
> **1975**: The TAC approves four roundtrips to the Rio Grande Valley via the Harlingen Airport each business day.
> **1976**: Southwest gets clearance from the TAC to fly to Austin, Corpus Christi, El Paso, Lubbock, and Midland/Odessa and places its sixth Boeing 737 into service.
> **1977**: The airline carries its five-millionth passenger, and its stock is listed on the New York Stock Exchange as "LUV."
> **1978**: After Lamar Muse steps down as president, Herbert D. Kelleher fills in as interim president, chief executive officer, and chairman of the board. Later in the year, Howard Putnam is unanimously elected president and chief executive officer, and Kelleher remains as permanent chairman of the board.
> **1979**: The airline extends service to the first city outside of Texas: New Orleans, Lousiana.
> **1980**: Southwest purchases its twenty-second Boeing 737, the first 737 in the Southwest fleet to be completely owned by Southwest Airlines.
> **1982**: Kelleher takes command as permanent president, chief executive officer, and chairman of the board. Southwest spreads its wings to San Francisco, Los Angeles, San Diego, Las Vegas, and Phoenix.
> **1985**: Southwest extends service to St. Louis, Missouri, and Chicago, Illinois.
> **1989**: Service begins from Oakland's International Airport.
> **1990**: Southwest passes the one-billion dollar revenue mark, becoming a major airline.
> **1993**: Southwest expands to the East Coast and begins service to Baltimore/Washington International Airport.
> **1994**: After Morris Air merges with Southwest, service begins to the Pacific Northwest cities of Seattle, Spokane, Portland, and Boise.
> **1995**: Southwest introduces "Ticketless Travel," or travel without a paper ticket, systemwide and adds service to Omaha.
> **1996**: Southwest inaugurates service into Florida and from Providence, Rhode Island.
> **1997**: Southwest initiates service to Jacksonville, Florida, the airline's fiftieth city, and later to Jackson, Mississippi.
> **1998-2000**: Southwest Airlines continues to expand throughout the Northeast, with new service to Manchester, New Hampshire; Islip, New York; Hartford, Connecticut; Albany, New York; and Buffalo-Niagara, New York.

In 1980, Southwest purchased its twenty-second Boeing 737. This plane was the first 737 in the fleet to be completely owned by Southwest Airlines.

In 1982, Kelleher took command as permanent president, CEO, and chairman of the board. Under his leadership, Southwest expanded its service area, spreading its wings to San Francisco, Los Angeles, San Diego, Las Vegas, and Phoenix. Southwest's next big expansion came in 1985, when the airline extended service to St. Louis, Missouri, and Chicago's Midway Airport. In 1989, service began from International Airport in Oakland, California.

In 1990, Southwest passed the billion-dollar revenue mark and became a major airline. With major airline status came an ever-widening geographic reach: in 1993, the company expanded to the East Coast and began service to Baltimore/Washington International Airport. Reaching out not only to the East Coast but also the Pacific Northwest, during the next year, 1994, Morris Air merged with Southwest. Service began to Seattle, Spokane, Portland, and Boise.

During this time, Southwest decided to take advantage of emergent technology to deliver better service to customers. Ticketless travel (travel with an electronic rather than a paper ticket) became available systemwide in January, 1995.

In 1996, Southwest started service into Florida: Tampa Bay and Fort Lauderdale in January, and Orlando in April. In October, Southwest inaugurated service from Providence, Rhode Island. Southwest started out 1997 with service to Jacksonville, Florida, its fiftieth city. Service to Jackson, Mississippi, was added in August. The following June, Southwest Airlines added service to Manchester, New Hampshire. In 1999, Southwest Airlines broadened service on the East Coast to include Islip, New York, in March and to Raleigh-Durham International Airport, in North Carolina, in June. Service to Hartford, Connecticut's Bradley International Airport began on October 31, 1999. New service to New York's Albany International Airport began in May, 2000, and to Buffalo-Niagara International Airport in October.

Financial Information

Southwest's common stock is traded under the symbol "LUV" on the NYSE. Net income for 2000 totaled $625.2 million, a result of having carried 63.7 million passengers. Southwest flights in 2000 were 70.5 percent full, on average. The company took in a total operating revenue of $5.6 billion.

An important component of Southwest's revenue is its World Wide Web site (www.Southwest.com). In 2000, Southwest reported that $1.7 billion, or approximately 30 percent of its 2000 revenue, was generated from online bookings. Southwest's World Wide Web site saves the company money, because having customers make reservations over the Internet is approximately ten times less expensive for the company than having to pay travel agents to book reservations.

Fleet

As of January 24, 2001, Southwest operated 346 Boeing 737 jets. On average, planes in the company's fleet were 8.2 years old. Southwest's flights average 492 miles in length and last 1.5 hours. Each aircraft makes eight flights per day on average, spending about twelve hours a day in the air.

Alexandra Ferry

Bibliography

Feldman, Joan M. "Seriously Successful: Southwest Airlines' Rapid-fire Growth, Consistent Profits and Employee Spirit Have Made It More Than Just an Airline." *Air Transport World* 31, no. 1 (January, 1994): 60-67. An article detailing the elements of Southwest's consistent growth.

Freiburg, Kevin. *Nuts! Southwest Airlines' Crazy Recipe for Business and Personal Success.* Austin, Tex.: Bard Books, 1996. An examination of Southwest's uniquely successful business strategy.

Henderson, Danna K. "Winning Ugly: Southwest Airlines Passengers May Find Its Livery Unsightly but Their Instant Recall Contributes to the Carrier's Unbridled Success." *Air Transport World* 34, no. 9 (September, 1997): 66-68. An article about one element of Southwest's marketing strategy.

Jennings, Mead. "Staying the Course: Southwest Airlines Has Proved to Be One of the Consistently Successful U.S. Carriers, and a Potential Bounty of Opportunity Is Arising from Failures and Cuts at Other Carriers." *Airline Business* (February, 1992): 52-55. Describes the airline's successes and potential successes.

See also: Air carriers; Airline industry, U.S.; Boarding procedures; Overbooking; Ticketing

Space shuttle

Date: Beginning on January 5, 1972
Definition: A reusable space launch vehicle developed by the United States to launch astronauts and large satellites into Earth orbit.
Significance: The space shuttle was the first reusable launch vehicle to carry humans into space.

Planning the Space Shuttle

The space shuttle program was initially conceived in the 1960's, when the National Aeronautics and Space Administration (NASA) began planning a comprehensive program for a permanent American presence in space. The plan included three components: a permanently crewed space station, a reusable vehicle to carry astronauts from Earth to orbit and back, and a space tug to move satellites around in orbit. However, the need to fund other national priorities resulted in cuts to the NASA budget at the end of the Apollo Program. Because this new space effort's cost far exceeded its budget, it was scaled back to include only the reusable launch vehicle, which was called the space shuttle. On January 5, 1972, President Richard M. Nixon officially announced the inauguration of the space shuttle program. NASA's ambitious schedule called for suborbital tests by 1977 and the first orbital tests by 1979. The shuttle was scheduled to begin regular launchings by 1980.

The Shuttle Vehicle

The space shuttle consists of three major components: a reusable, winged orbiter that carries the crew; a large external tank that holds fuel for the main engines; and two solid rocket boosters that provide most of the shuttle's lift during the first two minutes of flight. The space shuttle is designed to reach orbits ranging from about 115 miles to 400 miles high. Normally, space shuttle missions range from five to sixteen days in orbit. The smallest crew to fly on the shuttle was composed of two people, on the first few test flights, but the shuttle normally carries crews ranging from five to eight people, depending on the flight objectives. At liftoff, the space shuttle weighs about 4,500,000 pounds.

The orbiter, manufactured by the Space Division of Rockwell International, carries the crew, the payload, and the main propulsion system. The empty weight of the orbiter is about 150,000 pounds, approximately the same as that of a DC-9 jet aircraft. The crew compartment of the orbiter has three levels: the flight deck, the middeck, and a lower level equipment bay. The crew compartment is pressurized to 14.7 pounds per square inch with a mixture of 80 percent nitrogen and 20 percent oxygen, similar to the air pressure and composition at the earth's surface. The volume of the crew compartment is 2,325 cubic feet, about the equivalent of a 15-by-15-by-10-foot room.

The uppermost level of the crew compartment is the flight deck. The mission commander and the pilot are seated side-by-side in the forward portion of the flight deck. The mission commander and the pilot sit at workstations that contain the controls and displays used to guide the orbiter throughout the flight. Two seats for mission specialists are located directly behind the seats of the mission commander and the pilot. At the rear of the flight deck there are two overhead- and aft-viewing windows for observing orbital operations.

The middeck, which is directly beneath the flight deck, provides accommodations for additional crewmembers and contains three avionics equipment bays. Depending on the mission requirements, bunk sleep stations and a galley can be installed in the middeck. In addition, three or four seats of the same type as the mission specialists' seats on the flight deck can be installed in the middeck.

An airlock, located in the rear of the middeck, provides access to the payload bay. Normally, two extravehicular mobility units (EMUs) are stowed in the airlock. The EMU is an integrated spacesuit assembly and life-support system that enables flight crew members to leave the pressurized orbiter crew cabin and work outside the cabin in space. Removable panels in the middeck floor provide access to the equipment bay that houses the major components of the waste-management and air-cleaning and recirculating systems. This compartment has space in which to stow lithium hydroxide canisters, used to clean the air, and five separate spaces for crew equipment stowage. When on the ground, astronauts enter and exit the crew compartment through a side hatch in the middeck.

The payload bay, measuring 15 feet wide and 60 feet long, holds large payloads being carried to orbit. Two payload bay doors, each 60 feet long, are hinged at each side of the fuselage. The payload bay doors expose the payload bay to space when they are opened along the centerline. The back surface of the doors, which have a combined area of approximately 1,600 square feet, contains radiators that exhaust the heat generated by equipment on the orbiter. Seals on the doors provide a relatively airtight payload compartment when the doors are closed and latched.

The crew compartment of the orbiter does not contain sufficient space for experiments, and the payload bay is not pressurized, so astronauts working in the payload bay must wear spacesuits. To provide space for experiments, the European Space Agency (ESA) designed the Spacelab, a large, pressurized module that can be carried in the orbiter's payload bay. Astronauts enter the Spacelab through the airlock at the rear of the middeck of the crew compartment. The Spacelab provides electrical power and a pressurized working environment for astronauts to perform a variety of experiments.

The orbiter also contains the three liquid-fueled main engines. These engines burn liquid hydrogen and liquid oxygen, which is carried in the external tank attached to the orbiter. The top surface of the orbiter is covered with white silica material that protects the surface during reentry from temperatures of up to 1,200 degrees Fahrenheit. The bottom of the orbiter and the leading edge of the tail are covered with black silica heat-shield tiles, having very low thermal conductivity, which protect those surfaces from temperatures of up to 2,300 degrees Fahrenheit.

The orbiter's external tank, which was designed by Martin Marietta and built at NASA's Michoud Assembly Facility in New Orleans, Louisiana, contains all of the fuel, liquid hydrogen, and the oxidizer, liquid oxygen, for the orbiter's main engines. At the top of the external tank there is a conical nose cone that reduces the air drag on the vehicle and serves as a lightning rod. The oxygen tank, located beneath the nose cone, has a volume of 19,563 cubic feet. A 17-inch-diameter fuel line carries the oxygen to the orbiter with a maximum flow rate of 17,592 gallons per minute. The liquid hydrogen tank, which is located below the liquid oxygen tank, has a volume of 53,518 cubic feet. The 17-inch fuel line connecting the hydrogen tank to the orbiter has a maximum flow of 47,365 gallons per minute. Just before the shuttle reaches orbital velocity, the external tank is jettisoned, and it burns up on atmospheric entry.

The two solid-fueled rocket boosters are attached to the main tank. The solid rocket boosters are the largest solid-propellant motors ever flown and the first that were designed to be reused. The propellant mixture in each motor consists of ammonium perchlorate as the oxidizer, aluminum as the fuel, iron oxide as a catalyst, and a polymer binder that holds the mixture together. The fuel is shaped so that each rocket provides a high thrust at ignition and then reduces the thrust by approximately one-third after 50 seconds to prevent overstressing the vehicle during the time when it experiences maximum dynamic pressure. Because the solid boosters were too long to manufacture as a single unit, each booster consists of four segments. These segments are joined together using a system of clamps and O-ring seals, which are made of compressible material that fills the space in the joints to prevent leakage of high-pressure gas through the joints. Each solid booster weighs 1,300,000 pounds at liftoff and 192,000 pounds after the fuel has been burned. At liftoff, each of the solid boosters develops approximately 3,300,000 pounds of thrust. The solid rocket boosters also contain a parachute system, which allows them to descend into the Atlantic Ocean after use. They are recovered by ship and returned to the manufacturer for refurbishment and reuse.

The orbiter returns to Earth as a glider, using conventional flight controls and wings that provide lift. The wingspan is 78 feet. Each wing, constructed of aluminum alloy with a multirib-and-spar arrangement, has a maximum thickness of 5 feet and is approximately 60 feet long where it is attached to the fuselage. The main landing gear is stored in the wings and is extended only a few seconds before landing.

The Space Shuttle Flight Profile

The space shuttle is launched vertically from a transporter-launching pad that was modified from a Saturn V launching pad after the end of the Apollo Program. The shuttle can carry a crew of up to eight astronauts and can deliver a payload of up to 65,000 pounds into low-Earth orbit.

The liquid-fueled main engines ignite about seven seconds before the planned liftoff. A computer checks the performance of the main engines, which can be shut down if a problem is detected. If no problems are detected, the solid rocket boosters, which must burn until their fuel is exhausted, are ignited. At liftoff, the three main engines and the two solid-fueled booster rockets develop a total of more than 6,800,000 pounds of thrust. The solid rocket boosters, which provide most of the thrust to lift the space shuttle off the pad and up to an altitude of about 150,000 feet, burn for approximately two minutes. At an altitude of about 28 miles, just after they burn out, the solid boosters are jettisoned from the external tank by pyrotechnic separation devices. Eight small rockets on the solid boosters fire to carry them well clear of the orbiter. A parachute system slows the descent of the solid boosters, which are recovered from the ocean, about 170 miles from the launch site.

The external tank continues to provide fuel for the orbiter's three main engines until about eight minutes after liftoff. The main engines shut down at a

The space shuttle Columbia *is brought to Launch Pad 39B at the Kennedy Space Center in preparation for liftoff.* (NASA)

613

speed just below orbital speed, and the external tank is jettisoned. After a short period of coasting, two small maneuvering engines, fueled from tanks on the orbiter, fire to place the orbiter in Earth orbit.

Environmental control and life-support system radiators, used to cool the orbiter's systems, are located on the interior of the payload bay doors. Once the orbiter has achieved orbit, the payload bay doors are opened to allow proper cooling of the spacecraft.

During the mission, the path of the orbiter can be adjusted using the maneuvering engines. Once the mission is completed, the maneuvering engines serve as retrorockets, firing opposite the direction of the orbiter's motion and slowing the orbiter so that it reenters the earth's atmosphere.

Space Shuttle Missions

The first space shuttle orbiter, named *Enterprise*, was unveiled to the public on September 17, 1976, when it was rolled out of the Rockwell International hangar in Palmdale, California. Initially, the *Enterprise* was used for a series of ground tests. During 1976 and 1977, the *Enterprise* was carried aloft by a specially modified Boeing 747 aircraft, allowing engineers to study the aerodynamics of the orbiter. On August 12, 1977, the *Enterprise* separated from the Boeing 747 at an altitude of 22,800 feet, allowing the flight crew, Gordon Fullerton and Fred Haise, to perform approach and landing maneuvers at Edwards Air Force Base in California. After a series of unpowered flight tests, the *Enterprise*, which was never intended for powered flight, was retired. A fleet of four shuttles, *Columbia*, *Challenger*, *Discovery*, and *Atlantis*, was built for orbital operations.

The space shuttle *Columbia* was launched from NASA's John F. Kennedy Space Center at Cape Canaveral, Florida, on its first flight on April 12, 1981. John W. Young, a veteran of NASA's Gemini and Apollo Programs, was the commander, and Robert L. Crippen was the pilot. This was a test flight, and the only payload carried on the mission was a Development Flight Instrumentation Package, which contained sensors and measuring devices to record orbiter performance and the stresses that occurred during launch, ascent, orbital flight, descent, and landing. Post-flight inspection of *Columbia* revealed that an overpressure wave that occurred when the solid rocket boosters ignited resulted in the loss of 16 heat shield tiles and damage to 148 others. However, *Columbia*'s first flight demonstrated that the shuttle could perform a safe ascent into orbit and return to Earth for a safe landing.

The first five space shuttle missions were flown by *Columbia*, while the other space shuttle orbiters were under construction. The sixth shuttle flight, launched on April 4, 1983, was the first mission of *Challenger*. This mission deployed the first Tracking and Data Relay Satellite (TDRS), part of the satellite network used to relay shuttle communications to the ground. A malfunction of the inertial upper stage booster, which moves the satellite from the low orbit of the shuttle into the higher orbit required for global communications, resulted in an improper but stable orbit. Propellant aboard the satellite was used over the next several months to move the TDRS into the proper orbit.

Between April, 1981, and January, 1986, the space shuttles completed twenty-four missions. On June 18, 1983, the shuttle *Challenger* carried the United States' first woman astronaut, Sally K. Ride, into orbit and deployed two communications satellites, Anik C-2 for Telesat Canada and Palapa-B1 for Indonesia. During the *Challenger* mission launched on February 3, 1984, the first untethered space walk took place. Astronauts Bruce McCandless II and Robert L. Stewart used the Manned Maneuvering Unit (MMU) to fly in space unconnected to the orbiter. This mission also launched three satellites, but two, the Westar-VI and Palapa-B2, were placed into a low, elliptical orbit when the Payload Assist Module rocket motor, which should have boosted them into a high, circular orbit, failed. The shuttle *Challenger* carried the Long Duration Exposure Facility (LDEF) into orbit on April 6, 1984. The LDEF, whose purpose was to expose various materials to the space environment to monitor their stability or degradation in space and to determine the flux of micrometeorites and orbital debris, was supposed to be retrieved and returned to Earth after about two years.

The orbiter *Discovery* made its first flight on August 30, 1984, on a mission that launched three communications satellites. This mission also deployed a 102-foot-long, 13-foot-wide solar wing, which tested several different types of solar cells being considered for future space missions and demonstrated that very large structures could be deployed in space. The Spacelab space laboratory flew three times: carried into orbit by *Columbia* on November 28, 1983, and by *Challenger* on April 29, 1985 and July 29, 1985. The shuttle *Atlantis* made its first flight on September 20, 1985.

On January 28, 1986, the twenty-fifth space shuttle mission was launched from the Kennedy Space Center. The space shuttle *Challenger*, after a night of below-freezing temperatures, lifted off on its tenth mission into space at about 10:40 A.M. eastern standard time, carrying a crew of seven astronauts: Francis R. Scobee, the commander; Michael J. Smith, the pilot; Judith A. Resnik, Ellison S. Onizuka, and Ronald E. McNair, all mission specialists; Gregory B. Jarvis, a payload specialist; and America's first Teacher in Space, Sharon Christa McAuliffe. Seventy-four seconds after the launch, *Challenger* was destroyed, killing all seven crew members. A subsequent investigation established that the previous night's low temperature had hardened the O-ring seals between the segments of the solid-fueled rocket boosters. One joint in the right solid rocket booster had developed a leak, and the hot gases cut through metal on the shuttle to cause the disaster.

NASA immediately suspended the space shuttle program while the shuttle's overall safety was evaluated. The solid-fuel rocket booster joints were redesigned and the shuttle orbiter underwent more than two hundred modifications before the shuttle fleet returned to service. An escape system was added to the orbiter to allow astronauts to escape from a crippled shuttle and parachute to Earth. Construction began on a new shuttle, named *Endeavour*, to replace *Challenger*.

Shuttle flights resumed on September 29, 1988, when the shuttle *Discovery* carried a crew of five astronauts, commanded by Frederick H. Hauck, into orbit. This mission placed another TDRS communications satellite into orbit. Subsequent shuttle flights performed a variety of functions. On April 24, 1990, the shuttle *Discovery* placed the Hubble Space Telescope (HST) into orbit. The Hubble was designed to be serviced in orbit by future space shuttle missions. The first Hubble-servicing mission, flown by *Endeavour* and launched on December 2, 1993, accomplished its three primary objectives: restoring the planned scientific capabilities of the Hubble by installing a corrective lens designed to compensate for the incorrect shape of the mirror; restoring the reliability of Hubble's guidance system; and validating the concept of servicing while in orbit. The shuttle *Columbia* was launched on January 9, 1990, to place the SYNCOM IV-F5 defense communications satellite in orbit and to retrieve the Long Duration Exposure Facility (LDEF), which had been stranded in orbit after the *Challenger* accident.

The space shuttles have launched several interplanetary spacecraft. On May 4, 1989, the shuttle *Atlantis* launched the Magellan spacecraft, which went into orbit around Venus and performed radar mapping of its surface. On October 18, 1989, the shuttle *Atlantis* launched the Galileo spacecraft, which went into orbit around Jupiter, exploring that planet and its moons. On October 6, 1990, the shuttle *Discovery* launched the joint ESA/NASA Ulysses spacecraft, which was placed on a trajectory to pass Jupiter, where its orbit was altered to explore polar regions of the Sun.

In 1984, the U.S. government decided to build a space station, similar to the one that had been in the original 1960's plan. In preparation for this new space station, NASA began a series of space shuttle missions to Mir, the Russian space station. As part of this project, Russian cosmonaut Sergei Krikalev, the first Russian to be a crew member on an American spacecraft, flew on the space shuttle *Endeavour* in March, 1995. In June, 1995, the space shuttle *Atlantis* carried out the first mission to dock with the Mir Space Station.

On October 11, 2000, the shuttle *Discovery* flew the one-hundredth space shuttle mission, carrying a large truss, the Pressurized Mating Adapter-3, four large gyroscopes, and two heat pipes to the International Space Station. Before the launching of the shuttle *Discovery* in March, 2001, on a mission to bring the second crew to the International Space Station, James Kelly, the pilot, noted that, twenty years after the inception of the space shuttle program, the shuttle had finally realized its initial goal of transporting people to and from a permanent workplace in low-Earth orbit. During its first twenty years of operation, NASA's space shuttle fleet carried more than 600 astronauts and placed more than 3 million pounds of cargo into orbit.

George J. Flynn

Bibliography

Gurney, Gene. *Space Shuttle Log*. Blue Ridge Summit, Pa.: Tab Books, 1988. A history of the development of the space shuttle and its accomplishments on the early missions.

Joels, Kerry M., and Gregory P. Kennedy. *The Space Shuttle Operator's Guide*. New York: Ballantine, 1987. A "pilot's guide" to the space shuttle, written for general audiences and including information on the shuttle's systems, instrumentation, and flight procedures.

McConnell, Malcolm. *Challenger: A Major Malfunction: A True Story of Politics, Greed, and the Wrong Stuff*. New York: Doubleday, 1987. An extensive, well-illustrated account of the events leading up to the *Challenger* disaster.

See also: Accident investigation; Apollo Program; Crewed spaceflight; National Aeronautics and Space Administration; Spaceflight

Spaceflight

Also known as: Space exploration, space travel

Definition: Flight beyond Earth's atmosphere through the use of artificial satellites, space probes, or crewed spacecraft.

Significance: Spaceflight is considered the greatest scientific, technological, and human adventure of the twentieth century, allowing humans to explore what is considered by many to be the final frontier.

Background

Humans have long dreamed of leaving Earth to explore extraterrestrial worlds. Ancient writers told stories of trips beyond Earth, and natural philosophers speculated that heavenly bodies were made of an element completely different from terrestrial elements. In the sixteenth century, Polish astronomer Nicolaus Copernicus vastly expanded humanity's knowledge of the space containing these heavenly bodies by locating the Sun, instead of Earth, at the universe's center. As astronomical knowledge increased, storytellers imagined spaceflights of increasing sophistication.

In the nineteenth century, writers such as Jules Verne depicted space travel in elaborate technical detail. In the twentieth century, science-fiction writers described spaceflight with scientific accuracy, and their stories became more popular than they ever had been, as the practical means of going into space became a reality.

History

Just as Orville and Wilbur Wright had to solve several basic problems before achieving success in their first airplane, so, too, did spaceflight pioneers need to solve such problems as discovering a way to escape Earth's gravity. Rockets were first proposed for spacecraft propulsion in the twentieth century. The Russian engineer Konstantin Tsiolkovsky wrote extensively on the theory of spaceflight, including the need for multistage rockets, where two or more rockets are ignited in turn. The American physicist Robert H. Goddard designed, built, and launched the first liquid-fueled rockets. During World War II, the German rocket pioneer Wernher von Braun led a team of scientists who developed the first rocket-powered ballistic missile. Although the Germans designed this V-2 as a weapon, it became the model for all rockets—military, scientific, civilian, and commercial—that followed it.

Toward the end of World War II, the U.S. and Soviet military captured German scientists and engineers who had worked on the V-2 project. These scientists formed the core of postwar rocket-research programs. The United States launched more than fifty captured V-2 rockets and began using two-stage rockets for upper-atmosphere studies. Some of these vehicles achieved spaceflight, reaching the point where space begins, about 62 miles (100 kilometers) above Earth's surface. However, they did not have enough speed to go into orbit.

The Soviet Union was the first country to achieve orbital spaceflight when Sputnik 1 began to circle Earth on October 4, 1957. This first artificial satellite ushered in the age of spaceflight. A month later, the Russians launched Sputnik 2, which contained the dog Laika, the world's first space traveler.

These first Soviet spaceflights created a sensation around the world and especially in the United States, where it had long been assumed that Americans would be the first to achieve spaceflight. The Sputnik flights did much to change the nature of the Cold War from a political conflict between the United States and the Soviet Union to a comprehensive competition involving science, technology, and economics. Spaceflight became a symbol of the achievements of two different societies, capitalist and communist.

After civilian rockets failed to launch American satellites, President Dwight D. Eisenhower turned to the military for assistance. Five days after Sputnik 2 entered orbit, the U.S. Army used a Jupiter C rocket to orbit Explorer 1, whose instrumentation had been developed by University of Iowa physics professor James Van Allen. This Explorer mapped a doughnut-shaped region of high radiation surrounding the Earth that was later named the Van Allen radiation belts.

After the Soviet Union launched Sputnik 3 on May 15, 1958, U.S. leaders realized that the United States was falling behind in the space race. An acrimonious debate between Congress and the Eisenhower administration ensued, with the final resolution that the U.S. space program needed an effective legislative foundation. This legislation, the National Aeronautics and Space Act of 1958, created a civilian agency to explore space: the National Aeronautics and Space Administration (NASA). The act made no mention of crewed spaceflight, but its broad charter gave NASA the responsibility for the scientific, but not military, exploration of space.

During the first few years of the space age, uncrewed spaceflight characterized both U.S. and Soviet programs. These uncrewed spaceflights ranged from satellites in low-Earth orbit to probes aimed at interplanetary space. The first successful lunar probe was the Soviet Union's

Luna 1, which flew by the Moon in January, 1959. In March of that year, the United States Pioneer 4 glided by the Moon, and in September, the Soviet's Luna 2 became the first human artifact to land on the Moon. A month later, the Russians used their circumlunar probe Luna 3 to photograph the far side of the Moon.

Soon after these uncrewed satellites and probes were launched, both Soviet and American scientists began work on crewed space vehicles. Because of their lead in large rockets, the Soviet Union was able, on April 12, 1961, to launch the world's first crewed spacecraft, Vostok 1, a 3-ton sphere with a 2-ton service module. Soviet cosmonaut Yuri Gagarin thus became the first person to orbit Earth. After Gagarin's single orbit and safe return to Earth, the Soviet Union achieved several firsts and set several records. It launched several endurance record-setting crewed spaceflights and had a cosmonaut take the first space walk. Furthermore, Vostok 6 was piloted by Valentina Tereshkova, the first woman to make a spaceflight. The Soviets were also the first to orbit a spacecraft containing three cosmonauts.

The initial U.S. program for crewed spaceflight was called Mercury, and it became the responsibility of the newly formed NASA. A few months into John F. Kennedy's presidency and less than one month after Gagarin's flight, Alan Shepard became the first American astronaut launched into space, though his suborbital flight in a Mercury capsule lasted only about fifteen minutes. The first American orbital flight was made by astronaut John Glenn on February 20, 1962. Other Mercury flights stretched the spacecraft's orbital time to more than one day, and scientists and astronauts gained much valuable experience and information from the program, including the fact that humans should be active pilots rather than passive passengers during the missions.

While the United States and the Soviet Union developed their crewed spaceflight programs, both countries continued to develop uncrewed satellites and probes. For example, Americans launched the Television Infrared Observations Satellite (TIROS), the first weather satellite, in 1960, and it recorded more than 23,000 cloud images. Mariner 2, sent off by U.S. scientists in 1962, became the first spacecraft to explore another planet, Mars. From 1962 to 1965, the United States sent a series of Ranger probes to the Moon to take close-up photographs of its surface. The first successful soft landing on the Moon was that of the Soviet Union's Luna 9 on February 3, 1966. The United States achieved a successful soft landing on June 2, 1966, with its Surveyor 1. On April 3, 1966, the Soviet's Luna 10 became the first probe to successfully orbit the Moon. The first American lunar orbiter went around the Moon on August 14, 1966. With these and other lunar projects, it seemed obvious to many that the United States and the Soviet Union were engaged in a race to land humans on the Moon.

Crewed Lunar Spaceflights

The early Soviet successes in spaceflight placed intense political pressure on the U.S. president and lawmakers to find some accomplishment by which the United States could pull ahead of the Soviet Union. President Kennedy's advisors suggested a crewed landing on the Moon as such an achievement, and on May 25, 1961, Kennedy stood before Congress to ask the nation to "set the goal of landing a man on the Moon, before this decade is out, and safely returning him to Earth."

To attain this goal, NASA officials first had to decide how to get to the Moon. Eventually NASA scientists chose a lunar orbit rendezvous method, and consequently astronauts practiced rendezvous and docking techniques as part of the Gemini Program, a series of increasingly demanding missions with a two-person spacecraft. The Gemini missions had three phases. In the earliest missions, which began in 1965, astronauts tested the spaceworthiness of the Gemini spacecraft. They also performed the first American extravehicular activities (EVAs) and made the first-ever use of a personal propulsion unit. The middle Gemini missions, Gemini 4, Gemini 5, and Gemini 7, explored human endurance in space by progressively extending stays to two weeks, the maximum time that an Apollo lunar trip was expected to take. The final Gemini missions allowed astronauts to master the techniques of chasing a target vehicle and docking with it.

Apollo was the name of the mission to land men on the Moon. Tragically, before its first orbital trial, the Apollo Program came to an abrupt halt when, on January 27, 1967, a fire killed three astronauts, Roger Chaffee, Virgil "Gus" Grissom, and Edward White, in the Command Module (CM) during a countdown exercise. The spacecraft had a pure oxygen atmosphere and much flammable material, and a spark caused by an electrical short circuit ignited flames that rapidly engulfed the astronauts, who died of asphyxiation. Until the fire, the Apollo Program had proceeded without major difficulties, but these deaths delayed the first missions. NASA scientists redesigned the CM by minimizing flammable materials and changing the prelaunch cabin atmosphere to a mixture of 60 percent oxygen and 40 percent nitrogen.

The success of the Apollo missions depended on the gigantic Saturn V rocket that had been developed by

Wernher von Braun. The initial missions in the Apollo series were uncrewed tests of the Saturn and CM engines. For example, on April 4, 1968, the CM and the Lunar Module (LM) were tested on Apollo 8. The first crewed test, which began on October 11, 1968, was Apollo 7, the objective of which was to test the safety and reliability of all the spacecraft's systems. The first spaceflight involving humans leaving Earth orbit and traveling to the Moon was Apollo 8. This flight began on December 21, 1968, and the spacecraft went into lunar orbit on December 24, when the astronauts described the Moon's surface and read a passage from the first book of the Bible. The Apollo 9 mission in March, 1969, tested the Command and Service Module (CSM) and the LM in Earth orbit, and the Apollo 10 mission in May tested the CSM and LM in a lunar orbit.

Apollo 11, the lunar landing mission, took place between July 16 and July 24, 1969. On July 20, Neil Armstrong, after adeptly piloting the LM to its destination, became the first person to step onto the surface of the Moon, and he was later joined by Edwin "Buzz" Aldrin. Armstrong and Aldrin spent about two and one-half hours collecting rocks and setting up scientific experiments. Several hours later, their capsule, the *Eagle*, rocketed from the Moon to rendezvous with the CSM, the *Columbia*, which was piloted by Michael Collins. All three astronauts returned safely to Earth, where they received a jubilant reception.

From 1969 through 1972, six other Apollo missions traveled to the Moon, although Apollo 13 was unable to land on the lunar surface because of an explosion in one of its oxygen tanks. The Apollo 13 crew had to use the life-support systems of the LM *Aquarius* to help them survive the long trip back to Earth. NASA engineers consequently redesigned the oxygen tanks, and the final four Apollo lunar missions were able to explore the Moon safely and extensively. The hundreds of pounds of Moon rocks that were returned to Earth have given scientists a deep understanding of the origin and evolution both of the Moon and of the entire solar system.

Spaceflight After Apollo

Travel to the Moon was a risky and expensive enterprise, and neither the United States nor the Soviet Union made the trip in the 1980's and 1990 s. Critics of crewed spaceflight pointed out that science was much better and more inexpensively served by space satellites and probes. In the three decades after Apollo, robotic explorers such as Viking, Voyager, and Galileo proved to be highly efficient knowledge-gatherers. In 1976, two Viking spacecraft arrived at Mars: an orbiter that photographed the planet from above and a lander that analyzed rocks on the surface.

In 1977, two Voyagers were launched by NASA to start their twelve-year journey to the outer reaches of the solar system. The scientific instruments and cameras on the Voyagers sent back highly detailed information about the giant planets of Jupiter, Saturn, Uranus, and Neptune, along with the planets' fifty-seven moons. Voyager highlights included dramatic pictures of the turbulent storms of Jupiter's complex atmosphere, revelations of the complexities of Saturn's many rings, active volcanoes on Jupiter's moon Io, Neptune's Great Dark Spot, and nitrogen geysers on Neptune's moon Triton.

In 1997, Galileo became the first spacecraft to orbit an outer planet, and it has gathered much useful information about Jupiter's moons. The Soviets, too, used robotic probes in their scientific studies of the solar system. For example, in 1975, Venera 9 landed on the surface of Venus and returned the first pictures of its rocks and soil.

These uncrewed missions did not mean the end of crewed explorations of space. In 1971, Soviet scientists launched Salyut, the world's first space station. The Americans later launched their own space station, Skylab, which was visited by three-person crews in the 1970's, during which time astronauts made detailed studies of Earth's continents, oceans, and atmosphere. In 1975, the United States and the Soviet Union cooperated in the first international docking in space, when astronauts and cosmonauts performed an orbital rendezvous between an Apollo and a Soyuz capsule.

To make crewed spaceflight less expensive and more frequent, NASA developed the Space Transportation System (STS), commonly known as the space shuttle. Because landings at airfields are much less expensive than splashdowns at sea, and because it makes economic sense to reuse rockets, NASA engineers designed the space shuttle as a winged vehicle that was launched as a rocket, with two recoverable rocket boosters, and landed as an airplane.

In 1981, the space shuttle *Columbia* made its first flight. The other orbiting space shuttles of the 1980's and 1990's were *Challenger*, *Atlantis*, and *Discovery*. The missions of these shuttles included launching artificial satellites and retrieving them for servicing and repairs; performing scientific experiments in space; conducting secret military missions; and launching commercial communication satellites.

Despite NASA's aim for routine trips to space, the shuttle was plagued with problems, most notably the *Challenger* explosion on January 28, 1986. All seven crew members, including Sharon Christa McAuliffe, a New Hampshire schoolteacher, were killed. NASA stopped all shuttle missions while a special commission appointed by President Ronald Reagan studied the accident in order to determine the cause of the accident and the prevention of future such tragedies. The cause was a failure of a rubber ring that sealed the joint between two segments of one of the rocket boosters. To prevent any recurrence of this disaster, NASA engineers redesigned the booster joints and added a bail-out system that improved chances for crew survival in a crisis. The space shuttle resumed flying on September 28, 1988, with the liftoff of a redesigned *Discovery*.

One of the successes of the revamped STS was the Hubble Space Telescope (HST), which was launched from an orbiting shuttle in 1990. The HST was an uncrewed observatory far above the atmosphere of the earth, whose haze, clouds, and turbulence hampered telescopes on the ground. Unfortunately, after the HST was in orbit, astronomers discovered a problem with its mirror that seriously hindered its effectiveness. A shuttle repair mission in 1993 helped the HST achieve its astronomical potential. The HST was then able to take dramatic photographs of star births in the Eagle nebula and of galaxies 10,000,000,000 light-years away. It also measured an unimaginably gigantic burst of gamma rays in a distant galaxy that is the most powerful explosion ever observed.

The 1980's and 1990's were also characterized by an increasing number of spaceflights from countries other than the United States. On February 20, 1986, the Soviets launched the large Mir Space Station, which remained in orbit until 2001, when it was manipulated to fall harmlessly into the Pacific Ocean. During Mir's fifteen-year existence, cosmonauts set endurance records and learned much about how humans can live for long periods in space. After the Soviet Union ceased to exist in 1991, Russia took over the operation of Mir. Space cooperation between America and Russia resumed in 1995, when the space shuttle began to dock with Mir, which was periodically occupied by astronauts from various countries, including the United States.

With the end of Mir, crewed spaceflight centered on the International Space Station (ISS). The idea behind ISS was to share among several nations the cost of the construction and operation of a large space station. However, the structure and timetable of the ISS was continually changed during the presidencies of Ronald Reagan and Bill Clinton. The United States, Canada, Japan, Russia, and the European Space Agency (ESA) agreed to cooperate in building the redesigned ISS, whose construction actually began in outer space in 1998. The completed space station, planned to be the size of a football field, is the focus of spaceflights in the twenty-first century.

The participation of several nations in ISS was but another indication of the increasing involvement in spaceflight of countries around the world. Although the United States and the Soviet Union monopolized the early history of spaceflight, France launched its first satellite in 1965, and Britain its first in 1971. Fourteen nations founded the ESA in 1975 to combine their economic and scientific resources to develop new spacecraft for various missions. One of ESA's achievements was the space probe Giotto, sent to study Halley's comet in 1986. Japan also sent a probe to Halley's comet, and the nation's Advanced Earth Observing Satellite, launched in 1995, has gathered important information on Earth's lands, seas, and atmosphere. Other nations that have become actively involved in spaceflight are China, India, Canada, Israel, Australia, Brazil, Sweden, and South Africa.

Another trend of the late twentieth and early twenty-first centuries has been the commercialization of spaceflight. Various communications satellites have proved to be successful moneymakers for several companies. Some companies and governments have begun research on commercial crewed spaceflight, but these efforts have encountered serious difficulties because of the high cost of spaceflight. Similar problems have hindered plans for interplanetary travel, such as a crewed voyage to Mars. Critics of crewed spaceflight argue that it redirects funds from useful uncrewed programs and from important social and medical programs. In contrast, enthusiasts of crewed spaceflight emphasize the dreams that have energized scientists and engineers throughout history and the ineradicable desire to explore other worlds.

Robert J. Paradowski

Bibliography
Burrows, William E. *Exploring Space: Voyages in the Solar System and Beyond*. New York: Random House, 1990. An account of how rivalries—between the United States and the Soviet Union and between advocates of crewed and uncrewed spaceflight within NASA—drove lunar and planetary explorations.
Chaikin, Andrew W. *A Man on the Moon: The Voyages of the Apollo Astronauts*. New York: Viking Penguin, 1994. The definitive history of the Apollo Program, which put a man on the Moon, with an emphasis on the lives and personalities of the chief participants.
McDougall, Walter A. *The Heavens and the Earth: A Political History of the Space Age*. New York: Basic Books, 1985. A highly praised account of the space race between the United States and the Soviet Union

and its lessons about the relationship between technology and social change.

Murray, Bruce. *Journey into Space: The First Thirty Years of Space Exploration*. New York: Norton, 1989. An account of America's pioneering explorations of the solar system benefits from the insights of its author, director of the Jet Propulsion Laboratory from 1976 to 1983.

Neal, Valerie, Cathleen S. Lewis, and Frank N. Winter. *Spaceflight: A Smithsonian Guide*. New York: Macmillan, 1995. This heavily illustrated manual surveys the history of spaceflight from the dreams of the ancients to the speculations of the futurists.

See also: Aerospace industry, U.S.; Apollo Program; Wernher von Braun; Crewed spaceflight; Gemini Program; Robert H. Goddard; Manufacturers; Mercury project; National Committee for Aeronautics; National Aeronautics and Space Administration; Orbiting; Reentry; Rockets; Satellites; Saturn rocket; Space shuttle; Sputnik; Konstantin Tsiolkovsky; Uncrewed spaceflight; Uninhabited aerial vehicles; Vanguard Program

Spanish Civil War

Date: From 1936 to 1939

Definition: A military conflict resulting from a Nationalist rebellion, led by General Francisco Franco, against Spain's Republican government.

Significance: The Spanish Civil War has been considered the precursor to World War II and the testing ground for air power, including the German military tactic of the Blitzkrieg.

Background

Air power proved to be a major factor in the Spanish Civil War, a fratricidal conflict between Spain's two major antagonists during the 1930's. The Spanish Civil War resulted in the deaths of more than 300,000 combatants, of another 100,000 killed in murders and executions, and perhaps of an additional 200,000 who died from starvation and disease. Moreover, because most of the major European powers had become involved to a greater or lesser extent before the conflict finally concluded in March, 1939, the Spanish Civil War has been characterized as the opening round of World War II.

The war began in July, 1936, when Spain's conservative faction, subsequently known as the Nationalists, rose up in an attempt to overthrow the country's legitimate government, the Republicans, or Loyalists. Backed by the country's wealthy elite and the Catholic Church, a group of army officers started an insurrection in Spanish Morocco, across the Mediterranean Sea in North Africa. Spain's Republican government, also known as the Popular Front, supported by a wide spectrum of leftist elements and most of the country's urban population, reacted immediately to the threat.

The Popular Front government quickly secured the support of the Soviet Union, and, to a lesser extent, the governments of France and Great Britain. The latter two countries, in backing Spain's legitimate government, sought to stress the doctrine of nonintervention in what they considered Spain's internal affairs. Despite their sympathy for the Republicans, the French and British offered little in the way of material assistance.

The army rebels, led by Francisco Franco, Spain's youngest general, secured the backing of German chancellor Adolf Hitler and Italian dictator Benito Mussolini. Germany and Italy quickly began to furnish aid to the Moroccan rebels, who needed to transport their forces to the Spanish mainland. Also siding with Franco, although more or less surreptitiously, was Portugal's dictator, Dr. António de Oliveira Salazar, who feared the spread of the leftist ideology espoused by the Spanish Republicans to his own country.

Republican Spain itself had little in the way of a military force by which to defend itself against the rebel threat. Most of the regular army had joined the Nationalists, leaving the government's defense in the hands of inadequately armed and trained workers' militias. The Republicans had to acquire materials from abroad to counterbalance the military strength of their adversaries.

Foreign Assistance

Mussolini had had strong contacts with the Spanish monarchist government that had preceded the Popular Front. After the civil war commenced, he immediately pledged Italian aid to Franco's Nationalists. Both parties announced themselves as strongly anticommunist and saw the Loyalists as ideological enemies.

In the month following the outbreak of the rebellion in Morocco, Mussolini dispatched a number of trimotor Savoia bombers to both Melolla, Morocco, and Seville, Spain. The aircraft served both to bomb Loyalist naval vessels and military installations and to transport members of Franco's Moroccan troops to the Spanish mainland. Mussolini sent more than seven hundred aircraft to the Nationalists in the course of the war. By 1939, some 192 Italian pilots were serving in the Nationalist air force.

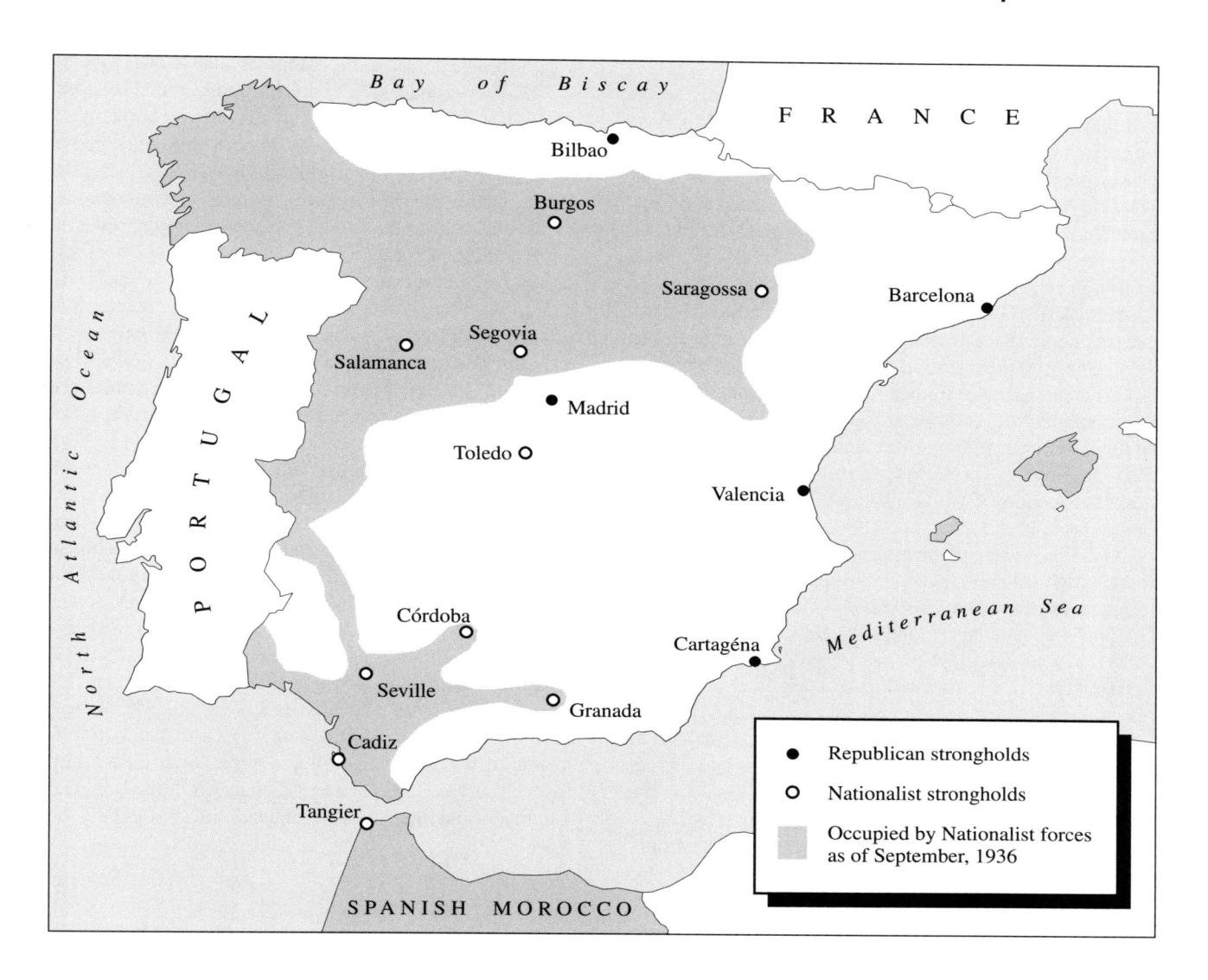

Although Hitler sympathized with Mussolini's ideological quarrel with the Republicans, his own decision to come to Franco's aid had much more practical applications. First, he wanted an ally, or at least a neutral power, on France's southern flank that would allow German forces access to the western Mediterranean and the Atlantic Ocean in the event of future hostilities. German submarines later used Spanish harbors to refuel and repair their submarine fleet during World War II. Hitler also sought to secure from Spain foodstuffs, wool, copper, and iron and pyrite ores to feed his war machine. Significantly, participation in combat against the Loyalist forces gave the Germans the opportunity to develop tactics that would be employed in the ensuing world war.

Within a month of the commencement of hostilities, Germany had dispatched eighteen new German Junkers trimotor bombers and six pursuit planes as well as thirty German pilots. As had the Italians, the Germans also furnished a substantial number of transport planes to aid the transfer of Franco's troops, especially the hardened and tough Moroccans, to the mainland. These airlifts became the first major aerial troop transports in military history.

The German fighters ordered by Hitler to Spain adopted the name the Condor Legion. They represented the best military force and equipment available in Germany at the time. Some nineteen thousand Germans served in the Condor Legion, whose equipment included planes, tanks, antiaircraft guns, artillery, transports, and seaplanes.

By war's end, the Germans had tried out twenty-seven different types of aircraft in Spain. In the combat's final year, they had replaced the Heinkels He-51, an inferior airplane, with what proved to be the fastest fighter used in the war, the Messerschmitt Me-109E. The German ace Captain Werner Mölders shot down fourteen enemy planes. Over the course of the conflict, Germany produced a total of fifteen aces, fighter pilots with five or more kills.

Many leftists in the French government had initially expressed support for Spain's Loyalist administration, but France nevertheless refused to supply arms to the Madrid government. Many of France's conservative and religious factions sided with the rebels. The French chose to take the route of nonintervention, even though the Italians and the Germans had already begun to supply Franco's forces with massive amounts of military aid, especially in terms of air power.

At the civil war's commencement, the Spanish government bought a small, inadequate supply of armaments on France's open market. The French writer André Malraux personally rounded up a number of aircraft, hired pilots to fly them, and delivered them to Spain. The aircraft involved were not state of the art, consisting of about thirteen unarmed Dewoitine and six Potex fighters. Malraux organized the Escuadrilla España, also called the First International Air Squadron, composed of volunteers and mercenaries, which represented the main air support for the Loyalist forces in the early stages of the war. At its beginning, Republican Spain's air force had consisted of only about sixty planes, twenty-five of which were fit for combat.

As did the French government, the British government, with a labor majority, expressed sympathy for the Loyalist cause. The British joined the French in maintaining a hands-off attitude in the struggle. They believed that the war would spread throughout Europe if they and the French entered the war on the Republican side. As events unfolded, however, a war involving most of Europe did break out as the Spanish Civil War itself came to a close in 1939.

The Soviet Union proved to be the only ally of Republican Spain that contributed any substantial aid to that country. The Russians provided both pilots and approximately eight hundred aircraft, consisting mostly of Polikarper 1-15's, called "Chatas," and Moskas. They also furnished military experts, guns, and tanks.

However, the distance from Russia to Spain proved to be a major obstruction in the Soviet's aid program. Few Russian ships of the type needed to move this war matériel were available. Most of the equipment had to be moved by water. Any ships seeking to deliver goods to the Loyalists faced Italian and German fighter aircraft and bombers.

Despite this harassment, the Soviet Union managed to make some fifty shipments to Republican Spain during the course of the war. The Republicans responded by paying the Soviet Union more than 500 tons of gold, valued at $518 million, from the Spanish treasury. Much of the equipment and ammunition performed poorly once employed in battle, for the Soviets had shipped a great deal of miscellaneous armaments for which they no longer had any use. The tanks and planes, however, did prove to be critical to the Republican defensive effort and protected Madrid itself from capture for most of the conflict.

Although Soviet leader Joseph Stalin wanted to keep the nation's aid program under wraps, the Soviets did make another major contribution to the Loyalist effort. They began a worldwide campaign to induce leftists and leftist sympathizers to join the ranks of the Republican government in their resistance to the Nationalists and their German and Italian allies. The International Brigades' forces broke down into separate national units. The Eleventh Brigade consisted of anti-Nazi Germans; the Twelfth, of a combination of Germans, Italians and French; the Thirteenth, of Poles, Czechs, and other Eastern Europeans; the Fourteenth, of French and Belgians; and the Fifteenth, of British, and North and South American volunteers. Malraux's First International Air Squadron had volunteers and mercenaries from countries throughout the world.

The Progress of the War

Despite the heroic efforts of the Spanish workers and their foreign volunteers, the poorly armed and equipped Loyalists proved in the long run to be no match for Franco's regulars and his Italian and German allies. The Soviet Union, in its attempts to supply the Republican government, encountered increasing difficulties from both the aggressive German and Italian interference with shipping and the French refusal to allow supplies shipped into their seaports to cross the frontier into Spain.

The Nationalist air force, composed primarily of German and Italian aircraft, flew over Republican positions with impunity, subjecting the major cities held by the government to regular bombing attacks. The Nationalists had gained permanent air supremacy by as early as October, 1936. On April 26, 1937, forty bombers of the Condor Legion attacked the northern Basque city of Guernica. Although the city was not an important military target, it was virtually destroyed, with more than one thousand civilian casualties from among the city's seven thousand inhabitants. The Germans would subject enemy cities to similar degrees of intense destruction during World War II.

As the Loyalist cause continued to deteriorate, aid furnished by foreign allies began to falter. The Soviet pilots who had made up a large part of the barely surviving Republican air force left the combat area by late 1937. Reduced to perhaps seven thousand volunteers near the conclusion of the war, the International Brigades withdrew at the request of the Spanish Republican government itself in November of 1938, ostensibly in a vain attempt to appeal for the withdrawal from Spanish soil of all foreign troops on both sides. Over the course of the war, the poorly armed Brigade forces suffered almost twelve thousand casualties: French, German, Italian, American, and Eastern European fighters who gave their lives in the struggle against Fascism.

Aftermath
Undoubtedly, the nonintervention pact signed by Great Britain and France played a major role in the ultimate defeat of the Spanish Republican government. Both Germany and Italy had poured both personnel and equipment into the Nationalist campaign. By the war's end, the Germans and Italians made up the bulk of the Nationalist military effort. Soviet aid, in contrast, had to be moved far greater distances and under constant attack. Despite the support of the majority of Spain's population, the Republican government could not survive Franco's rebellion.

Carl Henry Marcoux

Bibliography
Howson, Gerald. *Arms for Spain: The Untold Story of the Spanish Civil War.* London: John Murray, 1998. A review of the different approaches and attitudes of the European countries providing aid to the Nationalists and Republicans during the Spanish Civil War.

Puzzo, Dante A. *Spain and the Great Powers, 1936-1941.* New York: Columbia University Press, 1962. An examination of the differences between the open support of Germany and Italy for the Nationalists, the limited support of the Soviet Union for the Republicans, and the refusal of France and England to aid the legitimate Loyalist government.

Wheatley, Robert H. *Hitler and Spain: The Nazi Role in the Spanish Civil War, 1936-1939.* Lexington: The University of Kentucky Press, 1989. A discussion of Hitler's multiple objectives in providing aid to the Nationalists.

See also: Antiaircraft fire; Bombers; Fighter pilots; Guernica, Spain, bombing; Luftwaffe; Messerschmitt aircraft; Military flight; World War II

Spirit of St. Louis

Also known as: Ryan NYP (New York-to-Paris)
Date: Built in 1927
Definition: The first airplane to fly solo across the Atlantic, from New York to Paris, piloted by Charles A. Lindbergh.
Significance: Lindbergh's New York-to-Paris flight in the *Spirit of St. Louis* further proved the feasibility of transatlantic flight, changing the face of civil and military aviation.

In 1927, there was no more famous aviator in the world than Charles A. Lindbergh, and no more famous aircraft than the *Spirit of St. Louis*, the California-built Ryan monoplane that he flew alone and nonstop from New York to Paris that year. The flight was made in an attempt to win the $25,000 Orteig Prize, to be awarded to the first person to make a nonstop flight between New York and Paris.

Raymond Orteig offered his prize of $25,000, for the first pilot to fly nonstop from New York to Paris, in 1919. Originally, the prize was open for a period of five years, but airplane technology was not yet advanced enough for anyone to even make the transatlantic attempt in the early 1920's. When the prize was still unclaimed in 1926, Orteig extended the prize's term to 1931. By this time, transatlantic flight had begun to seem technically possible, and Lindbergh, who was already making a name for himself as a barnstormer, mechanic, and airmail pilot, was one of several aviators who decided to try his luck.

In 1926, Lindbergh raised $15,000 in backing from a consortium of St. Louis businessmen and set out to find a plane. Most people believed that multiple engines were the key to long-distance flight, but Lindbergh believed that he would have a better chance of success with the lightest possible plane, thereby increasing his fuel efficiency. He initially tried to purchase a single-engine plane from Columbia Aircraft Corporation, a New York company, but negotiations failed when the president of Columbia Aircraft wanted too much control over the project.

The Aircraft
Lindbergh had previously contacted the Ryan Aeronautical Company, a San Diego aircraft manufacturer, and in

623

The Spirit of St. Louis *was specially designed by the Ryan Aeronautical Company to Charles Lindbergh's specifications for his historic transatlantic solo flight in 1927.* (Hulton Archive)

February, 1927, Lindbergh finally contracted with the company for the aircraft. The plane, which cost $10,580, was custom-built for that one flight. Named for Lindbergh's financial backers, the *Spirit of St. Louis* was a high-wing monoplane constructed out of steel tubing, an aluminum cowling over the nose, spruce, and cotton cloth painted with aircraft dope covering the body of the plane. Much of the space in the aircraft was taken up by fuel tanks, according to Lindbergh's desire to fly solo so as to save weight and carry more gasoline. The pilot's position was behind the large fuel tank positioned just behind the engine, necessitating a small periscope for forward vision (the pilot could also look out of side windows); the plane carried a total of 451 gallons of fuel. The engine was a remarkably reliable 223-horsepower, nine-cylinder Wright Whirlwind air-cooled radial engine mounted in the nose of the aircraft. The plane was 27 feet, 8 inches from nose to tail and 46 feet from wingtip to wingtip. She weighed 2,150 pounds empty and 5,135 pounds fully loaded.

The Flight

Though U.S. Navy flying boats had made a crossing from Newfoundland to Portugal, with a stop in the Azores, in May, 1919, and British Royal Air Force officers John Alcock and Arthur Whitten Brown had flown nonstop from Newfoundland to Ireland the next month, Lindbergh's would be the first solo nonstop transatlantic flight, and his route was considerably longer. Lindbergh planned his flight carefully, and took off from Roosevelt Field in New York at 7:54 A.M. on May 20, 1927. At 10:24 P.M. on May 21, Lindbergh landed in Paris after a 33.5-hour flight, having fought exhaustion (he had not slept for twenty-four hours before his flight), hallucinations, and ice formation on the plane during the flight. Upon landing, the plane was mobbed by thousands of spectators and slightly damaged before it could be taken into a hangar. A week later, the plane repaired, Lindbergh flew the plane to Belgium, then to England, from where he and the crated airplane returned to the United States on an American cruiser.

The Aftermath

After a year of touring the United States and South America, the remarkable plane was donated on April 30, 1928, to the Smithsonian Institution, where it is now part of the permanent collection of its National Air and Space Museum in Washington, D.C. The flight catapulted Lindbergh (soon dubbed "Lucky Lindy") to a worldwide fame that would never leave him; he spent the rest of his life as an ambassador for the advancement of aviation and, later, for environmental causes. The accomplishment of the plane itself was also remarkable for many reasons. It showed that a small, single-engine aircraft could be rugged and reliable enough for the rigors of transatlantic flight; it further proved that nonstop crossings were feasible, and it showed that airplanes in general had reached a level of safety and reliability that meant they could be used for regular transportation.

Robert Whipple, Jr.

Bibliography

Berg, A. Scott. *Lindbergh*. New York: Berkeley, 1998. The Pulitzer Prize-winning biography of Lindbergh, which contains detailed information on the planning and construction of the aircraft.

Greenwood, John T., ed. *Milestones of Aviation: Smithsonian Institution, National Air and Space Museum*. New York: Hugh Lauter Levin, 1995. Covers the important markers in aviation history, including a detailed section on the *Spirit of St. Louis* and its transatlantic flight.

Lindbergh, Charles A. *We*. New York: Grosset & Dunlap,

1927. Lindbergh's story of his life up to and including the famous flight and its immediate aftermath.

Smithsonian Institution National Air and Space Museum. "Milestones of Flight." (www.nasm.edu/galleries/gal100/gal100.html) This World Wide Web site contains information on many historic aircraft, including a section on the *Spirit of St. Louis*.

See also: Airplanes; Charles A. Lindbergh; Monoplanes; Record flights; Transatlantic flight

Spitfire

Definition: The most important single-seat fighter used by the British Royal Air Force (RAF) during World War II.

Significance: The Spitfire served on the front lines of every theater of World War II and was produced in greater numbers than any other Allied fighter.

Evolution
Reginald J. Mitchell, the chief designer of the Supermarine company, designed the Supermarine Type 224 in response to a request for new RAF fighter aircraft to meet Air Ministry Specifications. The Type 224 flew for the first time in February, 1934. However, Mitchell was dissatisfied with the plane even before it flew and believed he could design a much better fighter aircraft by ignoring the specification. The Supermarine company undertook the work as a private venture, and the new design, the Spitfire, was accepted by the Air Ministry in January, 1935. Mitchell had previously designed a successful series of racing seaplanes for which the Rolls-Royce company had produced a powerful engine. Development of this engine produced the Rolls-Royce Merlin, which was chosen to power the Spitfire.

Description
The Spitfire was a low-wing, single-seater fighter aircraft of all-metal construction, featuring a retractable undercarriage and enclosed cockpit. Initially it was armed with eight 0.303-inch Browning machine guns, with which the Battle of Britain (1940) was fought. Later models carried gradually increasing armament, until the last, produced after the war, carried four 20-millimeter cannon. It could also carry bombs for use in the ground attack role. The most outstanding visual feature of the Spitfire, and the one by which it could always be recognized, was the elliptical wing shape featuring a smooth curve on the trailing edge to meet a lesser curve on the leading edge at the pointed wingtip.

In Service
The Spitfire went into service with RAF fighter squadrons in late 1938, and, by the start of the war in September, 1939, was being flown by nine squadrons. By the time of the Battle of Britain, it was being flown by nineteen squadrons. Although it was not the most numerically important British aircraft, as was the Hawker Hurricane, the Spitfire played a vital role. Equal in performance to the Luftwaffe's Messerschmitt Bf-109 fighter, it could take on the Bf-109 even though the British fighters were often outnumbered by the fighters that escorted the German bombers.

The Spitfire had been designed to intercept bombers attacking the British Isles, and, for this purpose, it did not need a great range. After the Battle of Britain had been won, the RAF gradually shifted, with increasing confidence, to a more offensive mode. The Spitfire was used to fight far from home, over enemy territory. In order to provide the necessary range, it was fitted with external fuel tanks to allow it to seek out the Luftwaffe in its home territory.

Development
The first Spitfires could reach speeds of 360 miles per hour and heights of 31,000 feet. By the end of the war, later models reached speeds of 460 miles per hour and heights of 44,000 feet. Later models received a newer, more powerful engine, the Rolls-Royce Griffon. The British Royal Navy also needed modern fighter aircraft, and the Spitfire was fitted with an arrester hook and catapult attachments to become the Seafire, in which guise it operated from aircraft carriers. The first Seafires were simply modified Spitfires. In order to render them fully suitable for naval use, they were redesigned to allow the wings to fold for storage purposes below decks.

Production
The advanced design of the Spitfire and its complicated elliptical wing initially caused production problems, because the hundreds of subcontractors necessary to ensure the required production rate were simply unused to the design. The bombing of the Supermarine works at Southampton during the Battle of Britain almost halted production, and it was quickly decided to disperse the factories, which added to production difficulties. However, new factories were built and additional men and women were trained, and, by the end of 1941, production of Spitfires was more or less satisfactory.

Fighting

The Spitfire was designed to fight other aircraft, and at this it was perhaps the best all-around fighter aircraft of World War II. Its real strength, however, lay in its superb maneuverability, which few aircraft could even approach. It could out-turn every German fighter, and although some models that were developed for a specific purpose did not have quite the same ability as others, generally speaking, the Spitfire was beloved by all who flew it.

The armament with which the Spitfire started the war soon became inadequate and was upgraded to include two 20-millimeter cannon in the Mark V and most subsequent models. However, some Spitfires were built with no armament at all. It had been found that the Spitfire, with modifications, could fly fast enough and high enough to avoid any attempts at interception and so, fitted with cameras, it became the backbone of RAF reconnaissance units.

Post-World War II Use

The end of World War II did not mean the end of the Spitfire, and the Seafire saw service with the British Royal Navy in Korea. In 1948, Israeli Spitfires flew alongside Israeli Bf-109's against Egyptian Spitfires in a confrontation in the Middle East. The RAF continued to use the Spitfire in a weather reconnaissance role until June, 1957.

Of more than 22,000 Spitfires and Seafires built, fewer than seventy are preserved, but approximately one-half of these remain airworthy and may be seen at flying displays all over the world.

Hugh Wheeler

Bibliography

Dibbs, John, and Tony Holmes. *Spitfire: The Flying Legend*. Oxford, England: Osprey, 2000. A tribute to the Spitfire, extensively illustrated with contemporary and archival photographs and featuring firsthand accounts from surviving Spitfire pilots.

Ethell, Jeffrey L., and Steve Pace. *Spitfire*. Osceola, Wis.: Motorbooks International, 1997. A history of the Spitfire in World War II, with bibliographical references and an index.

Morgan, Eric B., and Edward Shacklady. *Spitfire: The History*. Lincolnshire, England: Key Publishing, 2000. A wide-ranging and well-illustrated book describing the Spitfire in fine detail.

Oliver, David. *Jane's Supermarine Spitfire*. London: HarperCollins, 1999. Describes a typical Spitfire interception mission during the Battle of Britain.

See also: Airplanes; Battle of Britain; Fighter pilots; Luftwaffe; Messerschmitt aircraft; Military flight; Monoplanes; Reconnaissance; Royal Air Force; World War II

Spruce Goose

- **Also known as:** HK-1, HK-4 Hercules, Hughes H-4 Hercules, the Hughes Flying Boat, the "Flying Lumberyard"
- **Date:** Design work began in 1942; a prototype was completed and one test flight was accomplished in 1947
- **Definition:** In terms of wingspan, the largest aircraft ever built; because of its wooden construction, also one of the most controversial airplanes ever built.
- **Significance:** The *Spruce Goose* flying boat was designed during World War II to transport cargo or troops over long distances; its sole flight, over a distance of one mile in 1947, is a landmark in aviation history; its massive size and distinctive wooden construction have made it a true American icon.

Development

With a wingspan of 320 feet—longer than a football field—the *Spruce Goose* has the distinction of being the largest aircraft ever built. Planned and designed during World War II, when materials such as aluminum were in short supply and were reserved for the most urgent military projects, the *Spruce Goose* earned its name from its nearly all-wood construction. Only the flaps, or control surfaces, were made from fabric; the remainder of the plane was fashioned from layers of plywood especially constructed at the Hughes Aircraft Company plant in Culver City, California. Despite its nickname, the "*Spruce Goose*," only about 5 to 10 percent of the craft is constructed of spruce; the remainder is birch plywood. The name stuck, however, because, in the words of one worker, "nobody could think of a word that rhymed with birch."

The idea for such a gigantic seaplane originated with F. H. Hoge, Jr., a member of the Planning Committee of the War Production Board. After German submarines sank some 300,000 tons of British and American shipping during May, 1942, Hoge proposed to solve the submarine problem by building flying boats to transport cargo and troops across the Atlantic Ocean. Unlike conventional aircraft, flying boats could land or take off on bays or harbors and did not need long, land-based runways.

The idea intrigued the industrialist and shipbuilder Henry Kaiser, famous for building the Liberty Ships during World War II. In July, 1942, he suggested that the United States build an "aerial freighter" of at least seventy tons, a "gigantic flying ship" beyond anything imagined by the nineteenth-century science fiction writer Jules Verne. Kaiser asked for help from the billionaire Howard Hughes, a crack designer and pilot who had broken several airspeed records during the 1930's.

The project was approved in October, 1942. A team from Hughes Aircraft Company would design the craft and build one prototype and two additional planes. Once tests were completed, Kaiser's companies would begin regular production. The project was initially designated the HK-1 (HK for Hughes/Kaiser). Once design work had begun, Hughes employees voted to name it the H-4 Hercules. Hughes himself disliked the popular name of "*Spruce Goose*" and preferred to call the aircraft "the Flying Boat."

The project fell well behind schedule very early, mainly due to a multitude of design and construction problems. Kaiser dropped out of the project, and Hughes was forced by various government bodies to defend the project. Only continued support from the War Production Board and the personal intervention of President Franklin D. Roosevelt kept the project going.

Design

The problems involved in designing and building such an airplane were massive. Kaiser had suggested that the overall size of the first prototype be seventy tons, but Hughes made the work more challenging by changing the size to some two hundred tons. The goal was an aircraft that could carry 130,000 pounds of cargo or 750 troops (twice the passenger load of a modern Boeing 747).

Working at the Hughes Aircraft Company plant in Culver City, California, and at other sites, the Hughes team tested a variety of shapes for air and water efficiency. The final design model, based on decisions largely made by Hughes himself, recorded the lowest air drag of any seaplane ever tested at the National Advisory Committee for Aeronautics' Research Center at Langley Field, Virginia. Instead of a double-hulled plane, Hughes choose a single-hulled design which would require a wingspan 50 percent larger than the next largest plane of the time, the Martin JRM Mars. It was also decided that the aircraft would have a sizeable single vertical tail.

The final design divided the interior of the fuselage into two decks connected by a spiral staircase: a flight control deck for the operating crew and a cargo deck. Two railroad cars could fit in the interior cargo space, on a floor that was designed to carry 125 pounds per square foot. If planks were provided for its tracks, a 60-ton army tank could drive inside, under its own power, without the need to dismantle any part of the tank. The hull also contains eighteen watertight compartments, twelve of which might flood without sinking the craft.

In its final design, the *Spruce Goose* has an overall length of 218 feet. Its 320-foot wingspan exceeds even that of the U.S. Air Force's modern transport, the Lockheed C-5A Galaxy. The tail alone, at 113 feet, is more than eight stories high. The hull is 265 feet wide and the wings, at their thickest, are more than 11 feet thick. The craft has a gross weight of 400,000 pounds and a range of 3,500 miles. It cruises at 175 miles per hour and has a landing speed of 78 miles per hour.

Hughes chose to power the plane with Pratt & Whitney R-4360 engines. Eight of these twenty-eight-cylinder, 3,000-horsepower engines were mounted in the wings. The engines, radial in shape, sport four-blade Hamilton

---

Events in *Spruce Goose* History

May, 1942: Federal government official F. H. Hoge, Jr., proposes that the German submarine threat be countered by the construction of massive "aerial freighters" to fly cargo and troops across the Atlantic Ocean.

July, 1942: Industrialist Henry Kaiser proposes that the United States build "aerial freighters" of from 70 to 500 tons.

August, 1942: Kaiser suggests that billionaire and aviator Howard Hughes meet with him concerning the "aerial freighter" project.

November, 1942: A new Kaiser-Hughes corporation signs a federal government contract to design and manufacture *Spruce Goose* aircraft.

June, 1946: Sections of the *Spruce Goose* are moved from the Culver City, California, plant of the Hughes Aircraft Company to a final assembly site near Long Beach, California.

August, 1947: Hughes begins testimony before a congressional committee investigating the *Spruce Goose* project.

November, 1947: Hughes flies the *Spruce Goose* for the distance of a mile in Long Beach Bay.

February, 1982: The *Spruce Goose* is moved to become a public exhibit alongside the ocean liner *Queen Mary* in Long Beach.

October, 1992: The *Spruce Goose* is shipped via ocean barge to Portland, Oregon, to become a public exhibit in McMinnville, Oregon.

Standard propellers more than 17 feet in diameter. There are a total of 448 spark plugs to service and maintain. Although the total engine horsepower of 24,000 is impressive, the engines' ability to lift a craft of more than 400,000 pounds is a real achievement for both their makers and the Hughes team's overall design efforts.

Flight controls that would respond reliably and quickly were a special problem for such a gigantic aircraft. The layout of the flight controls on the flight deck is conventional—a dual column and wheel to turn the elevator and ailerons, and pedals for the rudder. Less conventional is the way that the craft was designed to respond to these controls. Instead of a mechanical system, Hughes and his team chose a hydraulic system in which pressurized oil moves the control surfaces. Purely mechanical links between the flight deck and the rest of the plane would have required the strength of 150 to 200 men just to turn the controls. Mechanical links also are unreliable in such a massive aircraft. The *Spruce Goose* is so large that changes in temperature could cause metal parts to expand and contract, possibly jamming in the process.

In addition to wing fuel tanks, there is a central fuel system in the hull. Fuel lines in the wings, however, have slip joints to allow for wing deflections of as much as 13 feet during flight.

The *Spruce Goose* pioneered the use of a 120-volt DC electrical system in airplanes. This relatively high voltage leaves a safety margin in case of electrical leakage in any of the 32 miles of wire inside the *Spruce Goose*. It also allows manageable wire sizes to be used. (A 24-volt system, the engineers calculated, would have required solid aluminum rods 2 inches in diameter in order to carry the current.) Electrical relays are specially designed to work at high altitudes.

Construction

A special building at Culver City, claimed to be the world's largest wooden building at the time, was used to build the subassemblies of the *Spruce Goose*. The most challenging construction problems involved the extensive use of wood. The Hughes team spent a great deal of time fashioning a wood construction process that would hold together in the stresses of flight. Although metal would be available in sufficient quantities during the last two years of World War II, that was not true when the *Spruce Goose* project began. At that time, aluminum and other key materials were reserved for higher priority war projects.

The structure of the aircraft was created from laminated layers of wood. The process chosen for laminating the wood, called Duramold, had first been used by Hughes in 1934 to construct parts of his record-breaking H-1 racer airplane. Birch was selected because it created a stronger plywood than spruce. To secure the most suitable birch wood, a team of specialists was sent to inspect and purchase trees in Wisconsin.

Layers of wood were bonded together with three different types of epoxy glues, and heat and steam were applied to "cure" the glues. The process required special jigs and construction techniques, some of which have remained secret. Workers had to wear gloves, since the oil from fingerprints might weaken a glue joint. For the wings, some 8,000 nails were used to hold the wood layers together until the glues had cured. All had to be removed later with special nail pullers.

Considerable sanding of the plywood exterior was necessary. A coat of wood filler was applied to all exterior surfaces, followed by a layer of sealer, a layer of rice paper, and two coats of spar varnish. The final step was a layer of aluminized spar varnish, which gave the *Spruce Goose* its silver color. These steps produced a smooth, glossy finish that was said to be more air efficient than aluminum skins, which require large numbers of rivets, which cause drag.

The Spruce Goose *sits in the water off Long Beach, California, during its only flight, on November 2, 1947.* (AP/Wide World Photos)

Assembly and Flight

In the summer of 1946, one year after World War II had ended, the subassemblies of the *Spruce Goose*, including the hull, tails, and wing sections, were transported to a dry dock and assembly site near Terminal Island, in the vicinity of the Long Beach naval base.

In 1947, the project came under attack from Republicans in the House of Representatives, who insisted that the *Spruce Goose* was a fitting symbol of the wastefulness of the Democratic administration of President Roosevelt. One congressman termed the flying boat "the flying lumberyard." Although Hughes defended the project passionately in congressional hearings, privately he told company workers to accelerate the project or "the next time you'll see me in jail." Hughes, who had spent much of his time during the war working on another aircraft, the XF-11, now worked at the assembly site for the *Spruce Goose* full time, although, characteristically, he did his work at night.

On November 2, 1947, a test of the plane was scheduled which involved taxiing the craft across Long Beach Bay. Some members of the press were invited to ride aboard the plane, and Hughes took the controls. After two successful trips across the bay, Hughes increased the plane's speed during the third attempt. He delighted a sizeable crowd of onlookers by lifting the plane off the water. After traveling for a mile at a height of about 70 feet, the craft landed smoothly. Although it was the only flight ever made in the *Spruce Goose*, it became a memorable moment in aviation history.

Although Hughes described the test flight as "just great," he never flew the craft again. There are varying opinions as to why he made no further attempts. Some argue that the plywood construction was not totally satisfactory (some workers claimed that Hughes attempted to address this by adding a corrugated aluminum skin and metal stiffeners into the gigantic wing). Others believe that Hughes saw congressional criticism as a challenge and lost interest after the successful flight.

Yet Hughes continued to spend money on the aircraft. Although the original plans had called for three *Spruce Goose*s, no other versions of the planes were ever produced. The prototype remained in Hughes's control for the remainder of his life, sitting in a hangar that was air-conditioned to provide the proper humidity to preserve the wood.

The craft was kept airworthy and the engines were fired up every month. The *Spruce Goose* was painted white. Hughes continued to make improvements, such as installing more powerful engines. When flooding damaged the *Spruce Goose*, Hughes built a larger hangar. While the United States government spent some $22 million on the project, Hughes spent an estimated $7 to $18 million dollars of his own money to complete and maintain the *Spruce Goose*.

The *Spruce Goose* as an Exhibit

Four years after Hughes' death in 1976, rumors circulated that the airplane was going to be disassembled so that pieces could be given to museums around the country. There were public protests, and the United States House of Representatives voted to declare the *Spruce Goose* a national treasure. Finally, the airplane was moved to another section of Long Beach, where it was put on display next to the ocean liner Queen Mary. Its new home was the world's largest geodesic dome, some 400 feet in diameter.

In 1988, the owner of the *Spruce Goose*, the Aero Club of Southern California/Aero Exhibits, sold the aircraft to the Evergreen Aviation Museum of the Evergreen Aviation Company in McMinnville, Oregon. A large section of the geodesic dome was removed to allow the *Spruce Goose* to be disassembled and placed on an ocean barge for its long journey.

Niles R. Holt

Bibliography

Barton, Charles. *Howard Hughes and His Flying Boat*. Fallbrook, Calif.: Aero, 1982. Makes excellent use of government documents to explain Hughes's struggles to save the *Spruce Goose* project from officials who wanted to close down the project. It is based on interviews with a large number of people who were involved in the project.

McDonald, John J. *Howard Hughes and the Spruce Goose*. Blue Ridge Summit, Pa.: Tab Books, 1981. This well-done and well-illustrated volume is the most detailed and readable book about the *Spruce Goose*. It has a separate chapter explaining the operating systems of the plane and contains more than eighteen pages of detailed drawings of different sections of the plane.

Odekirk, Glenn E. *HK-1 Hercules: A Pictorial History of the Fantastic Hughes Flying Boat*. Long Beach, Calif.: Frank Alcanter, 1982. This excellent volume includes some one hundred large photographs of the *Spruce Goose*, especially during different stages of assembly. Particularly interesting are the photographs of the move from Culver City to the dry dock near Long Beach. The author was one of Hughes's closest friends and fellow-workers on the *Spruce Goose* project.

See also: Airplanes; Howard Hughes; World War II

Sputnik

Date: Beginning October 4, 1957
Definition: The first man-made satellite to orbit Earth.
Significance: The launching of Sputnik 1 demonstrated that artificial satellites could be placed into orbit and transmit radio signals to Earth, opening the era of space exploration.

Early History of the Sputnik Program

The launching of the first man-made, Earth-orbiting satellite traces its history back to 1946, when Premier Joseph Stalin ordered the beginning of the Soviet Union's postwar rocket program. Soviet aeronautical engineer Sergei Korolev, later known as the father of the Soviet space program in the 1950's and 1960's, was appointed chief designer. Initially Korolev's group flew captured German V-2 rockets from Kapustin Yar, near Volgograd. Korolev, like many of his contemporaries, envisioned huge rockets that could be used for the exploration of space. However, political leaders could justify the large expense of a rocket development program only as part of a military system. The development of the atomic bomb required the construction of a long-range delivery system, either a long-range bomber or an intercontinental ballistic missile (ICBM). The first Soviet Earth-orbiting satellite came about as a result of both the interest of Korolev in exploring space and the interest of the Soviet premiers, Stalin and later Nikita Khrushchev, in having a rocket to deliver atomic bombs to the United States.

Sputnik's R-7 Rocket

Korolev's group developed the Soviet ICBM, a missile called the R-7. The design of the R-7 rocket remained secret until 1967, when the Soviet Union displayed the rocket at the Paris Air Show.

The R-7 is a one-and-one-half-stage ballistic rocket, measuring about 68 feet tall and about 34 feet across at its base. It consists of a central core surrounded by four strap-on booster rockets. The core of each of the strap-on booster rockets is a cluster of four rocket engines. At liftoff, the R-7 rocket employs twenty rocket engines, each generating 55,000 pounds of thrust, firing simultaneously. The liftoff thrust is more than 1 million pounds. When the four strap-on booster rockets exhaust their fuel, they drop off, leaving the four engines of the central core to provide the final thrust to deliver a warhead to its target or a satellite to orbit. The basic R-7 rocket can place about 3,000 pounds into a low orbit around the earth.

The R-7 rocket was successfully tested as an ICBM for the first time on August 27, 1957. It was used in unmodified form to launch the first three Sputnik satellites. As it became necessary to launch heavier satellites, a second stage was added to the R-7 to improve its performance.

The First Sputnik Satellite

Even before the R-7 rocket was test flown, Korolev suggested, in a secret memo to the Soviet government in 1954, the possibility of launching a satellite. Later, Korolev's group proposed to the Soviet National Academy of Sciences the possibility of launching an Earth-orbiting satellite using the new rocket. The International Geophysical Year, an eighteen-month period in 1957 and 1958 dedicated to the scientific study of the earth, provided the opportunity. Scientists recognized that many geophysical questions could be investigated only through the use of satellites. A satellite could be used to determine the density of the atmosphere high above the earth and could serve as a sensitive probe of the mass distribution in the earth, and satellite-borne instruments could monitor both radiation in space and the strength of the earth's magnetic field.

After Korolev was given the go-ahead to launch an Earth-orbiting satellite, a team to build the satellite was established. The satellite team set to work designing and building an ambitious, 3,000-pound satellite carrying an array of scientific instruments. This complex scientific satellite project fell behind schedule, and it appeared to Korolev that the R-7 rocket would be ready to loft the first satellite before there was a satellite ready to launch. Because the United States had announced its own plans to launch a satellite, it became imperative for the Soviets to launch their satellite as soon as possible.

Korolev's rocket design group decided to design and build a simple satellite in their own facility, in order to have something to launch when the R-7 was ready. In just two months, Korolev's group assembled what became the world's first artificial satellite, named "Sputnik," the Russian word for "traveler." This first Sputnik was simply an engineering test satellite that carried no scientific research instruments.

The R-7 rocket carrying Sputnik 1 lifted off from the Tyuratum Launch Facility on October 4, 1957. During the launch, Sputnik 1 was housed inside a protective nose cone on top of the R-7 rocket. After the core rocket had reached an altitude of 142 miles and a speed of 26,249 miles per hour, the rocket shut down, and Sputnik 1 was in orbit. The orbit was highly elliptical, with a low point of 142 miles and a high point of 588 miles above the earth's surface. Sputnik 1 circled the earth once every 96.2 minutes. Because its orbit was inclined about 65 degrees from the equator, Sputnik 1 traced out a path over the globe that took it over most of the populated regions of the world once every day.

Sputnik 1 was spherical in shape with a diameter of 22.8 inches and a weight of 184 pounds. The spherical shell was made of an aluminum alloy, and the interior was filled with nitrogen, a gas that would not condense even at the cold temperatures in space. At launch, four communications antennae, each about 9 feet in length, were folded to allow the satellite to fit into the nose cone of the R-7 launch vehicle. After Sputnik 1 was placed in orbit, the nose cone was jettisoned, the antenna were deployed, and the satellite separated from the core rocket. Sputnik 1 had two radio transmitters, working on frequencies of about 20 megahertz and 40 megahertz.

The temperature inside the aluminum shell of Sputnik 1 was monitored using sensors that produced small changes in the transmitter frequency with temperature. It was not known how much the temperature inside the satellite would vary as the Sputnik traveled from the sunlit to the dark side of the earth in a cycle that repeated every 96 minutes. These temperature measurements provided information on the design changes that might be needed on future satellites to maintain a uniform interior temperature.

The core rocket that carried Sputnik 1 remained in orbit for sixty days. The Sputnik 1 satellite remained in orbit for ninety-four days, although its batteries had drained and the transmitter had ceased to function after twenty-one days.

Although Sputnik 1 was designed only as an engineering test satellite, it did produce useful scientific results. The aerodynamics of spherical objects were well understood, so the rate at which the orbit of Sputnik 1 decayed as a result of air drag provided the first measurement of the air density at the orbital altitude. These measurements indicated that the air was ten times more dense than some scientists had previously modeled. In addition, the properties of the ionosphere, the upper region of the earth's atmosphere, were examined by monitoring how the 20- and 40-megahertz radio signals from the transmitters on Sputnik 1 were altered during passage through the upper atmosphere.

The First Scientific Sputniks

Sputnik 2, launched on November 3, 1957, was the first Earth-orbiting satellite to carry a full complement of scientific instruments. Sputnik 2, which weighed 1,118 pounds, was conical in shape, measuring about 12 feet long and about 6 feet in diameter, to maximize the use of the space available inside the R-7's conical nose cone. Sputnik 2 was placed into a highly elliptical orbit, coming within 140 miles of the earth's surface at closest approach and going out to 1,038 miles from the earth's surface, circling the earth once every 104 minutes.

The major purpose of Sputnik 2 was to study the effects of space travel, particularly weightlessness, on animals. The Soviet Union had previously launched animals, including dogs, on high-altitude rocket flights, providing extensive information on the response of animals to the liftoff acceleration. On previous rocket flights, however, weightlessness had lasted for only brief periods of time.

Sputnik 2 carried an 11-pound dog, named Laika, into orbit. The monitors on Sputnik 1 had already demonstrated that the interior temperature could be maintained in a range suitable for survival. However, the nitrogen atmosphere of Sputnik 1 was unsuitable to support life. To provide a suitable atmosphere, Soviet scientists used a system of reactive chemicals to give

Sputnik, launched by the Soviet Union on October 4, 1957, was the first artificial satellite to orbit Earth. (NASA CORE/Lorain Valley JVS)

off oxygen for Laika to inhale and another chemical system to absorb the carbon dioxide that Laika exhaled. Information on Laika's physical condition was radioed to Earth, and Soviet scientists concluded that animals could withstand weightlessness during orbital flight. Because the technology did not exist in 1957 to return Sputnik 2 and its passenger, Laika, to Earth, the dog was put to death by an injection of poison after providing seven days of biomedical data. Sputnik 2 fell from orbit on April 14, 1958.

Sputnik 2 also contained instruments to monitor the amount of solar and cosmic radiation penetrating the spacecraft's walls. The intensity of this radiation in orbit had not been known before Sputnik 2. This flight demonstrated that sufficient shielding could be provided by spacecraft walls in order to allow the short-term survival of animals in space.

Sputnik 2 demonstrated that animals, and presumably humans, could survive weightlessness and the radiation of the space environment and demonstrated techniques to provide oxygen, to clear the air of carbon dioxide, and to maintain a livable temperature in an orbiting spacecraft. Instruments on Sputnik 2 showed that the radiation intensity increased as the spacecraft's altitude and latitude increased. Later spacecraft showed that this was due to Sputnik 2 entering the edge of the Van Allen radiation belts, bands of high-energy-charged particles circling the earth beginning at an altitude of about 600 miles.

Sputnik 3, launched on May 15, 1958, made use of the full 3,000-pound lofting capability of the R-7 rocket. The satellite weighed 3,018 pounds, carrying 2,130 pounds of scientific and communications equipment. Unlike the biological mission of Sputnik 2, Sputnik 3 was designed to conduct a geophysical study of the space environment. It carried instruments to measure the solar and cosmic radiation outside the spacecraft, the earth's magnetic field, the rate of impact of micrometeorites, and the properties of the ionosphere. Sputnik 3 was placed in a very similar orbit to that of Sputnik 2, coming within 141 miles of the earth's surface at closest approach and going out to 1,168 miles from the earth's surface. Sputnik 3 took 106 minutes to circle the earth. Its instruments continued to function for almost two years, until Sputnik 3 reentered the earth's atmosphere on April 6, 1960.

Sputnik 3 performed a series of geophysical measurements. It began to map the belts of radiation that surround the earth. Sputnik 3 detected a sharp increase in the drag on the satellite in the same regions where the intensity of high-energy electrons hitting the satellite increased. The magnetometer on Sputnik 3 produced the first map of the earth's magnetic field.

Impact of the Sputnik Launches

The news that the Soviet Union had launched the world's first artificial satellite shocked much of the world. Although many people in Europe and North America had regarded Soviet science and engineering as inferior to that of the West, Sputnik 1 demonstrated Soviet capability in space technology. Within hours of the launching of Sputnik 1, U.S. senator Lyndon B. Johnson initiated a complete investigation into the state of the United States satellite and missile programs. Boris Chertok, the deputy director of the Soviet ICBM project, was surprised by the effect of the news of the launching of Sputnik 1. "We thought the satellite was just a simple thing: What mattered to us was to test the rocket again to gather statistics on how its systems were functioning. And suddenly the whole world was abuzz. It was only later that we understood what we had done." In response to Sputnik 1, the United States undertook a massive reform of education, with a new emphasis on science and mathematics courses.

Historically, most nations have claimed sovereignty over the airspace above their territories and have regulated flights of aircraft in their airspace. The launching of Sputnik 1 resulted in the development of new principles of international law, because Sputnik 1 passed over many nations, including the United States. Because these other countries did not protest when Sputnik flew over their territories, the principle was established that any nation can orbit a satellite over the territory of another nation.

George J. Flynn

Bibliography

Divine, Robert A. *The Sputnik Challenge*. New York: Oxford University Press, 1993. A thorough discussion of the social and political aspects of Sputnik and the space race, focusing particularly on the impact of Sputnik on the West.

Olberg, James E. *Red Star in Orbit*. New York: Random House, 1980. A comprehensive, well-illustrated account of the Soviet space program, including the Sputnik series of satellites and the development of the ICBM. Olberg's account, intended for general audiences, is drawn mainly from Soviet media reports.

Stoiko, Michael. *Soviet Rocketry*. New York: Holt, Rinehart and Winston, 1970. Chapter 6 describes the development of the R-7 ICBM that launched the early Sputniks. Chapter 7 provides an exhaustive discussion of the design, flight, and accomplishments of the first Sputnik satellites.

See also: Crewed spaceflight; Orbiting; Russian space program; Satellites; Spaceflight; Uncrewed spaceflight

ENCYCLOPEDIA OF
FLIGHT

Alphabetical Index of Entries

Accident investigation, 1
Advanced propulsion, 5
Advanced Space Transportation Program, 9
Aer Lingus, 12
Aerobatics, 14
Aerodynamics, 17
Aeroflot, 22
Aeromexico, 23
Aeronautical engineering, 25
Aerospace industry, U.S., 28
Ailerons and flaps, 32
Air Canada, 33
Air carriers, 34
Air Combat Command, 39
Air Force, U.S., 42
Air Force bases, 47
Air Force One, 50
Air France, 52
Air rage, 54
Air shows, 57
Air traffic control, 59
Airbus, 63
Aircraft carriers, 67
Airfoils, 70
Airline Deregulation Act, 72
Airline industry, U.S., 75
Airmail delivery, 81
Airplanes, 84
Airport security, 88
Airports, 92
Alitalia, 97
Altitude, 99
American Airlines, 101
Animal flight, 104
Antiaircraft fire, 108
Apache helicopter, 110
Apollo Program, 111
Neil Armstrong, 114
Astronauts and cosmonauts, 115
Jacqueline Auriol, 120
Autopilot, 120
Avionics, 122

Baggage handling and regulations, 125
Balloons, 127
Barnstorming, 131
Bats, 132
Battle of Britain, 134
Beechcraft, 137
Bell Aircraft, 139
Bermuda Triangle, 141
Biplanes, 143
Birds, 146
Black Sheep Squadron, 148
Blimps, 149
Blue Angels, 151
Boarding procedures, 153
Boeing, 154
Bombers, 157
Boomerangs, 161
Richard Branson, 163
Wernher von Braun, 164
British Airways, 165
Buoyant aircraft, 167
Richard E. Byrd, 170

Cargo aircraft, 172
Sir George Cayley, 174
Cessna Aircraft Company, 175
Octave Chanute, 177
Jacqueline Cochran, 179
Cockpit, 180
Bessie Coleman, 182
Commercial flight, 183
Communication, 187
Concorde, 190
Continental Airlines, 193
Corporate and private jets, 196
Crewed spaceflight, 198
Crop dusting, 202
Glenn H. Curtiss, 203

DC plane family, 205
Delta Air Lines, 208
Dirigibles, 211
Dogfights, 215
Jimmy Doolittle, 217

Doppler radar, 218
Dresden, Germany, bombing, 220
Hugh L. Dryden, 223

Eagle, 225
Amelia Earhart, 227
EgyptAir, 229
El Al, 231
Emergency procedures, 232
Enola Gay, 235
Evolution of animal flight, 237
Experimental aircraft, 241

Federal Aviation Administration, 245
Fighter pilots, 249
Fighting Falcon, 251
Firefighting aircraft, 253
Flight attendants, 256
Flight control systems, 259
Flight plans, 262
Flight recorder, 263
Flight schools, 265
Flight simulators, 269
Flying Fortress, 270
Flying Tigers, 272
Flying wing, 274
Fokker aircraft, 275
Food service, 278
Forces of flight, 281
Steve Fossett, 284
Franco-Prussian War, 286
Frequent flier miles, 287

Yuri Gagarin, 290
Roland Garros, 291
Gemini Program, 292
John Glenn, 295
Gliders, 297
Robert H. Goddard, 299
Goodyear blimp, 301
Gravity, 303
Guernica, Spain, bombing, 305
Guidance systems, 309

xv

Gulf War, 311
Gyros, 314

Hang gliding and paragliding, 318
Harrier jets, 320
Heavier-than-air craft, 322
Helicopters, 326
High-altitude flight, 330
High-speed flight, 333
Hijacking, 336
Hindenburg, 340
History of human flight, 343
Hornet, 349
Hot-air balloons, 351
Hovercraft, 353
Howard R. Hughes, 356
Human-powered flight, 357
Hypersonic aircraft, 360

Iberia Airlines, 364
Icing, 365
Insects, 367
Instrumentation, 370

Japan Airlines, 373
Jennys, 374
Jet engines, 376
Jet packs, 380
Jet Propulsion Laboratory, 381
Amy Johnson, 384
Johnson Space Center, 385
Jumbojets, 387

Kamikaze missions, 391
Kennedy Space Center, 394
Kites, 396
KLM, 398
Korean Air, 400
Korean War, 402

Landing gear, 405
Landing procedures, 407
Samuel Pierpont Langley, 409
Learjets, 410
Leonardo da Vinci, 411
Lighter-than-air craft, 413
Otto Lilienthal, 417
Charles A. Lindbergh, 419
Lockheed Martin, 420

Lufthansa, 423
Luftwaffe, 425

McDonnell Douglas, 429
Mach number, 431
Maintenance, 433
Manufacturers, 436
Marine pilots, U.S., 440
Beryl Markham, 442
MD plane family, 444
Mercury project, 446
Mergers, 449
Messerschmitt aircraft, 451
Microgravity, 453
Military flight, 455
Missiles, 460
Billy Mitchell, 463
Model airplanes, 464
Monoplanes, 465
Montgolfier brothers, 467

National Advisory Committee for Aeronautics, 469
National Aeronautics and Space Administration, 472
National Transportation Safety Board, 476
Navy pilots, U.S., 479
Ninety-nines, 481
Northwest Airlines, 483

Hermann Oberth, 485
Orbiting, 486
Osprey helicopter, 488
Overbooking, 490

Pan Am World Airways, 493
Paper airplanes, 495
Parachutes, 497
Parasailing, 499
Passenger regulations, 501
Pearl Harbor, Hawaii, bombing, 502
Auguste Piccard, 506
Pilots and copilots, 507
Piper aircraft, 510
Wiley Post, 513
Ludwig Prandtl, 514
Propellers, 515
Propulsion, 517
PSA, 522

Qantas, 524

Radar, 526
Ramjets, 530
Raptor, 533
Reconnaissance, 534
Record flights, 537
Reentry, 541
Hanna Reitsch, 544
Rescue aircraft, 545
Manfred von Richthofen, 547
Eddie Rickenbacker, 549
Sally K. Ride, 551
Rocket propulsion, 552
Rockets, 554
Roll and pitch, 558
Rotorcraft, 560
Royal Air Force, 562
Rudders, 565
Runway collisions, 566
Runways, 569
Russian space program, 570
Burt Rutan, 574

Safety issues, 576
Antoine de Saint-Exupéry, 579
Alberto Santos-Dumont, 581
SAS, 582
Satellites, 584
Saturn rockets, 588
Seaplanes, 591
707 plane family, 594
Alan Shepard, 598
Igor Sikorsky, 599
Singapore Airlines, 600
Skydiving, 601
Skywriting, 603
Sopwith Camels, 605
Sound barrier, 607
Southwest Airlines, 609
Space shuttle, 611
Spaceflight, 616
Spanish Civil War, 620
Spirit of St. Louis, 623
Spitfire, 625
Spruce Goose, 626
Sputnik, 630
Stabilizers, 633
Stealth bomber, 634
Stealth fighter, 635

Alphabetical Index of Entries

Strategic Air Command, 637
Stratofortress, 640
Superfortress, 643
Supersonic aircraft, 645
Swissair, 647

Tactical Air Command, 650
Tail designs, 651
Takeoff procedures, 655
Taxiing procedures, 658
Valentina Tereshkova, 660
Terrorism, 661
Test pilots, 666
Testing, 669
Ticketing, 672
Tomcat, 673
Training and education, 676
Trans World Airlines, 679
Transatlantic flight, 682
Transcontinental flight, 686
Transglobal flight, 689
Transport aircraft, 692
Triplanes, 696
Konstantin Tsiolkovsky, 697
Andrei Nikolayevich Tupolev, 698
Turbojets and turbofans, 699
Turboprops, 702
Tuskegee Airmen, 703

UFOs, 707
Ultralight aircraft, 712
Uncrewed spaceflight, 714
Uninhabited aerial vehicles, 717
United Air Lines, 720
US Airways, 723

Vanguard Program, 726
Jules Verne, 729
Vertical takeoff and landing, 730
Vietnam War, 731
Viking Program, 736
Virgin Atlantic, 738
"Vomit Comet," 740
Voyager Program, 742

Wake turbulence, 745
Weather conditions, 746
Whirly-Girls, 750
Richard Whitcomb, 752
Wind-powered flight, 753
Wind shear, 757
Wind tunnels, 758
Wing designs, 762
Wing-walking, 765
Winglets, 767
Winnie Mae, 768
Women and flight, 769

Women's Airforce Service Pilots, 773
World War I, 774
World War II, 779
Wright brothers, 785
Wright *Flyer*, 786

X planes, 789

Chuck Yeager, 793

Ferdinand von Zeppelin, 795

Glossary, 797
Bibliography, 803
Web Sites, 811
Organizations and Agencies, 822
Flight Schools and Training Centers in North America, 830
Museums of North America, 843
International Airports, 853
Air Carriers, 859
Airplane Types, 866
Time Line, 878
Air Disasters and Notable Crashes, 889

Categorized Index of Entries

Aerial Warfare
Air Combat Command, 39
Air Force, U.S., 42
Air Force bases, 47
Aircraft carriers, 67
Antiaircraft fire, 108
Balloons, 127
Battle of Britain, 134
Black Sheep Squadron, 148
Bombers, 157
Dirigibles, 211
Dogfights, 215
Jimmy Doolittle, 217
Dresden, Germany, bombing, 220
Eagle, 225
Enola Gay, 235
Fighter pilots, 249
Flying Fortress, 270
Flying Tigers, 272
Franco-Prussian War, 286
Guernica, Spain, bombing, 305
Gulf War, 311
Harrier jets, 320
Hijacking, 336
Hornet, 349
Jennys, 374
Kamikaze missions, 391
Korean War, 402
Luftwaffe, 425
Marine pilots, U.S., 440
Messerschmitt aircraft, 451
Military flight, 455
Missiles, 460
Navy pilots, U.S., 479
Pearl Harbor, Hawaii, bombing, 502
Raptor, 533
Reconnaissance, 534
Manfred von Richthofen, 547
Eddie Rickenbacker, 549
Royal Air Force, 562
Sopwith Camels, 605
Spanish Civil War, 620
Spitfire, 625
Stealth bomber, 634
Stealth fighter, 635
Strategic Air Command, 637
Superfortress, 643
Tactical Air Command, 650
Terrorism, 661
Tomcat, 673
Tuskegee Airmen, 703
Vietnam War, 731
World War I, 774
World War II, 779

Aerodynamics
Advanced propulsion, 5
Aerodynamics, 17
Aeronautical engineering, 25
Ailerons and flaps, 32
Airfoils, 70
Airplanes, 84
Altitude, 99
Autopilot, 120
Avionics, 122
Balloons, 127
Boomerangs, 161
Wernher von Braun, 164
Buoyant aircraft, 167
Sir George Cayley, 174
Octave Chanute, 177
Doppler radar, 218
Experimental aircraft, 241
Flying wing, 274
Forces of flight, 281-283
Gravity, 303
Jet engines, 376
Jet packs, 380
Kites, 396
Samuel Pierpont Langley, 409
Otto Lilienthal, 417
Mach number, 431
Microgravity, 453
Hermann Oberth, 485
Orbiting, 486
Paper airplanes, 495
Ludwig Prandtl, 514
Propellers, 515
Propulsion, 517
Ramjets, 530
Rocket propulsion, 552
Rockets, 554
Roll and pitch, 558
Saturn rockets, 588
Sound barrier, 607
Konstantin Tsiolkovsky, 697
Wake turbulence, 745
Wind tunnels, 758
Wing designs, 762
Winglets, 767
X planes, 789

Air Carriers
Aer Lingus, 12
Aeroflot, 22
Aeromexico, 23
Air Canada, 33
Air carriers, 34
Air France, 52
Airline Deregulation Act, 72
Airline industry, U.S., 75
Airplanes, 84
Airport security, 88
Airports, 92
Alitalia, 97
American Airlines, 101
Baggage handling and regulations, 125
Boarding procedures, 153
British Airways, 165
Commercial flight, 183
Continental Airlines, 193
Delta Air Lines, 208
EgyptAir, 229
El Al, 231
Flight attendants, 256
Food service, 278-280
Frequent flier miles, 287
Iberia Airlines, 364
Japan Airlines, 373
Jumbojets, 387
KLM, 398
Korean Air, 400
Lufthansa, 423
Maintenance, 433
Mergers, 449
Northwest Airlines, 483
Overbooking, 490
Pan Am World Airways, 493
Passenger regulations, 501
PSA, 522
Qantas, 524
SAS, 582
Singapore Airlines, 600
Southwest Airlines, 609
Swissair, 647
Ticketing, 672

Training and education, 676
Trans World Airlines, 679
United Air Lines, 720
US Airways, 723
Virgin Atlantic, 738

Aircraft Design
Advanced propulsion, 5
Advanced Space Transportation Program, 9
Aerodynamics, 17
Ailerons and flaps, 32
Air Force One, 50
Air shows, 57
Airbus, 63
Airfoils, 70
Airplanes, 84
Apache helicopter, 110
Autopilot, 120
Avionics, 122
Balloons, 127
Beechcraft, 137
Bell Aircraft, 139
Biplanes, 143
Blimps, 149
Boeing, 154
Bombers, 157
Buoyant aircraft, 167
Cargo aircraft, 172
Cessna Aircraft Company, 175
Octave Chanute, 177
Cockpit, 180
Concorde, 190
Corporate and private jets, 196
Crop dusting, 202
Glenn H. Curtiss, 203
DC plane family, 205
Dirigibles, 211
Eagle, 225
Enola Gay, 235
Experimental aircraft, 241
Fighting Falcon, 251
Firefighting aircraft, 253
Flight control systems, 259
Flight recorder, 263
Flying Fortress, 270
Flying wing, 274
Fokker aircraft, 275
Forces of flight, 281-283
Gliders, 297
Goodyear blimp, 301
Guidance systems, 309
Gyros, 314
Hang gliding and paragliding, 318
Harrier jets, 320
Heavier-than-air craft, 322
Helicopters, 326
Hindenburg, 340
History of human flight, 343
Hornet, 349
Hot-air balloons, 351
Hovercraft, 353
Hypersonic aircraft, 360
Instrumentation, 370
Jennys, 374
Jet engines, 376
Jet packs, 380
Jumbojets, 387
Landing gear, 405
Learjets, 410
Lighter-than-air craft, 413
Lockheed Martin, 420
McDonnell Douglas, 429
Maintenance, 433
Manufacturers, 436
MD plane family, 444
Messerschmitt aircraft, 451
Military flight, 455
Model airplanes, 464
Monoplanes, 465
National Advisory Committee for Aeronautics, 469
Osprey helicopter, 488
Paper airplanes, 495
Auguste Piccard, 506
Piper aircraft, 510
Propellers, 515
Propulsion, 517
Ramjets, 530
Raptor, 533
Reconnaissance, 534
Record flights, 537
Rescue aircraft, 545
Rotorcraft, 560
Rudders, 565
Burt Rutan, 574
Alberto Santos-Dumont, 581
Satellites, 584
Seaplanes, 591
707 plane family, 594
Igor Sikorsky, 599
Sopwith Camels, 605
Space shuttle, 611
Spirit of St. Louis, 623
Spitfire, 625
Spruce Goose, 626
Sputnik, 630
Stabilizers, 633
Stealth bomber, 634
Stealth fighter, 635
Superfortress, 643
Supersonic aircraft, 645
Tail designs, 651
Testing, 669
Tomcat, 673
Transport aircraft, 692
Triplanes, 696
Andrei Nikolayevich Tupolev, 698
Turbojets and turbofans, 699
Turboprops, 702
UFOs, 707
Ultralight aircraft, 712
Uninhabited aerial vehicles, 717
Vertical takeoff and landing, 730
"Vomit Comet," 740
Richard Whitcomb, 752
Wind tunnels, 758
Wing designs, 762
Winglets, 767
Winnie Mae, 768
Wright brothers, 785
Wright *Flyer*, 786
X planes, 789
Ferdinand von Zeppelin, 795

Animal Flight
Animal flight, 104
Bats, 132
Birds, 146
Evolution of animal flight, 237
Insects, 367

Aviation Careers
Accident investigation, 1
Aerobatics, 14
Aeronautical engineering, 25
Aerospace industry, U.S., 28
Air carriers, 34
Air Force, U.S., 42
Air shows, 57
Air traffic control, 59
Airline industry, U.S., 75
Airport security, 88
Airports, 92
Astronauts and cosmonauts, 115
Baggage handling and regulations, 125
Blue Angels, 151
Crop dusting, 202
Fighter pilots, 249
Firefighting aircraft, 253
Flight attendants, 256

Categorized Index of Entries

Flight schools, 265
Jet Propulsion Laboratory, 381
Johnson Space Center, 385
Kennedy Space Center, 394
McDonnell Douglas, 429
Maintenance, 433
Manufacturers, 436
Marine pilots, U.S., 440
National Aeronautics and Space Administration, 472
Navy pilots, U.S., 479
Pilots and copilots, 507
Strategic Air Command, 637
Tactical Air Command, 650
Test pilots, 666
Testing, 669
Training and education, 676

Instruments and Controls

Ailerons and flaps, 32
Air traffic control, 59
Autopilot, 120
Avionics, 122
Cockpit, 180
Communication, 187
Doppler radar, 218
Flight control systems, 259
Flight recorder, 263
Flight simulators, 269
Guidance systems, 309
Instrumentation, 370
Landing gear, 405
Radar, 526
Roll and pitch, 558
Rudders, 565
Stabilizers, 633
Winglets, 767

Manufacturers

Aeronautical engineering, 25
Aerospace industry, U.S., 28
Airbus, 63
Airline industry, U.S., 75
Airplanes, 84
Beechcraft, 137
Bell Aircraft, 139
Boeing, 154
Cessna Aircraft Company, 175
DC plane family, 205
Fokker aircraft, 275
Jet engines, 376
Lockheed Martin, 420
McDonnell Douglas, 429
Manufacturers, 436
MD plane family, 444
Messerschmitt aircraft, 451
Piper aircraft, 510
707 plane family, 594

Military Flight

Aerospace industry, U.S., 28
Air Combat Command, 39
Air Force, U.S., 42
Air Force bases, 47
Air Force One, 50
Aircraft carriers, 67
Antiaircraft fire, 108
Apache helicopter, 110
Jacqueline Auriol, 120
Battle of Britain, 134
Billy Mitchell, 463
Black Sheep Squadron, 148
Blimps, 149
Blue Angels, 151
Bombers, 157
Cargo aircraft, 172
Dirigibles, 211
Dogfights, 215
Jimmy Doolittle, 217
Dresden, Germany, bombing, 220
Eagle, 225
Enola Gay, 235
Fighter pilots, 249
Fighting Falcon, 251
Flying Fortress, 270
Flying Tigers, 272
Franco-Prussian War, 286
Guernica, Spain, bombing, 305
Gulf War, 311
Harrier jets, 320
Hornet, 349
Jennys, 374
Kamikaze missions, 391
Korean War, 402
Luftwaffe, 425
Marine pilots, U.S., 440
Messerschmitt aircraft, 451
Military flight, 455
Missiles, 460
Navy pilots, U.S., 479
Osprey helicopter, 488
Parachutes, 497
Pearl Harbor, Hawaii, bombing, 502
Raptor, 533
Reconnaissance, 534
Rescue aircraft, 545
Manfred von Richthofen, 547
Eddie Rickenbacker, 549
Royal Air Force, 562
Seaplanes, 591
Sopwith Camels, 605
Spanish Civil War, 620
Spitfire, 625
Stealth bomber, 634
Stealth fighter, 635
Strategic Air Command, 637
Superfortress, 643
Tactical Air Command, 650
Tomcat, 673
Transport aircraft, 692
Tuskegee Airmen, 703
Uninhabited aerial vehicles, 717
Vietnam War, 731
Women's Airforce Service Pilots, 773
World War I, 774
World War II, 779

Organizations, Programs, and Agencies

Advanced Space Transportation Program, 9
Air Combat Command, 39
Air Force, U.S., 42
Air Force bases, 47
Apollo Program, 111
Blue Angels, 151
Federal Aviation Administration, 245
Gemini Program, 292
Jet Propulsion Laboratory, 381
Johnson Space Center, 385
Kennedy Space Center, 394
National Advisory Committee for Aeronautics, 469
National Aeronautics and Space Administration, 472
National Transportation Safety Board, 476
Ninety-nines, 481
Royal Air Force, 562
Russian Space Program, 570
Strategic Air Command, 637
Tactical Air Command, 650
Vanguard Program, 726
Viking Program, 736
Voyager Program, 742
Whirly-Girls, 750
Women's Airforce Service Pilots, 773

People
Neil Armstrong, 114
Astronauts and cosmonauts, 115
Jacqueline Auriol, 120
Black Sheep Squadron, 148
Blue Angels, 151
Richard Branson, 163
Wernher von Braun, 164
Richard E. Byrd, 170
Sir George Cayley, 174
Octave Chanute, 177
Jacqueline Cochran, 179
Bessie Coleman, 182
Glenn H. Curtiss, 203
Jimmy Doolittle, 217
Hugh L. Dryden, 223
Amelia Earhart, 227
Fighter pilots, 249
Flight attendants, 256
Flying Tigers, 272
Steve Fossett, 284-285
Yuri Gagarin, 290
Roland Garros, 291
John Glenn, 295
Robert H. Goddard, 299
Howard R. Hughes, 356
Amy Johnson, 384
Samuel Pierpont Langley, 409
Leonardo da Vinci, 411
Otto Lilienthal, 417
Charles A. Lindbergh, 419
Marine pilots, U.S., 440
Beryl Markham, 442
Billy Mitchell, 463
Montgolfier brothers, 467
Navy pilots, U.S., 479
Hermann Oberth, 485
Auguste Piccard, 506
Pilots and copilots, 507
Wiley Post, 513
Ludwig Prandtl, 514
Hanna Reitsch, 544
Manfred von Richthofen, 547
Eddie Rickenbacker, 549
Sally K. Ride, 551
Burt Rutan, 574
Antoine de Saint-Exupéry, 579
Alberto Santos-Dumont, 581
Alan Shepard, 598
Igor Sikorsky, 599
Valentina Tereshkova, 660
Test pilots, 666
Konstantin Tsiolkovsky, 697
Andrei Nikolayevich Tupolev, 698
Tuskegee Airmen, 703
Jules Verne, 729
Richard Whitcomb, 752
Women and flight, 769
Women's Airforce Service Pilots, 773
Wright brothers, 785
Chuck Yeager, 793
Ferdinand von Zeppelin, 795

Procedures
Accident investigation, 1
Air traffic control, 59
Airport security, 88
Airports, 92
Baggage handling and regulations, 125
Boarding procedures, 153
Communication, 187
Doppler radar, 218
Emergency procedures, 232
Flight control systems, 259
Flight plans, 262
Flight schools, 265
Icing, 365
Instrumentation, 370
Landing procedures, 407
Maintenance, 433
Overbooking, 490
Runways, 569
Safety issues, 576
Takeoff procedures, 655
Taxiing procedures, 658
Ticketing, 672
Weather conditions, 746

Recreation
Aerobatics, 14
Air shows, 57
Airplanes, 84
Balloons, 127
Barnstorming, 131
Biplanes, 143
Blimps, 149
Blue Angels, 151
Boomerangs, 161
Buoyant Aircraft, 167
Hang gliding and paragliding, 318
Hot-air balloons, 351
Jennys, 374
Kites, 396
Model airplanes, 464
Paper airplanes, 495
Parachutes, 497
Parasailing, 499
Piper aircraft, 510
Skydiving, 601
Skywriting, 603
Triplanes, 696
Ultralight aircraft, 712
Wing-walking, 765

Safety Issues
Accident investigation, 1
Air rage, 54
Air traffic control, 59
Airline industry, U.S., 75
Airport security, 88
Airports, 92
Bermuda Triangle, 141
Boarding procedures, 153
Communication, 187
Concorde, 190
Doppler radar, 218
Emergency procedures, 232
Federal Aviation Administration, 245
Firefighting aircraft, 253
Flight plans, 262
Flight recorder, 263
Flight schools, 265
Hijacking, 336
Hindenburg, 340
Icing, 365
Landing procedures, 407
National Transportation Safety Board, 476
Runway collisions, 566
Runways, 569
Safety issues, 576
Takeoff procedures, 655
Taxiing procedures, 658
Terrorism, 661
Training and education, 676
Wake turbulence, 745
Weather conditions, 746
Wind shear, 757

Spaceflight
Advanced Space Transportation Program, 9
Aerospace industry, U.S., 28
Apollo Program, 111
Neil Armstrong, 114
Astronauts and cosmonauts, 115
Boeing, 154
Wernher von Braun, 164
Crewed spaceflight, 198
Hugh L. Dryden, 223

Categorized Index of Entries

Yuri Gagarin, 290
Gemini Program, 292
John Glenn, 295
Robert H. Goddard, 299
Gravity, 303
Jet packs, 380
Jet Propulsion Laboratory, 381
Johnson Space Center, 385
Kennedy Space Center, 394
Lockheed Martin, 420
McDonnell Douglas, 429
Manufacturers, 436
Mercury project, 446
Microgravity, 453
Missiles, 460
National Aeronautics and Space Administration, 472
Hermann Oberth, 485
Orbiting, 486
Reentry, 541
Sally K. Ride, 551
Rocket propulsion, 552
Rockets, 554
Russian space program, 570
Satellites, 584
Saturn rockets, 588
Alan Shepard, 598
Space shuttle, 611
Spaceflight, 616
Sputnik, 630
Valentina Tereshkova, 660
Konstantin Tsiolkovsky, 697
Uncrewed spaceflight, 714
Vanguard Program, 726
Viking Program, 736
Voyager Program, 742

Training
Cockpit, 180
Emergency procedures, 232
Federal Aviation Administration, 245
Flight control systems, 259
Flight schools, 265
Flight simulators, 269
Landing procedures, 407
Marine pilots, U.S., 440
Microgravity, 453
Military flight, 455
Navy pilots, U.S., 479
Piper aircraft, 510
Takeoff procedures, 655
Taxiing procedures, 658
Training and education, 676
"Vomit Comet," 740

Types of Flight
Aerobatics, 14
Airmail delivery, 81
Airplanes, 84
Animal flight, 104
Barnstorming, 131
Bats, 132
Birds, 146
Buoyant aircraft, 167
Commercial flight, 183
Concorde, 190
Corporate and private jets, 196
Crewed spaceflight, 198
Evolution of animal flight, 237
Experimental aircraft, 241
Gliders, 297
Hang gliding and paragliding, 318
Heavier-than-air craft, 322
Helicopters, 326
High-altitude flight, 330
High-speed flight, 333
History of human flight, 343
Hot-air balloons, 351
Hovercraft, 353
Human-powered flight, 357
Hypersonic aircraft, 360
Insects, 367
Lighter-than-air craft, 413
Military flight, 455
Orbiting, 486
Parasailing, 499
Record flights, 537
Rescue aircraft, 545
Rocket propulsion, 552
Rockets, 554
Rotorcraft, 560
Skydiving, 601
Spaceflight, 616
Supersonic aircraft, 645
Transatlantic flight, 682
Transcontinental flight, 686
Transglobal flight, 689
Transport aircraft, 692
UFOs, 707
Ultralight aircraft, 712
Uncrewed spaceflight, 714
Vertical takeoff and landing, 730
Wind-powered flight, 753

Women in Aviation
Jacqueline Auriol, 120
Jacqueline Cochran, 179
Bessie Coleman, 182
Amelia Earhart, 227
Amy Johnson, 384
Beryl Markham, 442
Ninety-nines, 481
Hanna Reitsch, 544
Sally K. Ride, 551
Valentina Tereshkova, 660
Whirly-Girls, 750
Women and flight, 769
Women's Airforce Service Pilots, 773